S0-AVW-345
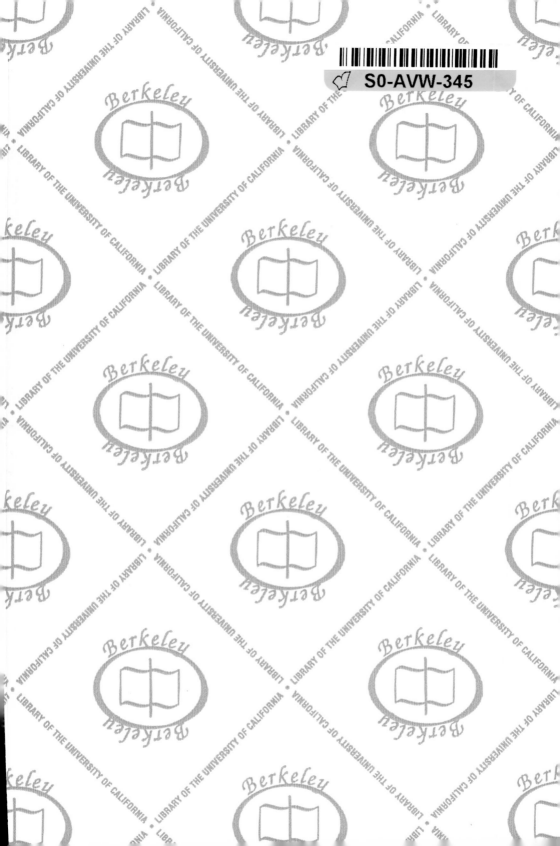

PROTEIN–PROTEIN INTERACTIONS

Edited by

C. FRIEDEN
Department of Biological Chemistry
Washington University School of Medicine
St. Louis, Missouri

L. W. NICHOL
Department of Physical Biochemistry
John Curtin School of Medical Research
Australian National University, Canberra

A Wiley-Interscience Publication
JOHN WILEY & SONS, New York · Chichester · Brisbane · Toronto

CHEMISTRY

6654-0306

Copyright © 1981 by John Wiley & Sons, Inc.

All rights reserved. Published simultaneously in Canada.

Reproduction or translation of any part of this work
beyond that permitted by Sections 107 or 108 of the
1976 United States Copyright Act without the permission
of the copyright owner is unlawful. Requests for
permission or further information should be addressed to
the Permissions Department, John Wiley & Sons, Inc.

Library of Congress Cataloging in Publication Data:

Main entry under title:
  Protein–protein interactions.

  "A Wiley-Interscience publication."
  Includes bibliographical references and indexes.
  1. Proteins—Reactivity.   2. Protein binding.
  I.   Frieden, Carl, 1928-   II.   Nichol, Lawrence Walter.
  [DNLM: 1. Proteins—Metabolism.   2. Drug interactions.
  QU 55 P96805]

QP551.P6975   574.19′245   80-29424
ISBN 0-471-04979-4

Printed in the United States of America

10   9   8   7   6   5   4   3   2   1

QP551
P6975
CHEM

Contributors

Dr. Leonard J. Banaszak
Department of Biological Chemistry
Washington University School of Medicine
St. Louis, Missouri

Dr. C. David Barry
Department of Physiology and Biophysics
Washington University School of Medicine
St. Louis, Missouri

Dr. Jens Birktoft
Department of Biological Chemistry
Washington University School of Medicine
St. Louis, Missouri

Dr. David Cox
Department of Biochemistry
Kansas State University
Manhattan, Kansas

Dr. Richard S. Dale
Department of Biochemistry
Kansas State University
Manhattan, Kansas

Dr. Carl Frieden
Department of Biological Chemistry
Washington University School of Medicine
St. Louis, Missouri

Dr. Gordon Hammes
Department of Chemistry
Cornell University
Ithaca, New York

Dr. Peter D. Jeffrey
Department of Physical Biochemistry
John Curtin School of Medical Research
Australian National University
Canberra, Australia

Dr. Lawrence W. Nichol
Department of Physical Biochemistry
John Curtin School of Medical Research
Australian National University
Canberra, Australia

Dr. Serge Timasheff
Department of Biochemistry
Brandeis University
Waltham, Massachusetts

Dr. Donald Winzor
Department of Biochemistry
University of Queensland
St. Lucia
Queensland, Australia

Preface

There are a variety of ways to discuss a topic as broad as that described by the term protein-protein interactions. In deciding to coedit this book, we felt that it had become increasingly important to discuss not only the experimental methods for the study of such interactions but also the chemical bases for and the biological consequences of these interactions. Fundamentally, a detailed understanding of the nature of protein-protein interactions rests on an appreciation of the nature of the domains of the polypeptide chains and, ultimately, upon an understanding of the nature of the forces involved. Accordingly, we have included a rather detailed accounting of structural aspects of protein molecules that emphasizes the complementary roles played by X-ray crystallographic studies and numerical estimates of conformational energy in elucidating the three-dimensional structure of a protein and the arrangement of subunits in those systems possessing quaternary structure.

In solution, a protein entity whether comprised of subunits or not may self-associate to form a series of higher polymers (or react with a dissimilar macromolecule) and, thus, the reader will find chapters devoted to the experimental elucidation of such interaction patterns utilizing mass migration (transport) and equilibrium methods. We have also included chapters in which the effects of protein-protein interactions are described with respect to fluorescent properties, to ligand binding, and to enzymatic activity. Among self-associating systems are those that are described as highly cooperative, and experimental approaches to the investigation of these systems, exemplified by tubulin and actin, are discussed.

We believe that the principles discussed in this book are applicable to a wide variety of systems ranging from those compartmentalized within a cell to those involved in antigen-antibody reactions, formation of multienzyme complexes, or hormone-receptor interactions. There is, of course, no way in which a single volume of this type can be truly comprehensive. On the other hand, it appeared to us that a complete presentation of the information included here is lacking in the biochemical literature. This volume should serve therefore as a source of information for the study of protein-protein interactions.

We want to thank those authors who have contributed to this book, especially as in many cases the information presented is not simply a review of available literature but includes new material or new approaches to the questions of protein-protein interactions. In a book of this kind it would be expected that different authors have different viewpoints in regard to the topic defined by protein-protein interactions. These are quite clearly delineated by the chapters themselves. Similarly, the symbolism in each chapter, in general, is consistent with symbolism used in that field in the literature, although attempts have been made to ensure some consistency throughout the book; the symbols used in a given chapter have been carefully defined.

Finally, we are conscious that a brief preface is insufficient, especially for the uninitiated, in presenting an overview of the terminology and interweaving concepts encountered in the field of protein-protein interactions. Accordingly, we commence the book with a chapter written in an attempt to overcome this difficulty. In discussing the diverse range of interaction patterns that are encountered in terms of thermodynamic, kinetic, and structural considerations, it presents a setting for and introduction of the detailed treatments to be found in succeeding chapters.

C. FRIEDEN
L. W. NICHOL

St. Louis, Missouri
Canberra, Australia
February 1981

Contents

Protein Interaction Patterns

L. W. NICHOL

It is the aim of this introductory chapter to delineate briefly the types of interacting systems that will be discussed in detail throughout this book and to establish certain basic structural, thermodynamic, and kinetic characteristics of these systems that will be utilized in succeeding chapters. The field is of evident relevance, since interactions of protein molecules with themselves, with dissimilar macromolecules, and with small compounds form sets of equilibria essential to the operation and control of many biochemical events. It is not surprising, therefore, that in the last two decades considerable advances have been made in the experimental elucidation of interacting protein systems and in studies aimed at the elucidation of their biological significance. It is hoped that in developing these dual themes, this book will prove to be a useful addition to the several existing treatments of the subject. These include early descriptions of the phenomena involved (1–3), reviews of spectral, migration, and equilibrium methods especially useful in their experimental elucidation (4–15), and discussions of particular interacting systems (16–22). This citation is by no means encyclopedic, as exemplified by the fact that other series (23–25) are also largely devoted to the consideration of protein interaction patterns of various types.

It is convenient to commence this discussion of the types of interacting protein systems encountered in practice by making some comment on the behavior in solution of a protein component that is not involved in self- or heterogeneous association reactions. This will serve as a reference point for the later classification of more complicated systems.

1.1 A SINGLE SOLUTE NOT CHEMICALLY REACTING

1.1.1 General Properties in Solution

Ovalbumin in solution provides an example of a protein that exists as a component characterized by a single-valued anhydrous molecular weight (26). There are of course, in this and like systems, equilibria between ionic constituents of the aqueous buffer and charged amino acid residues involved in the sequence of the protein; but we will take it that the solution has been dialyzed to equilibrium against the buffer so that the protein component (termed 2) is that defined by Casassa and Eisenberg (27), the macroion plus counterions required for electrical neutrality. If then, as discussed in detail in Chapter 5, a value of the apparent specific volume determined on the basis of an anhydrous concentration scale is used to determine the molecular weight of this protein component at infinite dilution, the anhydrous value, M_2^U, results (45,000 in the case of ovalbumin). There is likely to be "bound water" associated with this structure (28) so that the hydrated molecular weight is given by $M_2^H = M_2^U(1 + w)$, where w is the number of grams of water bound per gram of dry solute. The overall configuration of the hydrated structure, whether it be ovalbumin or another nonassociating protein such as aspartate transcarbamylase from *E. coli*, which is comprised of nonidentical subunits (29), will be that dictated by the requirement that the free energy of the whole system (including solvent) is at a minimum.

Chapter 2 and the associated Appendix presents a discussion of the energetics involved in the folding of the primary sequences of proteins to attain their final configurations. An understanding of the types of intramolecular forces involved is important, since they are the same types as those that operate in interactions between subunits within certain proteins and, indeed, intermolecularly in cases where a monomeric protein self-associates. A link is made in Chapter 2 between energetics and protein structure viewed at levels of hierarchical organization from primary structure through secondary structure to a survey of super-secondary structure and even higher orders of organization such as functional domains, lobes, and tertiary structure. Particular attention is paid to the organization of subunits in oligomeric proteins exhibiting quaternary structure and to subunit-subunit interactions. Thus symmetry rules based on simple rotation axes or combinations of rotation axes are considered in relation to the arrangements of subunits in oligomeric proteins, such as enzymes comprised of two or more subunits. As Chapter 2 notes, numerical estimates of the conformational energy of proteins and structures determined by X-ray crystallography play complementary roles in refining structural assignments and in elucidating dynamic fluctuations within the protein molecule. With this promise that Chapter 2 will delve deeply into structural considerations, the question may well be posed whether any other potentially useful concepts may be extracted from an introductory discussion of the properties of a nonassociating protein in solution. There is in fact the question of thermodynamic nonideality to be considered, which assumes considerable importance in the study of concentrated protein solutions and of multicomponent systems.

1.1.2 Consideration of the Activity Coefficient

If we consider again a solution of hydrated molecules each characterized by a molecular weight M_2^H, there is, even in the absence of chemical interaction, a potential energy of interaction, which may be specified with the use of statistical mechanics (30, 31) as a function of the center-to-center separation of two of the molecules in terms of the major contributions to this potential energy, covolume effects, and electrostatic interactions. These contributions comprise the major features that determine the nonideal behavior of the protein in solution. More rigorously, this nonideality may be expressed by introducing the activity coefficient y_2 as

$$y_2 = \frac{M_2^H a_2}{c_2^H} = \frac{M_2^U a_2}{c_2^U} \tag{1}$$

where a_2 is the thermodynamic activity of the hydrated component referred to a standard state on the molar concentration scale, and the symbol c denotes a weight concentration (g/liter). The connection between the statistical mechanical and macroscopic views of nonideality may be illustrated with reference to the first term of the virial expansion

$$\ln y_2 = \frac{\alpha_{22} c_2^U}{M_2^U} + \cdots \tag{2}$$

It has been shown (for like effective hard-sphere interactions) that (31)

$$\alpha_{22} = \frac{32 \pi N r_2^3}{3} + \frac{Z_2^2 (1 + 2\kappa r_2)}{2 I (1 + \kappa r_2)^2} - M_2^U \bar{v}_2^U \tag{3}$$

where the first term denotes the covolume (liter/mol) of the sphere of radius r_2 (N being Avogadro's number); the second term is an approximation of the electrostatic interaction written in terms of the net charge Z_2 borne by the macroion and κ, the inverse screening length of the supporting electrolyte, and the third term is the molar volume. The relationships between α_{22} and comparable virial coefficients according to the more rigorous formalism developed by Scatchard (32) will be given in Chapter 5. It suffices to note here that in studies conducted with a spherical protein at a reasonable ionic strength and low concentration the description of nonideality embodied in Eqs. (2) and (3) represents a very reasonable approximation (26). Moreover, this type of treatment has been extended to the description of activity coefficients pertinent to concentrated solutions where higher order terms in Eq. (2) must be considered, an excellent example being provided by the work of Ross and Minton (33), who used covolume calculations to estimate the concentration dependence of the activity coefficient of the $\alpha_2 \beta_2$ form of hemoglobin. The interesting result emerged that $y_2 \sim 62.8$ at 320 g/liter, a concentration pertinent to the erythrocyte.

1.1.3 Overall Geometry of the Macromolecule

Provided we are willing to regard the hydrated protein as an ellipsoid of revolution (prolate or oblate, the limiting case being a sphere), it is possible to obtain some information on the geometry of this entity. First, the concentration dependence of $\ln y_2$ may be found experimentally, and α_{22} may then be evaluated using Eq. (2). Figure 1a presents such results obtained from sedimentation equilibrium studies on ovalbumin (26). Second, the molar volume may be obtained from density measurements and Z_2 from titration or electrophoretic mobility data so that the magnitude of the covolume of the hydrated species, U_{22}^H, may be assessed as the first term on the right-hand side of Eq. (3). Third, the translational frictional coefficient, f_2^H, may be calculated from sedimentation or diffusion coefficient measurements, whereupon a function $\psi = U_{22}^H \eta^3 / N (f_2^H)^3$ may be evaluated, where η is the viscosity of the medium used to determine U_{22}^H and f_2^H. Figure 1b presents theoretical plots of

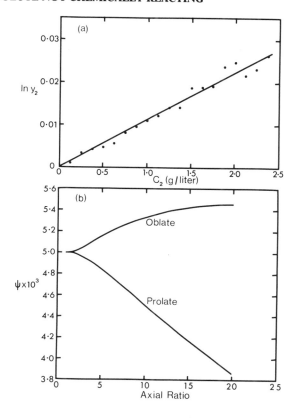

FIGURE 1

The overall geometry of a protein that does not chemically interact. (Adapted from ref. 26 with permission. Copyright 1977 American Chemical Society.) (*a*) The concentration dependence of the logarithm of the activity coefficient of ovalbumin obtained from sedimentation equilibrium results in acetate buffer, pH 4.59, 0.16 I, 20°C. The slope of the solid line obtained by least-squares regression equals α_{22}/M_2^U and corresponds using Eq. (3) to a covolume, U_{22}^H, of 5.0×10^5 ml/mol with $Z_2 = 0$ (at the isoelectric point). A similar value of U_{22}^H was obtained at pH 7.5 where $Z_2 = -14$. (*b*) Theoretically derived relations between axial ratios of ellipsoids of revolution and $\psi = U_{22}^H \eta^3 / N(f_2^H)^3$. For ovalbumin the viscosity of the medium, η, was 0.01016P and the translational frictional coefficient, f_2^H, was 5.60×10^{-8} g/sec so that the best estimate of ψ was 4.97×10^{-3}, corresponding to a prolate ellipsoid of revolution with axial ratio 2.5 : 1 and degree of hydration 0.37 g/g.

ψ vs axial ratio (26) calculated employing rigorous expressions for the covolumes (34) and frictional coefficients (35) of prolate and oblate ellipsoids of revolution. Since the plots for the different shapes diverge (from a value, $\psi = 8/162\pi^2$ for a sphere), interpolation using a value of ψ determined experimentally permits specification of the geometry of the hydrated species in these terms. Moreover, subject to certain reservations (26) sufficient information is also available to estimate w, the degree of hydration. This method of determining overall macromolecular geometry is certainly subject to error, but it leads to a less ambiguous result than conventional treatments involving frictional ratios (36) and intrinsic viscosities (37).

Information on the overall geometry of protein species is also available from other techniques such as small-angle X-ray scattering (Chapter 5). Fluorescence techniques are also noteworthy in this respect, and their principles are outlined in Chapter 6. There it is shown that the time dependence of fluorescence emission anisotropy is determined by the rotational motion of the fluorescent species. Rotational correlation times may therefore be related to the geometry of a species such as the Fab segment of IgG antibody labeled with ε-dansyl-L-lysine. This segment has the overall geometry of a prolate ellipsoid of revolution with axial ratio 2 : 1. Further details on the structure of IgG antibody and on the application of fluorescence emission anisotropy and resonance energy transfer techniques to other systems may be found in Chapter 6.

It seems that, despite the availability of certain detailed structures from X-ray crystallography, there continues to be a need for quantitative estimates of overall geometry of protein monomers. This is particularly true in the consideration of the assembly of such monomers to form oligomers: for example, recent calculations (38, 39) of the translational frictional coefficients and hence sedimentation coefficients of oligomers involving various geometrical arrangements of monomers is based on a knowledge of the ellipsoidal shape of the monomers. As an example, it was found (38) that the sedimentation coefficient of zinc insulin hexamer in solution was consistent with that calculated for a closed structure of six monomer units (each resembling a prolate ellipsoid) with the overall shape of an oblate ellipsoid of dimensions comparable with those found by X-ray crystallography. Moreover, as we will see, information on overall monomer geometry also provides the basis for the estimation in microscopic terms of composition-dependent activity coefficients pertinent in the study of chemically reacting systems, to which we now turn.

1.2   SELF-INTERACTING PROTEIN SYSTEMS

1.2.1   Isomerization and Self-Association

Mention is first made of the possibility that isomeric states of a protein, each with identical molecular weight, may coexist in equilibrium in a particular solution environment. The simplest type of such reaction is the two-state isomerization, $R \rightleftharpoons T$, discussed in Chapter 9 in relation to the theory of preferential ligand binding (40). The dimensionless equilibrium constant governing the reaction is given by a_T/a_R, which closely approximates c_T/c_R, since the activity coefficient ratio is likely to approximate unity. It follows that any weight-average quantity, $\Sigma c_i X_i / \Sigma c_i$ ($i = $ R, T and X_i is a molecular weight, elution volume, or sedimentation coefficient) will be independent of total concentration. The operation of rapidly reequilibrating isomerizations of this type is therefore difficult to detect by mass migration (sedimentation velocity, chromatography, and electrophoresis) or by equilibrium methods (such as light scattering or sedimentation equilibrium). If, however, an appropriate constraint is applied to the system, such as a change of pH or the addition of a ligand, changes in protein conformation are more readily studied, especially by spectral procedures.

In contrast, there is little difficulty in detecting the self-association of a protein in a fixed solution environment. Various types of intermolecular forces have been invoked to explain this widespread phenomenon that many proteins exist in solution as equilibrium mixtures of states of different molecular weight, M_i ($i = 1$, monomer; $i = 2$, dimer; etc.), a situation that specifies heterogeneity of the macromolecular component 2. Examples are provided by urease where the protomer of molecular weight 600,000 self-associates by intermolecular disulfide cross-links to form a series of higher polymers (41); by β-lactoglobulin A, where studies on other genetic variants have suggested that the self-association of the A variant to form octamer involves a hydrogen bond between aspartyl and glutamyl residues (19, 42); and by a range of proteins, including glutamate dehydrogenase (43), the protein from tobacco mosaic virus (44), and sulfatase A (45), where, among other evidence, the positive enthalpy change on polymer formation indicates that entropy-driven hydrophobic interactions (46) contribute significantly to a lowering of the total free energy of the whole system (including solvent). Very likely in most systems a combination of certain attractive forces (certainly including electrostatic interactions from charged chemical groups and induced and transient dipoles) contributes to the self-association. With certain systems, such as insulin, the domain of amino acid residues involved in polymer formation may well be those indicated by X-ray crystallography (47), whereas with lysozyme it appears from nuclear magnetic resonance studies (48) that there is no direct connection between the areas of contact in the crystal grown from acidic medium and the self-association operative in alkaline solutions.

The self-association of lysozyme around neutrality and at higher pH values proceeds by a head (active site)-to-tail mechanism (49, 50) and the extent of association is critically dependent on the contribution of net electrostatic repulsive forces. Thus at pH 5.0 the net charge borne by the lysozyme monomer ($M_1 = 14,400$) is about $+11.5$ (51), and little if any self-association is detectable in solutions of ionic strength 0.15. It may be possible to utilize this set of conditions or even a lower pH to explore the overall geometry of this monomer as outlined in Section 1.1.3. At pH 8.0, 0.15 I, however, the net charge for lysozyme has decreased (but still retains a positive value, $+7.3$) with the result that the free energy balance sheet is such that significant proportions of higher polymers coexist in equilibrium with the monomer at relatively high total concentration (31). The point is made with this example that in the characterization of a self-associating system and in the elucidation of its possible biological significance particular attention must be given to the effects of varying environmental parameters, which include pH, ionic strength, temperature, pressure, and the presence of other solutes.

Since the particular proteins mentioned above and several others that self-associate are discussed in later chapters, it is timely to comment on terminology to be encountered. In discussing the quaternary structure of a stable protein entity comprised of identical or nonidentical subunits, the terms dimers, trimers, and so on are frequently used (as in Chapter 2) to denote the numbers of subunits in the entity under discussion: the context of usage of these terms in these instances renders them unambiguous. However, of perhaps even wider occurrence in the literature, we find the term monomer of a protein (albeit comprised of subunits or not) being used to define that species with the lowest molecular weight that may be formed on dilution without breaking covalent bonds (22). In this connection it is noteworthy that at one stage in the investigation of the β-lactoglobulin A system it was thought that the species of molecular weight 36,600 was the monomer that proceeded to self-associate to a tetramer (146,400). Further studies, however, revealed that the 36,600 unit was in fact a dimer of the monomer (18,300), and thus the 146,400 species began to be termed an octamer. Clearly, confusion in terminology may result unless the molecular weights of species under discussion are specified and this specification (generally made in terms of anhydrous values) is recommended. The term protomer will also be encountered in connection with a species whose self-association is being studied in a particular range of total concentration. An example is provided by human oxyhemoglobin, which is now thought by some (52) to undergo self-association reactions of the types $2\alpha\beta \rightleftarrows \alpha_2\beta_2$; $2\alpha_2\beta_2 \rightleftarrows (\alpha_2\beta_2)_2 \rightleftarrows \cdots$. Of course all such species would coexist in equilibrium at *any* finite total concentration, but below ~ 1 g/liter the first equilibrium involving dimerization of the monomeric $\alpha\beta$ species ($M_1 \sim 32,000$) dominates, the relative proportions of polymers of the dimeric $\alpha_2\beta_2$ species being insignificant. If, however, investigations are conducted in the concentration range 10–320 g/liter, the proportion of $\alpha\beta$ species is insignificant, and only the postulated self-association of the protomer, $\alpha_2\beta_2$, is of relevance. In such cases the worker may justifiably use the molecular weight of the protomer for M_1 in relations that follow.

1.2.2 Composition of a Self-Associating System: Discrete and Indefinite Associations

The self-association of a monomer, P_1, in which charge is conserved on association, may be represented by the general scheme

$$P_1 + P_1 \rightleftarrows P_2$$
$$----- $$
$$P_{i-1} + P_1 \rightleftarrows P_i \tag{4a}$$
$$----- $$
$$P_{n-1} + P_1 \rightleftarrows P_n$$

With the use of abbreviated subscript notation ($i=1$ denotes monomer, etc.) the association equilibrium constants governing these equilibria may be written on the molar scale as

$$K_i = \frac{a_i}{a_{i-1}a_1} = \frac{y_i m_i}{y_{i-1}m_{i-1}y_1 m_1} \tag{4b}$$

where a_i, m_i, and y_i are, respectively, the thermodynamic activity, molar concentration, and activity coefficient of species P_i, and $K_1 = 1$ by reason of nomenclature. The values of a_i, which are independent of the pathway of formation of P_i, may thus be formulated as

$$a_i = \left\{ \prod_{l=1}^{l=i} K_l \right\} a_1^i \tag{5}$$

The total weight concentration of protein $\bar{c}$ (g/liter) is then given by

$$\bar{c} = \sum_i c_i = M_1 \sum_i i \left\{ \prod_{l=1}^{l=i} K_l \right\} \frac{a_1^i}{y_i} \tag{6}$$

Equation (6) forms the basis of the analysis, for example, of sedimentation equilibrium results obtained with self-associating systems where a_1 may be found directly as a function of $\bar{c}$ (53), as outlined in Chapter 5. The aim of such analysis is to characterize the system in terms of appropriate association constants and activity coefficients, and once it has been achieved Eq. (6) assumes even greater significance, since it permits definition of the detailed composition of solutions of the protein in terms of the relative proportions of monomeric and polymeric species comprising component 2 over the range of total concentration for which P_1 is (or may be regarded to be) the monomer. An appreciation of this detailed composition, and its variation with changes of environmental parameters, is basic if we are to seek biological relevance for protein self-associations, in terms of diffusional flows (Chapter 4), their contribution to osmotic effects, or to their interplay with ligand binding (Chapter 9). Equation (6) is considerably simplified if the approximation is made that $y_i/y_1^i = 1$, for then, as Adams and Fujita (54) originally noted, K_i defined in Eq. (4b) becomes $m_i/m_{i-1}m_1$ and Eq. (6) is simplified to

$$\bar{c} = M_1 \sum_i i \left\{ \prod_{l=1}^{l=i} K_l \right\} m_1^i; \qquad \frac{y_i}{y_1^i} = 1 \tag{7}$$

Although the "Adams–Fujita" approximation is discussed more fully in Chapter 5, we will turn later to a brief discussion of its validity; but for the present Eq. (7) will be utilized to introduce the two basic types of self-association, different aspects of which are discussed in several succeeding chapters.

1.2.2.1 Discrete (or definite) self-associations

These arise when the value of n in Eq. (4a) is finite so that a limited series of polymers coexist with monomer in solution. Examples are provided by a monomer–dimer system, such as bacterial α-amylase (55), and by a monomer –dimer–trimer–tetramer system, such as β-lactoglobulin A (56), for which M_1 equals 36,600. In general they may occur if a head-to-head interaction operates or if, by reason of protomer assembly geometry, the n-mer is a particularly stable structure. When $n > 2$, the improbability of multiple-bodied collisions suggests that polymers of size intermediate between monomer and n-mer may arise (as with β-lactoglobulin A), but there is no thermodynamic reason why these may not be insignificant in amount, whereupon the discrete association is likely to be termed a monomer–single higher polymer equilibrium ($nP_1 \rightleftarrows P_n$ or $nM \rightleftarrows P$). Consistent with Eq. (5) these cases are simply those where the product of all association constants up to K_n is much greater than any of the preceding products of equilibrium constants.

Since for discrete self-associations Eq. (7) is in closed form, it is possible, once n and the K_i have been evaluated, to solve the polynomial for m_1 at *any* $\bar{c}$ and hence to calculate the concentration dependence of solution composition utilizing $m_i = \{\Pi K_l\} m_1^i$, which is Eq. (5) with the approximation $y_i / y_1^i = 1$.

1.2.2.2 Indefinite self-associations

If n in Eq. (4a) is regarded as infinite, an unlimited series of polymers coexists in equilibrium with monomer, which suggests the presence of an array of three-dimensional networks or of polymer chains of ever increasing length. It may also eventuate with certain systems that the standard free energy changes accompanying successive additions of monomer units are identical (or nearly so), whereupon the indefinite self-association is termed isodesmic (57), and a single association constant, K_I, on the molar scale suffices to describe the system. Thus we find in solution environments reported by the authors values of K_I of 4.64×10^5 liter/mol for glutamate dehydrogenase, $M_1 = 309,000$ (58), of 4.61×10^2 liter/mol for lysozyme, $M_1 = 14,400$ (31), and of 1.28×10^2 liter/mol for oxyhemoglobin, $M_1 = 64,500$ (52). How may the composition of such systems be calculated for a series of $\bar{c}$ when the appropriate Eq. (7) is now in open form? First, we note that, when all $K_i = K_I$ (the isodesmic situation), $\{\Pi K_l\} = K_I^{(i-1)}$, and thus Eq. (7) may be written as

$$\bar{c} = M_1 m_1 \sum_{i=1}^{i=\infty} i (K_I m_1)^{i-1} \tag{8a}$$

The summation term may be written as

$$\xi = 1 + 2 K_I m_1 + 3 (K_I m_1)^2 + \cdots \infty \tag{8b}$$

so that

$$\xi (1 - K_I m_1) = 1 + K_I m_1 + (K_I m_1)^2 + \cdots \infty \tag{8c}$$

It is possible to sum the right-hand side of Eq. (8c) as a geometric progression to yield $1/(1 - K_I m_1)$ provided the series converges ($K_I m_1 < 1$), which has been justified from probability considerations (59). Thus for isodesmic indefinite self-association, combination of Eqs. (8a)–(8c) yields (57)

$$\bar{c} = \frac{M_1 m_1}{(1 - K_1 m_1)^2} \tag{9}$$

This closed solution provides a ready means of evaluating m_1 at any $\bar{c}$ and hence values of m_i once K_I has been obtained (Chapters 3 and 5) and provided $y_i / y_1^i \sim 1$. When this is done, for example, with the previously cited systems, glutamate dehydrogenase, lysozyme, and oxyhemoglobin, it emerges that identical values of the monomer weight fraction $(c_1/\bar{c})$ for these three systems arise at progressively increasing total concentrations: the related question of effective *in vivo* total concentration is therefore one of considerable interest.

There are types of indefinite self-association other than isodesmic. For example, both zinc-free insulin, $M_1 = 5734$, and α-chymotrypsin, $M_1 = 25{,}000$, in appropriate environments (60, 61) are systems of the type $i = 1, 2, 4, 6, \ldots, \infty$ in which a specific dimer is formed, which itself indefinitely self-associates. The appropriate equation analogous to Eq. (9) is (60, 62)

$$\bar{c} = \frac{M_1 m_1 \left\{ \left(1 - K_2 K_1 m_1^2\right)^2 + 2 K_2 m_1 \right\}}{\left(1 - K_2 K_1 m_1^2\right)^2} \tag{10}$$

which provides another example of a closed solution determining the composition of such systems. Further subclassification may be made on the basis of the particular species that undergoes indefinite self-association and relevant closed solutions may be formulated by summing geometrical progressions as illustrated above. Moreover, systems are encountered where in appropriate environments linear polymers formed by indefinite self-association further interact to produce higher order structures such as the two-dimensional sheets and helical tubes observed with glutamate dehydrogenase (63).

Particular mention should be made of a type of indefinite self-association that is the basis of self-assembly of protein monomer units to form rodlike structures, such as bacterial flagella, and microtubules. Chapter 8 treats this interesting problem in terms of a two-stage nucleated helical polymerization governed by two association constants. The first, K_n, describes the formation of dimers and successive polymers up to an n-mer, which acts as a nucleation center, the successive addition of further monomer units in the indefinite self-association being governed by the second association constant, K_h. One case of particular interest is that in which $K_h \gg K_n$ due to formation of a multibonded helical array once the n-mer has been formed. Comment is made in Chapter 8 on the variation of the equilibrium composition of such solutions with total protein concentration, which permits discussion of an apparent critical concentration above which the relative concentrations of higher polymers increases sharply in what could be termed, in a mechanistic sense, a highly cooperative interaction. In Chapter 8 Eq. (9) appears again with an extension appropriate to the nucleated polymerization process, together with a critical outline of experimental methods especially suited to the thermodynamic and kinetic elucidation of such systems. Consideration of screw symmetry principles in relation to the geometry of the final structures (macroscopically linear and microscopically helical) formed by this type of indefinite self-association is given in Chapter 2.

1.2.3   Consideration of Composition-Dependent Activity Coefficients

Calculations of solution composition from Eqs. (7), (9), and (10) with the implicit assumption that $y_i / y_1^i = 1$ will not have taken into account the actual composition dependence of the species activity coefficients. To do this we must extend Eq. (2) to become (31)

$$\ln y_i = \sum_j \alpha_{ij} m_j + \sum_j \sum_k \alpha_{ijk} m_j m_k + \cdots \tag{11}$$

where each of the subscripts $i, j, k, \cdots$ is allowed to span the set of monomeric and polymeric species independently. The constant coefficients α_{ij} and α_{ijk} are calculable from covolume and charge interaction considerations, provided one is willing to make assumptions concerning the geometry of the polymers and the net charges borne by them, based on experimental information on the corresponding quantities for monomer: the appropriate expressions are summarized in ref. 31 where, for example, the covolume contribution to α_{ij} is given by $4\pi N(r_i + r_j)^3 / 3$. This assumes spherical geometry, but other covolume expressions for different ellipsoid of revolution combinations are available (64).

The procedure (65) for determining the composition of a solution on the basis of calculated values for the α coefficients may be illustrated for simplicity with a monomer-dimer system, for which Eqs. (6) and (11) are written as

$$\bar{c} = M_1 \left(\frac{a_1}{y_1} + \frac{2 K_2 a_1^2}{y_2} \right) \tag{12a}$$

$$\ln y_1 = \alpha_{11} m_1 + \alpha_{12} m_2 + \cdots \tag{12b}$$

$$\ln y_2 = \alpha_{22} m_2 + \alpha_{21} m_1 + \cdots \tag{12c}$$

The following steps are then employed: (*a*) a value of a_1 is selected and the corresponding value of a_2 is determined as $K_2 a_1^2$ using the dimerization constant found experimentally (Chapter 5); (*b*) these values of a_1 and a_2 are substituted into Eqs. (12b) and (12c) as first estimates of m_1 and m_2 to find approximations of y_1 and y_2; (*c*) division of a_1 and a_2, respectively, by these y_1 and y_2 yields improved estimates of m_1 and m_2 for use in Eqs. (12b) and (12c) to find second approximations of y_1 and y_2; (*d*) the process is iterated until the values of y_1 and y_2 converge (65). Clearly with the joint use of Eq. (12a) this procedure leads to definition of the dependence of solution composition on $\bar{c}$, account having been taken of realistic estimates of the species activity coefficients.

Figure 2 presents activity coefficients for lysozyme species calculated by the iterative procedure employing α_{ij} and α_{ijk} values in Eq. (11) estimated on the basis of spherical geometry (31): for this isodesmic indefinitely self-associating system, the largest species in significant concentration at $\bar{c}$ of 20 g/liter is the decamer. It may be inferred from these results that the simplifying assumption that $y_i/y_1^i \sim 1$ is certainly reasonable at low values of $\bar{c}$. Previously it had received support from numerical calculations pertaining to uncharged model self-associating systems (66). However, with the charged lysozyme system (Figure 2) it is evident that the assumption becomes increasingly difficult to justify as the size of the polymer and of $\bar{c}$ increases. Iteration procedures based on Eq. (11) are likely to become more useful in the future if emphasis is given to the study of self-associating systems in a larger range of $\bar{c}$

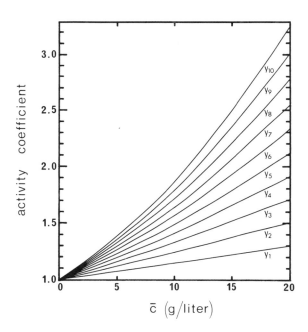

FIGURE 2

The dependence on the total weight concentration, $\bar{c}$, of calculated values of the activity coefficients of monomer and polymers (up to the decamer) of lysozyme, which indefinitely self-associates in diethylbarbiturate buffer, pH 8.0, 0.15 I, 15°C with $K_1 = 4.61 \times 10^2$ liter/mol. The calculations were based on the iterative use of Eq. (11) with values of α_{ij} and α_{ijk} computed assuming charge conservation ($Z_i = +7.3i$) on self-association and spherical geometry for all species. (Adapted from ref. 31. Copyright by North-Holland Publishing Company.)

than has commonly been employed in the past. It is not possible to be dogmatic about the number of nonideality terms that should be considered in different ranges of $\bar{c}$ because the magnitudes of these terms depend on both $\bar{c}$ and the magnitudes of the nonideality coefficients. These differ between proteins and even for the same protein as charge interactions are altered by changes of solution environment. It is preferable for the worker to estimate the magnitudes of these terms for his particular situation. Nevertheless, it might be helpful to note that for many studies conducted with globular proteins at ionic strengths 0.1–0.5, nonideality effects may reasonably be neglected at $\bar{c} < 1$ g/liter, that consideration of only first-order terms as in Eq. (12) will likely suffice in the range 1 g/liter $< \bar{c} < 10$ g/liter and that at higher total concentrations further terms must be progressively included.

It is timely also to note that Eq. (11) may be extended (by addition of the term $\alpha_{iY}m_Y$) to account for the effect of adding, for example, a macromolecular component Y to a self-associating system where Y does not chemically react with the monomer or polymers but does contribute to their activity coefficients. Such effects deserve more attention in relation to effective solution composition as the following example emphasizes. On the basis of thermodynamic parameters derived from experimental studies conducted with purified insulin at pH 7.0 in the presence and absence of zinc ions (60,67), it was concluded that at $\bar{c} \approx 3$ ng/ml (appropriate to serum) the zinc-free monomer ($M_1 = 5734$) predominates. It is hazardous, however, to utilize this rationale in support of the claim that this monomer is the only biologically relevant species in relation to membrane–receptor interaction, since clearly serum contains other components whose effect on the insulin self-association has yet to be elucidated. Thus in stressing that the composition of a self-associating system depends fundamentally on $\bar{c}$ as is done in this section, it is reemphasized that consideration must also be given to the way in which various environmental constraints (such as a variation in temperature, pressure, pH or the presence of other components) may operate to perturb the equilibria.

1.2.4 A Note on Kinetic Considerations

If a constraint is imposed on a self-associating system initially at equilibrium, the composition of the solution in terms of the relative proportions of monomer and polymer(s) may well be altered and questions arise concerning the rate of such a reequilibration. To introduce basic kinetic concepts in this context, let us consider a monomer-dimer definite self-association represented by

$$2P_1 \underset{k_r}{\overset{k_f}{\rightleftharpoons}} P_2; \quad -\frac{dm_1}{dt} = k_f m_1^2 - k_r m_2 \tag{13}$$

where k_f ($M^{-1}\text{sec}^{-1}$) and k_r (sec^{-1}) are the forward and reverse rate constants, respectively, t is time, and m_1 and m_2 are molar concentrations of monomer and dimer. In qualitative terms (3), reactions involving comparable proportions of reactants and products have been classified as slowly reequilibrating ($k_f \sim k_r$, both small), kinetically controlled (k_f, k_r both intermediate in magnitude) and rapidly reequilibrating ($k_f \sim k_r$, both large). This classification is useful in discussing the behavior of self-associating systems in the mass migration processes (also termed transport methods) of sedimentation velocity, chromatography, and electrophoresis (Chapters 3 and 4) where different migration rates apply to the monomeric and polymeric species. It is now well understood, for example, that with systems slowly reequilibrating (compared to the rate of differential migration of species under the influence of the applied field) experimentally observed boundaries or peaks may be directly related to the individual species (3,41), whereas with rapidly reequilibrating systems, reaction boundaries (3,5,68,69) will arise. Although the composition of the solution changes with total concentration across such reaction boundaries, equilibrium is effectively maintained between the species at every point. Accordingly, their interpretation in terms of weight-average migration rates corresponding to a plateau of total concentration (Chapter 3) leads to thermodynamic parameters, in particular the equilibrium constant(s) governing the self-association. Consideration of the shapes of reaction boundaries (Chapter 4) requiring an assessment of diffusional flows may permit further refinement or a choice to be made between possible alternative self-association patterns. Neither type of analysis gives quantitative information on k_f and k_r when both are large. In principle, information on rate constants may be available from migration experiments conducted with kinetically controlled systems (8,70–72), but more direct and general means for their evaluation are generally preferred (Chapters 6 and 7).

It will suffice here to mention relaxation methods that are based on a perturbation of an equilibrium by imposition of a constraint, such as a "jump" in temperature or pressure (73,74). The equilibrium constant, $K_2 = a_2/a_1^2$, will then vary according to

$$\left(\frac{\partial \ln K_2}{\partial T} \right)_P = \frac{\Delta H^0}{RT^2} \tag{14a}$$

$$\left(\frac{\partial \ln K_2}{\partial P} \right)_T = \frac{-\Delta V^0}{RT} \tag{14b}$$

where ΔH^0 and ΔV^0 are, respectively, the standard enthalpy and molar volume changes associated with the dimerization. Provided ΔH^0 (or ΔV^0, as appropriate) are nonzero, the composition of the solution must change following the imposition of the constraint, and this may be monitored over an interval of time by recording, for example, the variation of the weight-average molecular weight of the system measured by light scattering (74). The molar concentration of the monomer as a function of time may then be calculated: for example, with the monomer-dimer system of Eq. (13), $(m_1)_t = \bar{c}\{2M_1 - (M_w)_t\}/M_1^2$, with the assumption that nonideality effects are negligible. The slope of a plot of the logarithm of the difference between $(m_1)_t$ and the final equilibrium value $(m_1)_{t=t_{eq}}$ against time yields the relaxation time τ (for relatively small perturbations),

$$\tau = \frac{1}{2k_f(m_1)_{t=t_{eq}} + (k_r/2)} \qquad (14c)$$

This provides one relation for the evaluation of k_f and k_r at the final temperature; the second is given by the corresponding relation that $K_2 = k_f/k_r$, where K_2 is evaluated under the final conditions. Similar considerations apply to the study of indefinitely self-associating systems, an excellent example (which considered nonideality effects) being provided by the application of scattered light temperature jump (4 °C) and stopped-flow relaxation methods to the glutamate dehydrogenase isodesmic association (75). The results were interpreted in terms of a mechanism involving equilibrium reactions of the type $P_i + P_j \rightleftharpoons P_{i+j}$ ($i, j = 1, 2, \cdots, \infty$) with (at the final temperature of 15 °C) $k_f = 1.5 \times 10^6 M^{-1}$ sec^{-1} and $k_r = 5$ sec^{-1}, both being independent of chain length. This formulation of a "random association" governed by a single equilibrium constant, k_f/k_r, provides a revised mechanism for polymer formation than that given by the general scheme in Eq. (4a) with $n = \infty$, but nevertheless the relations based on Eq. (4a), notably Eqs. (6) and (9), remain valid, since the equilibrium concentrations of polymers are independent of the pathway of their formation.

It is timely to note that Eq. (14a) may be used to obtain estimates of ΔH^0 from the slope of a plot of ln K_2 vs $1/T$. In the event that the plot proves to be nonlinear, the temperature-dependence of ΔH^0 may be employed to calculate, either via the compensation temperature (76) or by direct application of Kirchhoff's law, ΔC_p^0, the change in heat capacity. Estimations of this kind, however, require the determination of the true equilibrium constant as a ratio of activities over a wide range of temperature and thus are best made on the basis of equilibrium measurements (Chapter 5) with due allowance for the composition dependence of activity coefficients as outlined in Section 1.2.3. Thus far, estimations of values of ΔC_p^0 for systems such as glutamate dehydrogenase seem to have been based on equilibrium constants derived on the basis of the "Adams–Fujita" approximation (76), an analysis that is associated with the surprising conclusion that the *apparent* second virial coefficient for glutamate dehydrogenase is a function of total concentration (76). The latter finding may have arisen in part from failure to express activity coefficients as functions of solution composition [Eq. (11)], a point of particular concern in attempts to determine ΔC_p^0 and to ascribe to it microscopic significance (76), since composition varies with temperature according to Eq. (14a).

Another means of perturbing the composition of a solution containing a self-associating protein is to add a ligand that binds preferentially to one form of the protein. This type of perturbation is discussed in Chapter 9, but there kinetic considerations are not emphasized because the prime objective is to explore the forms of binding curves after reequilibration, following ligand addition, has been effected. Such binding curves may nevertheless be directly relevant to the operation and control of in vivo binding responses, since many (but not all) self-associating protein systems are of the rapidly reequilibrating type. When the self-associating protein is an enzyme the concept is encountered that the initial velocity of the reaction catalyzed by the enzyme may be dependent on both the thermodynamic parameters governing the self-interaction and on the rate of reequilibration of the interaction following perturbation by preferential ligand (substrate or inhibitor) binding (77). Analogous considerations apply when the rates of ligand-induced conformational changes of enzyme structure are comparable to the rate of enzyme catalysis leading to hysteretic effects (78). These and other kinetic considerations are treated in Chapter 7.

1.3 MIXED (HETEROGENEOUS) ASSOCIATION OF TWO COMPONENTS

1.3.1 A General Framework

There are several types of interaction patterns that may arise on mixing in solution a protein (A) with a dissimilar component (B), and fundamental to any attempted classification of these schemes is the specification of the valency of the reacting species. If, for example, A is multivalent in that it possesses p reactive sites and B is monovalent, one encounters a situation, typified by the binding of drugs to a protein acceptor or by the interaction of a competitive inhibitor to a multisubunit enzyme, which is described by the set of equilibria

$$AB_{i-1} + B \rightleftarrows AB_i; \qquad i = 1, 2, \ldots, p \qquad (15)$$

If B is a compound of low molecular weight, it is usually termed a ligand, but it is also possible that B may be macromolecular, as, for example, in the formation of the trypsin–soybean trypsin inhibitor complex (79), a special case of Eq. (15) with $p = 1$. When the protein acceptor is monovalent and the ligand is bivalent, a cross-linking reaction may occur specified by

$$A + B \rightleftarrows AB; \qquad AB + A \rightleftarrows ABA \qquad (16)$$

An example is provided by the interaction of mercuric chloride with human mercaptalbumin where a mercuric ion acts as the ligand bridge between sulfhydryl groups on two mercaptalbumin monomers (80, 81). The remaining case of this particular set of mixed associations is one in which A is multivalent and B is bivalent, which leads to an array of equilibria involving the formation of the complexes $A_i B_j$ [$i = 1, 2, \cdots \infty; j = (i-1), i, (i+1), \cdots, i(p-1) + 1$]. This array is discussed in Chapter 9 in relation to model antigen-antibody reactions and is there arranged in the following fashion:

$$A_i B_j$$

$$
\begin{array}{llllll}
i=1 & A, & AB, & AB_2, & ,\ldots, & AB_p \\
i=2 & A_2B, & A_2B_2, & A_2B_3, & ,\ldots, & A_2B_{2p-1} \\
i=3 & A_3B_2, & A_3B_3, & A_3B_4, & ,\ldots, & A_3B_{3p-2} \\
\vdots & \vdots & \vdots & \vdots & & \vdots
\end{array}
\tag{17}
$$

This array shares features in common with the schemes described by Eqs. (15) and (16) in that the first row lists the type of complex evident in Eq. (15), while the first column of the array delineates complexes in which A molecules have been cross-linked via ligand bridges.

The above interaction patterns involving mixed association form a framework in which we will discuss in more detail the combinations of effects that may arise. But, first, it is relevant to note that, although the patterns encompass systems as diversified as acceptor (protein, membrane, etc.)–ligand binding and antigen-antibody interactions, the equilibria involved are describ -able at least for simple situations by the following relations (82). These relations involve reacted site probability functions, originally introduced by Flory to describe an open-ended linear condensation polymerization of a bifunctional monomer, the direct analog of an indefinite self-association in the context of reversible reactions: indeed, Eq. (9) may be derived on this alternative basis (63). For a mixed association of two components, the unbound (m_A) and total ($\overline{m}_A$) acceptor concentrations on the molar scale may be related by

$$m_A = \overline{m}_A (1 - P_A)^p \tag{18}$$

where P_A is defined as the probability that any of the p sites on A has reacted with a site on a B molecule. With similar notation for the v-valent B molecule we may write

$$m_B = \overline{m}_B (1 - P_B)^v \tag{19}$$

The conservation condition that the total concentration of reacted A sites must equal the total concentration of reacted B sites is formulated as

$$p P_A \overline{m}_A = v P_B \overline{m}_B \tag{20}$$

The basic relations are completed by defining a site-binding constant, k, as the ratio of the concentration of reacted A sites ($p P_A \overline{m}_A$) to the product of the concentrations of unreacted A sites [$p(1 - P_A)\overline{m}_A$] and unreacted B sites [$v(1 - P_B)\overline{m}_B$] such that

$$k = \frac{P_A}{v(1 - P_A)(1 - P_B)\overline{m}_B} \tag{21}$$

Of course a single equilibrium constant may be insufficient to describe the

Protein–Protein Interactions

equilibria encountered in practice, and this point is considered again later. Let us now utilize this basic framework to comment in more detail on various mixed associations, paying particular attention (as was done with self-associating systems) to the composition of such mixtures.

1.3.2 Interaction Between a Multivalent Acceptor and Univalent Ligand

When neither the acceptor nor the ligand is self-interacting Eq. (15) suffices to describe the operative equilibria. With $v=1$ Eq. (19) becomes $\bar{m}_B = m_B/(1-P_B)$, which on substitution into Eq. (21) yields $P_A = km_B/(1+km_B)$, and thus Eq. (18) gives the relation

$$\bar{m}_A = m_A(1+km_B)^p \qquad (22a)$$

Similarly, an expression for P_B in terms of P_A may be determined, which on substitution into Eq. (19) gives

$$\bar{m}_B = m_B + pkm_A m_B(1+km_B)^{p-1} \qquad (22b)$$

In an experimental situation it is useful to combine Eqs. (22a) and (22b) to formulate a binding function r, which may be measured as a function of m_B (Chapter 9). Thus

$$r = \frac{\bar{m}_B - m_B}{\bar{m}_A} = \frac{pkm_B}{1+km_B} \qquad (22c)$$

Equation (22c) may readily be linearized, for example, as a Scatchard plot (83) and the values of p and k determined. Conversely, once p and k are known the simultaneous Eqs. (22a) and (22b) may be solved for m_A and m_B for *any* initial mixing composition defined by values of $\bar{m}_A$ and $\bar{m}_B$. As elaborated in Chapter 9, the detailed composition of the solution follows from the relations

$$K_i = \frac{m_{AB_i}}{m_{AB_{i-1}} m_B}; \qquad K_i = \frac{(p-i+1)k}{i} \qquad (22d)$$

where K_i are stoichiometric equilibrium constants.

Two further points merit mention in relation to Eq. (22c). First, it is implicit in its derivation that activity coefficient ratios $y_{AB_i}/y_{AB_{i-1}} y_B$ approximate unity: even though the activity coefficients must be regarded as composition-dependent, there is some justification, at least on the basis of covolume considerations, for making this assumption when B is a ligand of low molecular weight. When B is also macromolecular, however, direct account of the composition dependence of activity coefficients should be made in the experimental determination of p and k and in their use to determine solution composition. The former endeavor has been discussed in relation to sedimentation equilibrium results obtained with certain heterogeneously associating systems (65), while the latter may be achieved by following a similar protocol as that described in Section 1.2.3 as outlined in ref. 65.

It is true, however, that composition-dependent nonideality has received scant attention in the experimental study of mixed associations and, while acknowledging the need for further development in this area, the remainder of the section will assume thermodynamic ideality.

Second, the binding equation Eq. (22c), is valid only when a single site-binding constant suffices to describe the system, which in turn requires that the p sites on A be *equivalent* and *independent* (2). Mixed associations are encountered where either or both of these conditions are not met. For example, when the binding of a ligand induces a conformational change in the acceptor, site binding constants may progressively increase or decrease and plots of r vs m_B will no longer be hyperbolic, the form of Eq. (22c), but rather will display the effects of positive and negative cooperativity (18). A discussion of these concepts is to be found in Chapter 9, which also presents a full account of a combination of interactions in which the acceptor self-associates prior to the addition of ligand, which, when added, preferentially binds to particular acceptor states. It suffices to note here that for these systems, too, expressions analogous to Eqs. (22a) and (22b) are available, which give the total molar concentrations of acceptor (comprising isomeric or polymeric states) and of ligand in terms of the concentrations of unbound reactants (40, 84): these are the basis for determining the compositions of such mixtures. When the protein acceptor is an enzyme and the ligand is its substrate, a preexisting self-interaction of the enzyme followed by substrate addition is of particular relevance in discussing the kinetics of the enzyme-catalyzed reactions. The reader is referred to Chapter 7 for information on this topic and for a critical discussion of the interrelationships between binding equations such as Eq. (22c) and their kinetic counterparts.

In addition to situations in which the preferential binding of a ligand perturbs a preexisting acceptor self-interaction, mixed association reactions may occur giving rise to a ligand-initiated association.

1.3.3 Ligand-Initiated Associations

There are situations where a protein acceptor has been shown not to self-interact in a particular environment (so that there is no preexisting equilibrium for a ligand to perturb); but, after the addition of a ligand, higher molecular weight forms of the protein have been detected. Clearly in such a situation the ligand has initiated an association by one of two basic ways (81).

1.3.3.1 Cross-linking of acceptor by a ligand bridge

The simplest example of this type of mixed association has already been given in Eq. (16). For this system Eqs. (18)–(21) with $p = 1$ and $v = 2$ may be combined to yield (by elimination of P_A and P_B) the following expression for the total (constituent) concentrations of A and B:

$$\bar{m}_A = m_A\{1 + 2km_B(1 + km_A)\} \tag{23a}$$

$$\bar{m}_B = m_B(1 + km_A)^2 \tag{23b}$$

It follows from the solution of the quadratic equation (23a) for m_A that the binding function, $(\overline{m}_B - m_B)/\overline{m}_A$, may be formulated as

$$r = \frac{6km_B - 1 + \sqrt{\Delta}}{4km_B + 2 + 2\sqrt{\Delta}} \tag{24a}$$

$$\Delta = (1 + 2km_B)^2 + 8k^2 \overline{m}_A m_B \tag{24b}$$

This solution is identical with Eq. (9) of ref. 81 with the substitutions $K_1 = 2k$ and $K_2 = k/2$, which are consistent with Eq. (22d) in the correlation of stoichiometric equilibrium constants (used by the previous workers) with the site-binding constant k.

Evidently, although the same pathway of formulation has been used, the binding equations, Eqs. (22c) and (24), differ dramatically due to the differing valencies of the ligand. In particular, the binding curves for the cross-linking scheme described by Eq. (24) must exhibit acceptor concentration dependence; numerical examples of such plots in Scatchard form are shown in Figure 3a, where the family of curves obtained with different values of $k\overline{m}_A$ is seen to intersect at the point where $(m_B = 1/2k, r = 0.5)$. In contrast, the Scatchard plot for Eq. (22c) is linear and independent of $\overline{m}_A$. It has been shown (81) that the point of intersection of the curves in Figure 3a arises at a value of m_B where the concentration of the complex ABA is at a maximum.

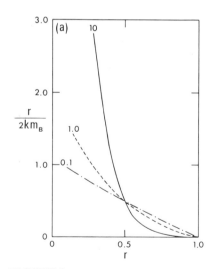
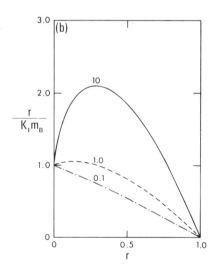

FIGURE 3
Scatchard plots computed for systems in which ligand initiates an association of the acceptor. (Adapted from ref. 81. Copyright 1976 American Chemical Society.) (a) Cross-linking of the acceptor by ligand, B, to form a complex ABA as described in Eq. (16). The numbers adjacent to each curve denote the values of $k\overline{m}_A/2$ used in Eq. (24) to simulate the curves. (b) Modification of the acceptor by ligand in the formation of the complex AB, which dimerizes (Eq. (25)). The curves were computed using Eqs. (26a) and (26c) and the indicated values of $K_2 \overline{m}_A$.

These basic properties of the simple cross-linked system shown in Eq. (16) have their exact counterparts with more complicated mixed associations of this kind involving the reversible interaction of bivalent ligand B with a p-valent acceptor to form the array of complexes $A_i B_j$ [Eq. (17)] comprising alternating A and B units in three-dimensional networks. Thus the reader will find in Chapter 9 that Eqs. (18)–(21) are again used (this time with p any value, and $v=2$) to derive the appropriate binding equation and to comment explicitly on the composition of such mixtures in terms of the concentrations of the $A_i B_j$ complexes. It suffices here to note that a family of binding curves is predicted similar in all respects to that shown in Figure 3a, the point of intersection corresponding to the value of m_B at which those complexes shown in Eq. (17) for which $j/i=p/2$ attain their maximal concentrations (82). The effects assume biological significance in relation to antigen–antibody interactions (Chapter 9) and may be quantitatively studied to determine p and k. In the latter connection the reader is referred to Chapter 5 where the analysis of sedimentation equilibrium results is discussed for a system conforming to Eq. (17), the analysis being performed in terms of the site probability functions, P_A and P_B, specified in Eqs. (18)–(21). The example there refers to the spectrum of electrostatic interactions which may arise on the mixing of two dissimilar proteins bearing opposite net charge (85).

1.3.3.2 The modification model of ligand-initiated association

Association of a protein acceptor may be initiated by addition of a ligand for reasons other than the formation of ligand bridges. Thus, even when acceptor and ligand are both univalent in relation to their heterogeneous association, the following simple interaction pattern may be visualized (81):

$$A + B \rightleftharpoons AB; \qquad BA + AB \rightleftharpoons BAAB \qquad (25)$$

This pattern suggests that on binding of a ligand to the protein A, this acceptor is modified either conformationally or by charge neutralization or both, so that the modified form may dimerize via groups, which are initially present (but prevented from interacting due to electrostatic repulsion) or are exposed as a result of the change in conformation of the acceptor. Quite different behavior is exhibited by such a system compared to the cross-linking case, as is exemplified by writing the relations

$$\bar{m}_A = m_A + K_1 m_A m_B + 2 K_1^2 K_2 m_A^2 m_B^2 \qquad (26a)$$

$$\bar{m}_B = m_B + K_1 m_A m_B + 2 K_1^2 K_2 m_A^2 m_B^2 \qquad (26b)$$

$$r = \frac{K_1 m_B (1 + 2 K_1 K_2 m_A m_B)}{1 + K_1 m_B + 2 K_1^2 K_2 m_A m_B^2} \qquad (26c)$$

where K_1 and K_2 are, respectively, the association equilibrium constants governing the equilibria specified in Eq. (25). Numerical examples conforming to Eq. (26) are shown as Scatchard plots in Figure 3b. As in Figure 3a, acceptor concentration dependence is exhibited, but the forms of the curves and the lack of an intersection point are contrasting features. Moreover, for the modification case, the concentration of BAAB will increase with increasing ligand concentration at fixed $\overline{m}_A$, whereas for the cross-linking scheme of Eq. (17) all complexes (except AB_p) are effectively removed at sufficiently high ratios of ligand to acceptor.

Binding curves of the form shown in Figure 3b have been found (86, 87) in the heterogeneous association of calcium ions and fragment 1 (the NH_2-terminal 156 residues) of bovine prothrombin. Moreover, from sedimentation studies it is known that calcium ions initiate a dimerization of fragment 1 (87, 88). Of course, the situation is more complicated than depicted in Eq. (25) in that several calcium ions bind to each molecule of fragment 1 and some cross-linking effects may be operative at relatively low calcium ion concentrations; but it is reasonable to speculate that dimer formation is effected primarily on the basis of the operation of a modification effect involving charge neutralization and possibly conformational changes. In turn this would suggest that at high concentration of calcium ions, prothrombin itself may comprise an equilibrium mixture of monomer and dimer with the dimeric form favored, an equilibrium of potential importance in the control of the amount of prothrombin monomer bound to the phospholipid vesicle in one step of the blood coagulation process (89, 89a). This example provides an illustration of a situation where the *ligand* (prothrombin) is the associating species, a type of interaction meriting further comment.

1.3.4 Self-Association of the Ligand

In addition to self-associating proteins, such as insulin, which act as the ligand in binding to membrane receptor sites, it is known that several compounds of low molecular weight, such as ATP, organic dyes, and cholesterol, also self-associate in solution. The types of interaction pattern and binding curves that may result when one state of the ligand binds preferentially to the acceptor (90) are discussed in Chapter 9. Moreover, it is not inconceivable that mixed associations may occur between acceptor and ligand both of which are capable of self-association. This situation visualized by Steiner (91) could potentially lead to the formation of complexes A_iB_j in which virtually no restriction is placed on the values of i and j defining stoichiometry. However, if the self-associations are discrete the problem becomes more tractable. For example, if both acceptor and ligand dimerize one must consider an interaction pattern involving equilibria between the species A, A_2, B, B_2, AB, AB_2, A_2B, and A_2B_2. Such restricted sets of equilibria are discussed further in Chapter 4.

The notion that mixed associations of various types may lead to complexes of various stoichiometries, exemplified by Eqs. (15)–(17) and the above discussion may, at first sight, appear daunting. It could be recalled, however, that the experimentalist is usually in a position to study both A and B separately to elucidate self-association if it occurs. Moreover, physical methods are available to detect a ligand-initiated association and to elucidate quantitatively situations where addition of a ligand imposes a constraint on a preexisting association equilibrium of the acceptor. Indeed, the aim of several succeeding chapters which deal with experimental methods is to show how results obtained using familiar procedures may be analyzed in these terms.

1.4   OTHER TYPES OF INTERACTION PATTERNS: CONCLUSION

The development in this chapter has been from consideration of a single solute whose concentration-dependent activity coefficient reflects physical interactions in solution to a variety of chemically reacting systems, including isomerizations, definite and indefinite self-associations, and mixed associations, such as acceptor-ligand binding, and heterogeneous association between macroentities. We have seen that there may be an interplay between ligand binding and protein association resulting from a ligand-initiated effect or from a perturbation of a preexisting self-interaction of the protein. It is hoped that sufficient theory has been presented at this stage to introduce basic concepts and to establish the need to characterize resultant interaction patterns. In the first instance, such an elucidation requires specification both of the types of species present in solution and of the relevant equilibrium constants, which determine the composition of the solution as a function of total concentration (for a self-associating system) and of initial mixing concentrations (for a heterogeneously associating system). Moreover, there are additional important properties to investigate, specifically concerning the nature of intra- and intermolecular forces involved in interacting systems, and the geometrical arrangement of subunits in monomeric species together with the way these assemble to form polymeric states. Questions also arise concerning rates of reequilibration of interacting systems and of enzyme-catalyzed reactions. All of these points receive discussion in the succeeding chapters, which present a selection of experimental procedures that have proved useful in elucidating interaction patterns: comment will also be found on the biological significance of the interactions and some areas requiring further investigation will be delineated.

In the latter connection it is a fair question whether all types of interaction pattern have been introduced in this chapter. The answer is in the negative. Scant attention has been paid to patterns involving heterogeneous association between three or more components. Such interactions are important in, for example, studies of enzymes in the joint presence of substrates and effectors (modifiers) or in the operation of a consecutive enzyme-catalyzed reaction in which heterogeneous association of different enzymes either as a tight complex or as a set of equilibria governed by smaller association constants is a possibility (92, 93). These particular systems will be treated later, but we have much yet to learn of the interactions between dissimilar proteins bound to membrane surfaces and other macrostructures: the related question of probing the properties of cell surfaces and phospholipid vesicles by fluorescence techniques is discussed in Chapter 6. The reader will also readily think of other types of interacting systems. Some of these may prove to be particular cases of interaction types already mentioned or combinations of them. Two examples will suffice to illustrate this point. First, early studies on pooled β-lactoglobulin indicated that a proportion of the protomer (molecular weight 36,600) failed to undergo self-association to its tetramer (94): in recent terminology (95) this would be referred to as a study of a mixture of competent and incompetent species. The problem of interpreting results, which were a combination of effects due to a definite self-association and the joint presence of a noninteracting macromolecular component, was overcome in the case of β-lactoglobulin when its genetic variants were separately prepared and studied (19, 96). Such separations of different forms of a particular state of a protein are, however, not always easy to obtain, and, even when this is achieved together with delineation of self-association behavior, there remains the need to perform a systematic series of reconstitution experiments to explore the possibility of mixed polymer formation. The solution behavior of certain hemocyanin solutions is a case in point (97). Second, the formation of micelles of a single solute is regarded by some as the separation of a bulk phase, the transition from solution phase occurring at a sharply defined "critical micelle concentration." This erroneous view (98) of a discontinuous relationship between monomer and micelle concentrations is corrected if micelles are treated as a separate *microscopic* phase with allowance for the variation of the entropy of the system due to their varying concentration (99). For monomeric ampholyte–globular micelle interactions, the latter treatment predicts a narrow range of micelle size, and it is not unreasonable to suggest that the behavior of at least some such systems may closely approximate that of a monomer–single larger polymer equilibrium governed by an association constant, equivalent to the relationship between the standard chemical potentials of monomer in free solution and in the micellar state, as discussed previously (99). If this proves to be the case, characterization of such systems in term of average micellar size and an average association constant may be possible by applying the appropriate interaction theory to migration or equilibrium results or to the sigmoidal curve that must result for a monomer–n-mer system when n is large and a weight-average property is plotted against total concentration. It is readily acknowledged, however, that micelle formation in protein solutions (particularly mixed micelle formation) is a very much more difficult problem to solve.

Possibly the only uniquely different *type* of interaction not so-far mentioned is a hybridization process, exemplified by $A(p_1p_2) + B(q_1q_2) \rightleftharpoons C(p_1q_1) + D(p_2q_2)$. Such equilibria are governed by a dimensionless equilibrium constant, a feature shared by isomerization reactions: indeed the behavior of hybridizing systems in mass migration (100) has been compared with that of isomerizing systems (9). In recent practice, however, little attention has been given to a characterization of possible equilibria of this type. Rather attention has been directed toward isolating hybrid forms of an enzyme obtained by mixing subunits of the enzyme obtained from different sources. An example is provided by hybrid formation of glyceraldehyde-3-phosphate dehydrogenases from rabbit muscle and yeast (101). This type of experiment provides a potential probe for the study by kinetic and thermodynamic methods of the involvement of subunit interactions in the binding of specific ligands to the enzyme.

Subunit interactions, isomerization, self-associations, and mixed associations are all encountered in the study of interacting protein systems and their elucidation offers the potential of comprehending common threads in aspects of seemingly diverse fields, such as enzymology, immunology, membrane function, and acceptor-ligand binding. The field of protein interaction patterns is, indeed, a broad one, and it cannot be expected that a single volume of this type will be encyclopedic. Nevertheless, it is hoped that the coverage which follows is sufficiently comprehensive to inform the reader of the current status of the field and to set the stage for future developments in this dynamic area.

REFERENCES

1. T. Svedberg and K. O. Pedersen, *The Ultracentrifuge*, Clarendon Press, Oxford, 1940.
2. I. M. Klotz, in H. Neurath, and K. E. Bailey, Eds., *The Proteins*, 1st ed., Vol. I, Part B, Academic Press, New York, 1953, p. 727.
3. L. W. Nichol, J. L. Bethune, G. Kegeles, and E. L. Hess, in H. Neurath, Ed., *The Proteins*, 2nd ed., Vol. II, Academic Press, New York, 1964, p. 305.
4. H. K. Schachman, *Ultracentrifugation in Biochemistry*, Academic Press, New York, 1959.
5. L. G. Longsworth, in M. Bier, Ed., *Electrophoresis, Theory, Methods and Applications*, Academic Press, New York, 1959, p. 91.
6. H. Fujita, *Mathematical Theory of Sedimentation Analysis*, Academic Press, New York, 1962.
7. E. T. Adams, Jr., in *Fractions Number 3* (*Feature Article*), Spinco Division of Beckman Instruments, 1967.
8. J. R. Cann, *Interacting Macromolecules*, Academic Press, New York, 1970.
9. L. W. Nichol and D. J. Winzor, *Migration of Interacting Systems*, Clarendon Press, Oxford, 1972.
10. J. W. Williams, *Ultracentrifugation of Macromolecules*, Academic Press, New York, 1972.
11. M. P. Tombs and A. R. Peacocke, *The Osmotic Pressure of Biological Macromolecules*, Oxford University Press, London and New York, 1974.
12. G. K. Ackers, in H. Neurath and R. L. Hill, Eds., *The Proteins*, 3rd ed., Vol. I, Academic Press, New York, 1975, p. 1.
13. K. E. van Holde, in H. Neurath and R. L. Hill, Eds., *The Proteins*, 3rd ed., Vol. I, Academic Press, New York, 1975, p. 225.
14. H. Kim, R. C. Deonier, and J. W. Williams, *Chem. Rev.* **77**, 659 (1977).

15. N. Catsimpoolas, Ed., *Physical Aspects of Protein Interactions*, Elsevier/North-Holland, New York, 1978.
16. E. R. Stadtman, *Adv. Enzymol.* **28**, 41 (1966).
17. J. Steinhardt and J. A. Reynolds, *Multiple Equilibria in Proteins*, Academic Press, New York, 1969.
18. D. E. Koshland, Jr. and K. E. Neet, *Annu. Rev. Biochem.* **37**, 359 (1968).
19. H. A. McKenzie, Ed., *Milk Proteins, Chemistry and Molecular Biology*, Vol. I, Academic Press, New York and London, 1970.
20. C. Frieden, *Annu. Rev. Biochem.* **40**, 653 (1971).
21. R. Jaenicke and E. Helmreich, Eds., *Protein–Protein Interactions*, Springer-Verlag, New York, 1972.
22. I. M. Klotz, D. W. Darnall, and N. B. Langerman, in H. Neurath and R. L. Hill, Eds., *The Proteins*, 3rd ed., Vol. I, Academic Press, New York, 1975, p. 293.
23. C. H. W. Hirs and S. N. Timasheff, Eds., *Methods Enzymol.* **27** (1973).
24. S. N. Timasheff and G. D. Fasman, Eds., *Subunits in Biological Systems*, Part A, Marcel Dekker, New York, 1971.
25. G. D. Fasman and S. N. Timasheff, Eds., *Subunits in Biological Systems*, Part B, Marcel Dekker, New York, 1973.
26. P. D. Jeffrey, L. W. Nichol, D. R. Turner, and D. J. Winzor, *J. Phys. Chem.* **81**, 776 (1977).
27. E. F. Casassa and H. Eisenberg, *Adv. Protein Chem.* **19**, 287 (1964).
28. C. Tanford, *Physical Chemistry of Macromolecules*, Wiley, New York, 1961.
29. D. C. Wiley and W. N. Lipscomb, *Nature (London)* **218**, 1119 (1968).
30. J. O. Hirschfelder, C. F. Curtis, and R. B. Bird, *Molecular Theory of Gases and Liquids*, Wiley, New York, 1954.
31. P. R. Wills, L. W. Nichol, and R. J. Siezen, *Biophys. Chem.* **11**, 71 (1980).
32. G. Scatchard, *J. Am. Chem. Soc.* **68**, 2315 (1946).
33. P. D. Ross and A. P. Minton, *J. Mol. Biol.* **112**, 437 (1977).
34. A. Isihara, *J. Chem. Phys.* **18**, 1446 (1950).
35. F. Perrin, *J. Phys. Radium* **7**, 1 (1936).
36. J. L. Oncley, *Ann. N.Y. Acad. Sci.* **41**, 121 (1941).
37. H. A. Scheraga and L. Mandelkern, *J. Am. Chem. Soc.* **75**, 179 (1953).
38. P. R. Andrews and P. D. Jeffrey, *Biophys. Chem.* **4**, 93 (1976).
39. D. C. Teller, E. Swanson, and C. de Haën, *Methods Enzymol.* **61**, 103 (1979).
40. J. Monod, J. Wyman, and J. -P. Changeux, *J. Mol. Biol.* **12**, 88 (1965).
41. J. M. Creeth and L. W. Nichol, *Biochem J.* **77**, 230 (1960).
42. J. McD. Armstrong and H. A. McKenzie, *Biochim. Biophys. Acta* **147**, 93 (1967).
43. R. F. Henderson, T. R. Henderson, and B. M. Woodfin, *J. Biol. Chem.* **245**, 3733 (1970).
44. S. Paglini and M. A. Lauffer, *Biochemistry* **7**, 1827 (1968).
45. L. W. Nichol and A. B. Roy, *Biochemistry* **5**, 1379 (1966).
46. M. A. Lauffer, in N. Catsimpoolas, Ed., *Physical Aspects of Protein Interactions*, Elsevier/North-Holland, New York, 1978, p. 115.
47. T. Blundell, G. Dodson, D. Hodgkin, and D. Mercola, *Adv. Protein Chem.* **26**, 279 (1972).
48. J. F. Studebaker, B. D. Sykes, and R. Wien, *J. Am. Chem. Soc.* **93**, 4579 (1971).
49. A. J. Sophianopoulos, *J. Biol. Chem.* **244**, 3188 (1969).
50. G. J. Howlett and L. W. Nichol, *J. Biol. Chem.* **247**, 5681 (1972).
51. C. Tanford and M. L. Wagner, *J. Am. Chem. Soc.* **76**, 3331 (1954).

52. L. W. Nichol, R. J. Siezen, and D. J. Winzor, *Biophys. Chem.* **10**, 17 (1979).

53. B. K. Milthorpe, P. D. Jeffrey, and L. W. Nichol, *Biophys. Chem.* **3**, 169 (1975).

54. E. T. Adams, Jr. and H. Fujita, in J. W. Williams, Ed., *Ultracentrifugal Analysis in Theory and Experiment*, Academic Press, New York, 1963, p. 119.

55. R. Tellam, D. J. Winzor, and L. W. Nichol, *Biochem. J.* **173**, 185 (1978).

56. L. M. Gilbert and G. A. Gilbert, *Methods Enzymol.* **27**, 273 (1973).

57. K. E. van Holde and G. P. Rossetti, *Biochemistry* **6**, 2189 (1967).

58. L. W. Nichol, R. J. Siezen, and D. J. Winzor, *Biophys. Chem.* **9**, 47 (1978).

59. H. Eisenberg, *Biological Macromolecules and Polyelectrolytes in Solution*, Clarendon Press, Oxford, 1976.

60. P. D. Jeffrey, B. K. Milthorpe and L. W. Nichol, *Biochemistry* **15**, 4660 (1976).

61. R. Tellam and D. J. Winzor, *Biochem. J.* **161**, 687 (1977).

62. E. T. Adams, Jr., W. E. Ferguson, P. E. Wan, J. L. Sarquis, and B. M. Escott, *Sep. Sci.* **10**, 175 (1975).

63. H. Eisenberg, R. Josephs, and E. Reisler, *Adv. Protein Chem.* **30**, 101 (1976).

64. L. W. Nichol, P. D. Jeffrey, and D. J. Winzor, *J. Phys. Chem.* **80**, 648 (1976).

65. L. W. Nichol and D. J. Winzor, *J. Phys. Chem.* **80**, 1980 (1976).

66. A. G. Ogston and D. J. Winzor, *J. Phys. Chem.* **79**, 2496 (1975).

67. B. K. Milthorpe, L. W. Nichol, and P. D. Jeffrey, *Biochim. Biophys. Acta* **495**, 195 (1977).

68. G. A. Gilbert, *Proc. R. Soc. London*, *Ser. A.* **250**, 377 (1959).

69. L. W. Nichol and A. G. Ogston, *Proc. R. Soc. London*, *Ser. B.* **163**, 343 (1965).

70. G. G. Belford and R. L. Belford, *J. Chem. Phys.* **37**, 1926 (1962).

71. L. W. Nichol and D. J. Winzor, *J. Phys. Chem.* **78**, 460 (1974).

72. S. J. Lovell, L. W. Nichol, and D. J. Winzor, *FEBS Lett.* **40**, 233 (1974).

73. M. Eigen and L. de Maeyer, in A. Weissberger, Ed., *Technique of Organic Chemistry*, Vol. 8, Part 2, Wiley-Interscience, New York, 1964, Chapter 18.

74. G. Kegeles, *Methods Enzymol.* **27**, 308 (1978).

75. D. Thusius, P. Dessen, and J. -M. Jallon, *J. Mol. Biol.* **92**, 413 (1975).

76. P. W. Chun, in N. Catsimpoolas, Ed., *Physical Aspects of Protein Interactions*, Elsevier/North-Holland, New York, 1978, p. 79.

77. B. I. Kurganov, in T. Keleti, Ed., *Symposium on Mechanism of Action and Regulation of Enzymes*, Akadémiai Kiadó Budapest and North-Holland, Amsterdam, 1975, p. 29.

78. C. Frieden, *J. Biol. Chem.* **245**, 5788 (1970).

79. J. Lebowitz and M. Laskowski, Jr., *Biochemistry* **1**, 1044 (1962).

80. H. Edelhoch, E. Katchalski, R. H. Maybury, W. L. Hughes, Jr., and J. T. Edsall, *J. Am. Chem. Soc.* **75**, 5058 (1953).

81. L. W. Nichol and D. J. Winzor, *Biochemistry* **15**, 3015 (1976).

82. P. D. Calvert, L. W. Nichol, and W. H. Sawyer, *J. Theor. Biol.* **80**, 233 (1979).

83. G. Scatchard, *Ann. N.Y. Acad. Sci.* **51**, 660 (1949).

84. L. W. Nichol, W. J. H. Jackson, and D. J. Winzor, *Biochemistry* **6**, 2449 (1967).

85. P. D. Jeffrey, L. W. Nichol, and R. D. Teasdale, *Biophys. Chem.* **10**, 379 (1979).

86. S. P. Bajaj, R. J. Butkowski, and K. G. Mann, *J. Biol. Chem.* **250**, 2150 (1975).

87. F. G. Prendergast and K. G. Mann, *J. Biol. Chem.* **252**, 840 (1977).

88. C. M. Jackson, C. -W. Peng, G. M. Brenckle, A. Jones, and J. Stenflo, *J. Biol. Chem.* **254**, 5020 (1979).

89. F. A. Dombrose, S. N. Gitel, K. Zawalich, and C. M. Jackson, *J. Biol. Chem.* **254**, 5027 (1979).

89a. L. W. Nichol, in K. G. Mann and F. B. Taylor, Eds., *The Regulation of Coagulation*, Elsevier/North Holland, New York, 1980, p. 43.

90. L. W. Nichol, G. D. Smith, and A. G. Ogston, *Biochim. Biophys. Acta* **184**, 1 (1969).

91. R. F. Steiner, *Biochemistry* **7**, 2201 (1968).

92. L. W. Nichol, P. W. Kuchel, and P. D. Jeffrey, *Biophys. Chem.* **2**, 354 (1974).

93. G. R. Welsh, *Prog. Biophys. Mol. Biol.* **32**, 103 (1977).

94. S. N. Timasheff and R. Townend, *J. Am. Chem. Soc.* **83**, 464 (1961).

95. D. A. Yphantis, J. J. Correia, M. L. Johnson, and G. -M. Wu, in N. Catsimpoolas, Ed., *Physical Aspects of Protein Interactions*, Elsevier/North Holland, New York, 1978, p. 275.

96. H. A. McKenzie, W. H. Sawyer, and M. B. Smith, *Biochim. Biophys. Acta* **147**, 73 (1967).

97. P. D. Jeffrey, *Biochemistry* **18**, 2508 (1979).

98. C. Tanford, *The Hydrophobic Effect: Formation of Micelles and Biological Membranes*, Wiley, New York, 1973.

99. J. N. Israelachvili, D. J. Mitchell, and B. W. Ninham, *J. Chem. Soc., Faraday Trans. II* **72**, 1525 (1976).

100. L. W. Nichol and A. G. Ogston, *Proc. R. Soc. London, Ser. B*. **167**, 164 (1967).

101. M. R. Holloway, H. H. Osborne, and G. M. L. Spotorno, in H. Sund, Ed., *Pyridine Nucleotide-Dependent Dehydrogenases*, Walter de Gruyter, Berlin, New York, 1977, p. 101.

CHAPTER **2**

Protein—Protein Interactions and Protein Structures

LEONARD J. BANASZAK, JENS J. BIRKTOFT, AND
C. DAVID BARRY

2.1   GENERAL PRINCIPLES

The crystallographic determination of the molecular structure of a number of proteins comprised of one or more subunits as well as numerous monomeric proteins has resulted in a wealth of new data, much of which has yet to be assimilated into the realm of the chemistry of macromolecules. In the text that follows an attempt is made to describe selected examples of these structures and wherever possible to relate the results to what still must be called evolving principles of protein conformation. A common thread used throughout this chapter is the relationship of conformation and energetics. Although considerably more space is devoted to conformation as obtained from X-ray crystallographic structure studies, the reader should try to link the idea of conformation and energy. If this rather obvious link is made, then it is apparent that the stabilization of the conformation of proteins at several different hierarchial levels is always the resultant of the same atomic forces.

The idea that the structure of proteins could be viewed from a hierarchial point of view was put forward by Linderstrøm-Lang as far back as 1952 (1). According to this concept, protein structures could be considered at a primary, a secondary, a tertiary, and a quaternary level, and these levels of organization continue to be useful in describing proteins. The primary structure is the linear covalent assembly of amino acids. The secondary structure is the folding of shorter contiguous segments of the polypeptide chains into regular arrangements typified by a characteristic set of constant torsional angles for the polypeptide backbone called ϕ and ψ (2). This level of conformation includes helices, the strands that make up β structures, and certain "hairpin loops." Such loops or turns do not have constant values of ϕ and ψ but rather a recurring combination of values, which generate the same tight turns. Segments of secondary structure, together with irregularly folded intervening polypeptide chain segments, associate into the globular protein creating the tertiary structure. Finally, two or more globular units may associate thus forming the quaternary structure or oligomeric structure central to this chapter.

This original hierarchial concept set forth by Linderstrøm-Lang is essentially unchanged, except some new levels have been added. Within a given protein a limited number of the secondary structural elements will frequently associate into regular organized assemblies, which have been labeled super-secondary structures (3). In turn, forms of super-secondary structure can further join into larger assemblies creating domains or lobes. As is described in a later section, forms of super-secondary structure may even extend across subunit-subunit interfaces.

Finally, throughout this chapter a discussion of helical forms of fibrous polypeptides is intentionally avoided. Oligomeric proteins such as collagen aggregate by the intertwining of extended polypeptide chains. The polypeptide chains in such aggregates frequently have constant ϕ and ψ torsional angles and by the definitions developed in this chapter represent a type of secondary or super-secondary structure. Because of their unique rodlike character, fibrous proteins tend to have somewhat different molecular structures and properties, and are not easily described along with their globular counterparts.

Noting this one omission, the chapter is divided into three principal parts. In Section 2.1 a brief outline of the nature of nonbonded interactions is presented. The details of the nature of these forces are expanded upon in the appendix, Section 2.6. Section 2.1 also contains a description of the geometrical principles of symmetry and a brief outline of the limitations of structures based on X-ray crystallographic results.

Section 2.2 is a summary of the nature and principles of protein conformation at all of the forementioned hierarchial levels. To view the molecular structure of a protein containing multiple subunits one must first be familiar with the evolving principles at these other levels of conformational organization.

Sections 2.3 and 2.4 deal directly with the molecular structure and properties of multisubunit proteins. Examples of symmetrical and asymmetrical oligomers are given and last of all some examples of conformational changes mainly involving subunit-subunit rearrangements are given.

2.1.1 The Energetics of Protein–Protein Interactions

Fundamental to the stabilization of oligomeric proteins are several forms of interatomic forces and the thermodynamic energy derived from entropic factors related to water and the protein itself. While it has not yet been possible to predict the molecular structure of proteins by minimization of the conformational energy, numerical estimation of this energy based on crystal structures is becoming increasingly important. Energetic calculations of this sort have been used to refine protein structures and to study dynamic fluctuations within the protein (4, 5). In spite of the complexity of such calculations, the energetics of protein conformation is a vital factor in linking protein conformation in a crystal to the subtle variations of this structure that are probably related to function.

In consideration of the growing importance of conformational energy calculations as related to protein function, the details of how such calculations can be applied to globular proteins are contained in Section 2.6. To calculate the magnitude of these interatomic forces, semiempirical functions must necessarily be used. Electrostatic contributions from charged chemical groups, and induced and transient dipoles must be taken into account. Repulsive forces and the energetics of distortion from canonical values are equally important and are described later.

The hydrogen bond, which is a special form of nonbonded electrostatic interactions, also has an important role in oligomeric protein systems. As will be shown in a subsequent section, hydrogen bonds are observable by distance calculations using the crystallographic coordinates of a protein. Especially pertinent to oligomeric proteins is the fact that hydrogen bonds have been observed in all subunit-subunit interfaces.

The so-called hydrophobic energy contribution to protein conformation, including the formation of subunit-subunit interfaces, is somewhat more difficult to evaluate. However, current approaches to this problem are also described in Section 2.6. They center mainly on the calculation of accessibility of the solvent to the protein atoms, something that changes dramatically during protein folding or upon subunit-subunit aggregation.

The aggregation of globular protein subunits into symmetrical oligomers is a direct result of the multiplicity of a set of favorable energetic interactions. Geometrical symmetry generated by such favorable energetics is an important means of describing the molecular organization of oligomeric proteins.

2.1.2   Symmetry

A great number of proteins, in particular those found within a cell, are oligomeric and thus are composed of a relatively small number of subunits. The subunits are in most instances chemically identical, although protein molecules containing different subunit types are also found. The association of identical subunits follow rules, which will result in some type of symmetry within the final assembly. Hence symmetry is important not only for understanding the structure and assembly mechanism of oligomeric proteins, but is of relevance as well when dealing with dynamic biological properties such as cooperativity or allosteric behavior. In addition the basic rules of symmetry play a fundamental role in X-ray crystallography, which, of course, is one of the primary sources of information on the structure of proteins. What follows is a brief outline of some simple principles of symmetry as well as a description of how they relate to an assembly of subunits, that is, to an oligomeric protein. Also included is a discussion of some of the methods used to determine molecular symmetry in oligomeric proteins. For those readers who would like to see simple examples of symmetry operations illustrated in three dimensions, an excellent book by Bernal, Hamilton, and Ricci can be recommended (6).

Symmetrical aggregation of subunits was first observed when the low-resolution X-ray studies of hemoglobin were completed by Perutz and co-workers (7). They found that the $\alpha_2\beta_2$ forms of hemoglobin could be described by a set of simple symmetry operations. It was also realized that the simple geometric relationship of protein atoms in the symmetrical $\alpha_2\beta_2$ structure formed the basis of multiple and specific noncovalent interactions between the subunits. The symmetrical aggregation also has energetic implications, which will be discussed subsequently. Since the early studies of hemoglobin, many examples of symmetrical aggregation in oligomeric proteins have been found, and to summarize these observations some simple definitions of the terms and the nature of these geometrical relationships are necessary.

The word *symmetry* is used to describe some repeating motif of objects, herein only protein subunits. A *symmetry operation* is the physical motion or mathematical transformation imposed on a member of a set to produce the motif. Because of the chiral nature of amino acids, the only operations that apply to proteins are *rotation* operations. Symmetry operations such as *reflections* and *inversions* through points, lines, or planes are not allowable in protein molecules. In discussing protein aggregates and symmetry one other definition is necessary, that of a *symmetry element*. A symmetry element is a point, line, or plane about which the symmetry operation occurs. Since only rotation axes are found within oligomeric protein molecules, the only symmetry element pertinent to our discussion is a line.

The simplest form of symmetry that is found in oligomeric proteins is variously called twofold rotational or dyad symmetry. The words rotational and symmetry are frequently omitted and symmetry and symmetry element is simply called twofold and twofold axis, respectively. The presence of twofold rotational symmetry within a protein molecule means that each atom of the protein has a symmetry-related second atom. This second atom is located at a position such that if it is rotated exactly 180° around the twofold rotation axis, it is congruent with the first atom.

A representative example of twofold rotational symmetry as found in oligomeric proteins is shown in Figure 1. One segment from each of the two subunits of the dimeric protein, alcohol dehydrogenase (8) is shown as well as the twofold rotation axis, the symmetry element relating the two segments. For any protein known to form a stable dimer it should be expected that the subunits within a single molecule will be related by twofold rotational symmetry. Exceptions are, however, possible.

To describe oligomeric proteins containing three or more subunits the definitions already given are extended first to include threefold, fourfold, and *n*-fold rotational symmetry. Hence a protein containing three subunits can be expected to have them arranged around a threefold rotation axis, and the symmetry operation generates congruency after each of three 120° rotations. The aggregation of protein subunits into circular assemblies containing *n* subunits occur with *n*-fold rotational symmetry, and congruency will occur after each of *n* rotations of 360°/*n* around the rotation axis. This is a necessary requirement if all subunits are to be in the same environment and make identical interactions with their immediate neighbors. It should, however, be pointed out that as far as pure rotational symmetry in oligomeric proteins is concerned, only two- and threefold rotational have been observed in crystalline protein structures. Other types of rotational symmetry have only been observed in combination with other (rotational) symmetry elements.

Higher symmetry of a different form from simple rotational is equally possible for oligomeric protein containing 2*N* subunits (*N* > 2) or, in other words, an even number of four or more subunits. In this higher symmetrical arrangement, the protein subunits are located in three dimensions around a central point, although rotation axes (lines) still play the principal role. Because the subunit motif occurs around a central point, the resulting

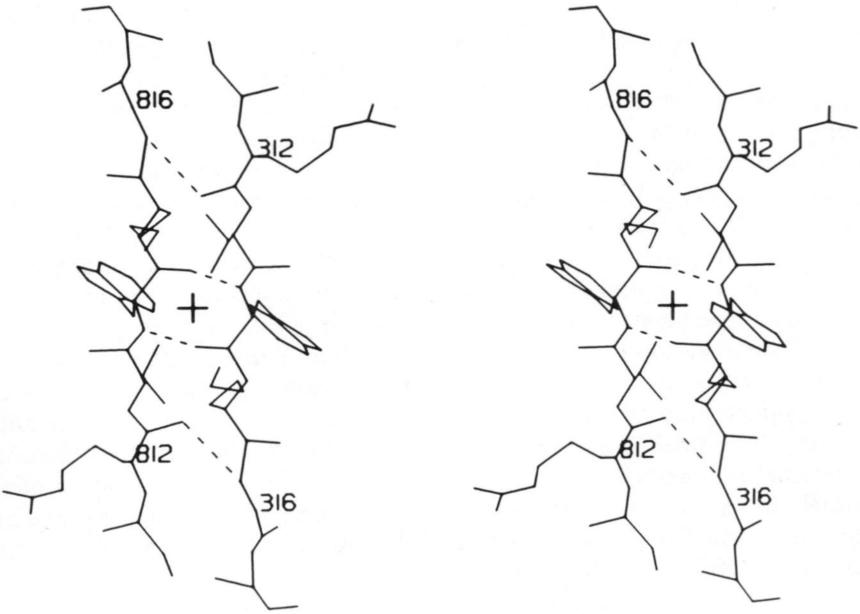

FIGURE 1

Twofold rotational symmetry. The stereodrawing shows seven amino acid residues from each subunit in horse liver alcohol dehydrogenase (8). Subunit 1 on the right contains residues 311–317. Residue numbers for those in subunit 2 are offset by 500 (811–817). The cross indicates the position of the molecular twofold symmetry axis, which is perpendicular to the plane of the paper. The dotted lines represent hydrogen bonds occurring between the two subunits. The coordinates used to generate this and the other stereodrawings in the chapter were obtained from the Protein Data Bank at the Brookhaven National Laboratory. All residue numbers are placed to the right of the corresponding α-carbon atom.

arrangement is referred to as a *point group*. A very common arrangement of protein subunits combines twofold rotational symmetry with an *n*-fold rotation axis. This combination of rotation axes are frequently grouped together as a class and called the *dihedral* point groups. The simplest dihedral arrangement occurs when the *n*-fold axis is a twofold rotation, and the second twofold axis is found perpendicular to and intersecting it at the very center of the protein molecule. In this one instance the combination of two mutually perpendicular and intersecting twofold rotation axes generates a third dyad axis perpendicular to the other two.

Several proteins containing four identical or nearly identical subunits have this so-called 222 symmetry. As an example of this geometric arrangement, a small segment of the enzyme lactate dehydrogenase (9) is shown in Figure 2 to illustrate the 222 point group symmetry. Only a single α-helical segment of each subunit is shown, and the reader is advised to study the drawing by

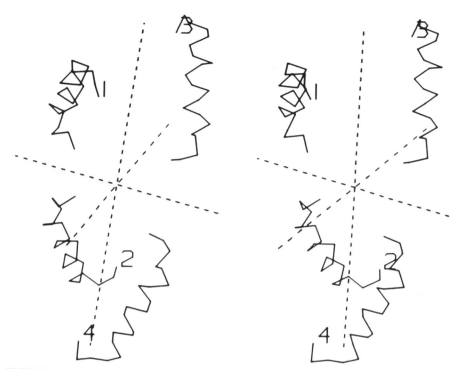

FIGURE 2

Dihedral 222 symmetry. The helical segment containing residues 53–73 from each of the four subunits in dogfish heart lactate dehydrogenase (9) is shown in the stereodiagram. Only α-carbon atoms are shown. The first residue in each chain segment is labeled with the subunit number. The stippled lines represent the three intersecting twofold rotational symmetry axes.

using stereoglasses. In stereo it should be possible to visualize the effects of a 180° rotation around the twofold axes, which are shown by the dotted lines.

The next highest form of dihedral symmetry combines a threefold rotation axis with the twofold rotation axis and is called 32 dihedral symmetry. Proteins containing six subunits would be expected to be organized with this symmetry, and such is the case for aspartate transcarbamylase, which contains the subunits in a 32 arrangement (10, 11). To form other dihedral point groups one simply takes the n-fold rotation symmetry axis and adds a twofold rotation axis perpendicular to it. In the final arrangement of symmetry elements, additional twofolds are generated by the n-fold rotation axis. These relatively simple rules of dihedral symmetry can be used to predict the arrangement of subunits in oligomeric proteins of unknown structure. For example, octameric proteins might belong to the class 42, decameric molecules should have 52 symmetry, and dodecameric proteins might be expected to belong to the so-called 62 point group. Through electron microscopy and

X-ray diffraction, examples of all of the forementioned symmetrical subunit arrangements have now been identified, and some will be described in more detail in a later section.

Besides simple rotational symmetry and the dihedral class of subunit arrangements, two other major types of symmetry are found in biological structures, namely, *icosahedral* and *helical* symmetry. For example, the most complex form of symmetry found in oligomeric systems is that of the spherical viruses. In the outer shell of these viruses the coat protein subunits aggregate in a way that is described by a point group with so-called icosahedral symmetry. An icosahedron is a regular solid bounded by 20 faces and the underlying symmetry of this polyhedron combines twofold, threefold, and fivefold rotation axes. In the simplest case the icosahedral aggregation of protein subunits places a single subunit at each of the vertices of the equilateral triangle comprising the faces of the icosahedron (60 subunits). Caspar and Klug, by introducing the concept of quasi-equivalence, demonstrated that even larger numbers of protein units can also be incorporated into the symmetry of the icosahedron (12, 13). By assuming equivalent subunit-subunit contacts (or bonds) around fivefold and sixfold rotation axes, this can be accomplished in a quantized manner. Since their introduction in the early 1960s, no exceptions to these rules have yet been found among the organization of the coat proteins in spherical viruses. Indeed recently detailed molecular conformational mechanisms for quasi-equivalence is beginning to evolve from high resolution X-ray analysis of crystalline viruses, and such mechanisms will be described in a subsequent section (14).

The underlying icosahedral symmetry of spherical viruses is not found in any other protein aggregate. This is due to the fact that with simple globular shaped proteins the icosahedral point group generates a shell-like particle useful for encapsulating other material such as nucleic acids. However, another form of symmetrical aggregation common to viruses is found in other polymerizing systems. In rodlike viruses such as tobacco mosaic virus the coat protein units form a cylindrical shell with each member related to the aggregate by helical symmetry. Long continuous polymers of proteins like sickle cell hemoglobin (15, 16), actin (17, 18), and tubulin (19, 20) have helical symmetry, even though they may not form cylindrical shells like those found in the rodlike viruses.

To describe the symmetry of helical aggregates, only a few parameters are necessary. The symmetry element for such particles is again a line located in the center of the cylinder describing the particle. The symmetry operation is somewhat more complex than a simple rotation axis and is called a *screw* axis. In the helical motif the protein unit is rotated around as well as translated in the direction of the screw axis in both cases by a precise angle and distance, respectively. Congruency may not occur in a single turn of the screw, that is, there may be a nonintegral number of protein subunits per turn. The properties of the helical aggregate are usually described by the distance between turns measured along the screw axes itself and by the number of protein subunits contained in one turn.

Although helical viruses and continuous aggregates of other proteins can both be described by helical screw symmetry, their final appearance is somewhat different. Caspar and Klug showed that for cylindrical shells of proteins in the rodlike virus, specific packing can be represented by a closely packed plane net (12). Such a planar net rolled into a cylinder produces a cylindrical shell with a varying size hole in the center. Rodlike polymers can also be formed, which have a solid core. In helical aggregates such as those formed by sickle cell hemoglobin, multiple strands of helical subunits are packed closely together producing an almost solid filamentlike structure (15).

The rules of symmetry, which describe the motif of protein subunits in biostructures as small as enzymes containing only two subunits and as large as tobacco mosaic virus, have their basis in the fact that aggregation is the result of specific protein-protein interactions (21). With the exception that quasi-equivalence may occur under special circumstances, the interaction sites and aggregation energy between protein subunits in the oligomeric system are always identical. The specific physical forces and hence energy comprising such interactions have been described in Section 2.6. The closed symmetrical structures described by the various forms of point group symmetry multiply the energetically favored subunit-subunit interaction by a symmetry factor. In the simplest case of the protein comprised of two identical subunits, the symmetry factor is 2. For example, if a region labeled A1 on subunit 1 of the protein interacts with a region B2 on subunit 2 (A1 to B2), then the twofold rotational symmetry generates a second identical contact, which would be A2 to B1, and the stabilization energy is increased by a factor of 2.

Exceptions to the symmetrical formation of oligomers are possible. Furthermore, even where the rules of symmetry are observed, in a relatively small volume near the symmetry element itself, the symmetry may break down. Again using the twofold symmetrical protein as an example, if an atom (or side chain) in subunit 1 is positioned on or very near the twofold rotation axis, then clearly its mate in subunit 2 cannot occupy the same volume. The twofold symmetry in such circumstances does not apply exactly (22). This special property of symmetrical proteins has chemical significance. In those regions of the oligomer near the symmetry element a stoichiometry of less than the value predicted by the number of subunits is possible. Sometimes chemical reactivity of groups further away from the symmetry element may even be different because of this subtle conformational effect.

In summary, the simple principles of point group symmetry permit predictions about the overall geometrical structure of closed well-defined oligomeric proteins. In general terms the symmetry is the result of specific subunit-subunit interactions. Simple rotation axes or combinations of rotation axes are the principal forms of symmetry found in these closed oligomeric proteins.

However, in continuous aggregates of proteins another form of symmetry is possible, and this is the screw symmetry that was described for helical aggregates.

To define the symmetry of subunits present in an oligomeric protein both chemical and structural data are necessary. Precise knowledge of molecular weights for the component subunits and the oligomeric form of the protein is frequently critical to the determination of its symmetry. Methods for determining the molecular weight of a purified protein are discussed in Chapter 5, while the determination of subunit molecular weight is now almost trivial using SDS electrophoresis methods. The symmetry or lack of symmetry may be determined either directly from electron density maps obtained crystallographically or, less reliably, from the projected images of molecules seen on electron micrographs. Furthermore, even if an electron density map cannot be calculated, single crystal X-ray data can often be used indirectly to arrive at the correct symmetry of the protein molecule.

Turning first to the use of electron microscopy, because of resolution limits on electron micrographs including the effects of stain, electron beam, and vacuum, and because of the fact that one is always observing a projection of the specimen, this is generally a difficult way of determining molecular symmetry. To take one successful example, Eisenberg, Josephs, and Reisler have summarized the results of electron microscopic studies on bovine glutamate dehydrogenase (23).

Depending on which projected view is seen in the electron micrograph the arrangement of the six subunits in the glutamate dehydrogenase molecule produces some distinctive images that suggest that this protein has dihedral 32 symmetry. The reader is referred to the review article to study the original electron micrographs (23). In the case of glutamate dehydrogenase and for that matter any protein in which the molecular symmetry has been deduced from electron microscopy, the major sources of errors were listed in the previous paragraph. On the other hand, if the particle itself is a large continuous aggregate such as a helical polymer or alternatively thin fragments of crystalline protein can be formed, the micrographs contain additional information. Much more powerful methods such as optical diffraction or image reconstruction can be used to aid in the determination of the molecular symmetry. Such methods in principle are similar to those used in X-ray crystallography and do not require a special descriptive section (24). The added reliability obtained from imaging fiberlike aggregates or crystal fragments is attributable to the multiple copies of the molecular image contained in a definable orientation.

Single crystal X-ray diffraction studies are the most reliable method for determining the symmetry relating the subunits in an oligomeric protein, and several different levels of sophistication can be used to apply these methods. At the simplest level a three-dimensional electron density map of the crystalline protein in question is available. During scrutiny of even a low-resolution electron density map it is generally possible to see the component subunits in the symmetrical motif.

As an example of such an approach the simple two subunit protein cytoplasmic malate dehydrogenase can be used. The crystalline pig heart enzyme was studied by single crystal X-ray methods using isomorphous heavy atom derivatives and an electron density map at 5 Å resolution was obtained (25). In this map relatively small contact areas existed between subunits in the crystalline array, except in one case where a broad contact area was visible. Assuming this to be the interactive region between subunits in the dimeric protein, it was also apparent from the map that this pair of selected subunits was arranged with twofold rotational symmetry (25). A number of other examples of direct observation of subunit symmetry in electron density maps have been documented; in fact, hemoglobin cited at the beginning of this section was the first. However, it is quite common for the symmetry to be known before electron density maps are calculated, and this is possible by using methods that will be described subsequently.

At higher resolution, greater than about 3.5 Å, a molecular model and atomic coordinates are generally obtainable from the electron density map of the oligomeric protein. Keeping in mind the fact that two identical objects can always be moved into the same position in space by a general rotation and translation about a line, it is possible to calculate and even refine the nature of the symmetry relationships among the atoms in the subunits comprising the protein (26, 27). After the precise coordinate transformation related to the symmetry operation is defined by such refinement procedures, "conformational" departures from the symmetry are detectable by simply comparing the rotated and unrotated coordinates.

The direct observation of subunit symmetry in an electron density map is easy to envision. Two more subtle crystallographic approaches can also be used to arrive at the symmetry contained in oligomeric proteins, and both have been extensively described in a review article by Matthews and Bernhard (28). The two approaches can be labeled as (a) crystallographic symmetry-volume relationships and (b) noncrystallographic symmetry detection.

The symmetry-volume relationships are used in the following way to arrive at molecular symmetry. The *unit cell* of any crystal is defined as the parallelpiped, which when translated one unit repeat distance in the directions of the Cartesian axes describing the lattice will generate the entire crystal. This unit cell can frequently be subdivided into smaller volumes called *asymmetric units*. In all instances, the asymmetric units comprising the crystal unit cell are related to one another by one or more symmetry operations. Indeed crystals where the unit cell and asymmetric units are the same are rare. If the entire protein molecule is found in one of these asymmetric units, there is no useful direct physical (or crystallographic) expression of the oligomeric protein symmetry. If, on the other hand, the volume of the asymmetric unit will only accommodate a fraction of the molecule, then that subunit will be related to another by the same symmetry operation that relates the asymmetric units to each other.

Symmetry operations relevant to protein crystals that are permissible in three-dimensional lattices include two-, three-, four-, and sixfold rotation and screw axes, and such forms of rotational symmetry in oligomeric proteins can be detected by symmetry-volume relationships. The symmetry operations present in any crystal lattice are described by the so-called space group, which can be obtained from preliminary X-ray diffraction photographs from single crystals of the protein in question. The volume of the unit cell and an asymmetric unit can be obtained from dimensions measurable on the same diffraction photographs. The number of protein subunits present in an asymmetric unit is a function of its volume, the density of the crystals, the partial specific volume, and molecular weight of the protein in question (29,30). In the absence of density measurements a simple rule of thumb is that the protein occupies 50% of the volume of the unit cell and that it has a partial specific volume of 0.74 cm³/g. Knowing these factors the number of protein subunits in an asymmetric unit can be assigned. If this number is some integer fraction of the number of subunits present in the protein, then the molecular symmetry is the same as the elements of the crystal symmetry relating one asymmetric unit to another.

When the asymmetric unit contains one or more oligomeric molecules low-resolution X-ray diffraction data from the protein crystals might still be useful in analyzing the molecular organization. The diffraction data, even without reaching the stage of electron density map calculations, can be analyzed for what is now being called noncrystallographic symmetry. The term noncrystallographic symmetry, when used in conjunction with X-ray diffraction data, is synonymous with molecular symmetry. Although beyond the scope of this chapter, methods for detecting noncrystallographic symmetry in X-ray diffraction data have been devised and widely used to study crystalline oligomeric proteins (31). These methods depend first on measuring the X-ray crystal data usually only to low resolution and analyzing this data iteratively to detect both the type (twofold, threefold, etc.) and orientation of molecular rotational symmetry present in the X-ray diffraction data.

2.1.3 Protein Conformation in the Crystalline State

Most of the detailed structural information for oligomeric proteins has resulted from single crystal X-ray diffraction studies. More limited but still significant contributions have come from the areas of neutron and electron diffraction and electron microscopy. Neither space nor the scope of this chapter permits us to provide the reader with a description of the methodology of diffraction studies, but several excellent texts are referenced here for those who want to read about the more technical aspects of these methods (24,30,32). X-ray crystallographic studies have some inherent limitations and several interrelated factors should be taken into account when discussing the molecular structure of a protein. These factors include (a) the relationship of the molecular structure in the crystalline state to that in solution; (b) the accuracy of structural data derived from both electron density and difference electron density maps; (c) the nature of conformational disorder as found in the crystalline state.

The question of crystal structure vs solution structure has been given a great deal of attention since the early results of X-ray analysis were reported. Although no major differences have ever been found, several factors should be considered in relating solution properties of a protein with a crystal structure. Clearly X-ray diffraction analysis yields an essentially static image of a protein structure. The time needed for X-ray data collection is many orders of magnitude longer than the time scale considered when discussing any dynamic property of a protein. A protein molecule in a crystal lattice may have segments of polypeptide chain that have certain restrictions on forms of conformational variability, which are not present in solution. Such restrictions may be the result of crystal packing phenomena. Since such conformational variations are small and generally rare, and since they are often observable in the crystalline state as well, this is not a major difficulty. Finally, the ionic environment for a protein molecule in a crystal can be assumed to be essentially identical to that in solution. Based on this fact alone the structure of a protein in the crystalline phase must be similar to the predominant conformation present in a solution of similar pH and ionic strength.

Of the many tests possible for verifying the identity of protein conformation in the crystalline and solution status the measurement of enzymatic activity is among the most sensitive. Several enzymes have been found to be fully active in the crystal form (33,34), whereas others have been observed to have only somewhat reduced enzymatic activity (35,36). A reduced level of enzymatic activity can be explained in a number of different ways. Many enzymes are known to undergo subtle conformational changes during the binding of substrates or during catalysis. In the crystalline form lattice effects might prevent these changes from occurring in the same way as they do in solution. Based on somewhat similar effects, it has been observed that in some instances protein crystals will disintegrate upon the addition of substrates, cofactors, or other ligands. Such effects are due to an accompanying conformational change with a concomitant breakdown of the crystal lattice.

In instances where a crystalline enzyme is inactive, the simplest explanation is that the active site is sterically blocked by adjacent protein molecules in the crystal lattice. Hence substrates cannot reach the active site of the enzyme, even though it is in the appropriate active conformation (37).

Another important observation that serves to establish the identity of crystal and solution structure is related to polymorphic crystal forms. At least two proteins have been crystallized from very different solvents and as a result appear in different crystal lattice systems. The two proteins are subtilisin and ribonuclease (38,39). Comparison of the independently determined molecular structures have shown that few if any significant conformational differences exist in spite of the polymorphic crystal habits and different chemical environments. Comparison of structures of biologically related proteins have shown that they are also conformationally very similar despite the fact that they may come from widely different biological sources and were crystallized using different chemical conditions (40).

Last of all, a variety of other physical-chemical methods confirm the identity between crystal structure and molecular conformation in solution. Chemical modification studies, hydrogen ion exchange studies, and spectroscopic studies of protein-bound chromophores all affirm the similarity between protein in the crystalline state and in solution. An excellent review article on motion in proteins by Gurd and Rothgeb (41) touches on these physical chemical methods and results. After more than ten years of considering the crystal-solution relationship, it is now quite clear that only subtle differences are likely to be found for proteins in these different states. The acceptance of the principle of identity or near-identity between conformations in these two states is significant. It means that the more sophisticated physical-chemical methods can now be used to study dynamic processes in proteins using the crystal structure as a basis.

The second factor regarding the crystal conformation of proteins that must be considered is the accuracy of the coordinates and the reliability of conformational differences observed through protein modification in the crystalline state. The nature of the X-ray method and of protein crystals in general makes the achievable reliability of atomic coordinates near to a few tenths of an angstrom. By measuring X-ray data corresponding to very high resolution (better than 1.5 Å), and by using refinement methods the atomic coordinates can be improved even further.

However, a few additional considerations must be made. It has long been known that in electron density maps of proteins, some parts of the polypeptide chain appear clearer and better resolved than others, that is, conformational disorder exists in protein crystals. While in some instances this can be attributed to experimental errors, in others the disorder must be an intrinsic property of the protein. Several reasons may explain the absence or reduced electron density in specified regions of a protein (42). Conformational polymorphism, where segments of the protein appear to be able to assume a number of stable conformations, is one reason, and such effects have been observed in several crystalline proteins (43,44). In such cases if the side chain is restricted to only two or three alternative conformations all may appear in the electron density map, although at less than unit weight (42). In instances where more conformations are possible no electron density would be observable for that segment of the polypeptide chain.

Thermal effects may also vary in different parts of the electron density map of a protein. Recent developments have shed some light on this effect in proteins, although not yet to oligomeric systems. Refinement of protein crystal structures, using the methods of small molecule crystallography, have been successfully carried out on a number of proteins. In this kind of refinement both the positional parameters and the so-called "temperature" factor of all atoms can be fitted to the measured X-ray data. The temperature factor is primarily an estimate of the thermal mobility of each individual atom. Wherever atomic or near atomic resolution can be achieved, the atomic temperature factor is probably influenced by its location in the protein molecule. To simplify refinement an overall temperature factor is frequently assigned to each amino acid in the protein, but again the final value seems to be a measure of the conformational position of that residue in the overall structure. Hence residues located in the interior of proteins have temperature factors similar to the value for small organic molecules. Near and at the surface of the molecule the temperature factor increases.

The variation in temperature factor along the polypeptide chain may also be related to the conformation for classes of proteins. For example, lysozyme from two different species have been extensively refined at high resolution (45). The temperature factor variation for human and hen egg-white lysozyme are quite similar in related elements of conformation (45), and these similarities occur in spite of differences in the amino acid sequence.

As noted in the introduction to this section, crystallographic studies can also be used to determine conformational differences between proteins. Two different experimental approaches are possible. If the change in conformation is relatively minor straightforward difference Fourier analysis can be used. The accuracy of difference methods is better than that of the original coordinate determination. Frequently differences approaching 0.1 Å can be found, whereas the original coordinate determinations may be reliable only to about an angstrom. If the conformational changes cause a major alteration in crystal lattice parameters, or a new crystal form results, a de novo structure determination is required. In such a situation the overall conformational differences may not be reliable unless they exceed about one-half angstrom. Furthermore, when two conformations arising from different crystal studies are compared, the effect of different crystal environments must also be taken into account.

As an example of how two or more independent X-ray analyses produce almost identical results, the molecular structure of chymotrypsin may be used. A detailed comparison of the α and γ forms of chymotrypsin show no discernable conformational differences. α-Chymotrypsin obtained at pH 4.2 is comprised of two identical subunits (44), and γ-chymotrypsin is a monomeric species obtained at pH 5.6 (46). Aside from this difference only a few exposed side chains seem to differ in conformation. On the other hand, exposure of α-chymotrypsin crystals to high pH values does not destroy crystallinity, but extensive conformational changes are evident in several parts of the molecule (47). Under these circumstances, the two molecules in the α-chymotrypsin dimer undergo different conformational changes. This asymmetry would not occur in solution, since they appear to result from the crystal lattice effects (22,44,47).

The close similarity between the crystal and solution structure of both simple and oligomeric proteins is well established. Where different forms are observable in solution, they can generally be observed in the crystalline phase or vice versa (48). Conformational mobility more generally attributed to protein molecules in solution is also found in the crystalline state. Stable conformational substates different from the reference state can be defined if different crystalline forms are obtainable or occasionally in a single electron density map. Difference Fourier methods may also be used to detect conformational changes. X-ray measurements at very low temperatures along with refinement methods may also be useful in studying motional properties of atoms in a given structure.

2.2   HIERARCHICAL LEVELS OF PROTEIN STRUCTURE

While the idea of forms of secondary structure such as α-helices is commonplace in discussing protein conformation, principles of super-secondary structure and the idea of lobes and domains in tertiary organization is relatively new. This section briefly describes both the old and new levels of protein organization. The results are again derived from crystallographic analysis. A description of the underlying energetics that generate these higher levels of organization is largely omitted except for those relating to the hydrogen bond. This type of noncovalent interaction can be roughly defined from the crystal coordinates, and hence it is easily discussed along with the structure.

The discussion of tertiary structure (Section 2.2.3) emphasizes some unique consideration about both monomeric and oligomeric proteins. This is the emerging concept of unique definable lobes within a single globular unit. The reader should pay special attention to the apparent confusion between the use of the terms super-secondary, domains, and lobes. Each of these terms has a different structural meaning, but it should become clear in the text that follows that their definitions, to a certain extent, overlap.

2.2.1   Secondary Structure

The secondary structure of a protein refers to the stable regular folding of a polypeptide chain. No term has yet been given to irregular conformations, that is, those with no obvious characteristic features. Occasionally the term random coil is used for irregular folding, but this should be reserved for the randomly fluctuating polypeptide chains generally associated with denatured proteins. As already noted, secondary structure is typified by a folding pattern where the polypeptide backbone dihedral angles, ϕ and ψ, have a unique set of values producing a helical conformation. For polypeptides with planar peptide bonds the helical pitch and the number of units per turn is uniquely determined by the values of ϕ and ψ. By increasing the number of units per turn, a whole spectrum of helices are generated. However, only a few are relevant to protein structures, and they occur where hydrogen bonding between backbone amido and carbonyl groups within the helix are possible.

Minimization of the intramolecular free energy that stabilizes secondary structure has shown that the α-helix, sometimes labeled 3.6_{13}, is the most favorable (2). This particular structure is characterized by 3.6 residues per turn and by nearly linear hydrogen bonds between an amido group and a carbonyl group four residues back along the chain. Nearly all helical structures observed in crystalline proteins are of this type. The 3.0_{10}-helix is characterized by three amino acids per turn and by hydrogen bonds, less linear than in the α-helix. The hydrogen bonds in this form of helix occur between an amido group and a carbonyl group three residues back. Only very short pieces containing two to three hydrogen bonds and one or two turns have been observed in proteins of known structure. Free-energy calculations show that the α-helix is more stable than the 3_{10}-helix by about 2 kcal/mol (2).

The β-strand, a nearly fully extended polypeptide chain, is a form of secondary structure that is rarely seen as an isolated unit. Rather two or more strands of polypeptide chain are arranged adjacent to each other in such a way that interstrand hydrogen bonds involving backbone amido and carbonyl groups are formed. An extended structure is not normally called a β-structure unless it is associated with another extended structure in such a manner. The arrangement of member strands can be parallel, antiparallel, or a mixture of both. In all cases the β-sheets that result could equally well be defined as a form of super-secondary structure. Antiparallel β-sheets have been observed in numerous proteins, both globular and fibrous. Parallel and mixed β-sheet have, on the other hand, only been observed in globular proteins. Furthermore in globular proteins, this type of secondary structure has been generally found in the interior of the protein and removed from solvent.

Several other considerations of strands and helices are noteworthy. For example, secondary structure, when observed in crystalline globular proteins, frequently deviates from the ideal models. Bends have been observed in the middle of helices. The C-terminal end of many helices often change from an α-helix toward a 3_{10}-helix. The intermediate stage has been labeled the α_{II}-helix, and noteworthy is the fact that no hydrogen bonds are formed in this structure (49).

β-sheet structures also show deviations from the ideal form. Water molecules or other potential dual hydrogen donor and acceptor groups are sometimes found inserted between the strands. Most often this happens at the end of β-sheets in such a way that the last hydrogen bond is mediated through an atom not covalently linked to any part of the β-sheet itself (44, 50).

Sometimes simple antiparallel β-secondary structures contain a small bend. This feature has been called the β-bulge and is defined as a region between two consecutive β-type hydrogen bonds, which includes two residues on one strand opposite one residue on the other strand (51). In other words, one residue in one strand is omitted in the hydrogen bonding scheme. With few exceptions the β-bulge is found only in antiparallel β-sheets. It generates a sharp local twist in the sheets, a fact that facilitates the formation of super-secondary structures such as the closed β-barrel. The geometry of polypeptide conformation in the β-bulge arrangement makes it tempting to suggest that a mutation generated insertion or deletion of an amino acid can be accommodated in a β-sheet without causing major distortions (51).

One additional form of secondary structure has been identified in globular proteins, and it has been alternatively labeled hairpin loop, β-bend or chain reversal (52,53). The common structural feature of the β-bend is the organization of four consecutive amino acid units where the first and last residue are close to each other, that is, separated by less than 5 Å. A hydrogen bond between the carbonyl group of the first residue and amido group of the fourth residue is frequently but not always observed. Most β-bends can be classified into one of three principal types depending on the ϕ and ψ values of the second and third residue (52). In type III β-bends or 3_{10}-turns these ϕ and ψ values are similar to those of the 3_{10}-helix. The β-bend is in general located on the molecular surface, and it provides a form of secondary structure leading to a drastic change in chain direction, an important factor when folding a long polypeptide chain into a globular unit (54).

The unique handedness of naturally occurring amino acids has an effect on the forms of secondary structure found in proteins. For example, a helical structure in principle can have either a left- or a right-handed twist. As far as the polypeptide backbone itself is concerned, the left- and right-handed helix is equally stable, and potential energy calculations for polyglycine show that each right-handed helix has a left-handed counterpart of identical energy (2). Energy calculations have shown, however, that interactions between side chains and the backbone make the right-handed helix the more stable and the preferred choice for polypeptide chains of L-amino acids irrespective of the type of helix (2). The energy difference has been estimated to be between 0.3 and 2.0 kcal/mol depending on the type of parameters used in the calculation (2,55). Observations among crystalline proteins support these calculations. No left-handed helices have been observed so far.

In summary, there are two principal forms of secondary structure common to all globular proteins: helices and extended or β-conformation. Helical conformations are further subdivided into two types called α and 3_{10} and have a unique form of handedness related to the chirality of the amino acids. Extended or β-conformations are rarely found as a single conformational segment, but rather in multiple-stranded forms containing interstrand hydrogen bonds. Sometimes well-defined combinations of β-strands alone or of β-strands and helices are found in a large number of proteins, and in such instances they represent a form of super-secondary structure.

2.2.2 Super-Secondary Structure and Domains

In the immediately preceding section a rudimentary description of the various types of secondary structure that have been found in proteins was described. These different kinds of secondary structure can be combined into a higher level of organization sometimes called *super-secondary* structure. Historically the idea of super-secondary structure probably originated with Rossmann's comparison of the molecular structure of dogfish lactate dehydrogenase with other nucleotide binding proteins (27). Proteins as diverse as lactate dehydrogenase and flavodoxin contained a so-called "nucleotide binding fold" and questions arose as to which similarities were due to the conservation of biological function and which were a manifestation of energy factors producing a thermodynamically unique and stable conformation. At the same time another concept, *domain*, was introduced. This term was primarily used to describe conformational similarities between proteins or fractions of proteins having obvious functional relatedness. Furthermore, such conformational similarities have also been observed between proteins of widely different function. This has added a new degree of complexity to this area of molecular biology, since it has not yet been possible to completely distinguish between structural homology resulting from evolution and those attributable to energetic considerations.

Precise definitions of the terms super-secondary structure and domain are therefore difficult to make, since, as already noted, both terms have been used in the literature to describe the same type of conformational similarities among proteins. In this chapter a distinction between super-secondary structure and domain is made, and it is summarized as follows: *Super-secondary structure* is the assembly of elements of protein secondary structural elements, such as β-strands and α-helices, into recognizable and recurring patterns of polypeptide chain folding. It has been called *topological connectivity* by Richardson (56) and *packing of secondary structure* by Levitt and Chothia (57). The term *domain* will be reserved for conformationally homologous protein structures or fractions of protein structures and is characterized by two additional features. An apparent similarity in biological function must exist, although that feature might not always be immediately obvious. Additionally the domain must be formed from a continuous segment of polypeptide chains. Thus as one traces the polypeptide conformation through a domain, it cannot wander into another segment of the protein before returning to complete the domain structure. Domains and similar regions of super-secondary structure become indistinguishable when the domains are of relatively small volumes, have similar biochemical functions, and contain *only* elements of super-secondary structure known to be found in other proteins of unrelated functions. Last of all, questions as to whether homologous segments of proteins should be classified as domains or super-secondary structures are of little consequence if one is not interested in the biological pedigree of the molecules.

Based on the forementioned definitions related forms of super-secondary structure in proteins have been uncovered by many workers, and it is now generally accepted that such forms of conformation have their basis in favorable energy considerations. At least five different factors must be considered in describing this new hierarchial order of conformational organization. These factors are as follows: (*a*) The linear order and type of connectivity of the elements of secondary structure must be catalogued. (*b*) The steric arrangement or handedness of connectivity of the secondary structure must also be described wherever variations are possible. (*c*) The contributing energetics of the combinations of secondary structure must be determined if possible. (*d*) Special patterns in the underlying amino acid sequences leading to the combinations of secondary structure should be tabulated. (*e*) Combinations of super-secondary structure into even higher orders of organization such as domains, lobes, and tertiary structure must also be studied.

To some degree all of these factors are interrelated and hence they serve mainly as useful means of categorizing the forms of super-secondary structure that have so far been uncovered. For example, Richardson has devised a simple way of defining the linear order and type of connectivity in β-sheet structures (56). There are two possible ways of connecting the member strands of a β-sheet structure. Richardson defined one category as *hairpin connections* in which the polypeptide backbone chain reenters the same end of the β-sheet from which it left. The other type of β-strand connectivity loops around (or crosses over) to enter the β-sheet super-secondary structure on the opposite end from which it left and hence is called a *crossover connection*; frequently it is an α-helix that forms the crossover. This particular unit, $\beta\alpha\beta$, is a commonly occurring form of super-secondary structure.

Next the order of connectivity usually needs to be defined. Adjacent connected β-strands in the β-sheet may not be contiguous in the covalent sequence. To use a five-stranded β-sheet as an example, the first two sequentially connected strands could be adjacent in the sheet or be separated by up to three other strands. In 70% of the sheet structures, adjacent strands are sequentially connected (56). In addition to a consideration of the ordering of strands the type of connections must also be noted. As described in the previous paragraph, the connection can be either hairpin, crossover, or complex. It is complex if the polypeptide chain makes an excursion into other parts of the protein before returning to the β-sheet super-secondary structure. Such an excursion between different super-secondary structural elements is not that uncommon (50, 58), whereas similar meandering between domains by definition does not take place. The organization of helices in super-secondary structure are somewhat more difficult to describe. Few recurring forms of super-secondary structure involving only helices have so far been identified (57, 59). Hence a notation similar to that developed for β-sheets have not yet been worked out for any helical assemblies.

The handedness or chirality of forms of super-secondary structure is another factor that must be considered, and it is generally more difficult to describe. Most β-sheet structures display a pronounced twist, right-handed if viewed along the polypeptide strands, left-handed if viewed perpendicular to the chain direction (60). The conformational effect of the twist can be seen in Figure 3. Each strand of polypeptide chain within the parallel β-sheet is represented by a broad arrow. The warp as seen in Figure 3 is caused by a

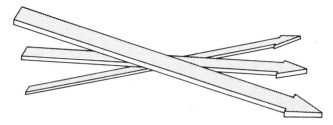

FIGURE 3
Schematic representation of the left-handed twist present in most β-sheet structures. Each segment of polypeptide chain in this three-stranded parallel sheet is represented by an arrow.

slight right-handed twist in the component β-strands and is ultimately attributable to the chirality of the component L-amino acid units. It has in fact been shown that for an extended polypeptide conformation a local potential energy minimum exists for the right-handed twisted β-strand (60). The extent of the twist per residue as observed in proteins of known crystal structure varies, but it is consistently right-handed and is independent of whether the β-sheet is of the parallel, antiparallel, or of the mixed type. A form of super-secondary structure, which is called the β-barrel, contains a β-sheet conformation arranged in cylindrical form (44). The same left-handed rotation found between strands of the β-sheet super-secondary structure results in the strands of a β-barrel appearing to form a right-handed helical structure about the barrel axis (61, 62).

As already noted, types of super-secondary structure that contain both α-helices and β-strands may also have a unique or a favored handedness. A simple example of such a form of chirality in super-secondary structures can be found in the β-strand–α-helix–β-strand unit, which is designated βαβ. This simple form of super-secondary structure has been observed 57 out of 58 occurrences to have a right-handed arrangement (63). The only exception is found in subtilisin (63).

To combine the factors of type, connectivity, and right-handedness in a single example, Figure 4 shows a portion of the super-secondary structure, β-strand–α-helix–β-strand. The specific example is a polypeptide chain segment containing only α-carbon atoms from triose phosphate isomerase (64). In the Richardson notation this form of β-structure would be denoted 1X, the X indicating a crossover connection (56).

While the handedness of types of super-secondary structure are derived from the chirality of the amino acid building blocks, the actual combinations of elements of secondary structure into larger units must result from energetic factors. Hydrogen bonding involving polypeptide backbone groups in strands of β-polypeptide conformation is clearly one important contributing factor. Participation of side chains in hydrogen bonds, including ion pair formation,

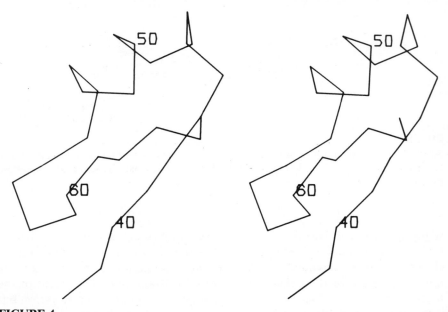

FIGURE 4

The super-secondary structure called $\beta\alpha\beta$. The stereodiagram contains an α-carbon model of residues 38-65 from subunit 1 in triose phosphate isomerase (64).

might also be important, but such noncovalent bonds should occur randomly in globular proteins and do probably play a lesser role in the generation of forms of super-secondary structure. Hydrophobic energy must definitely play a major role, although again when dealing with super-secondary combinations the precise nature of this contribution is more obscure. Although presently not clearly delineated, the arrangement of α-helices, sheet-sheet orientations, and so on is currently being studied to determine if systematic forms of packing might be found in different types of super-secondary structures and in combinations of super-secondary structural units into the final globular protein (65,66).

Turning to the concept of a domain, there is no need to reemphasize factors such as chirality and order of connectivity. Recall also that the distinction between super-secondary structure and domain is a rather fluid one and in some proteins a domain and super-secondary structural unit are one and the same. This is exemplified by chymotrypsin and other serine proteases (44,62) where the β-barrels are both well-defined super-secondary structures and distinguishable functional domains. In other proteins a domain can be composed of several forms of super-secondary structures. Such is the case with several NADH-dependent dehydrogenases in which the nucleotide binding domain contains multiple forms of super-secondary structures (67).

The number of known types of functional domains in proteins is still relatively small and hence is somewhat easier to illustrate than the evolving principles of super-secondary structure. Domains have been identified in heme proteins that transport oxygen, in nucleotide binding proteins, especially dehydrogenases, in proteins binding Fe-S clusters, in proteins binding Ca^{2+} ions, and in the so-called serine proteases. Figure 5 presents one typical example of a protein domain. It shows both the α-carbon positions and that of the Ca^{2+} ion in the protein parvalbumin (68). As can be seen in Figure 5, only about 30 amino acid residues are found in this domain. It is an especially useful example to study because another nearly identical Ca^{2+} binding domain is found in the next segment of the same polypeptide chain. Hence the Ca^{2+} ion binding domain is also an example of a functionally homologous structure appearing more than once in the same polypeptide chain.

An example of a domain that is considerably larger in size is the nucleotide binding domain of dehydrogenases, which is shown in Figure 6. As already noted, this homologous structural unit is found in numerous dehydrogenases and in flavodoxin (67). The nucleotide binding domain generally consists of six strands of parallel β-structure (β-sheet) with four α-helices forming the interconnecting segments. This domain is characterized by the fact that it also contains several elements of super-secondary structure and the reader should recognize both secondary and super-secondary elements in the stereodiagram of the nucleotide binding domain. Several $\beta\alpha\beta$ units are clearly visible. The nucleotide binding domain shown in Figure 6 is also a good example of the confusion that can arise between the concepts of domains and super-secondary

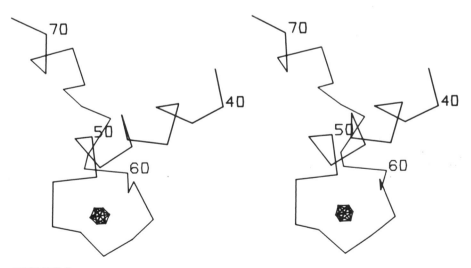

FIGURE 5
One of the two calcium binding domains in parvalbumin. The stereodiagram shows an α-carbon model of residues 39–71 of parvalbumin (68). The calcium ion is represented by the octahedron and every 10th residue is labeled.

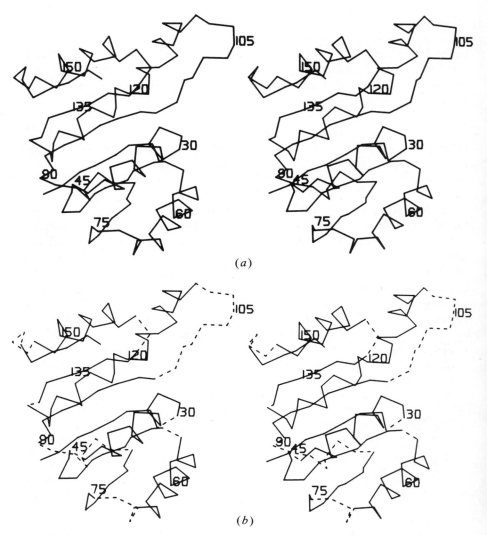

FIGURE 6
The nucleotide binding domain present in lactate dehydrogenase. The stereodiagram contains an α-carbon model of residues 22–163 of lactate dehydrogenase (9). Different secondary structural elements are emphasized in (*b*), (*c*), and (*d*). In part (*b*), both α-helices and β-strands are shown as continuous lines. The rest of the domain, largely turn regions of polypeptide chain are shown stippled. In part (*c*), only helices are shown as lines, and in part (*d*) only β-strands are represented by continuous lines. The domain can be divided near residue 90 into two similar super-secondary structures. Every 15th residue is labeled.

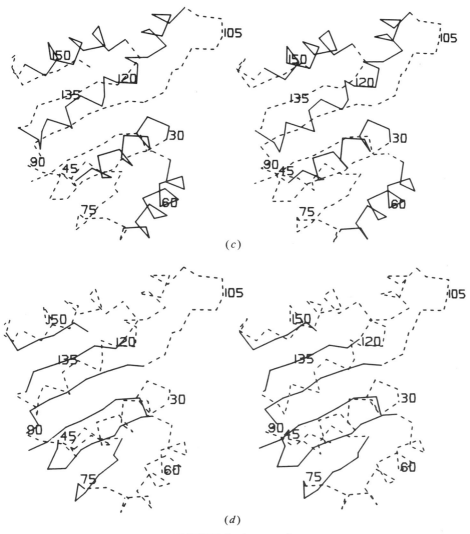

(c)

(d)

FIGURE 6 (*Continued*)

structures. The nucleotide binding fold is a functional domain, in that the same structure will bind the dinucleotide NADH in a variety of enzymes and yet is also known to contain well-defined elements of super-secondary structures, which will occur in many different and unrelated proteins.

In summary, a few examples of forms of super-secondary structure found in globular proteins have been described. Factors that must be considered in studying this new form of hierarchial organization such as linear order, type, and handedness have also been described, and a few examples from known protein structures illustrate two units of super-secondary structure, the β-sheet and the $\beta\alpha\beta$ units. A number of other forms of super-secondary structure are known. Some are easily recognizable, such as the four nearly parallel helices found in hemerythrin (69), cytochrome b562 (70), and tobacco mosaic virus coat protein (71). Other forms may still have gone undetected. Related to these conformational similarities, which must be due to energetic considerations, were those probably stemming from evolutionary factors. Such protein units, herein called domains, may also contain one or more units of super-secondary structure. Thus the nucleotide binding *domain* of dehydrogenases contains several elements of the super-secondary structural unit, β-strand–α-helix–β-strand. The evolving systematics and the interrelationships of these hierarchial levels may serve in an important way to protein chemists. Thus it is now possible to visualize the entire structure of triose phosphate isomerase (64) or concanavalin A (50) or other proteins simply by remembering the appropriate units of super-secondary structure that comprise the protein.

2.2.3   Tertiary Structure

The next level in the hierarchical organization of protein structures has been called tertiary structure. This term describes the assembly of super-secondary structures, lobes, and domains as well as irregular conformations that together constitute the completely folded polypeptide chain. For the sake of future discussion, the term "lobe" is used to describe a larger subassembly of the polypeptide chain that appears to be stable even if the chain connections to other parts of the protein were to be cleaved (57). A lobe has all the structural characteristics of an entire globular protein with respect to distribution of types of amino acids.

When a lobe of tertiary structure possesses evolutionary and functional relationships to another protein or another lobe of the same protein it can also be defined as a domain. In such instances the domain may also contain established forms of super-secondary structure. This extends the overlap of definitions, which was described in the previous section. When considering smaller proteins, it is often found that a domain constitutes the whole protein and the term lobe is inapplicable. Glucagon (72) with a single α-helix and rubredoxin (73) with a β-barrel conformation are such examples. An even more complex situation arises when we consider the nucleotide binding domain common among most NADH-dependent dehydrogenases (67). The structure and folding pattern of this domain, for example, in lactate dehydrogenase (9), is essentially the same as the flavin binding domain in flavodoxin (74). In the former case this domain constitutes only one-half of the total folded polypeptide chain and no visible lobes are present, whereas in the latter case the identical domain, with respect to folding pattern, is the complete molecule.

The occurrence of lobes within a polypeptide chain appears to be a function of the length of the polypeptide chain. As noted by several authors, many proteins can be divided into a number of distinct lobes (75,76). The minimum number of amino acids in such a lobe seems to be around 40–50, whereas the upper limit is more uncertain. Some have suggested 150 amino acids as near the upper limit (76). It is probably inadvisable to set size limitations on a lobe, but clearly small proteins would rarely be expected to have multiple lobes. In describing the tertiary structure of proteins one convenient approach is to view the acquisition of tertiary structure as the assembly of super-secondary structure or lobes or domains. For a multi-domain structure, this directs the attention to obvious functional and evolutionary features that may be evident in the overall tertiary structure.

The tertiary structure of a protein containing only a single lobe or a single form of super-secondary structure is relatively easy to describe. The interior of the molecular structure is closely packed with atoms arranged in a manner similar to that found in crystals of organic molecules (77). There are few polar side chains located in the interior, and if so, they are with rare exceptions, all involved in hydrogen bonds. Most ionizable side chains are almost uniformly scattered about the external surface, although an occasional ion pair located somewhat in the interior of the molecule have been observed.

As the size of the protein increases more than one form of super-secondary structure and more than one lobe may be discernable. If multiple lobes are present, the central core of each is predominantly hydrophobic with polar groups again located on or near the molecular surface. In proteins containing a single lobe but multiple forms of super-secondary structure the interfaces between elements of super-secondary structure tend to be hydrophobic. Solvent molecules trapped in the protein interior are as a rule located between elements of super-secondary structure where they mediate hydrogen bonds (44, 78).

In many respects the interfaces between elements of super-secondary structure or domains are similar to subunit-subunit interfaces. Sometimes even symmetry is detectable where homologous units occur. For example, the covalently linked mate to the Ca^{2+} binding domain shown in Figure 5 would be observed in an orientation related by twofold rotational symmetry in the part of the structure not shown (79). Features such as the location of polar groups, hydrogen bond and ionic bond formation, and trapping of solvent molecules follow the same pattern in both tertiary and quaternary structure organization. Furthermore, a degree of flexibility may be observed between domains just as it may occur between subunits. Such is the case between domains in horse liver alcohol dehydrogenase and the coat protein in crystalline tomato bushy stunt virus (80, 81). Parenthetically, the evolutionary conservation of residues, which in glyceraldehyde 3-phosphate dehydrogenase is involved in subunit-subunit interaction is higher than those residues involved in the interdomain contacts within one subunit (82). It should be expected, however, that the converse might equally well occur.

Most enzymes studied so far seem to consist of at least two domains, and sometimes these domains are contained within identifiable lobes. Frequently this means that the molecular structure has a deep cleft that divides the molecule into two distinct halves. This cleft sometimes serves as the substrate binding site, and the catalytic residues present in the structure belong to two separate domains. Well-documented examples of cleft-containing proteins are lysozyme (37) and the acid proteases (83). In other cases no cleft is readily apparent and the domains are packed closely together. In the two domains found in NADH-dependent dehydrogenases, separate roles have been assigned to the individual domains (67). In functional terms the structural segment containing the nucleotide binding domain is principally involved in binding and orienting the bound NAD^{2+}. The catalytic domain, on the other hand, contains conformational segments whose function may be to carry out the actual oxidation-reduction reaction.

Triple domain enzymes have also been described; examples are pyruvate kinase (84) and glutathione reductase (85). In the latter enzyme, a catalytic domain, a NADPH binding domain, and a FAD binding domain, is discernible. Furthermore, this enzyme containing two subunits has the rather unusual feature that the catalytic residues for a single active site are contributed from two different subunits. This then is a proven case where only the oligomeric form of the enzyme can be catalytically active.

The most direct parallel between the association of domains to form the teriary structure of a protein and subunit assembly to produce the quaternary organization can be found among those proteins where the same domain is repeated more than once in a single continuous polypeptide chain. Gene duplication followed by gene fusion must be the principal evolutionary mechanism for this to occur, since extensive amino sequence homologies are also often apparent. The spatial relationship between the repeated domains may often be similar to that found in oligomeric proteins. If two domains are present pseudo-twofold rotational symmetry may be found like that already

TABLE 1
Molecules with Internal Symmetry

	MW	No. Copies	Seq. Homo.	Symmetry
Ferredoxin (88)	6,000	2	Yes	2-fold
Myogen (68)	11,500	2	Yes	2-fold
Rhodanese (89)	33,000	2	Weak	2-fold
Pepsin family (83)	35,000	2	Weak	2-fold
Trypsin family (62)	25,000	2	No	Complex
Soybean trypsin inhibitor (90)	22,000	3	No	3-fold
Wheat germ agglutinin (91)	17,000	4	—[a]	Complex
Immunoglobulin (86, 87)				
Light chain	25,000	2	Yes	Complex
Heavy chain	50,000	4	Yes	Complex

[a]Probable; no chemical sequence data are available, and the homology is based on a tentative "X-ray sequence."

described for parvalbumin. More complex geometric relationships are also observed, as seen with the immunoglobulins (86, 87) and the serine proteases (62). By way of conjecture, the development of this type of tertiary structure, internal twofold rotational symmetry between domains, seems to follow from the known structure of a protein with two subunits. After gene duplication a symmetrical domain-domain set of interactions adds the usual symmetry factor to the stabilization energy.

In Table 1 is listed the names of proteins of known structure where internal symmetry has been detected. In many other proteins extensive blocks of amino acid sequence repeats have been observed, suggesting internal structural domains that might be duplicated. Structural data are not available for these systems (92).

Rhodanese is a protein of known structure consisting of two nearly identical domains arranged in a symmetrical manner and is a good example of tertiary structure containing multiple domains. It consists of a single polypeptide chain of 293 amino acids divided into two different domains of approximately 140 amino acids each (89). A stereodiagram containing only α-carbons is shown in Figure 7. The view is approximately down the twofold

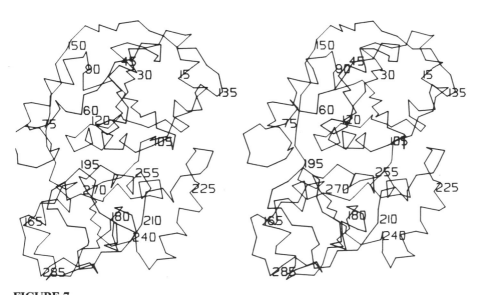

FIGURE 7

The double domain structure of rhodanese. The stereodiagram is an α-carbon representation of the entire molecule (89, 93). The direction of view is approximately along the intramolecular twofold symmetry axis relating the two domains. Every 15th α-carbon atom is labeled. To aid in observing the similarity in the conformation of the two domains, residues 75 and 225 mark the beginning of a conformationally homologous α-helical segment. When viewed in stereo, the reader should be able to find many other examples of homologous elements of secondary structure within the two domains.

rotation axis relating the domains and clearly shows that they have nearly identical structures. At the center of each domain is a five-stranded parallel β-sheet surrounded by three helices on one side and two on the other. The hydrogen bonding scheme as well as the topological connections within the two β-sheets are extremely similar. A least-squares refinement of the distance between equivalent α-carbon atoms showed that the root-mean-square deviation is 1.95 Å for 117 α-carbon atom pairs (93). Within the error limits expected for this kind of analysis the matched α-carbon atoms in the two domains are related by a proper twofold rotation axis.

The twofold symmetry is, however, only exact as far as the α-carbon atoms are concerned; when taking into account all the atoms in both domains, the symmetry relationship degenerates somewhat. This is a direct consequence of the lack of any significant amino acid sequence homology between the two domains. Even when topologically identical residues were aligned, only 15 pairs out of 117 were found to be identical. Of these 15 identities, all pairs except one are located within elements of secondary structure (89, 93). Despite the great dissimilarity in the amino acid sequences of the two domains, their internal structure have similar conformational properties. In each domain the parallel β-sheets donates side chains to each of two hydrophobic cores, located on both sides of the sheet super-secondary structure. The rest of the two hydrophobic clusters is made up of side chains from the helices.

The domain interface contains predominantly hydrophobic residues, but a significant number of polar interactions are also formed. Twenty-six hydrophobic contacts, eight hydrogen bonds, and two salt bridges are found in the domain interface (93). In all of the hydrogen bonds at least one participating atom is from a side chain. There are no hydrogen bonds between the domains that involve backbone atoms alone. Even though there are few homologous amino acids in the two domains, the hydrophobic interactions follow roughly the twofold symmetry pattern, whereas the polar interactions do not.

Last of all, the active site, cys 247, is located at one end of the domain interface (Fig. 7). Most of the interdomain hydrogen bonds are in fact located near the active site, and this is where the symmetry in interdomain interactions differs the most.

In summary, the tertiary structure of many simple proteins consists of a unit of conformation that cannot be subdivided in any reasonable way. Sometimes, however, the tertiary structure of a protein may also be viewed as an assembly of elements of super-secondary structure occasionally arranged in a manner that contains multiple lobes. Evolution has also produced tertiary folding of a single polypeptide chain that contains multiple copies of a unique conformational domain. The arrangement of domains can be complex or symmetrical orientations as seen in rhodanese can occur. The symmetrical arrangement of domains in a single folded polypeptide chain appears very similar to the symmetrical arrangement of subunits in an oligomeric protein.

2.3 STRUCTURE OF OLIGOMERIC PROTEINS

The principles of symmetry and how they relate to the assembly of oligomeric proteins were briefly described in Section 2.1.2. In that section an outline of the evidence or methods that can be used to detect the presence of symmetry elements in crystalline proteins was also provided. However, up to this point no data have been presented as to the number and types of proteins that actually obey these rules. The number of oligomeric proteins for which the structure and the presence of symmetry elements have been analyzed by diffraction methods is now quite large. A complete tabulation is outside the scope of this chapter but can be found in recent reviews by Matthews and Bernhard (28,30). In this section a limited number of well-documented oligomeric protein structures will be used to illustrate the principles discussed in Section 2.1.2. As throughout this chapter, the emphasis is placed on systems where single crystal X-ray diffraction analysis has been the principal tool of investigation. An exception is Section 2.3.4, which describes continuous or helical protein aggregates and which contains models based largely on electron micrographs. At the end of this section detailed information on the subunit-subunit interactions in one oligomeric protein, glyceraldehyde 3-phospate dehydrogenase is presented. Some of these details are unquestionably special for this protein. However, the energetic and conformational principles described for the one selected example are likely to be of a general nature and should with only minor modifications be applicable to other oligomeric systems.

2.3.1 Symmetrical Proteins

The simplest type of homogeneous oligomeric protein contains two identical subunits. As discussed in Section 2.1.2, the only symmetry element possible for such an oligomer is a twofold rotation axis. Proteins containing two subunits and as widely different as malate dehydrogenase (25), triosephosphate isomerase (64), β-lactoglobulin (48), Bence-Jones proteins (86,87), and many others, have their component subunits arranged with such twofold rotational symmetry. While exceptions to this symmetry rule may exist, they appear to be exceedingly rare (cf. Section 2.3.2). Thus dimeric proteins containing identical polypeptide subunits have their subunits arranged with twofold rotational symmetry.

Proteins containing three subunits appear to be relatively rare but still appear to aggregate in the expected symmetrical manner. The structure of two known proteins, bacteriochlorophyll protein (94) and 2-keto-3-deoxy-6-phosphogluconic aldolase (95), have their component subunits arranged with threefold rotational symmetry. With the possibility of exceptions yet to be noted it is safe to generalize that proteins comprised of three identical polypeptide chains will have threefold rotational symmetry.

In the case of proteins containing four identical subunits two symmetrical subunit arrangements are possible, but only one seems to be found in proteins. To date no tetrameric protein with the subunits arranged in a fourfold rotationally symmetric fashion have been observed, rather they seem to favor the dihedral symmetry motif, 222 (See Section 2.1.2). Typical examples of tetrameric proteins with 222 symmetry include glyceraldehyde 3-phosphate dehydrogenase (96), lactate dehydrogenase (9), and phosphoglycerate mutase (97) and perhaps the best known, hemoglobin (7). Although the latter contains two types of subunits, they are sufficiently homologous that to the first approximation they are arranged in a 222 fashion. Hence proteins containing four polypeptide chains generally have their subunits arranged with dihedral, 222 symmetry, noting that fourfold rotational symmetry is possible, but no example has yet been reported.

Aggregates of five protein subunits have not been found in purified proteins, although symmetry arguments would suggest that they should occur with fivefold rotational symmetry. However, proteins containing six subunits have been frequently identified. Predictably, they contain the subunits in a 32 dihedral symmetry arrangement, although sixfold rotational symmetry is also possible. For example, glutamic dehydrogenase, mentioned with respect to the use of electron microscopy in determining subunit symmetry (Section 2.1.2), is thought to have 32 dihedral symmetry (23,98). However, the most detailed description of a protein having the subunits arranged in a 32 dihedral motif is found in the X-ray studies of aspartate transcarbamylase (11,99). Because two different types of protein subunits are present, the so-called regulatory (R) and catalytic (C) subunits, the overall arrangement is somewhat unique. Nevertheless, the six (RC) subunit pairs are arranged in such a manner that the overall point symmetry of this molecule obeys the dihedral 32 arrangement. A more detailed discussion of the assembly of aspartate transcarbamylase is given in Section 2.3.3. Proteins containing six subunits appear to prefer the combination of threefold and twofold rotational symmetry found in the 32 dihedral group. One would expect other yet undocumented proteins with six subunits to also have this subunit arrangement. No examples of sixfold rotational symmetry have yet been described.

With few exceptions oligomeric proteins are assembled in a symmetrical manner. One can never be certain about how many examples are needed before empirical rules can be formulated, but in the case of simple oligomeric proteins this now seems possible. Clearly proteins with two subunits have twofold rotational symmetry, with three subunits threefold axes, while those with four subunits belong to the dihedral point group 222, and those with six subunits appear to favor the dihedral 32 rules. In the case of proteins that have eight or more subunits only a few examples have been studied, and no empirical rule can yet be given. A simple extension of the symmetry principles that have so far been discovered suggests that proteins with eight subunits should have dihedral 42 symmetry. Hemerythrin, an oxygen binding protein frequently found in a form containing eight subunits, obeys this rule (69).

2.3.2 Nonsymmetrical Proteins

In the previous section, examples of the symmetrical aggregation of subunits into oligomeric protein molecules was described. The geometrical symmetry seen in these proteins was observed directly or indirectly using X-ray crystallographic methods. With the same experimental techniques, a few exceptions to the symmetry rules appear to have been found. As already noted, coordinate refinement procedures can detect even relatively small variations from the underlying molecular symmetry. Such departures from the rules of symmetry can occur at two levels of organization, either quaternary or conformational (tertiary).

For oligomeric proteins to be nonsymmetrical at the quaternary level, the subunits are conformationally identical, but their assembly does not obey any form of symmetry. An example of a nonsymmetrical aggregate is the form of yeast hexokinase where the two identical subunits are not related by twofold rotational symmetry (100). This case will be discussed in more detail later. As was noted in Section 2.1.2, stabilization energy from a complementary subunit-subunit interface is multiplied by two in the twofold rotationally symmetric dimer. When this symmetry is absent the twofold multiplication in stabilization energy must be compensated for by the additional complementarity present in a unique subunit-subunit contact region(s).

At the subunit conformational or tertiary level somewhat more subtle departures from symmetry might occur in an oligomeric protein. The subunit association itself may be symmetrical, but minor structural differences between the subunits may exist. Generally such asymmetry may occur only in the crystalline form of the proteins, where symmetrical members of an oligomeric protein might find themselves in anisotropic crystal environment. In such situations the asymmetry can occur in regions quite removed from the symmetry axis. Although no structural data are available in solution, departures from the symmetry would probably occur only near the symmetry element where steric affects could prevent identical conformations (see Section 2.1.2). Such asymmetry has been observed in crystalline proteins, for example, α-chymotrypsin (22) and insulin (101). Temporal departures from protein symmetry in solution and even in the crystalline state must also occur but will be ignored in this discussion.

Last of all, it should be noted that departures from symmetry could also involve the combination of conformational and quaternary structural differences. To use a hypothetical example, a nonsymmetrical dimer of identical (amino acid sequence) subunits in which the member subunits are arranged in a manner that lacks twofold rotational symmetry is possible. In this case one protein subunit would have to have a different conformation than its mate. In such an oligomeric protein the energy contribution from dimerization contributes significantly to the tertiary or conformational energy of the subunits in a direct manner. In fact refolding of the polypeptide chain(s) must occur during the assembly of the aggregate.

Yeast hexokinase, crystal form BII, is presently the single exception to symmetrical aggregation of identical protein subunits (100). In this enzyme, the two chemically identical subunits are related to each other by a 156° rotation accompanied with a 13.8 Å translation along the rotation axis, rather than the expected 180° rotation (twofold) with no translation component. One of the properties of unsymmetrical aggregates is that different residues in each subunit form the subunit-subunit interactions. Recalling that the letter represents a region of a designated subunit, denoted by the numbers 1 and 2 (cf. Section 2.1.2), such contact sets could be denoted by A1 to B2 and C2 to D1. In symmetrical proteins containing two subunits a given contact is always repeated: A1 to B2 and A2 to B1. Such singularity in the subunit-subunit interface is precisely what is found in the molecular structure of yeast hexokinase.

Steitz and co-workers have also dealt with the problem of why subunit association does not continue beyond the assembly of the initial molecule, thus creating endless aggregates (100). That is, in the protein with two subunits described above, with contacts denoted A1-B2, C2-D1, why cannot new subunit interactions of the types A2 to B3 and C1 to D4, and so on be formed? In the yeast hexokinase molecule this does not occur because once the dimer is formed potential binding surfaces (A2, B3, etc) are no longer sterically accessible to other subunits.

Nonsymmetrical subunit association such as observed for hexokinase can generate nonequivalence in the affinities for ligands and in the reactivity of functional groups. In its extreme half-site reactivity results. Hexokinase contains two different types of ATP binding sites; one of these is present with a stoichiometry of only one per hexokinase dimer (100). It is located between the subunits of the nonsymmetrical dimer, and clearly other such intersubunit binding sites locations might also possess half-site stoichiometry. Parenthetically other regions not necessarily in the subunit contact area may also be singularly present in the dimer.

Last of all, this special case of nonsymmetrical aggregation must be examined to see if conformational differences between the two subunits are present. Steitz and his co-workers have compared the conformation of the individual subunits using models at 3.5 Å resolution and found them very similar with only a few small changes present (100). In summary, the two subunit form of yeast hexokinase is nonsymmetrical with no *major* conformational differences between the member subunits. In the hierarchial notation it is nonsymmetrical at the quaternary level.

The molecular structure of the hexameric form of insulin contains examples of a different type of deviation from the usual rules of subunit symmetry (101). In the crystalline form of insulin, six insulin molecules plus two zinc ions are arranged such that three insulin dimers are related by a crystallographic and therefore an exact threefold rotation axis. The two zinc ions are located on the threefold axis. Each monomer in these three dimers is related by a noncrystallographic twofold axis. Chemical data indicate that the same hexamer is also present in solution (101). The conformational differences between the insulin monomers in the symmetrical dimer only occur near the twofold rotation axis. In this region hydrogen bonds are observed between extended segments of the B chains of two molecules and a short segment of antiparallel β-sheet structure is formed. With atoms of two subunits approaching very close to the molecular twofold rotation axis, steric packing phenomena comes into effect. This overcrowding can be relieved by having differing conformations in segments of the neighboring subunits. The departures are limited and only the relative position of a side chain (phe-B24 and B'24) seems to differ (101). The polypeptide chain conformations of the two insulin subunits appear identical.

Nonsymmetrical aggregates of proteins containing identical subunits thus seem to fall into three classes. (I) At the tertiary or conformational level departures from symmetry mainly occur near a symmetry element for obvious steric reasons. Other such subtle conformational variations may also occur in the structure of a crystalline protein where the pertinent subunits are in an anisotropic environment. In the latter instance, such variations would have no significance in the solution form of the protein. Examples of class I types departures from the rules of symmetry are probably very common. (II) At the quaternary level it is possible for two conformationally similar (or identical) protein subunits to form a nonsymmetrical aggregate. In these instances continuous polymerization is prevented by steric factors, and the dimeric form of yeast hexokinase appears to be the only presently known example of this nonsymmetrical class of oligomers. They appear to be a rare exception. (III) Conformational and quaternary (I and II) departures are possible realizing that only conformational differences are sufficient. In such a yet hypothetical aggregate, identical polypeptide chains form unique oligomers with each subunit in a different conformation. No examples are presently known.

2.3.3 Proteins Containing Different Types of Subunits

Oligomeric proteins containing different types of polypeptide chains are nearly as commonplace in biological systems as those with identical subunits. However, only in a few instances is much known about their molecular structure. If one can extrapolate from these few examples it appears clear that the same underlying symmetry rules and hence energetic principles apply equally well to oligomeric proteins containing two or more different types of polypeptide chains as they do to the homogenous aggregates. Such being the case the symmetry arguments (see Sections 2.1.2 and 2.3.1) can frequently be used in a simple way to predict the stoichiometry and the crude arrangement of units in the oligomeric protein. X-ray crystallographers are acutely aware of these principles, but protein chemists may not be; two known examples are discussed here in sufficient detail that the common principles will be apparent.

Two types of subunit assemblies containing different polypeptide chains can be described. The different types of subunits can be present in equal amounts, that is, $(\alpha\beta)_m$, $(\alpha\beta\gamma)_m$, and so on, where the symbols α, β, and γ are the different subunit types and m is the stoichiometry number. Alternatively the stoichiometric ratio can be different for each subunit type, and the oligomer can be represented by $\alpha_n\beta_m$, $\alpha_n\beta_m\gamma_p$, and so on.

The simplest type of a heterogenous aggregate is a $\alpha\beta$ dimer, that is, $m=1$, and such oligomers are frequently found in biological systems. In terms of structural detail, the best-known and characterized examples are the complexes between trypsin and trypsin inhibitors and a stereodrawing of an α-carbon model is shown in Figure 8 (102, 103).

High-resolution X-ray studies have shown the contact area between the two proteins at nearly atomic resolution. As is visible in Figure 8, the actual

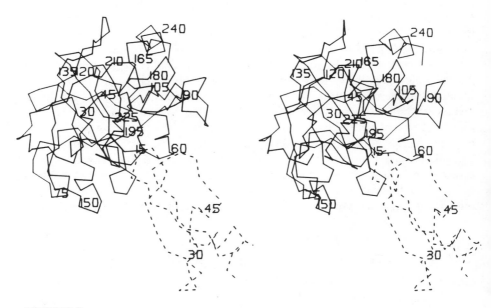

FIGURE 8

The bovine trypsin–bovine pancreatic trypsin inhibitor complex. The stereodiagram contains only α-carbon atoms and shows the molecular structure of the trypsin-trypsin inhibitor complex (102). Trypsin is shown with continuous lines, and the inhibitor is shown stippled. Every 15th residue in each protein is numbered. A covalent bond (not shown) is formed between Ser 195 and Lys 15. In stereo, the reader should be able to observe which residues in each molecule might be involved in protein-protein interactions.

contact region between trypsin and trypsin inhibitor is relatively small. However, with all the atoms present it can be seen that the molecular surfaces fit closely together forming about six hydrogen bonds between the two molecules (102). As expected, there is complementarity at the conformational level between the two protein molecules. Furthermore, the conformations of trypsin and the pancreatic trypsin inhibitor are essentially the same in the native and complexed state. Hence the structural features necessary for the specificity of the recognition process preexist in the two protein components.

At least two cases of higher aggregates of proteins containing two different polypeptide chains are known, hemoglobin and aspartate transcarbamylase. For hemoglobin the molecular structure of several forms are now known to near-atomic resolution (104). Noteworthy but not changing its usefulness as an example is the fact that hemoglobin is a somewhat special case of an oligomeric protein with different subunit types. It is special because of the near identity in polypeptide conformation of the α- and β-chains. Parenthetically, the conformational similarity occurs in spite of relatively large differences in amino acid sequences. The structure of hemoglobin can be represented by the symbols used earlier, $(\alpha\beta)_2$. As previously mentioned, the four subunits are arranged with pseudo-222 dihedral point symmetry; this is shown schematically in Figure 9. The exact twofold rotation axis relating the two $\alpha\beta$ pairs is shown as the horizontal dotted line. The pseudo-twofold rotation axes are also represented by dotted lines and the usual crystallograpic dyad symbol as shown in Figure 9. One twofold rotation axis is perpendicular to the plane of the drawing and is simply indicated by the centralmost dyad symbol. The lines interconnecting the subunit symbols indicate potential subunit-subunit contacts. Perutz noted that, even at low

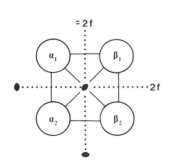

FIGURE 9

Schematic representation of the subunit-subunit interactions in hemoglobin. The symbol ● or the letter 2f indicate a twofold rotation axis which is shown schematically by the dotted lines. One such axis is perpendicular to the plane of the paper and shown only by the symbol ● in the centermost part of the drawing. The horizontal symmetry axis is an exact twofold rotation axis producing the congruency of α_1 upon α_2 and β_1 upon β_2 subunits. The other two symmetry elements are only pseudo-twofold rotation axes, since they involve conformational homology between α and β subunits. Potential subunit-subunit contacts are shown by the fully drawn lines. Six such contacts can be seen but the symmetry shows that they occur as pairs of three different types.

resolution, the magnitude of subunit contacts differed notably for different pairs, for example, $\alpha_1 : \alpha_2$, $\alpha_1 : \beta_1$, and so on. Only a relatively small number of mainly polar contacts existed between the α_1 and α_2 subunits, and the β_1 and β_2 subunits in the tetramer (7,105). On the other hand, a relatively broad subunit contact area existed between α_1 and β_1 and its symmetry-related mate, α_2 and β_2. Detailed tabulation of the subunit-subunit interactions in hemoglobin have been published and will not be repeated here (106, 107).

The presence of detectable amounts of dissociated forms of hemoglobin in solution at neutral pH and moderate ionic strength and the magnitude of each of the different subunit-subunit contacts in the electron density map led Perutz to suggest that dissociation of the $(\alpha\beta)_2$ form occurs in a manner that generates $\alpha\beta$ molecules (7). The other possible dissociation would lead to α_2 plus β_2 molecules. The presence of an $\alpha\beta$ oligomer in solution has been substantiated by chemical methods, reviewed by Baldwin (105). Thus the crystallographic structural information about subunit-subunit contacts as was available in the case of hemoglobin aided in understanding association-dissociation phenomena occurring in solution.

In addition the structural data describing subunit-subunit contacts has another important facet. Chemical properties related to association are of special interest for hemoglobin and other aggregates that function in an allosteric or cooperative manner. Both for homogeneous and heterogeneous oligomeric proteins cooperative chemical phenomena must be communicated through the subunit contact regions. The complexity of cooperativity at the structural level therefore is attributable to the intricacies of the noncovalent interactions in the contact areas between component subunits (see Section 2.3.4).

The only other structurally well-defined oligomeric protein containing different types of subunits is of the type $(\alpha\beta)_6$. Aspartate transcarbamylase, also labeled aspartate carbamoyl transferase, contains six catalytic (C) and six regulatory (R) subunits arranged with 32 symmetry (11). While the arrangement of subunits obeys the 32 symmetry, the packing and contacts of R and C subunits is somewhat surprising. Thinking of three catalytic subunits (C_3) as the central unit, the molecule contains two such C_3 oligomers in a nearly eclipsed arrangement. The two C_3 units are related by a twofold rotation axis (11). The C subunits in each C_3 unit have few contacts with the C subunits in the second. Instead each C unit is linked through a R_2 dimer to another C unit in the opposite C_3 unit (11). The C subunits connected in this manner are $120°$ apart around the molecular threefold rotation axis. Thus, whereas the subunits of aspartate transcarbamylase are arranged in a fashion that obey the usual symmetry rules, they do so in a rather unique manner. Incidentally the tightly associated R subunits contain a form of super-secondary structure which has been observed in subunit-subunit contacts in other proteins such as prealbumin (58), alcohol dehydrogenase (8), and concanavalin A (50). An eight-stand β-sheet structure is formed, which contains four strands from one R subunit and four strands from its twofold rotationally related mate.

The X-ray structure of aspartate transcarbamylase when described in terms of subunit organization and principal contacts, just as in the case of hemoglobin, has several implications in assembly and dissociation processes. The six regulatory subunits appear to form very close subunit-subunit contacts in pairs, suggesting that a dimeric form of the regulatory subunits is a relatively stable form of these protomers. Similarly the tight packing of catalytic subunits around the molecular threefold rotation axis of the aspartate transcarbamylase molecule suggest that this might be a relatively stable form of the catalytic subunits. Hence both during assembly and dissociation reactions, if any intermediate forms of this C_6R_6 protein were to appear, they would probably occur in the form of C trimers and R dimers. Earlier chemical studies had shown that in the presence of mercurials aspartate transcarbamylase dissociated into two catalytic subunits, C_3 trimers, and three regulatory subunits, R_2 dimers (108, 109). Just as was the case for hemoglobin major subunit-subunit contacts observed crystallographically, C-trimers and R-dimers, can suggest which intermediate oligomeric units occur during dissociation and probably during assembly processes as well.

In summary, proteins that are composed of different types of polypeptide subunits contain no new structural features. The same symmetry rules that apply to homogeneous oligomeric proteins can be used to describe heterocomplexes. Allowing for possible exceptions to appear in the future, proteins composed of four subunits $(\alpha\beta)_2$ will most likely occur with twofold rotational symmetry, proteins containing six subunits $(\alpha\beta)_3$ with a threefold rotation axis, and so on. In even higher numbered aggregates, it could be expected that the appropriate forms of simple rotational or dihedral symmetry should also occur.

In such oligomeric systems of higher symmetry caution must be used in predicting dissociative intermediates. At first sight such intermediates might be thought to be related to the symmetry. On this basis one would expect that the R_6C_6 form of aspartate transcarbamylase would have formed intermediates either of two C_3 and R_3 trimers or three C_2 and R_2 dimers. Instead the major subunit contacts observed in the higher resolution crystal structure show why mixed forms of intermediates occur upon dissociation, *three* R_2 and *two* C_3 subunit forms!

2.3.4   Proteins Forming Continuous Aggregates

In Section 2.1.3 protein aggregates that contain subunits arranged with a form of screw symmetry were introduced. Examples of globular proteins that aggregate in such a continuous manner range from enzymes such as glutamate dehydrogenase (23) and catalase (110) to proteins whose biological function is related to their ability to polymerize, such as actin and tubulin. Actin (18) and tubulin (20) in their polymerized form occur as cellular organelles, and hence the polymer form appears to be the functionally relevant aggregation state.

Several factors are worth noting before citing a few examples of such helical aggregates. First, almost all of the structural data on these helical particles come from studies of electron micrographs supplemented occasionally by low-resolution X-ray diffraction data. The newer methods of optical diffraction and image reconstruction, combined with electron microscopy, have been particularly important in describing the low-resolution structural organization of helical protein aggregates. However, because the starting information is an electron micrograph of a negatively stained particle, the highest resolution obtainable is not much better than about 20 Å.

The second factor regarding structures of continuous protein aggregates is that the extent of formation can be dependent on several quite different chemical factors. Aggregation may be influenced by pH changes, metal ions, small organic molecules and, in the case of sickle cell hemoglobin, even O_2. Since the formation of the polymerized form of the globular protein may be dependent on a variety of chemical factors, it is not surprising that polymorphs are found. Rather than provide an exhaustive list of the various forms of helical aggregates that have been identified, a few selected examples are given in Table 2.

Perhaps the simplest helical polymer to describe is the muscle protein actin. As can be seen in Figure 10, it contains only two twisted strands of globular units. The helical twist is relatively small (or the repeat distance large) such that it produces a repeat about every 13 subunits (17, 18). By using shadowing methods and electron microscopy the muscle actin filaments were shown to have a right-handed screw sense (111). An actin filament can thus be pictured as two strands of beads twisted together only slightly; each "bead" or actin monomer at low resolution appears to be globular in shape much like a typical protein subunit. In a formal sense each actin monomer makes three classes of subunit-subunit contacts. One class occurs between axially adjacent neighbors in the same strand and are indicated by the symbols A to B in Figure 10. The other two classes are oblique contacts to subunits in the neighboring actin strand and are labeled D to F and C to E in Figure 10 (18).

It should be noted that nonmuscle forms of actin are generally found in a more complex form than the simple twisted two-stranded system described above. In nonmuscle cells multiple actin filaments are combined with other proteins to form cablelike structures. For example, six actin filaments, each double-stranded, are combined in a hexagonal manner in the actin aggregate found in the acrosomal process of horseshoe crab sperm (112). This polymorphic form of actin plus another protein of MW 55,000 may be common to similar systems observed in other plant and nonmuscle animal cells. In all cases, however, the basic repeating subunit in the fundamental two-stranded actin filament is a globular protein of diameter about 55 Å, measured in the direction of the helical axis.

Tubulin, also listed in Table 2, is a different example of helical aggregate because in its polymerized form, it is a hollow cylinder. Although several polymorphic froms of tubulin can occur, the best characterized polymer

TABLE 2
Examples of Polymeric Proteins with Helical Symmetry

Protein	Component(s)	MW	Strands	Pitch or Surface Lattice	Diameter of Aggregate (Å)	Repeat Distance (Å)	Size of Globular Unit[a] (Å)	Ref.
F-actin, rabbit muscle	G-actin	45,000	2	13 subunit/turn	80	~720	~55	17,18
Tubulin (A)	α-chain } β-chain	110,000	13	13-filament, 3-start	250 (110 central hole)	113	~40	19,20
Hemoglobin S	α-chains } β-chains (β6glu→val)	64,000	14	14-filament, 7-start	200	~3200	~60	15

[a]Measured in direction of helical axes.

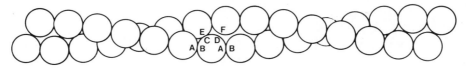

FIGURE 10

Schematic representation of actin filaments. Each subunit of actin is indicated by a circle. The three different types of monomer–monomer contacts are labeled as A:B, C:E and D:F (17, 18).

contains a 13-filament aggregate with approximate dimensions as given in Table 2. Just as was the case for actin the basic protein unit has a globular shape but of somewhat smaller dimensions, appearing to be roughly 40 Å long in the direction of the helical symmetry axis (19, 20). In tubulin the closest contact between monomeric units occurs within a strand that runs parallel to the helical axis of the cylinder. The staggering or rise between units in adjacent strands of tubulin is about 8–9 Å so that in 13 repeats, the distance is equivalent to three tubulin monomers. Hence the helical symmetry is described as 3-start as noted in Table 2 (19, 20).

Tubulin represents a continuous aggregate formed by nearly straight strands of globular units producing a cylinder with a hollow central region of diameter equal to about 110 Å. Each globular unit of roughly 55,000 MW appears to have a bilobal structure, but no details are yet available on the molecular structure of the individual units.

Fibers of sickle cell hemoglobin are another example of globular proteins forming long continuous helical aggregates, but in this case considerable information about the molecular structure of the basic unit, hemoglobin is available (16). In fact there is no reason to believe that the molecular structure of sickle cell hemoglobins is different from normal hemoglobin A except at the site of the single amino acid change in the β-chains (β-6).

Although several polymorphic forms have been identified, one probable fundamental structure contains 14 strands and is described further in Table 2 (15). The 14 strands viewed in cross section have the hemoglobin S molecules in roughly a hexagonal close-packed arrangement so that there is no central hole, as was the case for tubulin. Additional symmetry present in the aggregate show that each pair of strands can be in seven different environments (15). Molecules in the paired strands are thought to be related by a twofold molecular screw axis (15). Such pairing resembles the packing of hemoglobin molecules in crystals of deoxyhemoglobin S where the four subunit entities are packed in an assembly of strands in the crystal lattice (16). Adjacent molecules in each of a pair of strands in the crystalline form are again related by a local twofold screw axis. Hence the overall organization in the crystals may be similar to that described for the 14-standed polymeric form described above and viewed by electron microscopy. In the crystalline form of hemoglobin S the molecular structure of normal hemoglobin itself was used to obtain X-ray phase information so subtle conformational differences between the mutant and parent forms would not be apparent at the limiting resolution used, that is, 5 Å. However, the residues involved in protein-protein contacts about the local twofold screw axis relating strand 1 to strand 2 and in the direction of single strand can be surmised from the crystal study (16). If this morphological homology between strandlike packing in the crystal and the globular strands in the helical aggregate is correct a great deal is known about the protein-protein contacts in hemoglobin S, and the reader is referred to the paper by Wishner et al. (16), which lists these intermolecular contacts.

Perhaps the best-understood protein subunit participating in a helical protein assembly is that which forms the coat of tobacco mosaic virus. A high-resolution electron density map (2.8 Å) from crystals containing a "disk" of tobacco moasic virus protein units alone has been obtained and the polypeptide chain traced through this map (71). In addition X-ray studies of paracrystalline forms of the virus itself have resulted in an electron density map at 4 Å resolution (113). The combined studies on crystalline disks of the coat protein and paracrystalline virus have produced information about polypeptide conformational changes accompanying viral assembly, a factor that must always be considered in describing the specific aggregation. In addition the combined crystal and paracrystal structural studies should eventually produce details about the specific subunit interactions in this helical polymer (71, 113).

In summary, helical aggregates of globular proteins can be thought of as beaded chains. The number of chains or strands present in a single aggregate varies for different protein types, and each chain or strand may have a varying twist. In some instances the final molecular aggregate may be hollow or tubelike. To describe the structural nature of the aggregate it is frequently necessary to select more than one chain to begin the helical lattice, and an example of 3-start helical organization, tubulin, has been described.

Specific subunit-subunit contacts along a component strand and between strands determine the unique form of the final polymerized structure. In some helical structures contacts between several monomeric units in the so-called helical lattice make it impossible to identify a unique stable strand or strands. In other systems relatively close contacts between defined globular units and sometimes between specific strands suggest intermediates in the assembly process, just as they do with simple oligomeric proteins. Thus in the case of the 13-stranded tubulin aggregates, the globular strands forming chains running parallel to the helical symmetry axis are probably the protofilaments. In the presence of Mg^{2+} or Zn^{2+} two different sheet forms of tubulin have been observed, and in one case the sheets are nothing more than the opened and flattened tubules (114). In the other case, those sheets obtained in the presence of Zn^{2+}, adjacent protofilaments have opposite polarity, but the strands again appear to be the same as the straight filaments in the tubelike aggregate (114). In contrast, the intermediate protein oligomer for tobacco mosaic virus assembly is not a strand, but a disk. In this case further polymerization, that is, disk-disk aggregation, leading to a helical assembly probably involves conformational changes within individual globular units (113). The specific subunit-subunit interactions must also change in the transition from disk structure to the final helical tobacco mosaic virus particle.

Finally, the continuity in the rules that govern the symmetry of closed protein oligomers and continuous helical polymers is typified by the structure of hemoglobin *S*. The two α and β subunits are arranged with typical 222 point group symmetry in both forms of hemoglobin. This closed tetrameric unit then polymerizes into a unique 14-stranded continuous helical polymer under appropriate chemical conditions.

2.3.5   Subunit–Subunit Interactions

Throughout the previous sections reference has been made to specific noncovalent protein-protein interactions and their importance to symmetry in molecular structure and assembly. In addition these interactions play an important role in protein function and indeed form the basis for such phenomena as cooperativity. As noted throughout this chapter, the same kinds of specific noncovalent interactions are responsible for conformation at all levels of structural organization. At the quaternary level and in the case of closed oligomeric proteins there are now multiple examples of crystal structures to select and study the nature of such subunit-subunit interactions. In this section one such oligomeric protein is described in detail, glyceraldehyde 3-phosphate dehydrogenase.

Glyceraldehyde 3-phosphate dehydrogenase is an enzyme composed of four identical subunits (115). The structure of the enzyme from several species have been determined, those from lobster tail muscle (96) and from *Bacillus stearothermophilus* (116) at high resolution. In all the systems analyzed the four member subunits were found to be arranged with exact or near exact 222 molecular symmetry. This symmetry arrangement is shown schematically in Figure 11. The structure of the lobster enzyme is the best-analyzed and documented and is the species to be discussed in detail here. Because of the molecular symmetry the electron density of initially four subunits and later only of pairs of subunits have been averaged to improve the quality of the electron density map, and hence in this species no asymmetry in subunit conformation can be present across this axis (117, 118). As can be seen in Figure 12*a*, the contact region between subunits 1 and 2 is relatively small. In fact the crystal structure of glyceraldehyde 3-phosphate dehydrogenase shows that only two hydrogen bonds are formed in this interface and that they occur between asp 276 (#1, #2) and tyr 46 (#2, #1) (118).

The subunit contact between subunits 1 and 4 occurring across the *P* twofold rotation axis is the most extensive found in glyceraldehyde 3-phosphate dehydrogenase and is shown in Figure 12*b*. Most of the contact

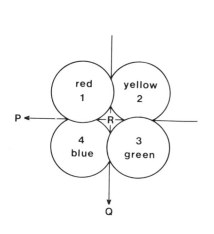

P

red
1

yellow
2

R

4
blue

3
green

Q

FIGURE 11

Schematic representation of subunit organization in glyceraldehyde 3-phosphate dehydrogenase. The schematic representation of the glyceraldehyde 3-phosphate dehydrogenase molecule is similar to one shown in reference (117). The three twofold rotational symmetry axes are labeled P, Q, and R, while each subunit is schematically represented by a circle. Since the subunits are conformationally identical, this representation can be used to label the different subunit–subunit contacts, which will be shown in Figure 12. For example, one type of subunit-subunit contact occurs between subunit 1 and 2 across the Q-axis. This particular contact can be seen in more detail in Figure 12a. Also see text.

residues are contained in antiparallel β-pleated sheets containing member strands from each subunit. Several hydrogen bonds are formed between a side chain and a carbonyl oxygen atom contained in the polypeptide backbone of the adjacent subunit (117). Because of the extensive region of close atomic contacts between #1 and #4, this interface has been suggested to be the most stable of the three types that are present in glyceraldehyde 3-phosphate dehydrogenase (117).

The last set of subunit-subunit contacts present in glyceraldehyde 3-phosphate dehydrogenase are those occurring between subunits 1 and 3 across the R twofold rotation axis. As illustrated in Figure 12c, this subunit-subunit interface involves amino acid residues from positions 178 to 202 in the polypeptide chain. A series of H bonds again are found in the contact region with contributing atoms from side chains as well as from carbonyl and amido groups within the polypeptide backbone (117). The subunit contact occurring across the R twofold rotation axis has special significance to the catalytic function of the enzyme, since residues from both subunits found in or near this contact region are involved in binding of $NAD^+(H)$ and probably glyceraldehyde 3-phosphate as well (117). Thus because of this subunit interface active sites from each of the two subunits are brought relatively close to one another.

The cooperativity or half-site reactivity observed in this protein can be tentatively accounted for in terms of the different types of subunit-subunit interactions observed in the crystal structure. The Q-axis subunit interface (Figure 12a) is found to be an exact twofold rotation axis in the human enzyme (118). Considerations of the extent of interactions across the P- and R-axes, respectively, suggest the former would be the more stable subunit-subunit interface. Thus any dimer-dimer asymmetry is thought to take place

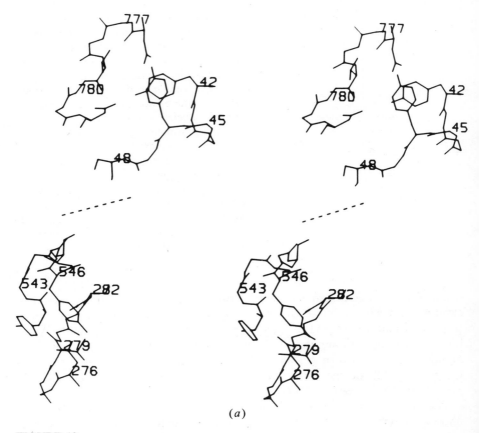

(a)

FIGURE 12
Subunit-subunit interaction in lobster glyceraldehyde-3 phosphate dehydrogenase. The stereodiagrams are based on information in Table IV of ref. 117. All polypeptide backbone atoms are included in the segments of polypeptide chain which are shown. Side chains are only shown if they participate directly in the subunit-subunit interaction. The stippled line indicate the appropriate twofold rotation axis found in the enzyme molecule.

(a) Q-axis interactions including residues 42–48 and 276–282 from subunits #1 (red) and #2 (yellow). Residue numbers for subunit #2 are offset by 500. In stereo, the identity of the two contacts should be visible. The top subunit–subunit contact involves $(42-48)_{su1}$ to $(276-282)_{su2}$ while the bottom contact contains $(42-48)_{su2}$ to $(276-282)_{su1}$. Similar pairing can be observed in the stereodiagrams shown in parts (b) and (c).

(b) P-axis interactions including residues 169–175, 193–207, 223–234, 239–245, 276–282, and 296–308 from subunits #1 (red) and #4 (blue). Residue numbers of subunit #4 are offset by 500.

(c) R-axis interactions including residues 9–13, 35–49, 178–202, and 232–235 from subunits #1 (red) and #3 (green). Residue numbers for subunit #3 are offset by 500.

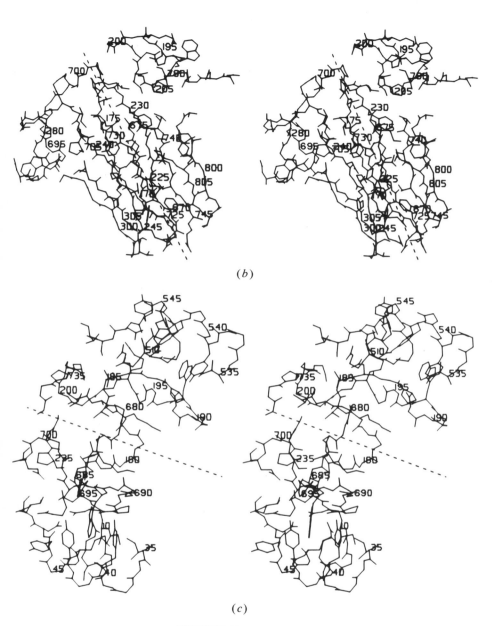

(b)

(c)

FIGURE 12 (*Continued*)

by changes in the relationship of the 1–4 pair of subunits to the 2–3 pair (117). This is equivalent to changes in subunit-subunit interactions across the R-axis. Further support to these suggestions comes from the fact that active sites are in close contact across the R-axis.

In summary, an example of a tetrameric protein, glyceraldehyde 3-phosphate dehydrogenase, illustrates several important facts about subunit-subunit interactions. (a) The 222 symmetry of the molecule generates at least three well-defined but different contact regions. In the case of glyceraldehyde 3-phosphate dehydrogenase they are defined relative to the symmetry axes labeled P, Q, or R. (b) The magnitude of surface complementarity differs considerably for each of the three types of contact regions. A relatively small number of residues from each subunit are in close proximity in the #1 to #2 (Q-axis) contact compared to the number of amino acids defining the contact regions in the #1 to #4 (P-axis) and in the #1 to #3 (R-axis) contacts. (c) For the #1 to #3 (and #2 to #4) interface, the active sites of member subunits are in close proximity with each other, and it is through this interface that the conformational changes creating half-site reactivity might be generated. (d) Hydrogen bonds involving donors and acceptors from the side chains and the polypeptide backbone chain itself have been identified in all of the subunit interfaces. (e) Amino acid residues involved in subunit-subunit contacts may come from a relatively narrow segment of the polypeptide chain (R-contact, mainly near residue 185). Or the contact segments could come from numerous regions scattered along the linear amino acid sequence (P-contact, #1 to #4). (f) The 222 arrangement of subunits at least in glyceraldehyde 3-phosphate dehydrogenase is not precisely maintained and this, together with the proximity of active sites which occur near the R-contact as mentioned in (c), results in subtle asymmetry and conformational differences between otherwise structurally identical polypeptide chains (117).

Knowing the nature of subunit-subunit contacts in oligomeric proteins, a few more general observations can now be described. Cytoplasmic malate dehydrogenase comprised of two subunits is conformationally highly homologous with the tetrameric enzyme lactate dehydrogenase (67). In addition the subunit-subunit interface in malate dehydrogenase is identical to one of the three unique subunit interfaces in lactate dehydrogenase (67). Seemingly lactate dehydrogenase has four subunits and cytoplasmic malate dehydrogenase has two subunits, only because of an additional 20 amino acid residues at the N-terminal end of lactate dehydrogenase. It would seem that, just as evolutionary accidents have generated related but different biochemical functions, similar accidents have produced different levels of oligomeric assembly. Furthermore, as noted in the early sections of this chapter and now shown in detail in the subunit interfaces of glyceraldehyde 3-phosphate dehydrogenase, no unique energetic or conformational principles have been observed at the level of protein-protein interactions. Interactions at the quaternary level are essentially the same as those found in elements of secondary and super-secondary structures in globular proteins.

2.4 CONFORMATIONAL CHANGES

Changes in the conformation of a protein are observable using X-ray crystallographic methods as described in Section 2.1.3. As might be expected, conformational changes may be categorized as to which of the hierarchial organization is affected by the conformational change. Changes in structure affecting secondary and super-secondary structures should be quite readily observable by X-ray methods, but have so far not been documented. This is probably due to the fact that these types of structures contain numerous hydrogen bonds. Conformational changes that result in a breakdown of some or all of these bonds are energetically unfavorable and will most likely only take place upon complete denaturation. Minor changes in secondary structures, such as opening up of the end of helices, introduction of minor bends, or twist in β-structures are possible. It is significant that wherever such changes have been observed no changes in hydrogen bonding have been noticed.

The next level of organization is the tertiary structure, but conformational changes at this level can be all inconclusive, that is, every conformation change must include a tertiary change. If, on the other hand, tertiary conformational changes were to be limited to those which do not affect domain-domain interactions as well as subunit-subunit rearrangements, a more meaningful division results. Simple changes in tertiary conformation under varying chemical conditions have been observed for practically every protein of known crystal structure. Quite often simple tertiary conformational changes accompany the binding of small compounds to crystalline proteins. The change may vary in magnitude from a slight reorientation of a single amino acid side chain to the movement of an entire segment of the polypeptide chain. The movement of the so-called "loop" region in lactate dehydrogenase accompanying the binding of NAD$^+$ is an example of the latter (67).

A discussion of simple tertiary conformational changes is beyond the scope of this chapter. Instead we will describe two other forms of structural changes that have direct bearing on oligomeric proteins. The first type is those that affect the domain-domain interactions within a single polypeptide chain. The second type concerns changes in subunit-subunit contact regions. Clearly combinations of the two types are possible, and neither form is likely to occur without an accompanying change in tertiary structure.

2.4.1 Domain–Domain Conformational Changes

An example of small conformation changes in the orientation of two domains relative to each other can be found in the structure of the coat proteins in crystalline tomato bushy stunt virus (81). In Section 2.1.2 (on symmetry) the importance of quasi-equivalence in the structure of spherical viruses was discussed. The quasi-equivalence of the coat protein subunits in this icosahedral shell can be achieved in only two ways. Either the coat protein itself is rigid and more than one type of interaction between identical subunits exists, or alternatively the subunits are flexible, and, whereas the intersubunit interactions are essentially unchanged (quasi-equivalent), the internal structure of the subunits display some conformational variability.

The molecular structure of tomato bushy stunt virus is composed of two distinct globular domains connected by a hinge region (81). The internal folding of the domains remains virtually unchanged in every subunit, but their relative interdomain positions depend on whether the subunit interaction are symmetrical or quasi-symmetrical. Changes in the hinge angle by about 20° are a consequence of this variation of domain-domain interaction (14). The two component domains of tomato bushy stunt coat protein can be in two distinct arrangements, and this conformational degeneracy allows the subunit-subunit contacts to be equivalent.

Another class of proteins which show domain-domain conformational variability is the antibodies (86, 87). The structure of the IgG antibody molecule is built up from six distinct, but nearly identical, domains with four in each heavy chain and two in each light chain. The domains have been labeled $V_L, C_L, V_H, C_{H1}, C_{H2}, C_{H3}$ where the subscripts indicate whether they are found in the light (L) or heavy chains (H). The two halves of the IgG molecule are related by twofold symmetry. In each half of the molecule there is additional symmetry describing the domain-domain relationship. However, the twofold symmetry axis that relates V_L and V_H domains to each other does not coincide with a twofold axis relating C_L to C_{H1}. Furthermore, the angle between these two dyad axes varies for different antibodies. Even the same antibody or fragment thereof in different crystal environments displays different interdomain angles at this so-called switch peptide region (86). A point of domain-domain flexibility is located in the hinge peptide region. This connection occurs between domains in the F_{AB} and F_c regions. In at least one instance, IgG Kol, there must be a multitude of conformations available to the F_c part of the structure, since no significant electron density is observed in the crystalline state (119, 120).

Another example of changes in domain-domain interactions can be found in yeast hexokinase, a protein which was described in an earlier section since it seems to form a nonsymmetrical dimer. Hexokinase (100) and phosphoglycerate kinase (121) belong to a group of enzymes having the common property of transferring phosphate from ATP to another compound. A unifying feature of these enzymes seems to be a bilobal double domain structure with a distinct cleft between the domains (122). The binding of glucose to hexokinase causes a closing of this cleft, which is created by a movement in the hinge region linking the two domains (123). The domain-domain conformational change observed in the crystalline states should cause a reduction in the radius of gyration of the protein in solution. Small-angle X-ray scattering experiments have in fact confirmed this conformational change in both hexokinase (124) and a similar one in phosphoglycerate kinase (125).

Domain-domain conformational changes represent one additional way for proteins to exist in more than one conformational state. In cases where the domains appear to exist as distinct lobes connected by a small segment of polypeptide chain, such conformational changes would seem to require little driving energy. Domain-hinge-domain flexibility is especially useful for providing quasi-equivalence in virus coats proteins. For the antibody molecule and in enzymes such conformational flexibility appears to be related to the binding of a ligand and hence also directly to some biological function.

2.4.2 Quaternary Conformational Changes

Some conformational changes can best be described by considering them at the quaternary level. And indeed such structural changes often are of unique biological importance because they may mediate biochemical phenomena such as enzyme cooperativity. In the case of a symmetrical oligomer of identical subunits, the quaternary structural change may take place in two principal ways. (I) A simple tertiary structural change occurs in a fraction of the subunits present in the oligomer producing asymmetry in the molecule. (II) Simple tertiary conformational changes occur simultaneously in all subunits and the symmetry is conserved. It should be emphasized that, although the symmetry remains, new subunit-subunit contacts may be formed. Variations of these two types of quaternary changes are numerous; only a few examples are given here.

As an example of asymmetrical behavior of a symmetrical oligomeric protein, a protein containing two subunits is the easiest of visualize. As a word of warning, several crystalline proteins display asymmetrical or cooperative behavior in their interaction with ligands. Sometimes solution properties of these proteins do not indicate any degree of cooperativity, and it is clear that restrictions imposed by the crystal lattice might be part of the explanation for the observed asymmetry present in only the crystalline state. For example, the two subunits in crystalline cytoplasmic malate dehydrogenase show different affinities for the coenzyme NAD^+, even though the subunits are related by twofold rotational symmetry (126). However, a careful comparison of the structures of the apo- and holo- forms of the enzyme argue in favor of a crystal lattice-mediated effect (127). For this enzyme and other similar systems such as α-chymotrypsin (22) molecular asymmetry preexists in the crystalline structure by virtue of lattice interactions with neighboring molecules. Ligand interaction and the resulting conformational changes may reflect this nonequivalence, but only in the crystalline state.

Of the oligomeric proteins that have demonstrable chemically cooperative properties, two have been studied in several different forms using crystallographic methods. Hemoglobin generally exhibits positive cooperativity in binding oxygen. Glyceraldehyde 3-phosphate dehydrogenase usually exhibits negative cooperativity in the binding of NAD^+ and sometimes shows half-site reactivity for other active site reagents as well. The molecular structure of glyceraldehyde 3-phosphate dehydrogenase from lobster (117) and *Bacillus stearothermophilus* (128) has been determined. Both enzymes crystallize with the complete molecule of four subunits in the asymmetric unit. As noted in Section 2.3.5, the glyceraldehyde phosphate dehydrogenase molecule possesses 222 symmetry. Studies on the lobster enzyme show that there are no noticeable changes in quaternary structure or in tertiary structure when three of the four bound NAD^+ molecules are removed (129). It was thus suggested that any of the conformational changes that are known to take place in the enzyme would occur upon binding of the first molecule of NAD^+. This suggestion was essentially verified in the analysis of the effects of NAD^+ binding to the bacterial glyceraldehyde 3-phosphate dehydrogenase (128, 130). This enzyme can be crystallized with a NAD^+ content per four subunits ranging from zero up to four molecules. The largest conformational change takes place when the first molecule of NAD^+ is bound, and the crystals of the apoenzyme are in fact unable to accommodate the structural changes accompanying coenzyme binding. Crystals grown with 1–4 mol NAD^+/enzyme molecule can be interconverted quite readily. Comparison of the apo- and hologlyceraldehyde 3-phosphate dehydrogenase structures at 6 Å resolution shows a number of significant conformational changes. Recall from Section 2.3.5 that the active sites are relatively close to one another in pairs in this oligomeric enzyme. Although the atomic details of the conformational change accompanying the binding of the first NAD^+ are not fully known, the entire coenzyme binding domain appears to have rotated away from the NAD^+ binding site in the holoenzyme. The axis of rotation is located near the central region between the domains. This movement results in atomic displacements of up to 5 Å in some parts of the coenzyme binding domain (130). Thus while the structural differences between the holo- and apo- forms of glyceraldehyde 3-phosphate dehydrogenase are not known in great detail, the binding of NAD^+ seems to lead to a domain-domain conformational change, which is propagated directly to the subunit-subunit interface.

Events in the cooperative transition can then be summarized as beginning with (*a*) a simple tertiary conformational change concomitant with the apoenzyme binding its first NAD^+ molecule. The conformational change produces (*b*) a relatively large movement in the coenzyme binding domain relative to the remainder of the molecule. The movement of the coenzyme binding domain means that the simple tertiary conformational change is propagated to the subunit interface and hence generates similar changes in the other subunits (128, 130).

In another system crystallographic analysis has resulted in an even better understood quaternary conformational change; the one that accompanies oxygen binding to hemoglobin. Recall that it was X-ray studies of crystalline hemoglobin that first demonstrated the presence of symmetry in an oligomeric protein. It has also been long recognized that hemoglobin has allosteric or cooperative oxygen-binding properties. In the late 1960s, Perutz and his co-workers were able to show that the quaternary structure of hemoglobin differs for the oxy- and deoxy- forms of the molecule. For the first time a structural explanation for allosteric phenomena was shown to be attributable to these two quaternary states.

At that time Perutz and his co-workers were comparing human deoxyhemoglobin with horse oxyhemoglobin. Both states have a single twofold rotation axis relating $\alpha\beta$ pairs as well as pseudo-twofold axes, which define the arrangement of α to β subunits (see also Section 2.3.3.). Even at low resolution the quaternary transition was definable without including any major conformational changes within each subunit. Small subunit rotations occurred in a manner that preserved the overall symmetry of the hemoglobin molecule but produced a new set of subunit contacts (26). The initial resolution of the electron density maps were insufficient to define the precise conformational changes that accompany this transition, but these have been increasingly understood as high-resolution X-ray data have been accumulated (131, 132).

Knowing that the X-ray studies define only two final states for the hemoglobin molecule, it is wise to ignore controversies centering on whether or not intermediate forms of oxy- and deoxyhemoglobin exist. Furthermore, the crystallographic two-state model may be analyzed to determine the simple tertiary conformation changes that accompany the transition. Since it is the binding of oxygen that initiates the transition, conformational changes must begin at a heme iron atom. Next it is equally clear that changes in conformation must be propagated toward subunit-subunit interfaces. It is only through the maze of noncovalent contacts at the subunit-subunit interface that one heme can communicate with another.

Recalling that the four subunits in hemoglobin can be labeled α_1, α_2, β_1, β_2, the subunit-subunit contacts can then be denoted by the symbols $\alpha_1\beta_1$, $\alpha_2\beta_2$, $\alpha_1\beta_2$, and so on (Fig. 9). In this notation the dimer pairs of subunits related by the exact twofold rotation axis of the hemoglobin molecule are represented by $\alpha_1\beta_1$ and $\alpha_2\beta_2$. Baldwin and Chothia have recently summarized the significant facts related to the oxy- and deoxytransition, and what follows is taken largely from their description (132). To better understand the nature of the transition the reader must be acquainted with the structure of the hemoglobin–myoglobin family of oxygen-binding proteins. Recall that the folding contains eight α-helical segments labeled A thru H. Helix F contains a histidine side chain covalently linked to the iron atom of the heme moiety and is often called the proximal histidine.

The first notable fact about the quaternary transition is that the interface between α_1 and β_1 (also α_2 and β_2!) subunits is unaffected. In addition the conformation of the central most parts of both subunits of this pair, including the B, C, G, and H helices and the D helix of the β subunit has the same structure in both states. The key tertiary change begins with electronic events accompanying the O_2 molecule binding to the iron-porphyrin system. Changes in the orientation of the proximal histidine result and this triggering change is propagated to the subunit interfaces by movement of the F-helix. The movement of the ends of this helix, particularly the FG corner, produces quaternary changes between $\alpha_1\beta_2$ and its symmetrical mate $\alpha_2\beta_1$.

In this highly oversimplified description of the oxy- to deoxyhemoglobin transition numerous small repositioning of atoms within the oligomeric molecule have been ignored. Most all of these changes are known through the crystallographic studies (132).

However, the events can be summarized in a rather general way, perhaps serving as a model for similar changes in other proteins. The allosteric change begins with (a) electronic effects on the iron-porphyrin system which occurs upon binding oxygen. The next step is (b) a simple tertiary conformational change involving the proximal histidine. Changes in the orientation of the proximal histidine (c) bring about a movement in an element of secondary structure (F-helix). The movement of the helix (d) propagates the conformational change to one or more subunit interfaces. The subunit-subunit interface(s) (e) accommodate changes such as (d) in the neighboring subunits. And now, in reverse order, the change of the subunit interface is transmitted back to the second ligand binding site through the symmetry equivalent element of secondary structure. If one speculates about other cooperative changes, events numbered (a) through (d) could be the same in a quaternary transition producing negative cooperativity only (e) need be different. Instead of accommodating or facilitating the binding of an additional ligand, it would inhibit such a chemical event. The return to a symmetrical oligomer is the key to these cooperative events.

In summary, conformational changes in oligomeric systems have unique biochemical significance. It is possible for chemical binding events to alter the nature of the same process on an adjacent subunit. This can occur either because the binding site is itself at or near the subunit interface similar to the active site of glyceraldehyde 3-phosphate dehydrogenase, or that the chemical event can propagate conformational changes to the subunit-subunit interface as it occurs during the oxy- to deoxyhemoglobin transition. It is the specificity and energetics of noncovalent protein-protein interactions at the subunit interface which have imparted special biochemical properties to oligomeric protein systems.

2.5 FUTURE EXPECTATIONS AND ACKNOWLEDGMENTS

As the number of molecular structures derived from oligomeric proteins increases, fundamentals governing all hierarchial levels of conformation will be more apparent. Certainly predictive and energetic estimates of secondary, super-secondary and tertiary conformation will become increasingly more accurate. At the quaternary level the relationship between molecular structure and functional properties such as cooperativity should be definable for many more oligomeric systems. The quaternary rearrangement governing cooperative oxygen binding by hemoglobin may be only one mechanism for such allosteric phenomena. If the resolution limits of electron microscopy can be extended, considerably more structural information on helical polymers should be obtainable. In instances where three-dimensional crystals of the protein itself can also be obtained, methods are being developed for fitting the molecular structure into maps of the total helical aggregate. Should this be possible, the precise conformational changes governing such aggregates may be definable.

Finally, we feel the need to make a few general comments about the results that have been presented. Throughout this chapter an effort has been made to emphasize principles and general notions about protein conformation rather than listing numerous examples. To our colleagues who are directly involved in X-ray crystallographic studies of proteins or in studies related to energetics, predictive or empirical cataloging of conformation, we apologize for not citing numerous pertinent references. We remind the reader that this chapter is an attempt to condense for them important new principles and cite examples. No claim is made to any original generalities or principles in any of these examples; they have only been summarized from the existing literature.

2.6 APPENDIX: ENERGETIC ASPECTS OF PROTEIN–PROTEIN INTERACTIONS

2.6.1 Interatomic Forces—Their Physical Basis and Functional Description

While the hierarchy for protein-protein interactions has been established with the single amino acid as the minimum organizational unit, the physical forces that account for these interactions and lead to their stabilization operate at a lower, atomic level. These interatomic forces are often classified as being *strong* or *weak*, depending upon the magnitude of the potential energy of the interaction compared with the energy associated with thermal motions within the protein. In considering intramolecular interactions as opposed to inter-molecular reactions, we are concerned almost entirely with *weak* forces. The primary, covalent structure of the interacting entities remain unchanged, and hydrogen rather than ionic bonds are important because of the relative number of interactions involved. Additional factors such as the influence of environment and the distance range of the interaction can also play a part in determining the relative importance of the various types of interactions at each level of the hierarchy.

2.6.1.1 Physical basis for atomic interactions

All interatomic forces can be attributed to interactions between or re-organization of orbital electrons moving in the field of the nuclear charge. As such they often require use of quantum rather than classical mechanics in their analysis. The study of covalent interactions, which involve the establishment of new or modified molecular orbitals for the bonding electrons, or the computation of molecular properties such as the distribution of atomic charges and the energy required to delocalize an electron, require a full quantum-mechanical calculation. While much of the formalism and methodology for such quantum calculations was established in the 1920s, implementation of these calculations for all but the simplest molecule has only recently become feasible. Major simplifying assumptions have still to be made and the calculations are essentially in vacuo, the quantitative description of solvent effects remaining a research goal. Even then the analysis of flexible molecules with more than a few internal degrees of freedom (rotatable bonds) is still impractical using quantum mechanics. Some other molecular properties, such as the conformational energy, depend primarily on knowledge of atomic rather than electronic parameters and can be estimated using a semiclassical approach that has become known as molecular mechanics. In this approach atoms are treated as classical particles subject to various forces. The character of these forces are selected to reproduce known atomic or molecular properties and represent classical mechanical analogs of atomic quantum phenomena.

Thus, while the basis of an atomic interaction may be the Pauli exclusion principle and require the functional dependencies to be established quantum mechanically, its effect may be represented through a classical potential energy function whose parameters may be determined empirically. Interaction of charged atomic species can be calculated using Coulomb's law but with the charge in general being delocalized and distributed over several neighboring atoms. Neutral molecules may exhibit permanent dipoles (or higher order multipoles), which can again be treated using Coulomb's law and a delocalized charge distribution. In both instances the electrostatic energy can be computed using the concept of partial charges, nonintegral point charges being associated with each atom or at the centers of bonds so as to reproduce the net electrostatic field of the molecule.

Nonpolar molecules by definition have no permanent multipole moments but can, in common with polar molecules, exhibit both induced and transient multipole effects. These reflect changes in the electron distribution of the molecule that occur as a consequence of a neighboring multipole (permanent or transient) or fluctuations that occur spontaneously as a consequence of the probabilistic nature of the motions of the orbital electrons. The magnitude of these effects depends upon a parameter known as the atomic polarizability, and, although individually small (of the same order as thermal energies) because of the number of such interactions that occur, they make an important contribution to the overall energy of both inter- and intramolecular interactions. Hypothetically, as two neutral nonpolar atoms are brought together any electronic fluctuation of one will induce a field at the other. This field will in turn influence the electrons of the second leading to a complementary fluctuation, the sense of the perturbation being such that the energy of interaction of the transient dipoles (or multipoles) will be negative (attractive). These transient dipole-induced transient dipole phenomena were first proposed by London (133) and are commonly known as London dispersion forces.

At very short interatomic separations, usually below 3 Å, the attractive dispersion forces give way to a much stronger interaction stemming from a more persistent interaction of the electron clouds. While a semiclassical model would predict the strong electrostatic repulsion that is observed, in many cases a quantum-mechanical treatment is really required and was first carried out for the hydrogen molecule by Heitler and London (134) in the 1920s. The interactions between nonbonded atoms will have a strongly repulsive core limiting the minimum center-to-center approach distance of these atoms to approximately two times the bonding distance of atoms. While the theoretical determination of atomic bond lengths or nonbonded repulsive energy for most biologically important molecules is still not a routine calculation, characterization of the energetics of distortions of covalently bonded atoms can be described quite successfully using a semiclassical Hooke's law-type model.

It is interesting to note that in many treatments of nonbonded atomic interactions the dipole, dispersion, and hard-core repulsion terms are collectively known as van der Waals forces. Although chronologically van der Waals predates quantum mechanics by 50 years, his work on the way in which gases deviate from the ideal gas laws relates to the macroscopic effects of atomic interactions. On the basis of experimental observations he proposed modification of the perfect gas law,

$$pV = NkT \tag{1}$$

to the form

$$\left(P + \frac{aN^2}{V^2}\right)(V - bN) = NkT \tag{2}$$

In fact this is only a good approximation at relatively low concentration, but the form of the correction terms are significant. Specifically they provide for a reduction in the volume available to the molecules by a quantity bN and for an increase in the pressure experienced by the gas molecules by a quantity aN^2/V^2. The parameter b is a volume which for spherical gas molecules will be four times the volume excluded by a single molecule and can give an estimate of the radius of the repulsive core of the molecule, that is, the radius at which the repulsion becomes greater than the average kinetic energy of molecular collisions. The coefficient a parameterizes an internal pressure effect. Qualitatively it relates to an adhesion between the molecules, because they loosely associate. Even in a gas they appear to be responding to a pressure greater than that applied externally. In the modern kinetic theory of gases these effects are embodied in *virial* coefficients and can be directly related to two-body interaction potentials via the technique of cluster expansion.

2.6.1.2 Potential energy functions

For the purpose of semiclassical calculations on the conformational energy of molecules it is necessary to specify a set of scalar potentials that describe the functional dependence of the atomic interactions. The potential energy of a conformation is obtained directly by summing the values of the functions for all interactions. The force acting on a selected atom is a vector whose magnitude and direction are obtained from

$$F = -\nabla \left[\sum V_{(r)} \right] \tag{3}$$

where the summation runs over all interactions involving the selected atom. These relationships also form the basis of calculations on the dynamic behavior of molecules using either a Newtonian or a Lagrangian approach to setting up the equations of motion for the atoms in a classical fashion.

The total conformational energy of a molecule can be considered to be the sum of terms representing different classes of interaction. Each term will be a function of the generalized atomic coordinates (r) and will be summed over all appropriate interactions. Thus

$$V_{(r)}^{\text{Total}} = V_{(r)}^{\text{Bonded}} + V_{(r)}^{\text{Electrostatic}} + V_{(r)}^{\text{London}} + V_{(r)}^{\text{Hydrogen bond}} + V_{(r)}^{\text{Solvent}} \tag{4}$$

Bonded interactions. The bonded interactions represent strain-energy terms arising from the deviation of the covalently bonded atoms from ideal stereo-geometries. They can be separated into terms representing bond length, bond angle, and torsion angle distortions. The bond length and bond angle terms are normally assumed to be quadratic in their deviations from the ideal, strain-free, equilibrium values. The torsion angle exhibits a cosine dependence on the deviations. Equilibrium values can be obtained through an analysis of crystal structures determined by X-ray diffraction, while in general the force constants can be deduced from the frequencies observed in infrared or Raman spectra for stretching and bending modes of molecules containing the bond of interest (135).

$$V = \frac{1}{2} \sum_{\text{bonds}} Kb(b - b_0)^2 + \frac{1}{2} \sum_{\substack{\text{bond} \\ \text{angles}}} K\theta(\theta - \theta_0)^2$$

$$+ \frac{1}{2} \sum_{\substack{\text{torsion} \\ \text{angles}}} K\phi \left[1 + \cos n(\phi - \phi_0) \right] \tag{5}$$

where b and b_0 are the observed and equilibrium values of the bond length in angstroms, θ and θ_0 and ϕ and ϕ_0 corresponding values for bond angles and torsion angles in radians. The parameter n is set to 2 or 3 to describe a 2- or 3-fold symmetry for the arrangement of atoms about the bond, the associated values of ϕ_0 being 0 and $\pi/2$, respectively.

Typical values of the force constants K are (2,135–138):

$$Kb: \quad 200–1000 \, \text{kcal/mol-Å}^2$$
$$K\theta: \quad 40–100 \, \text{kcal/mol-radian}^2$$
$$K\phi: \quad 1–6 \, \text{kcal/mol-radian}^2$$

Distortions of 0.03 Å, 4° and 45°, respectively will produce strain energies compatible with the energy of thermal motion (0.3 kcal/mol).

An additional contribution to the bonded interaction is sometimes added to account for the strain energy associated with bonds that are planar due to resonance (e.g., the peptide bond). This term will have the form

$$V = \frac{1}{2} \sum_{\substack{\text{planar} \\ \text{bonds}}} KxX^2 \qquad (6)$$

where X measures the deviation from planarity in radians, and Kx has typical values of $1–10$ kcal/mol-radian^2 so that thermal energies correspond to variations of order 10 degrees (2, 135, 136).

While it is often assumed that the force constants for a given chemical group are transferable from one molecule to another, Bixon and Lifson (139, 140) report that their attempts to obtain a best fit of these parameters in a given series of molecules indicates a considerable variation in the b_0 and θ_0 parameters even within a closely related series of molecules. This predicates against the common practice of using *off-the-shelf parameters* in calculations and suggests that any attempt at obtaining meaningful quantitative predictions for a given structure should be firmly based on either an experimental probe of the structure (spectral and diffraction studies) or when this is not practical a careful analysis of a series of closely related molecules.

Electrostatic interactions. The electrostatic potentials will, in this text, be defined to represent the effect of all permanent (nontransient) charge distributions with the exception of those associated with hydrogen bond formation. Essentially the interactions in this class are coulombic in nature, based on pairwise interactions of the form

$$V = \frac{332 q_1 q_2}{\varepsilon r_{12}} \quad \text{kcal/mol} \qquad (7)$$

where the interacting charges are expressed in terms of the electronic charge q_1, and q_2, the separation distance r_{12} in angstroms and ε the effective dielectric constant for the medium between the charges. In the case of polar molecules that carry no net charge but do have an asymmetrical charge distribution corresponding to the existence of permanent multipoles the potential energy can be computed from expressions for the interactions of these multipoles. For *point* dipoles where the distance between the dipoles, r_{12}, is large compared with the dipole charge separation, the interaction

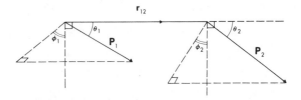

FIGURE 13 The geometry of dipole–dipole interactions.

energy will be dependent on the relative orientations of the dipoles,

$$V = \frac{14 \cdot 4 P_1 P_2}{\varepsilon r_{12}^3} \times \left[\cos(\phi_1 - \phi_2) \sin\theta_1 \sin\theta_2 - 2\cos\theta_1 \cos\theta_2 \right] \text{kcal/mol} \quad (8)$$

where ϕ_1, θ_1 and ϕ_2, θ_2 are the spherical polar angles for the dipole orientations, the polar axis corresponding to the vector r_{12} (Figure 13). The atomic dipoles P_1 and P_2 are in debyes (1 D = 10^{-18} esu) so that a dipole in which unit charges are separated by 1 Å has a moment of 4.8 D.

Computation of the dipole energy contribution from the above equation is appropriate when coupled to experimental determination of the effective dipole strengths, although they may be computed directly from knowledge of the molecular wavefunctions. In a third approach the charge distribution is represented by a set of point charges whose value and location reasonably approximate the inferred external electrostatic field of the molecule for all conformations. These point charges are termed *partial* charges, as their magnitudes are usually fractions of an electron charge. Typically they are located at atom centers or at the midpoint of covalent bonds.

Under circumstances where the interacting dipoles are subject to independent thermal motions an average must be taken over all possible orientations, the distribution of orientations being given by a Boltzmann factor. For strong interactions the dipoles will line up at or close to the minimum energy configuration with the dipoles collinear. Then

$$V = \frac{-28.8 P_1 P_2}{\varepsilon r_{12}^3} \text{ kcal/mol} \quad (9)$$

with the previously defined notation and units. For weak interactions the Boltzmann average will lead to the expression

$$V = -\frac{2}{3}(14.4)^2 \frac{P_1 P_2}{\varepsilon r_{12}^3} \times \frac{P_1 P_2}{\varepsilon r_{12}^3 kT}$$

$$= -\frac{69,600}{T} \times \frac{P_1^2 P_2^2}{\varepsilon^2 r_{12}^6} \text{ kcal/mol} \quad (10)$$

where T is the temperature in degrees Kelvin. If the interacting dipoles are coupled so that the thermal motions are not independent a more complex analysis has to be performed. Under these circumstances the above expressions will represent the lower bound on the interaction energy.

An additional inductive effect has also to be included in the electrostatic potential. It arises when the field produced, for example, by a permanent dipole, P, in one part of the molecule is able to polarize a second, essentially nonpolar group inducing in it a dipole moment. This induced dipole will be parallel to the inducing field and will be proportional to both the polarizability of the group, α, and the field strength at the group. The interaction potential will be

$$V = \left(\frac{14.4P^2}{\varepsilon^2 r_{12}^6} \right)(1 - 3\cos^2\theta)\alpha \text{ kcal/mol} \tag{11}$$

where the notation and units are as before with θ the angle between the dipole P and the vector r_{12} and α the polarizability of the group in units of Å^3. Typical values of α are in the range 1–6 Å^3 and follow an approximate formula given by Setlow and Pollard (141):

$$\alpha = \frac{332a^2}{I} \text{Å}^3 \tag{12}$$

where a represents the linear size of the atom or group in angstroms, and I is its ionization potential in kcal/mol.

Similar but more complex expressions can be derived for quadrupole and higher multipoles and for interactions between mixed multipoles such as dipole-quadrupole. In general the $1/r^6$ distance dependence found for the dipole will be replaced by $1/r^8$ and $1/r^{10}$ for the quadrupole-dipole and quadrupole-quadrupole interactions, respectively. At small distances r_{12} approaching 1 Å, these energies would become significant compared with those for a dipole. However, as previously discussed, for such distances the interactions will be dominated by a hard-core repulsion. Thus for all practical purposes the dipole approximation will provide a reasonable estimate of interaction energies.

London-type interactions. As stated in Section 2.6.1.1, the dispersion forces arise from the transient fluctuations in charge distributions that are predicted by quantum mechanics, occur even in nonpolar molecules and are associated with frequencies in the optical range (10^{15} H). The interaction is in effect between a transient dipole and an induced dipole so that the dispersion term will be similar in form to those of the inductive interactions but with the magnitude of both dipoles depending on the polarizability of both interacting groups.

While Debye (142, 143) in 1920 inferred correctly the basis of the dispersive interaction and suggested that the potential energy would be proportional to the product of the polarizabilities ($\alpha_1\alpha_2$) and inversely proportional to the sixth power of the separation, his attempt at a qualitative evaluation using an electrostatic model was unsatisfactory. The effect is quantum-mechanical in origin and required the development of a quantum formulation to produce expressions consistent with experimental data at least for simple molecules. In 1931 Slater and Kirkwood (144) proposed the expression

$$V = -\frac{3\pi e_0^2 a_0^{1/2}}{\varepsilon^2 r_{12}^6} \times \left[\frac{\alpha_1 \alpha_2}{(\alpha_1/n_1)^{1/2} + (\alpha_2/n_2)^{1/2}} \right] \tag{13}$$

where e_0 is the electronic charge, a_0 the Bohr radius, n_1 and n_2 the number of external electrons in the interacting systems and ε the effective dielectric constant. This work was followed by a more exact treatment by London (133), which produced the equation

$$V = -\frac{3}{4} \frac{I_1 I_2}{I_1 + I_2} \times \frac{\alpha_1 \alpha_2}{\varepsilon^2 r_{12}^6} \tag{14}$$

where I_1 and I_2 are the ionization energies in kcal/mol of the interacting species.

In both formulations it should be noted that because the interaction has its physical basis in optical frequency fluctuations, the high-frequency limit of the dielectric constant must be used. In these expressions therefore ε will have a value that will approach the square of the refractive index of the interposing medium, even if this is a polar solvent such as water. In contrast, the ε required for the electrostatic interactions will correspond to the zero frequency limit of the dielectric constant.

The other nonbonded interaction is the repulsion that must dominate at short distances ($r_{12} < 2$–3 Å) and tend to infinity as $r_{12} \to 0$ to be consistent with the space filling properties of atoms and molecules. Unlike the dispersive term where there is general agreement on the functional dependence of the potential, the distance dependence of the core repulsion is unresolved, the only real concensus being that it is a strong function of the interatomic separation.

The following functions, among others, have been proposed for the repulsive core (135, 140, 145, 146).

Hard sphere (146–151)

$$V_{(r)} = 0 \qquad r \geqslant R$$

$$= +\infty \qquad r < R \tag{15a}$$

where R is chosen to represent the sum of the van der Waals radii of the two atoms or groups.

Lennard–Jones (136, 152–155)

$$V_{(r)} = \frac{+B}{r^{12}} \tag{15b}$$

Buckingham (156–160)

$$V_{(r)} = +B\exp(-\mu r) \tag{15c}$$

Kitaigorodsky (161–163)

$$V_{(r)} = +B\exp(-\mu r) \tag{15d}$$

The Buckingham and Kitaigorodsky functions essentially differ only in the way in which the μ parameter is chosen.

Comparison of these functions is best done by combining the core and dispersive term $(-A/r^6)$ and redefining variables to obtain a Universal (dimensionless) form for the nonbonded potential (135, 161, 162). In all cases the function will exhibit a minimum with respect to r_{12} corresponding to the equilibrium separation for the nonbonded but interacting groups of atoms. The location of this minimum $(r_{12} = R)$ and the depth of the potential minimum $[V(R) = -V_0]$ can be used to normalize r_{12} and V, the relationships between R, V_0 and the A, B, and μ coefficients being established from the requirement that when $r_{12} = R$, V is minimized and has a value of $-V_0$.

Defining the dimensionless variable $Z = r_{12}/R$ the following results for $V(Z)/V_0$ are obtained:

Hard sphere

$$\frac{V_{(Z)}}{V_0} = 0 \qquad Z \geqslant 1$$

$$= +\infty \qquad Z < 1 \tag{16a}$$

R = sum of van der Waals radii (V_0 is indeterminate).

Lennard–Jones (also known as the 6–12 potential)

$$\frac{V_{(Z)}}{V_0} = Z^{-12} - 2Z^{-6}$$

$$V_{(Z)} = 0 \qquad \text{for } Z = 0.89$$

$$V_0 = \frac{A}{2R^6} = \frac{B}{R^{12}} = \frac{A^2}{4B}$$

$$R = \left(\frac{2B}{A}\right)^{1/6} \tag{16b}$$

Buckingham and Kitaigorodsky

For both we define $K = \mu R$ and have

$$\frac{V_{(Z)}}{V_0} = \left(\frac{K}{K-6}\right)\left\{\frac{6}{K}\exp[K(1-Z)] - Z^{-6}\right\}$$

$$V_0 = \frac{A}{R^6}\left[\frac{K-6}{K}\right] = B\exp(-K)\left[\frac{K-6}{6}\right] \tag{16c}$$

For the Buckingham potential μ is set to $4.6(K=4.6R)$ for all atoms, and B is adjusted so as to give a value of R consistent with the sum of van der Waals radii.

The equation linking A, B, μ, and R is

$$\mu R = \ln\left(\frac{\mu B}{6A}\right) + 7\ln R \qquad (17)$$

while $V_{(z)}=0$ for the value of Z fitting the equation

$$Z - \frac{6\ln Z}{K} = 1 - \frac{\ln(K/6)}{K} \qquad (18)$$

Kitaigorodsky observed that for many atom pairs K could be set to a constant $(K=13)$ and that $V_{(z=2/3)}$ could be set to 3.5 kcal/mol. This leads to an equation in which V_0 is replaced by $V_{(z=2/3)}$ as a normalizing factor.

$$\frac{V_{(z)}}{3.5} = \left[8600\exp(-13Z) - 0.0422Z^{-6}\right] \qquad (19)$$

V_0 is then constant $= 0.079$ kcal/mol

$$V_{(z)} = 0 \qquad \text{for } Z = 0.887$$

and

$$R = \left[\frac{(K-6)A}{KV_0}\right]^{1/6} \approx (6.82A)^{1/6}$$

Recently Hagler and co-workers (164–167) have started to use a 6–9 potential modeled after the Lennard–Jones 6–12 function but with a repulsive term of the form

$$V_{(r)} = \frac{+B}{r^9} \qquad (20)$$

A universal form of this potential can also be obtained and the appropriate equations are

$$\frac{V_{(z)}}{V_0} = 2Z^{-9} - 3Z^6$$

$$V_{(z)} = 0 \qquad \text{for } Z = 0.87$$

$$V_0 = \frac{A}{3R^6} = \frac{B}{2R^9} = \frac{4A^3}{27B^2}$$

$$R = \left(\frac{3B}{2A}\right)^{1/3} \qquad (21)$$

Examination of the plots of the Universal forms of these potential functions as shown in Figure 14 brings out both similarities and differences. In the attractive range the curves can be superimposed—even the Buckingham

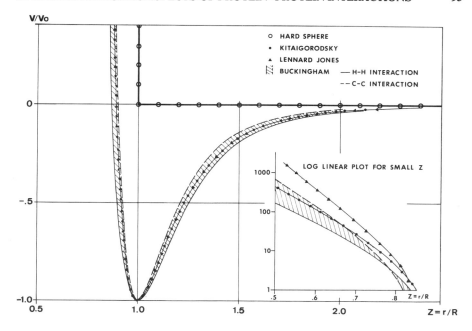

FIGURE 14 Universal form of potential energy functions.

function for which the form is dependent on the interaction type through the parameter K shows only a small divergence when the H–H and C–C interactions are plotted. The energy scale factors, V_0, for the different interactions and functional expressions does vary and indicates some major differences (Table 3). The Kitaigorodsky expression represents the weakest interaction with a maximum attraction of 80 cal/mol for each atomic pair, independent of their type. The Buckingham potential leads to a much stronger interaction with greater variation with atom type, 112 cal/mol for H–H to 357 cal/mol for N–N. The Lennard–Jones function lies between these two extreme models. At small distances ($Z < 0.75$) the repulsive portion of the functions dominate and show major differences—the Buckingham and Kitaigorodsky functions becoming unrealistic, as they predict an attraction as Z tends to zero.

Values of the distances scale factor, R, are interaction-dependent but quite consistent. For the hard-sphere potential R is in general 10–20% percent smaller than the values of R used with the other potentials. This, however, is a consequence of the parameterization, in the hard-sphere case R corresponds in both physical and numerical terms to the value of r_{12} at which the potential becomes repulsive, while for the softer potentials this occurs for values of r_{12} in the range 0.87–$0.89R$.

TABLE 3
Nonbonded Potential Function Parameters

Interactions	R (Å)[a]					V_0 in(cal/mol)[a]			
	1A	1B	2	3	4	1A,B	2	3	4
C–C	3.0–3.2	2.9	3.4	3.4	3.4	0	120	239	79
H–H	1.9–2.15	1.8	2.4	2.4	2.4	0	122	112	79
C'–C'	2.8–2.85	2.4	2.9	2.9	2.9	0	108	153	79
C–N	3.15	2.65	3.25	3.25	3.25	0	155	290	79
C–O	2.7–2.8	2.7	3.22	3.22	3.2	0	165	246	79
N–N	2.6–2.7	2.4	3.10	3.10	3.1	0	205	357	79
N–O	2.6–2.65	2.45	3.07	3.07	3.05	0	218	306	79
O–O	2.6–2.75	2.50	3.04	3.04	3.0	0	232	267	79
O–H	2.35–2.55	2.15	2.72	2.72	2.7	0	153	159	79
N–H	2.5–2.6	2.1	2.75	2.75	2.75	0	145	190	79

$$r_{(V=0)} = R \qquad r_{(V=0)} = 0.87\text{–}0.89\ R$$

[a]Set 1: Hard sphere A, Hopfinger (135); B, Gabel, Rasse, Scheraga (239); Set 2: Lennard–Jones, Scott and Scheraga (55,147); Set 3: Buckingham, Brant and Flory, Ramachandran (156,2); Set 4: Kitaigorodsky, Venkatachalam and Ramachandran, Kitaigorodsky (163,161).

Hydrogen bonds. Because of its enormous importance in biological systems the hydrogen bond is perhaps the single most studied nonbonded interaction (168–170). Yet despite a wealth of facts that have been collected about the hydrogen bond, using a very wide range of experimental techniques, including calorimetry, spectroscopy, nuclear magnetic resonance, X-ray, and neutron diffraction, there is still no universally accepted model for the interaction.

In principle it is accepted that the bond has as major components the electrostatic and nonbonded-type interactions discussed above and embodied in the Stockmayer equation used by De Santis and Liquori (171). However, other factors have been added to improve the agreement with experimental observations. Brant (172) introduced an angle-dependent term, which took into account the weakening of the interaction for nonlinear arrangements of the atoms and made a smooth transistion to the nonbonded form for large deviations from linearity. Magnasco and Gay (173) introduced a charge transfer term represented by a Morse potential (174). Moulton and Kromhout (175) had fitted NMR data by adding an angle-dependent factor akin to Brant's to the function proposed by Lippincott and Schroeder (176) based on the interaction of two diatomic, dipolar, species X—H and H—Y. However, recently Hagler and Lifson (153, 167) have found that these additions can be made redundant, at least within a series of amide crystals, by using optimized atomic parameters for the electrostatic and nonbonded interactions. While these optimized parameters for the A and B coefficients of the Lennard–Jones

TABLE 4

Hagler and Lifson Hydrogen Bond Parameters (153)[a]

Atom	Partial Charge in Electron Charges	Lennard–Jones Parameters			
		A (kcal/mol-Å^6)	$B \times 10^{-3}$ (kcal/mol-Å^{12})	R (Å)	V_0 (kcal/mol)
H	+0.28	0	0	0	0
N	−0.28	1230	2270	3.93	0.167
O	−0.36	500	275	3.21	0.228
C	+0.36	1340	3020	4.06	0.148

[a] The effective hydrogen bond potential is computed from the sum of the electrostatic and nonbonded interactions for H–O, H–C, N–O, and N–C pair interactions. The A, B, and V_0 coefficients for the interacting pairs are taken to be the geometric mean of the appropriate atomic parameters, while the arithmetic mean is used for the R coefficients.

potential and for the partial charges on the H, C, O, and N atoms differ somewhat from *typical* values such as those presented in the preceding text and references, in all but one instance they agree well enough to be within the limits of experimental error. The parameters for the peptide bond atoms are included in Table 4.

The single exception in Hagler and Lifson's coefficients is of great significance and concerns the nonbonded parameters of the hydrogen itself. These, when optimized, become zero, the conclusion being that, while the partial charge on the hydrogen (−0.28 electron charges) is an essential part of the interaction, the nonbonded effects, dispersion and repulsion, are screened by the amide nitrogen. This model has found important confirmation in a quantum-mechanical model proposed by Allen (177) based on the ab initio molecular orbital wave functions.

Solvent or hydrophobic interactions.   The term hydrophobic bond is often encountered in connection with solvent interactions, implying, to the unwary, the existence of specific atom-atom interactions with perhaps a well-defined functional dependency. However, such descriptions of these interactions are not currently available, the difficulties in establishing a theoretical model being related to the more entropic rather than enthalpic nature of the effects and the absence of a model of bulk water itself at a molecular level.

Expressions for the various interaction potentials given in the preceding text represent contributions to the enthalpy, H, of the system. While in fact the enthalpy change during a molecular interaction establishes the binding energy of the interaction, the stability of a conformation depends on the Gibbs free energy, G, which involves the temperature, T, and an entropy term, S.

$$G = H - TS \tag{22}$$

In statistical mechanics, entropy provides a measure of the disorder of a system, the entropy of a state being given by the expression

$$S = R \ln W \quad \text{kcal/mol-degree} \tag{23}$$

where R is the gas constant and W represents the number of ways in which the state can be achieved. An isolated protein in going from a random coil to a folded, native conformation undoubtedly experiences a decrease in enthalpy, the significant pairwise atomic interactions increasing in number and taking on lower, more negative values. At the same time the protein will become more ordered and thus will experience a corresponding decrease in entropy. As, at constant temperature the changes in G, H, and S indicated by ΔG, ΔH, and ΔS are related by the equation, $\Delta G = \Delta H - T\Delta S$, the sign of ΔG will depend on the balance between the change in enthalpy and entropy and, moreover, will be temperature-dependent. If ΔG is negative the net change will be from random coil to folded conformation.

Inclusion of solvent modifies this picture. In the random coil state there will be a large number of interactions between the protein and the solvent. Solvent molecules will be bound, be ordered, and have a low entropy. In the folded state the area of contact between the protein and the solvent will decrease, the protein forming a compact globular structure with solvent largely excluded from the internal region. The number of bound waters will decrease, the solvent can become more disordered and will have a higher entropy.

To a first approximation for polar solvents, such as water, all atoms will be interacting to their maximum capabilities. For each pair of protein-solvent interactions that must be broken in the transition to the folded state one protein-protein and one solvent-solvent interaction should result. As again to a first approximation the interaction strengths will be equal, the expression for the net enthalpic change will be small and the expression for ΔG will reduce to

$$\Delta G = -T(\Delta S \text{ protein} + \Delta S \text{ solvent}) \tag{24}$$

Nemethy and Scheraga (178–180) have made estimates of the quantity ΔS protein $+\Delta S$ solvent, for the transfer of various amino acid side chains from water into a nonpolar environment and given values for this of between $+9$ and $+16$ cal/mol-degree depending on the side chain. Chothia (181) argues for a value of $\Delta S = +70$ cal/mol-degree for the entropy gained by restoring the translational and rotational degrees of freedom to a small (solvent) molecule with a smaller negative ΔS being expected for the removal of the 2 or so internal degrees of freedom of a protein side chain. In both cases the models would predict that ΔG would be significantly less than zero —favoring the folded conformation.

In nonpolar solvents the direction of the changes indicated in Table 5 will be correct but the magnitude of the effects will be different. Both protein-solvent and solvent-solvent enthalpy changes might be expected to be diminished due to the absence of dipole-dipole interactions and hydrogen

TABLE 5

Effects of the Transition from Random Coil to Native Conformation

Item	Direction of Change	
Protein-protein interactions	Increase	$\Delta H < 0$
Protein-solvent interactions	Decrease	$\Delta H > 0$
Solvent-solvent interactions	Increase	$\Delta H < 0$
Protein disorder	Decrease	$\Delta S < 0$
Solvent disorder	Increase	$\Delta S > 0$

bonds. This reduction will also lessen the ordering of the solvent by the protein so that the solvent entropy increase accompanying the folding of the protein will be smaller. The net result will be a reduction or even a change in the sign of ΔG from the aqueous solvent value.

Krimm and Venkatachalam (182) have outlined a procedure for handling systems containing bound water molecules. This is based largely on the use of electrostatic and nonbonded functions with suitable parameters but has an added entropy term, which is computed from the formula $S = R \ln W$ given earlier. W is interpreted as being the statistical mechanical partition function measuring the number of states that are isoenergetic with the conformation of interest, the internal degrees of freedom being the angles that define the orientation of the water molecule with reference to the bonding group. In the case of poly-L-proline, the inclusion of the bound water had a significant effect on the computed free energy and on the dependence of the energy as a function of the internal angles of the monomer unit. Krimm's prediction of the relative stability of the cis and trans forms of the polymer and the solvent dependencies involved are confirmed by experiment. The method neglects the effect of unbound solvent, that is, the major hydrophobic interaction and requires extensive amounts of computer time to implement. Extensions of the method to handle unbound waters does not appear feasible.

Several empirical approaches to solvent interactions have been proposed based on a more macroscopic view of the interactions and incorporating experimental data on molecular hydrophobicity, solubility, and solvent partition coefficients. Gibson and Scheraga (183) and Hopfinger (135, 184, 185) have both adapted the hydration shell model (186) to provide a solvent free energy term, which is a function of the molecular conformation. This is computed by estimating the number of solvent molecules that would be removed from the first hydration shell to accommodate the test conformation, up to a maximum equal to the number of solvent molecules in the hydration shell. Then to each solvent molecule displaced, a free-energy contribution which takes into account the nature of the solvent and the solute atoms is assigned. In a similar manner Chothia (187) has used Nozaki and Tanford's data on hydrophobicity (188) derived from experiments on the solubility of amino acids in organic solvents, and Richards and Lee's estimates of their accessible surface areas (189) to produce a figure for the average free-energy

TABLE 6
Free Energies Gained by Displacing Solvent Molecules

| Atom or Group | Aqueous Solution[a] (Volume of Solvent Molecule = 21.1 Å³) | | | Ethanol[b] (Volume of Solvent Molecule = 63.7 Å³) | |
	No. of Molecules in Hydration Shell Set 1, Set 2	ΔG per Solvent Molecule (cal/mol) Set 1	ΔG per Solvent Molecule (cal/mol) Set 2	No. of Molecules in Hydration Shells Set 3	ΔG per Solvent Molecule (cal/mol) Set 3
Amide N	2	630	630	2	180
Aromatic C	2	110	630	2	150
Aromatic CH	3	110	110	2	400
Carbonyl O	4,2	940	1880	2	1180
Carboxyl O	5,4	4800	4200	2	2450
Hydroxyl O	6,2	840	1580	1	570
Amide H	2	310	310	1	280
Hydroxyl H	2	310	310	1	570
Carboxyl H	2	310	310	1	880
Aliphatic CH	2	−130	−130	2	390
Aliphatic CH$_2$	3,4	−130	−100	3	390
Aliphatic CH$_3$	8	−130	−130	4	410

[a]Set 1, Gibson and Scheraga (183); Set 2 Hopfinger (184).
[b]Set 3 Forsythe and Hopfinger (185).

change accompanying the removal of 1 Å^2 of protein surface from contact with aqueous solvent.

For typical hydrocarbon chains in aqueous solutions, both Scheraga (180) and Hopfinger (185) propose a free-energy change of -130 cal/mol for each solvent molecule displaced from the hydration shell. For hydrogen $\Delta G = +300$ cal/mol, while for polar groups such as carbonyl oxygens, amide nitrogens, and so on, ΔG is in the range 600–4500 cal/mol. The data are shown in Table 6. Chothia's composite figure for proteins is $\Delta G = -25$ cal/Å^2 removed from the solvent accessible surface. When combined with an estimate of 6 Å^2 for the cross-sectional area of a water molecule, this value would correspond to a $\Delta G = -150$ cal/mol per water molecule displaced. Thus, while Chothia's model may be extreme, and while the early computations of accessible surface are being questioned (190, 191), the three methods would seem to be in broad agreement on the free energy associated with the so-called hydrophobic bond.

Summary of potential functions.   The picture that emerges from the preceding survey is of functions, based both on theory and experimental observation that are capable of quantitatively describing the major classes of nonbonded interactions involved in protein energetics. While in principle a self-consistent set of functions and parameters can be obtained for these relationships, great care has to be taken in making these selections. Individual authors will have developed optimized parameters to fit particular data sets, usually accounting for the data with only a subset of the interactions, by making the assumption of rigid geometry, or in vacuo interactions. This leads to the possibility for partial duplications of interactions to occur inadvertently. For example, the torsional strain energy terms in the bonded interactions will embody nonbonded interactions for atoms that are members of the group defining the bond; if a torsional term is to be included then a careful analysis is necessary to distribute the interactions for these atoms between the bonded and the nonbonded interactions. It should be noted that the torsional term is not made redundant by the nonbonded interactions as it will include bond-bond as well as atom-atom contributions. Other possible duplications will involve the hydrogen bond functions with both nonbonded and electrostatic terms.

Another potential hazard lies in the choice of the dielectric factor ε. It has already been noted that in the theoretical treatment of the electrostatic and the dispersive contribution to the nonbonded interaction different values of ε are called for. The former requires the use of the zero frequency limit, the latter, the use of the high frequency or optical limit. Most of the parameters of the potential functions have been developed using ε in the range 3 to 4 (55, 156) for the zero frequency limit justifying this even in aqueous solvents as either the microscopic limit (2) or the value for typical, proteinlike, material. Other authors, including Hopfinger (135), Ralston (192), Warshel (154), and Greenberg (193), suggest that a distance-dependent function must be introduced for ε, for both theoretical and practical reasons. In particular

Greenberg (193) found it necessary in predicting or analyzing amino acid crystal structures to describe ε by a step function,

$$\varepsilon_{(r)} = 1.0 \qquad r < 3.5\,\text{Å}$$
$$= 3.5 \qquad r \geqslant 3.5\,\text{Å} \qquad (25)$$

Functions or coefficients proposed by authors using different models for the dielectric cannot be combined.

In the case of small molecules the strategy of choice in establishing parameters for use with a series of molecules is to use data available for a subset to optimize the coefficients of the potential functions (160, 166, 194). This extrapolation or bootstrapping process has been used in conjunction with energy minimization to make predictions on a wide variety of structures, including peptides (2, 146, 195–200). It is difficult to judge objectively whether these predictions demonstrate the value or the shortcomings of this approach. Many workers claim to have generalizable functions that predict successfully the conformation of small molecules as observed in crystals. However, it is also true that much of the information available from crystal data will have been built into the optimized potential functions and that other workers (193) have reported that the energy minimum located at or near the crystal conformation is not always a global minimum when parameters for the geometry of the unit cell are included in the minimization. On the other hand, the prediction of solution conformations, which are in particular needed to validate solvent interaction terms (hydrophobic bond potentials) are difficult to evaluate. Available experimental techniques provide qualitative rather than quantitative conformational data.

Verification of the general validity of potential functions for use with proteins can, however, be obtained by examination of the structural and conformational information available for the 100 or so proteins that have been studied by X-ray diffraction in the crystalline state. Comparisons can be made of the location and frequency of the ϕ and ψ angles observed in the backbone of these proteins with Ramachandran plots of the conformational energy of the N-acetyl N'-methyl amides of all 20 naturally occurring amino acids, the amino acid side chains being allowed to adopt their minimum energy conformation for each backbone conformation. After taking into account the standard deviations that are to be encountered in the experimental data (± 30 degrees or so in ϕ or ψ), the Ramachandran plots based on the hard sphere, nonbonded potential show consistency with the location of observed allowed and disallowed regions (2, 146–150). Inclusion of hydrogen-bond and solvent terms in the calculations and replacement of the hard-sphere nonbonded function by Lennard–Jones, Buckingham, or Kitaigorodsky functions define potential energy surfaces that are consistent with the frequencies of occurrence of the allowed ϕ and ψ angles (2, 195, 201). Likewise, Pohl's empirical energy function (202), established by fitting protein data to a Boltzmann energy distribution, shows up no major discrepancies, agreeing well with typical theoretical plots for an alanine-like residue, the differences between the various amino acids being averaged out. However, while these agreements are encouraging, it must be kept in mind that the observed distributions of the ϕ, ψ angles for even a single residue type in the protein represents a summation of distributions. The sum observed is for this residue in different environments (surface, buried, polar, nonpolar, helical, etc.) rather than a single distribution function arising from a homogeneous population.

Current trends are toward the development of better techniques for obtaining optimized potential functions (194) and toward a reconciliation of quantum-mechanical and semiempirical potential function calculations (145, 155, 164, 203–206). Scheraga and co-workers (145) have refined parameters for the various amino acid interaction terms on the basis of an extended crystal structure data base. Although in this work there are no bond length or bond angle strain terms they do allow for each amino acid type to have a different geometry to reflect the effect of side chain-backbone interactions. On the basis of their analysis they propose that the repulsion parameters of the nonbonded interactions for atoms separated by three bonds of which the center one is rotatable (1–4 nonbonded interactions) be screened to 50% of the normal values to make them consistent with the repulsions computed quantum mechanically. Similar screening of this interaction in the case of the nonbonded hard-sphere potential was suggested in earlier work by this group (55) but was also challanged by Ramachandran (2). Robson and co-workers (164) have made ab initio quantum calculations on N-formyl N'-methyl amides of glycine and alanine and report good agreement with the calculations performed by Hagler and Lifson (153, 167) using semiempirical functions incorporating a 6–9 nonbonded potential. They report that the agreement is better for nonhydrogen bonded conformations and suggest a correction to the ab initio calculation for the hydrogen bond contribution. Hagler and co-workers (165) have examined several different methods for predicting the conformations of oligopeptides, also using a 6–9 nonbonded potential. Differences in the predictions based on Monte Carlo (see Section 2.6.2.4), and fixed or flexible geometry models were found and are being evaluated by comparison with experimental data on the peptides obtained from analysis of nmr, IR, and CD spectra. As well as incorporating an entropic factor for solvent, this work provides information for including vibrational free-energy terms—a prelude to considerations of the dynamics of molecular conformations and a link to the molecular dynamics of Karplus and the protein-folding simulations of Levitt, Scheraga, and others (see Section 2.6.2).

2.6.2 Conformational Calculations and Conceptual Models of Proteins

2.6.2.1 Polypeptide geometry

Information on the geometry of polypeptide and protein chains comes almost entirely from the analysis of single crystal X-ray diffraction data on single amino acids or oligopeptides. Much of these data have been compiled and reviewed by Gurskaya (207) and Marsh and Donohue (208). Table 7 summarizes their findings for the geometry of the dipeptide unit and contains for comparison the values used by several groups actively involved in energy calculations. Figure 15 indicates the conventional labeling of a dipeptide unit. The angles at the α-carbon atom, which would be 109.47° for ideal tetrahedral geometry, are subject to the most variation, values in the range 108°–112° being considered acceptable. However, it should be noted that

TABLE 7
Peptide Geometry[a]

	Bond Lengths (Å)				
	A	B	C	D	E
N–CA	1.47	1.45(5)	1.47	1.47	1.45(3)
CA–C′	1.53	1.51	1.53	1.53	1.53
C′–N	1.32	1.32(5)	1.32	1.32	1.32(5)
N–H	—	—	1.00	1.00	1.00
CA–CB	1.51	1.52(5)	—	1.53	1.53
C′–O	1.24	1.24	1.24	1.24	1.23

	Bond Angles (deg)				
	A	B	C	D	E[b]
C′–N–CA	123	122.0	126	123	121
C′–N–H	123	119.0	121	123	124
HA–N–CA	—	—	115	114	115
N–CA–C′	110	111.0	110	109.5	108.0–111.1
N–CA–CB	—	—	110	109.5	108.0–113.7
CB–CA–C′	—	—	110	109.5	108.3–111.0
CA–C′–N	114	116.0	118	114	115
CA–C′–O	121	120.5	119	121	120.5
O–C′–N	125	123.5	123	125	124.5

Torsion Angles (deg)

CA–C′–N–CA = ω =   0°   cis-Peptide
CA–C′–N–CA = ω = 180°   trans-Peptide
C′–N–CA–C′ = ϕ
N–CA–C′–NA = ψ

[a]Sets: A, Gurskaya (207); B, Marsh and Donohue (208); C, Ramachandran (2); D, Scheraga (146); E, Momany (145).

Abbreviations (also used in Figure 16): N, nitrogen atom; CA, α-carbon atom; C′, carbonyl carbon atom; O, carbonyl oxygen atom; CB, β-carbon; HA, α-carbon proton.

[b]To account for differences between the X-ray structures of different amino acids used by Momany (145), we show, where appropriate, a range of values.

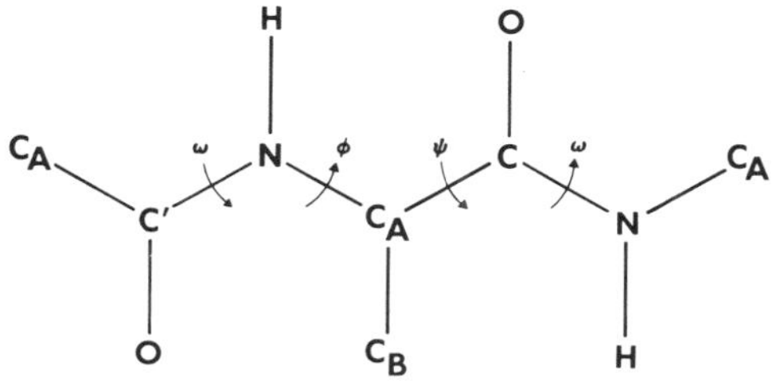

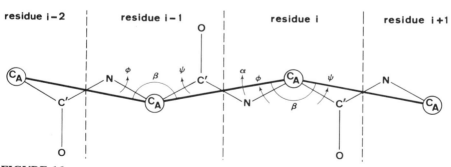

FIGURE 15 Dipeptide unit.

because this geometry is used M times over in a chain of M residues any differences are compounded. For example, the end to end distance for a polypeptide chain will be quite sensitive to the choice of the basic peptide geometry. Methods for generation of the polypeptide or protein coordinates from standardized geometry have been embodied in widely distributed programs. The review by Ramachandran (2) and the paper by Nemethy and Scheraga (209) describe two methods, but many others exist, often optimized to fit particular circumstances.

Both Levitt (210, 211) and Robson (212) use a simplified representation of the protein chain. Levitt basically follows the virtual bond model suggested by Flory (213), which makes use of the invariance in a cis or trans peptide of the distance between consecutive α-carbons. He defines α-angles, which are the torsion angles measured for four consecutive α-carbons and β-angles, which are the angles between adjacent α-carbon to α-carbon vectors. The nature of these geometrical properties is shown in Figure 16. A mathematical

residue i−2   residue i−1   residue i   residue i+1

FIGURE 16
Relationship between ϕ, ψ, and Levitt's α, β angles. The angles are defined thus:

$$C_{A_{i-2}} - C_{A_{i-1}} - C_{A_i} - C_{A_{i+1}} = \alpha_{i-1} = \text{function of } (\phi_{i-1}, \psi_{i-1}) \text{ and } (\phi_i, \psi_i)$$

$$C_{A_{i-2}} - C_{A_{i-1}} - C_{A_i} = \beta_{i-1} = \text{function of } (\phi_{i-1}, \psi_{i-1})$$

$$C_{A_{i-1}} - C_{A_i} - C_{A_{i+1}} = \beta_i = \text{function of } (\phi_i, \psi_i)$$

$$C_{A_j} - C_{A_{j+1}} = 3.81 \text{ Å for transpeptide bond.}$$

relationship between the conventional ϕ and ψ angles and α and β can be obtained using spherical trigonometry.

2.6.2.2 Energy minimization

Minimization of the conformational energy of a whole protein, with or without consideration of solvent, involves dealing with a quantity that is the sum of many thousands of atomic interactions and is a function of many hundreds of conformational variables. Identification of the conformer of minimum global energy is a major computational task beyond the limits of current computational instrumentation. Not only is the magnitude of the calculation of the energy associated with a single conformer significant but the complexity of the dependence of the energy on the conformational variables makes it certain that there will be many local energy minima and that the true global minimum will be associated with a relatively small radius of convergence.

Nemethy and Scheraga (209) attempted the analysis of an octapeptide loop that occurs in ribonuclease and is constrained by a cystine bridge (residues 65–72) using minimization techniques. While the cyclic constraint lead to only a small number of conformations being identified, the crystal structure elucidated later by X-ray diffraction (39) was not 1 of the 15. As a followup Scheraga (214) examined in detail the application of potential energy minimization to selected oligopeptides that occur in lysozyme (37). He found that the computed energy minimum conformation of a residue at the center of an oligopeptide could be made to agree with the crystal observations but only when it was flanked on either side by several residues, usually four or more whose conformations were set to those found in the protein crystal. This suggests again that the potential functions available are realistic and that medium-range interactions, that is, those involving residues that are close neighbors in the protein amino acid sequence, provide the major stabilization of residue conformations. However, this work also demonstrates the small radius of convergence mentioned earlier; the residues adjacent to the central residue have to be in a conformation close to that of the crystal before the computed global minimum will match the observed minimum for the central residue.

The problem of multiple local energy minima may be avoided if the minimization is started at or near to the crystallographically determined structure as this can be presumed to be at or close to the true energy minimum. This is the basis of the technique known as energy refinement, which was used by Levitt (137,215,216) to restore polypeptide geometry to sets of coordinates obtained from physical models and therefore subject to errors of measurement. He used an energy function consisting of strain energy terms and a Lennard–Jones nonbonded potential. When applied to the X-ray coordinates of lysozyme, the minimization led to a structure which had acceptable geometry and was still in close agreement with the best fit to the electron density maps. Scheraga, Hermans, and their co-workers (217–221) introduced more elaborate functions including electrostatic and hydrogen bond terms and applied these to both lysozyme and rubredoxin. Changes produced by the energy refinements were mostly small and in the direction of an improved geometry. The larger changes were to be found in regions where the crystal showed substantial thermal motion, that is at the ends of the polypeptide chain and in long amino acid side chains. The overall conclusions to be drawn from this work lie less in these conformational results than in the demonstration of the existence of functions that can provide a reasonable description of the interactions.

Reduction in the computational complexity associated with energy minimization can be achieved by reducing the number of variables used to model the structure. This can be done by fixing the conformation of local or secondary structures, by removing from consideration their internal degrees of freedom, the rationale being that the global minimum will involve only arrangements of these stable entities. Alternatively, variables can be removed by replacing the full peptide geometry in which all nonhydrogen atoms are explicitly represented, with a simplified version in which atoms are ignored or groups of atoms are represented by a single, composite, or superatom. Both techniques have been used but even with these simplifications the computations will still be extensive. Most investigators have therefore concentrated on the modeling of the smaller proteins such as bovine pancreatic trypsin inhibitor (BPTI), which has 58 residues (222–224). BPTI has the advantage that its folding pathway has been the subject of experimental investigation by Creighton and others (225).

Burgess and Scheraga (226) formulated a quantized model for native BPTI in which each residue was assigned one of five conformation states, which were defined on the basis of the population density observed in Ramachandran plots of the protein data base and allows individual ϕ, ψ angles to be represented to within 30°. Starting from this model, which now represented a perturbation of the native structure, they tested the performance of three folding algorithms. Two of these were based on artificial potentials, which forced the formation of cystine bridges with and without the constraint that the chain should be self-avoiding and that the sum of the squares of the changes in dihedral angle in the backbone (ϕ and ψ) from the X-ray observed values should be minimized. The third algorithm sought minimization of a potential function in which electrostatic, nonbonded and torsional terms, developed from work by this group on oligopeptides, were used. Although in no case was the native conformation of BPTI recovered, the procedure using the *realistic potentials* had started to show nativelike ordering in the conformations generated when the minimization was terminated because of the computer time involved. It was concluded, however, that such a procedure has the potential to recover the native conformation, but that a rather accurate prediction of the topography of the native conformation would have to be incorporated in the starting model. Again the problem is seen as one of convergence, the third algorithm allowing relaxation of a perturbed structure but not its global minimization.

To study recovery of the native conformation from conformers even remotely resembling a denatured state, it is apparent that minimizations will have to be run for many more steps. To keep these computations within reasonable bounds, most workers have adopted models that have less detail and/or few internal degrees of freedom. Levitt and Warshel (210) essentially follow a virtual bond model proposed by Flory (213) and represent the residues by two spherical superatoms centered on the α-carbon and centroid of the side chain. A new conformational variable α is used, which corresponds to the dihedral angles in the α-carbon chain (Section 2.6.2.1 and Figure 16). Variation in the interlink angles, β, which would normally be a function of two pairs of ϕ, ψ angles, is replaced by an empirically determined dependence on α. In a second paper (211) Levitt expands the model to provide positional data on the backbone nitrogen and oxygens and allows for a more complex description of side chains at the cost of introducing a second independent variable. Interaction potential parameters for these superatoms as a function of the angle α have been developed from an analysis of six representative dipeptides. The resulting model, while retaining many of the specifics of the protein, has many fewer interactions and variables. The refolding of BPTI was used as a test of the model and was attempted from three separate starting states, the idealized native state produced by fitting the reduced geometry model to native coordinates and two extended coformations, one of which included a preformed carboxyl-terminal helix. During the minimization a procedure described as *normal mode thermalization* was used to get out of local energy minima, which in this case corresponded to apparently stable intermediates whose conformational energy was still high and which possessed relatively little order compared to the native structure. The idealized native structure had a root-mean-squared (rms) deviation from the crystal structure of 2.5 Å, which, while resembling the crystal structure, is not a detailed match. Specific features such as the characteristic twist in the β-sheet were absent (227). Folding from the extended conformations resulted in structures with rms values of 6–8 Å when compared to the native protein. Again these showed superficial resemblances, although the carboxyl-terminal helix was only found in instances where it persisted from the preformed nucleus.

In another paper Levitt (228) incorporated six permanent α-helical regions into the reduced geometry model of the carp myogen protein and studied the formation of α-helical subassemblies. The resulting model was similar to major portions of the myogen crystal structure. This success lends support to the contentions of the authors that long-range interactions, that is, those involving residues widely separated in the primary sequence, are also of major importance in the determination of tertiary structure.

Kuntz (229) has also made use of a simplified geometry modeling using single, β-carbon based spheres to represent residues and with Cartesian coordinates as variables. Constraints were imposed on interresidue distances so as to characterize protein geometry. Interaction parameters are represented by a matrix whose entries are specific to the interacting residue types and include a term to promote disulfide bridge formation. Tests were made using rubredoxin and BPTI, the primary aim being to investigate factors influencing the formation of compact globular structures using interactions not necessarily having a theoretical basis. Nevertheless, structures with rms values of 4–5 Å were reported, which again superficially resembled the native proteins.

Robson (212) has recently reported a more detailed modeling of BPTI. A single conformational variable, γ, was used to parameterize the geometry and energetics of dipeptide units, but unlike the α parameter of Levitt (210,211) γ was defined so that ϕ and ψ angles can be recovered and the full backbone structure be regenerated. The ellipse in the ϕ, ψ angle space for this mapping was chosen to pass through the populated positions observed for the principle secondary structures in proteins (195,201,202). This represents a nice generalization of the five-state model of Burgess (226), although the continuous nature of the variable γ does not preclude residue conformers that are sterically disallowed. Interactions between dipeptide units were parameterized as functions of the center to center separations, the coefficients representing the combined van der Waals, electrostatic, hydrogen bond, and solvent interactions. A specific potential was introduced to promote correct pairing of the disulfide bridge residues, although simulations seemed to be insensitive to its strength. Local minima were avoided without the use of the *normal mode thermalization* (210,211,227) by alternating between two minimizing procedures having different characteristics with regard to escape from local minima. While the starting configuration did contain predicted secondary structure, these were not locked in during minimization and modifications could and did occur. Comparison of minimized structures with native BPTI had rms values of order 6 Å. Once again broad similarities with the native structure could be found in these structures, the authors commenting in particular on the presence of a β-sheet and the conservation of the predicted carboxyl-terminal helix.

In principle the simplified models used should allow identification of the types of interaction that are important in folding and promote thinking about the way in which the native structure is formed and stabilized (229). Claims that the structures produced by the minimization experiments surveyed are close to the biologically relevant set, and therefore that these procedures can be used to obtain meaningful information about the specifics of native conformations of new proteins from primary sequence information alone, have received critical review (195,212,227,230). The main contentions are that (a) the initial starting conformation, the potentials, or the model itself are biased in favor of a return to the specific native conformation; and (b) the criteria used for judging the similarities of the native and computed structures are not sufficiently discriminating.

By way of illustrating the second point Hagler (227,230) used a full geometry model for BPTI with potentials derived from oligopeptide work

(166,197) but with a sequence consisting of only glycine and alanine. Starting from a completely extended structure, the structure was allowed to minimize with respect to the ϕ, ψ backbone angles (there are no side-chain rotations for glycine or alanine), with *normal mode thermalization* (210,211) used to avoid trapping in local minima. Superficially the resultant structures resemble the native BPTI with an antiparallel β-sheet and a carboxyl-terminal helix (left-not right-handed, though), which packs against the sheet. The typical rms value of 6.8 Å was comparable to that produced by other workers, only Kuntz (229) perhaps being significantly lower. However, a more detailed examination of these structures (211,227,230) showed the absence of key features of the native PBTI, namely, the characteristic bend in the β-sheet and the specific chain threading required for cystine bridge formation. The authors (227) conclude that the superficial resemblances reported by other workers can be achieved on the basis of backbone interactions alone. Features introduced into models to account for side-chain specifics play little or no role in achieving the overall shape and fail to reproduce structural features that would be expected to be sequence-dependent.

2.6.2.3 *Empirical prediction of structures*

A more empirical approach to the nonexperimental determination of native protein structure has been embodied in the secondary structure predictive schemes already referred to. These are based on the detection and exploitation of sequence-structure correlations in proteins and have been reviewed recently by Chou and Fasman (231), who present an extensive bibliography of the subject.

Analysis of the amino acid sequences that occur in the neighborhood of features such as α-helices, β-sheets, and β-bends in proteins, whose structures have been solved crystallographically, shows a variety of correlations. Most prediction schemes attempt to identify the sequence features that correlate strongest with the occurrence of a particular feature, usually examining the amino acids that occur within the structure. These schemes have a reasonable success rate (232) but it is clear that, while the amino acid sequence does contain specification of the secondary structure, the coding is either very complex or somewhat ambiguous. Certain amino acids do appear to favor a helical structure, but is is also true that no amino acid type has been found only in, or never in, a helix. The success of prediction schemes, which only identify one conformation, only examine local correlations and ignore the effect of long-range and solvent interactions, provides evidence that local interactions involving only atoms in adjacent residues will sometimes determine the local secondary structure. However, because this is not true in general, correlations discovered will not apply in every case and predictions can be expected to exhibit the characteristics of a message received over a noisy communication channel.

A technique is being developed (Barry, unpublished), which seeks to optimize the location of secondary structures by looking for agreement between predictors of different aspects of the structural feature. For example, analysis of the crystal structures allows a determination of the correlations between the occurrence of individual amino acids and the overall percentage of helix observed in the protein. This correlation can be used as a measure of the likelihood of finding a helix associated with a particular type of residue. It is different from that used by Chou and Fasman (232) in that it is based on not just residues *within* a helix. Residues may be grouped according to the correlation, and classes may be identified whose percentage occurrence can be used to estimate the total percentage of helical structure in a protein.

A more detailed analysis of the distribution of amino acid type involving an examination of the occurrence of amino acids at specific locations relative to the designated start and finish of helices also shows some characteristic preferences. These are statistically most significant for the five or so residues found either side of the *begin* and *end* residues of the helix and can be used to predict likely *begin* and *end* markers in the protein sequence. Overall prediction of a helix is then based on the identification of a suitable *begin* marker followed by a string of residues that are helix-favoring or neutral, interrupted at most by a single antihelix (coil) class residue and terminated by an *end* marker. Solitary markers, which occur in conjunction with a short sequence of helix-favoring residues preceded and proceeded by longer sequences of coil-type residues, correlate well with the occurrence of β-bends in proteins and can be used for their prediction. This correlation is strongest for proteins predicted to have a low or zero helix content based on the percentage occurrence of both the helix and coil class residues. Disagreement of the estimates of the helical content coming from these classes can be used to signal a *noisy* protein in which predictions will be unreliable. Most prediction methods fail to work well for some proteins (231, 233). It should also be noted though that, while individual schemes may be quite unreliable in specific instances, the joint prediction histograms (234–236) based on the results of 10 or so independent schemes can be used to provide a more generally reliable basis for secondary structure identifications.

In the absence of hard conformational data on proteins whose sequence is known, empirical prediction methods have a role to play—suggesting secondary structure content or structural-homology with other proteins whose crystal conformation is known. In a few instances models of whole proteins have been built on the basis of predictions of secondary and tertiary structure (237–241), which can be used to provide the basis for experimental evaluation of the underlying concepts. In a similar manner, the sequence-structure correlations forming the basis of the predicting methods, themselves represent observations that can be used to evaluate the potential functions as these correlations should have their origins in the energetics of atomic interactions. Their major importance, however, would appear to be the provision of starting points, which bear sufficient resemblance to the biologically relevant conformations that techniques including energy minimization can be used for refinement and be capable of achieving the correct structure.

2.6.2.4 Monte Carlo methods

The Monte Carlo procedure was first developed in connection with the evaluation of multidimensional integrals where normal methods were too slow by many orders of magnitude to be practical and where even an estimated value was useful. Instead of approximating the integral using formulas based on a regular sampling of the function throughout the ranges of the integration variables, the integral is estimated from values of the function at randomly selected settings of the variables. When applied to the study of systems such as proteins where conformational states are distributed according to a Boltzmann factor, a modified form of the method is used (242). Instead of choosing conformations randomly and then weighting them with the exponential factor, conformations are chosen with a probability corresponding to the Boltzmann distribution and are then weighted evenly. This is done by generating the next random conformation, evaluating its energy and comparing it with the energy of the previous conformation. If the energy has decreased the new conformation is accepted, if the energy has increased the move is accepted with a probability equal to the Boltzmann factor. Low-energy states will thus be retained for several moves and averages (Boltzmann weighted) will simply be the average taken over all accepted moves. Conformations with low probabilities (high energies) will appear only infrequently in the ensemble of accepted conformations rather than appearing often but then being applied with very low weights in computing averages. In this way functions that vary more rapidly than it is practical to sample systematically or functions that have large but localized anomalies can be treated, even a small sample giving an estimate of the ensemble average accompanied by a measure of confidence in the result. It must, however, be noted that the estimates are probabilistic in nature and can sometimes represent atypical values. Two areas of application suggest themselves. True global minimization of the potential energy function for whole proteins is impractical, but the exploration and partial characterization of the properties of the potential energy surface using a Monte Carlo procedure can be considered. Likewise, although the statistical mechanics of the helix-coil transition in polypeptides has been studied extensively using analytic techniques and now provides models for the cooperativity believed to exist in the formation of secondary structures in proteins,* other models are not amenable to analytic treatments but can be studied by Monte Carlo techniques.

Two approaches based on different representations of the protein have been used. In the first, called the *lattice* approach, the specifics of the protein geometry are sacrificed, the protein being represented as a set of connected units occupying sites belonging to a regular lattice. This simplifies the

---

*This work is beyond the scope of this text but is well documented in books by Flory (213), Volkenstein (243), Poland and Scheraga (244), and Hopfinger (135). Reviews covering both the experimental and theoretical aspects are also available and include those by Lotan and Katchalski (245), Anfinsen and Scheraga (197), Tanford (246,247), and Kautzmann (248).

computation of both the conformation and the conformational energy of the protein model, increasing the number of states that can in practice be generated and analyzed and therefore improving the statistics associated with derived properties of the model. The individual units of the model will, in the case of proteins, usually represent whole residues and can be assigned specific attributes. These attributes can be used to simulate volume or energy characteristics of the residues and must be chosen so that in conjunction with the rules governing the occupancy of the lattice the behavior of the model is consistent with that of proteins in general. In the second, the *nonlattice* or *real-space* approach, the model retains the geometry of the protein, although this may be simplified and conformational parameters may be restricted to discrete values following the *rotational isomer-type* modeling of Flory (213).

Statistical averages.   Application of Monte Carlo techniques to the charting of the potential energy surface is well illustrated in the paper by Hagler (165), which reports studies on the conformational properties of several oligopeptides in solution. Average free energy, entropy, and end-to-end distances were calculated using a partition function derived from a very large number of trial conformations (5×10^5), generated using full but rigid geometry and evaluated using potential functions for nonbonded, electrostatic, and hydrogen bond interactions.

The folding of proteins and the renaturation of globular proteins have also been investigated from the statistical mechanical standpoint. Hermans (249) used a simple lattice model to explore the three-dimensional equivalent of the one-dimensional Zimm–Bragg (250) model for helix-coil transitions and correlated the results to experimental data on proton exchange rates. Crippen has studied the properties of peptide conformations using a self-avoiding random walk on a two-dimensional square lattice (251) and has also used the rotational isomer approach with an α-carbon model to investigate the equilibrium constants for the oxidation of reduced BPTI (252). Specifically the model allowed predictions to be made for the probabilities of various disulfide bridges to form under denaturing and renaturing conditions that were consistent with experimental observations (225). Using the real-space, rotational isomer approach Scott and co-workers (253a, b, c) have estimated the partition function for homopolymers of glycine and alanine, their N-methyl derivatives and simple copolymers. While they use explicit peptide geometry rather than a lattice or α-carbon model, initial results were obtained with only a coarse sampling of the monomer conformational space (three or four states). However, in later work the number of states considered for each monomer unit was increased significantly so as to represent a uniform sampling (every 10 degrees in ϕ and ψ) of the regions of the Ramachandran plots which are sterically allowed on the basis of hard-sphere potentials, with all monomer conformations assigned equal weights. The numerical estimate of the partition function obtained was then used to predict bulk properties of the system such as the radius of gyration, mean end-to-end distance and average dipole moment together with their dependence on chain length and composition. It can also be used to investigate helix-coil transitions and to make estimates of the conformational entropy per residue (253c). Similar studies on short polyalanine and polyglycine chains were carried out by Hermans, Premilat and Hesselink (254–256).

Simulations. The work by Levitt, Robson, Hagler, and co-workers (210–212, 227, 228) was directed primarily at obtaining minimum energy conformations for their protein models, but meaning was also attached to the way in which the minima were approached and to the characteristics of intermediate conformations. The underlying concept of a folding pathway is apparent in these papers, the minimization of the conformational energy of the model being analogous to the natural folding process during which free-energy will also be minimized. Viewed in this way the minimization procedure becomes a simulation of the folding (210). However, the recently reviewed experimental work of Creighton and others (225) point to the existence of multiple folding pathways, which funnel down to a set of well-defined native conformations while work of Cooper (257), Wuthrich (258), Phillips (259), and others provide evidence for the existence of quite large-scale conformational fluctuations even in the folded state. These observations taken together indicate the need for a more statistical type of approach.

It has been pointed out by Go and others (260–262) that the Monte Carlo technique can be employed to simulate the approximate time course of a system behaving stochastically as well as to evaluate equilibrium values and to estimate the extent of probable fluctuations. The concept of temperature is introduced into the simulation by requiring that at equilibrium (stationary state) the probability of states should fit a Boltzmann distribution, while because the method implicity takes into account the density of states and thus the entropic factors, transition rates will already be based on Gibbs free energy differences (see Section 2.6.1.2: Solvent or Hydrophobic Interactions). This technique can therefore be used to simulate the helix–coil transition in polypeptides and to study the temperature dependence on both chain length and the strength and form of interactions (262).

More recently Go and co-workers (260, 261, 263–265) have used the simulation technique in conjunction with a two-dimensional square lattice model to study the statistical mechanics of protein folding, unfolding, and fluctuations. The protein is represented as a chain of nonintersecting units (residues) whose character is incorporated into the model through the specifics of interunit (interresidue) interactions. A folded, native conformation can be defined by specification of a characteristic set of unit interactions which will occur for this conformation. Despite the failure of the lysozyme model to fold from all but partially folded states (260), some general conclusions were drawn from the lattice models which appear likely to hold true for real proteins:

1. In the refolding process nucleation is a rate-limiting step.

2. Short-range interactions accelerate folding and unfolding transitions as well as determining local secondary structure.

3. The all or none type of transition from native to denatured state depend primarily on highly specific interunit, long-range interactions. These are essential for the highly cooperative stabilization of the native conformation.

4. Nonspecific parts of the long-range interaction (hydrophobic interactions, for example) counteract the short-range effect and cause a deceleration of the folding kinetics. They allow locally organized regions to aggregate in nonnative arrangements.

5. Under certain conditions, which can be quantified from the behavior of entropy and enthalpy (S vs H plots) during the transitions and appear to relate directly to the amount of well-defined secondary structure in the native state, the all-or-none nature of the transition can be lost.

Tanaka and Scheraga (266) have also used the Monte Carlo simulation technique in conjunction this time with a real space model, to repeat the experiments carried out by Burgess (226) in which minimization techniques were used to study the relaxation of perturbed BPTI conformations in a solvent environment. At the same time the simulation was used to support the proposal of a three-step folding mechanism involving: (a) formation of ordered backbone structures by short-range interactions–residue pairs within four of each other in the amino acid sequence; (b) formation of small contact regions by medium-range interactions–residue pairs still from the same nonapeptide; and finally, (c) association of the small contact regions of (b) into the native structure by long-range interactions–residue pairs distant in the amino acid sequence.

The various stages were simulated, in order, by application of different types of random perturbations to the model but using the same potential functions throughout. No artificial potential was used to bias the formation of disulfide bridges. While the degree to which the resulting structures resembled the native BPTI is not clear, the experiment indicated plausibility for the three-step mechanism and led to a subsequent paper (267) in which empirical residue-residue interaction parameters were developed that included solvent effects. However, no report of results obtained using these was given.

2.6.2.5 Molecular dynamics

There remains one important computational alternative to Monte Carlo simulation for the study of conformation fluctuations. This is the molecular dynamics approach of Karplus and co-workers (4). Stated simply, it is possible, given interaction potentials and atomic geometry, to set up and solve the equations of motion for a protein in the manner of a problem in classical mechanics. Because of the large velocities but small distances encountered at the atomic level, the time steps for the numerical solution of these equations has to be small, of the order 10^{-15} sec. Simulations are then feasible for events occurring on a time scale of the order of 10–100 p sec. Using BPTI for the model, fluctuations about the observed X-ray structure were simulated. Both correlated fluctuations, in which disturbances of the main chain atoms was minimal, and concerted motions, in which major structural features oscillated as a whole, were found to be present. The authors also concluded that vibrational energy can be localized for a comparatively long period of time (10 psec) in proteins, despite the availability of efficient relaxation pathways. The overall picture obtained is of a structure that behaves in a fluid like manner at room temperatures, there being fluctuations of atoms about some average position, which are dominated by collisions with neighboring atoms in much the same way as are those of atoms diffusing in a fluid.

Exciting as these procedures are, they represent calculations many orders of magnitude more complex than any other surveyed in this section. Even when the issues that have been raised by this work relating to the sensitivity of the simulation and the general validity of conclusions that can be drawn from it, or to the choice of potential functions or the importance of the starting geometry of the model, are resolved, the application of molecular dynamics to the study of protein-protein interactions as they are modeled during folding appears to be greatly limited by computational considerations. The figure normally suggested for the ratio between the rate of folding of a protein as observed in nature and the rate at which these motions can be simulated in the computer, that is, $10^{12}:1$ represents, unfortunately, a major under estimate for molecular dynamic calculations on proteins.

2.6.2.6 Environment

Modifications of the solvent environment of a protein can have a profound effect on its conformational state, often leading to folding or unfolding of the structure. Reviews by Tanford (246, 247) and Pace (268) provide details on a wide spectrum of physical and chemical agents that can cause such changes. In this section only a brief outline of how such solvent effects enter into the computational framework that has been surveyed will be given.

Inclusion of the solvent itself in calculations is the first step and this has already been discussed in Section 2.6.1.2: Solvent or Hydrophobic Interactions, with Table 6 or those compiled by Hopfinger (135, 184, 185), providing the basis for computing the effects to be expected upon changing solvents. A second-order effect may result if there is an accompanying change in the dielectric constant. As was indicated in Section 2.6.1.2: Summary of Potential Functions, the dielectric constant for even a polar solvent such as water is already reduced to a value of 3 or 4 by most workers in the potential function calculations. Temperature is probably the next most important variable. In the Monte Carlo treatments and in Karplus's molecular dynamics studies, it enters explicitly through a Boltzmann factor. It, however, also enters other aspects of the calculation implicitly. The coefficients for the dispersive attractions in the nonbonded interactions and the dielectric constant and the coefficient in the electrostatic terms are functions of temperature for the same basic reason. At higher temperatures dipoles, whether permanent or induced, have a reduced effect as their alignment in an electric field is less precise and subject to thermal oscillation. Likewise in the hydrophobic bond data, the coefficients for the free-energy lost or gained per unit area of surface or per molecule of solvent displaced, are also temperature-dependent.

Addition of chemical agents to the solvent in varying concentrations may effect the pH, ionic strength, or hydrogen bonding and/or conformational state of the solvent. pH changes will result in a change of the partial charges for groups that are solvent accessible, while change in the ionic strength will modify the Debye–Hückel screening interactions (269) and hence again the effective charge distributions. Agents like guanidinium hydrochloride or urea cause denaturation through hydrogen bonding effects, acting almost as an additional solvent, modifying the hydrophobic terms through their action on both the protein and the original solvent. Agents like lanthanum chloride on the other hand probably lead primarily to a change in the solvent structure, forming a less fluid, more icelike state for which the entropic/enthalpic balance and hence the hydrophobic bond coefficient will be different.

Of the papers cited in Sections 2.6.2.2–2.6.2.5 only those by Hesselink (270) and Crippen (252) include consideration of environmental effects other than temperature. Hesselink incorporates both pH and salt concentration into the Monte Carlo study of helix-coil transitions of poly-L-lysine, while Crippen again uses the Monte Carlo method to study the differences in behavior of oxidized and reduced BPTI under both denaturing and renaturing conditions.

While the mechanisms for introducing such environmental effects into energy calculations are available, their lack of use is indicative of the fact that at present the major challenge is seen to be in understanding more fundamental aspects of the folding process. Environmental effects are far more important when considering true interprotein interactions between two known structures. However, in these cases the complexity of the system precludes, in general, use of detailed atomic level calculations and relies on techniques that are subjects of other chapters.

2.6.2.7 Conceptual models

The information necessary to determine the three-dimensional structure of a folded protein is contained in its primary amino acid sequence placed in the appropriate chemical environment (271). It should therefore be possible in principle to predict or compute the conformation of a protein from its primary sequence. From the survey presented in Sections 2.6.2.2–2.6.2.6, it is apparent that, while this is still considered possible it remains a research goal and may continue to do so for some time. Determination of the structure of some 100 or so proteins by X-ray crystallography provides a quite extensive data-base against which to check evolving theories. Other experiments such as those of Creighton and Wetlaufer (76,225), which follow the formation of specific bonds (disulfide bridges), or of Wuthrich (258) or Williams (272,273), which use NMR techniques to monitor the motions of individual residues or the accessibility of surface and internal protons, do not provide the structural detail of crystallography but do provide clues to the way in which folding occurs. These experiments have all stimulated much thought about protein structure, folding, and stabilization and have led to quite definite models being proposed.

These models have in turn provided the basis for computational strategies. In particular the concept of a *folding-pathway*, first discussed by Levinthal (274) as a way to explain the rapidity with which a protein folds, is to be found embodied in most minimizations and in the Monte Carlo simulations of proteins. As set out in extensive reviews by Anfinsen and Scheraga (195,197), most workers in this area have subscribed to a model for folding which involves three stages. These are characterized by defining interactions described as short-, medium-, or long-range, the range referring to the separation of the interacting residue pairs in the primary sequence of the protein rather than to spacial separations in the folding or native protein structure. The analysis of these interactions in terms of contributing atomic interactions will be the same, independent of range, the potentials surveyed in Section 2.6.1 being suitable for their functional representation. Short-range interactions reflect the dependence of the backbone (ϕ, ψ) angles, of a residue on both its type and the type and conformation of its close neighbors in the sequence. It is this correlation that has formed the basis for empirical prediction methods, so that in general these short-range interactions are assumed to relate to the formation of helices and β-strands and bends. Medium range interactions involve residues separated by four or five others in sequence which are brought into contact partly through the effect of the short-range interactions on the conformations of the intervening residues. They will be important in stabilizing the hinge regions (226,266,267,275,276) and surface bends (229) in proteins. Nucleation, defined as any localized conformational event that can significantly increase the rate of formation of the native structure from its unfolded state (277), will in general be associated with medium-range interactions. According to Baldwin (278) the formation of both α-helices and β-structures follow nucleation-dependent kinetics. Nagano (279) considers specifically medium range interactions between residue pairs, one with helix potential the other with β-structure potential, as the key to nucleation, while Matheson focuses on the formation of hydrophobic pockets (277). Once nucleation has occurred the long-range forces, between residues now distant in primary sequence but due to short- and medium-range interactions, close in space, take over, completing the folding. These interactions will for the most part be typified by rather nonspecific hydrophobic effects. In Ptitsyn's self-organizational model for apomyglobin folding (280), and to some extent in Levitt's myogen model (228), final folding is preceded by the folding of sets of two or three helices against each other to form *centers of crystallization.* Other helices then organize around these centers before the final structure is formed from the folding of these units together to form a highly compact structure.

Explanations for many of the detailed features seen in native proteins (Section 2.2) can be given in energetic terms based on specific atomic interactions. Examples include the high incidence and related stability of both the α-helix and the β-sheet (281); the preponderance of right- over left-handed helices (2,55,195,282); the preference for a right-handed twist in β-sheets (60,283); and the packing of helices and sheets (57,65).

Some of the more general properties of globular proteins have also been examined from the standpoint of atomic interactions. Analysis of protein structures carried out by Richards (77) and Chothia (65,78,284–286) show proteins to have few internal spaces caused by packing defects and to have a high packing density. Examination of the character of the solvent accessible surface changes in going from an extended to the folded conformation showed that the formation of secondary structures such as helices and β-sheets buries a greater proportion of the polar rather than the nonpolar surface and that the interfaces between such secondary structures are very hydrophobic. Chothia (78) concludes that the folded protein consist of secondary structural entities stabilized internally by polar, hydrogen bond interactions and externally by hydrophobic interactions with other entities. He argues that the hydrophobic nature of these interfaces will greatly simplify the packing involved in producing a stable compact structure avoiding the problems that would be associated with the simultaneous matching of, hydrogren bonding by, and removal of bound water from appropriate pairs involved in polar interactions. This is also consistent with the modeling described in which secondary structures such as helices or β-sheets form first then rearrange.

Chothia's interpretation however conflicts with a model put forward by Wuthrich (258). This is based on the experimental determination and comparison of the rotational motion of aromatic rings and amide protons in the interior of BPTI using nuclear magnetic resonance techniques and depicts the protein as a collection of hydrophobic clusters linked by interaction of polar groups located on their surface. In a recent review of the considerable body of information that has been obtained on the folding of BPTI, and to a lesser extent ribonuclease, by studying the disulfide-bridge pairings in folding intermediates, Creighton (225) also proposes a model in which hydrophobic clusters play a key role.

The first step is one in which nonpolar groups are brought together out of the solvent to produce very unstable and flexible globules, which are compact but are in rapid equilibrium with fully unfolded states. These involve the whole peptide chain but will unfold more readily than they will undergo the transition to the fully folded state. However, within the conformations of the starting globule are ones in which a critical number of specific stabilizing interactions may be encountered simultaneously. The second step involves the formation of such a productive intermediate, while the third step is the rapid generation of the fully folded state by formation of the remainder of the stabilizing interactions in a highly cooperative manner, this now being more probable than the unfolding of the intermediate. The productive intermediates are likely to have few specific stabilizing interactions but may exhibit a significant number of nonspecific hydrophobic interactions of the sort that ultimately stabilize the folded state. The rate-limiting step in this model is step 2 in which the critical number of specific stabilizing interactions must be encountered simultaneously. Creighton (225) also notes that the required precision of the close packing coupled to the pairing of polar groups and the expulsion of water and so on, involved in formation of the almost folded state, makes this step improbable. However, his conclusion is different from Chothia (78) in that he argues that this is in fact what has to happen and that it provides the explanation for the observed, rate-limiting step occurring late in the folding pathway.

Creighton's model is easily matched to the pictures proposed by Cooper (257), of a structure which is precisely folded and tightly interlocked but which exhibits fluctuations which are both frequent and dramatic, and by Karplus in both his molecular dynamics (4) and diffusion-collision models (287). It is still possible that Creighton and Wuthrich's conclusions are not general, holding only for BPTI, which is a small protein with less than average helical content. Although unlikely, results obtained for BPTI may represent a special case.

To conclude, while there are differences between the models for protein folding that currently underly much of the computational work using Monte Carlo simulation or minimization and the models developed from the more experimental investigations, the similarities are perhaps more important. Both have proteins folding by a pathway as opposed to a fully random search process, stress the importance of specific polar-type interactions and nonspecific hydrophobic interactions, and distinguish between long, medium and short-range interactions. Differences in fact then really involve only discussion of whether the interactions can be modeled as occurring in series (short, then medium, then long) or whether the order is less well demarcated, contains a considerable element of parallelism and is initiated by predominantly long-range interactions. At present there is probably insufficient data to rule out either possibility, although there may be evidence of a subtle shift in the position of the theoreticians in that a recent paper by Matheson and Scheraga (277) introduced the concept of a hydrophobic pocket, stabilized by short range interactions, as a nucleation site in proteins.

REFERENCES

1. K. U. Linderstrøm-Lang and J. A. Schellman, "Protein Structure and Enzyme Activity," in P. D. Boyer et al., Eds., *The Enzymes*, Vol. 1, 2nd ed., New York, Academic Press, 1959, p. 444.

2. G. N. Ramachandran and V. Sasisekharan, *Adv. Protein Chem.* **23**, 283 (1968).

3. M. G. Rossmann and A. Liljas, *J. Mol. Biol.* **85**, 177 (1974).

4. J. A. McCammon, B. R. Gelin, and M. Karplus, *Nature (London)* **267**, 585 (1977).

5. A. Jack and M. Levitt, *Acta Crystallogr.* **A34**, 931 (1978).

6. I. Bernal, W. C. Hamilton, and J. S. Ricci, *Symmetry. A Stereoscopic Guide for Chemists*, W. H. Freeman, San Francisco, Calif. 1972.

7. M. F. Perutz, *J. Mol. Biol.* **13**, 646 (1965).

8. H. Eklund, B. Nordström, E. Zeppezauer, G. Söderlund, I. Ohlsson, T. Boiwe, B-O. Söderberg, O. Tapia, and C.-I. Brändén, *J. Mol. Biol.* **102**, 27 (1976).

9. J. J. Holbrook, A. Liljas, S. J. Steindel, and M. G. Rossmann, in P. D. Boyer, Ed., *The Enzymes*, Vol. 11, 3rd ed., Academic Press, New York, 1975, p. 191.

10. D. C. Wiley and W. N. Lipscomb, *Nature (London)* **218**, 1119 (1968).

11. H. L. Monaco, J. L. Crawford, and W. N. Lipscomb, *Proc. Natl. Acad. Sci. USA* **75**, 5276 (1978).

12. D. L. D. Caspar and A. Klug, *Cold Spring Harbor Symp. Quant. Biol.* **27**, 1 (1962).

13. A. Klug, J. T. Finch, R. Leberman, and W. Longley, in G. E. W. Wolstenholme and M. O'Connor, Eds., *Principles of Biomolecular Organization*, Ciba Foundation Symposium, Little, Brown, Boston, Mass., 1966, p. 158.

14. S. C. Harrison, *Trends Biochem. Sci.*, **3**, 3 (1978).

15. G. W. Dykes, R. H. Crepeau, and S. J. Edelstein, *J. Mol. Biol.* **130**, 451 (1979).

16. B. C. Wishner, K. B. Ward, E. E. Lattman, and W. E. Love, *J. Mol. Biol.* **98**, 179 (1975).

17. J. Hanson and J. Lowy, *J. Mol. Biol.* **6**, 46 (1963).

18. P. B. Moore, H. E. Huxley, and D. J. DeRosier, *J. Mol. Biol.* **50**, 279 (1970).

19. L. A. Amos and A. Klug, *J. Cell Sci.* **14**, 523 (1974).

20. H. P. Erickson, *J. Cell Biol.* **60**, 153 (1974).

21. D. L. D. Caspar, in G. E. W. Wolstenholme, and M. O'Connor, Eds. *Principles of Biomolecular Organization*, Ciba Foundation Symposium, Little, Brown, Boston, Mass., 1966, p. 7.

22. A. Tulinsky, R. L. Vandlen, C. N. Morimoto, N. V. Mani, and L. H. Wright, *Biochemistry* **12**, 4185 (1973).

23. H. Eisenberg, R. Josephs, and E. Reisler, *Adv. Protein Chem.* **30**, 101 (1976).

24. T. L. Blundell and L. N. Johnson, *Protein Crystallogr.* Academic Press, London, 1976.

25. D. Tsernoglou, E. Hill, and L. J. Banaszak, *J. Mol. Biol.* **69**, 75 (1972).

26. H. Muirhead, J. M. Cox, L. Mazzarella, and M. F. Perutz, *J. Mol. Biol.* **28**, 117 (1967).

27. S. T. Rao and M. G. Rossmann, *J. Mol. Biol.* **76**, 241 (1973).

28. B. W. Matthews and S. A. Bernhard, *Annu. Rev. Biophys. Bioeng.* **2**, 257 (1973).

29. B. W. Matthews, *J. Mol. Biol.* **82**, 513 (1974).

30. B. W. Matthews, in H. Neurath and R. L. Hill, Eds., *The Proteins*, Vol. 3, 3rd Ed., Academic Press, New York, 1977, p. 403.

31. M. G. Rossmann, Ed., *The Molecular Replacement Method*, Gordon and Breach, New York, 1972.

32. K. C. Holmes and D. M. Blow, "The Use of X-ray Diffraction in the Study of Protein and Nucleic Acid Structure," *Methods Biochem. Anal.* **13**, 113 (1965).

33. G. Eichele, D. Karabelnik, R. Halonbrenner, J. N. Jansonius, and P. Christen, *J. Biol. Chem.* **253**, 5239 (1978).

34. S. J. Bayne and M. Ottesen, *Carlsberg Res. Commun.* **41**, 211 (1976).

35. F. A. Quiocho and F. M. Richards, *Biochemistry* **5**, 4062 (1967).

36. P. J. Kavinsky and N. B. Madsen, *J. Biol. Chem.* **251**, 6852 (1976).

37. T. Imoto, L. N. Johnson, A. C. T. North, D. C. Phillips, and J. A. Rupley, in P. D. Boyer, Ed., *The Enzymes*, Vol. 7, 3rd ed., Academic Press, New York, 1972, p. 665.

38. J. Drenth, W. G. J. Hol, J. N. Jansonius, and R. Koekoek, *Eur. J. Biochem.* **26**, 177 (1972).

39. F. M. Richards and H. W. Wyckoff, in P. Boyer, Ed., *The Enzymes*, Vol. 4, 3rd ed., Academic Press, New York, 1971, p. 647.

40. M. N. G. James, L. T. J. Delbaere, and G. D. Brayer, *Can. J. Biochem.* **56**, 396 (1978).

41. F. R. N. Gurd and T. M. Rothgeb, *Adv. Protein Chem.* **33**, 73 (1980).

42. R. Huber, *Trends Biol. Sci.* **4**, 271 (1979).

43. T. Takano, *J. Mol. Biol.* **110**, 537 (1977).

44. J. J. Birktoft and D. M. Blow, *J. Mol. Biol.* **68**, 187 (1973).

45. P. J. Artymiuk, C. C. F. Blake, D. E. P. Grace, S. J. Oatley, D. C. Phillips, and M. J. E. Sternberg, *Nature (London)* **280**, 563 (1979).

46. D. M. Segal, G. H. Cohen, D. R. Davies, J. C. Powers, and P. E. Wilcox, *Cold Spring Harbor Symp. Quant. Biol.* **36**, 85 (1971).

47. R. L. Vandlen and A. Tulinsky, *Biochemistry* **12**, 4193 (1973).

48. D. W. Green, R. Aschaffenburg, A. Camerman, J. C. Coppola, P. Dunnill, R. M. Simmons, E. S. Komorowski, L. Sawyer, E. M. C. Turner, and K. F. Woods, *J. Mol. Biol.* **131**, 375 (1979).

49. G. Nemethy, D. C. Phillips, S. J. Leach, and H. A. Scheraga, *Nature (London)* **214**, 363 (1967).

50. G. N. Reeke, Jr., J. W. Becker, and G. M. Edelman, *J. Biol. Chem.* **250**, 1525 (1975).

51. J. S. Richardson, E. D. Getzoff, and D. C. Richardson, *Proc. Natl. Acad. Sci. USA* **75**, 2574 (1978).

52. C. M. Venkatachalam, *Biopolymers* **6**, 1425 (1968).

53. J. J. Birktoft, D. M. Blow, R. Henderson, and T. A. Steitz, *Phil. Trans. R. Soc. London* **B257**, 67 (1970).

54. I. D. Kuntz, *J. Am. Chem. Soc.* **94**, 4009 (1972).

55. R. A. Scott and H. A. Scheraga, *J. Chem. Phys.* **45**, 2091 (1966).

56. J. S. Richardson, *Nature (London)* **268**, 495 (1977).

57. M. Levitt and C. Chothia, *Nature (London)* **261**, 552 (1976).

58. C. C. F. Blake, M. J. Geisow, S. J. Oatley, B. Rérat, and C. Rérat, *J. Mol. Biol.* **121**, 339 (1978).

59. P. Argos, M. G. Rossmann, and J. E. Johnson, *Biochem. Biophys. Res. Commun.* **75**, 83 (1977).

60. C. Chothia, *J. Mol. Biol.* **75**, 295 (1973).

61. M. J. E. Sternberg and J. M. Thornton, *Nature (London)* **271**, 15 (1978).

62. A. D. McLachlan, *J. Mol. Biol.* **128**, 49 (1979).

63. M. J. E. Sternberg and J. M. Thornton, *J. Mol. Biol.* **105**, 367 (1976).

64. D. W. Banner, A. C. Bloomer, G. A. Petsko, D. C. Phillips, C. I. Pogson, I. A. Wilson, P. H. Corron, A. J. Furth, J. D. Milman, R. E. Offord, J. D. Priddle, and S. C. Waley, *Nature (London)* **255**, 609 (1975).

65. C. Chothia, M. Levitt, and D. Richardson, *Proc. Natl. Acad. Sci. USA* **74**, 4130 (1977).

66. F. E. Cohen, T. J. Richmond, and F. M. Richards, *J. Mol. Biol.* **132**, 275 (1979).

67. M. G. Rossmann, A. Liljas, C.-I. Branden, and L. J. Banaszak, in P. Boyer, Ed., *The Enzymes*, 3rd Ed., Academic Press, New York, 1975, p. 61.

68. P. C. Moews and R. H. Kretsinger, *J. Mol. Biol.* **91**, 201 (1975).

69. I. M. Klotz, G. L. Klippenstein, and W. A. Hendrickson, *Science* **192**, 335 (1976).

70. F. S. Mathews, P. H. Bethge, and E. W. Czerwinski, *J. Biol. Chem.* **254**, 1699 (1979).

71. A. C. Bloomer, J. N. Champness, G. Bricogne, R. Staden, and A. Klug, *Nature (London)* **276**, 362 (1978).

72. K. Sasaki, S. Dockerill, D. A. Adamiak, I. J. Tickle, and T. L. Blundell, *Nature (London)* **257**, 751 (1975).

73. K. D. Watenpaugh, L. C. Sieker, and L. H. Jensen, *J. Mol. Biol.* **131**, 509 (1979).

74. R. D. Anderson, P. A. Apgar, R. M. Burnett, G. D. Darling, M. E. Lequesne, S. G. Mayhew, and M. L. Ludwig, *Proc. Natl. Acad. Sci. USA* **69**, 3189 (1972).

75. D. C. Phillips, *Proc. Natl. Acad. Sci. USA* **57**, 484 (1967).

76. D. B. Wetlaufer, *Proc. Natl. Acad. Sci. USA* **70**, 697 (1973).

77. F. M. Richards, *Carlsberg Res. Commun.* **44**, 47 (1979).

78. C. Chothia, *J. Mol. Biol.* **105**, 1 (1976).

79. R. H. Kretsinger and C. E. Nockolds, *J. Biol. Chem.* **248**, 3313 (1973).

80. H. Eklund and C.-I. Bränden, *J. Biol. Chem.* **254**, 3458 (1979).

81. S. C. Harrison, A. J. Olson, C. E. Schutt, F. K. Winkler, and G. Bricogne, *Nature (London)* **276**, 368 (1978).

82. K. W. Olsen, D. Moras, M. G. Rossmann, and J. I. Harris, *J. Biol. Chem.* **250**, 9313 (1975).

83. J. Tang, M. N. G. James, I. N. Hsu, J. A. Jenkins, and T. L. Blundell, *Nature (London)* **271**, 618 (1978).

84. D. I. Stuart, M. K. Levine, J. Muirhead, and D. K. Stammers, *J. Mol. Biol.* **134**, 109 (1979).

85. G. E. Schulz, R. H. Schirmer, W. Sachsenheimer, and E. F. Pai, *Nature (London)* **273**, 120 (1978).

86. D. R. Davies, E. A. Padlan, and D. M. Segal, *Annu. Rev. Biochem.* **44**, 639 (1975).

87. L. M. Amzel and R. J. Poljak, *Annu. Rev. Biochem.* **48**, 961 (1979).

88. E. T. Adman, L. C. Sieker, and L. H. Jensen, *J. Biol. Chem.* **248**, 3987 (1973).

89. J. H. Ploegman, G. Drent, K. H. Kalk, W. G. J. Hol, R. L. Heinrikson, P. Keim, L. Weng, and J. Russell, *Nature (London)* **273**, 124 (1978).

90. A. D. McLachlan, *J. Mol. Biol.* **133**, 557 (1979).

91. C. S. Wright, *J. Mol. Biol.* **111**, 439 (1976).

92. W. C. Barker, L. K. Ketcham, and M. O. Dayhoff, *J. Mol. Evol.* **10**, 265 (1978).

93. J. H. Ploegman, G. Drent, K. H. Kalk, and W. G. J. Hol, *J. Mol. Biol.* **123**, 557 (1978).

94. B. W. Matthews, R. E. Fenna, M. C. Bolognesi, M. F. Schmid, and J. M. Olson, *J. Mol. Biol.* **131**, 259 (1979).

95. I. M. Mavridis and A. Tulinsky, *Biochemistry* **15**, 4410 (1976).

96. M. Buehner, G. C. Ford, D. Moras, K. W. Olsen, and M. G. Rossmann, *J. Mol. Biol.* **90**, 25 (1974).

97. J. W. Campbell, H. C. Watson, and G. I. Hodgson, *Nature (London)* **250**, 301 (1974).

98. J. J. Birktoft, F. Miake, L. J. Banaszak, and C. Frieden, *J. Biol. Chem.* **254**, 4915 (1979).

99. S. G. Warren, B. F. P. Edwards, D. R. Evans, D. C. Wiley, and W. N. Lipscomb, *Proc. Natl. Acad. Sci. USA* **70**, 1117 (1973).

100. T. A. Steitz, R. J. Fletterick, W. F. Anderson, and C. M. Anderson, *J. Mol. Biol.* **104**, 197 (1976).

101. T. Blundell, G. Dodson, D. Hodgkin, and D. Mercola, *Adv. Protein Chem.* **26**, 279 (1972).

102. A. Rühlmann, D. Kukla, P. Schwager, K. Bartels, and R. Huber, *J. Mol. Biol.* **77**, 417 (1973).

103. R. M. Sweet, H. T. Wright, J. Janin, C. H. Chothia, and D. M. Blow, *Biochemistry* **13**, 4212 (1974).

104. M. F. Perutz, *Br. Med. Bull.* **32**, 195 (1976).

105. J. M. Baldwin, *Prog. Biophys. Mol. Biol.* **29**, 225 (1975).

106. G. Fermi, *J. Mol. Biol.* **97**, 237 (1975).

107. R. C. Ladner, E. J. Heidner, and M. F. Perutz, *J. Mol. Biol.* **114**, 385 (1977).

108. J. G. Gerhart and H. K. Schachman, *Biochemistry* **4**, 1054 (1965).

109. G. R. Jacobson and G. R. Stark, in P. D. Boyer, Ed., *The Enzymes*, Vol. 9, 3rd ed., Academic Press, New York, 1973, p. 225.

110. N. A. Kiselev, D. J. DeRosier, and A. Klug, *J. Mol. Biol.* **35**, 561 (1968).

111. R. H. Depue and R. V. Rice, *J. Mol. Biol.* **12**, 302 (1965).

112. D. J. DeRosier, E. Mandelkow, A. Silliman, L. Tilney, and R. Kane, *J. Mol. Biol.* **113**, 679 (1977).

113. G. Stubbs, S. Warren, and K. C. Holmes, *Nature (London)* **267**, 216 (1977).

114. T. S. Baker and L. A. Amos, *J. Mol. Biol.* **123**, 89 (1978).

115. J. I. Harris and M. Waters, in P. D. Boyer, Ed., *The Enzymes*, Vol. 13, 3rd Ed., Academic Press, New York, 1976, p. 1.

116. G. Biesecker, J. I. Harris, J. C. Thierry, J. E. Walker, and A. J. Wonacott, *Nature (London)* **266**, 328 (1977).

117. D. Moras, K. W. Olsen, M. N. Sabesan, M. Buehner, G. C. Ford, and M. G. Rossmann, *J. Biol. Chem.* **250**, 9137 (1975).

118. H. C. Watson, E. Duee, and W. D. Mercer, *Nature (London) New Biol.* **240**, 130 (1972).

119. P. M. Colman, J. Deisenhofer, and R. Huber, *J. Mol. Biol.* **100**, 257 (1976).

120. M. Matsushima, M. Marquart, T. A. Jones, P. M. Colman, K. Bartels, and R. Huber, *J. Mol. Biol.* **121**, 441 (1978).

121. R. D. Banks, C. C. F. Blake, P. R. Evans, R. Haser, D. W. Rice, G. W. Hardy, M. Merrett, and A. W. Phillips, *Nature (London)* **279**, 773 (1979).

122. C. M. Anderson, F. H. Zucker, and T. A. Steitz, *Science* **204**, 375 (1979).

123. W. S. Bennett and T. A. Steitz, *Proc. Natl. Acad. Sci. USA* **75**, 4848 (1978).

124. R. C. McDonald, T. A. Steitz, and D. M. Engelman, *Biochemistry* **18**, 338 (1979).

125. C. A. Pickover, D. B. McKay, D. M. Engelman and T. A. Steitz, *J. Biol. Chem* **254**, 11323 (1979).

126. E. Hill, D. Tsernoglou, L. Webb, and L. J. Banaszak, *J. Mol. Biol.* **72**, 577 (1972).

127. M. Weininger, J. J. Birktoft, and L. J. Banaszak, in H. Sund, Ed., *Pyridine Nucleotide-Dependent Dehydrogenases*, W. deGruyter, Berlin, 1977, p. 87.

128. A. J. Wonacott and G. Biesecker, in H. Sund, Ed., *Pyridine Nucleotide-Dependent Dehydrogenases*, W. deGruyter, Berlin, 1977, p. 140.

129. K. W. Olsen, R. M. Garavito, M. N. Sabesan, and M. G. Rossmann, *J. Mol. Biol.* **107**, 577 (1976).

130. G. Biesecker and A. J. Wonacott, *Biochem. Soc. Trans.* **5**, 647 (1977).

131. M. F. Perutz, *Nature (London)* **228**, 726 (1970).

132. J. Baldwin and C. Chothia, *J. Mol. Biol.* **129**, 175 (1979).

133. F. London, *Trans. Faraday Soc.* **33**, 8 (1937).

134. W. Heitler and F. London, *Z. Physik.* **44**, 455 (1927).

135. A. J. Hopfinger, *Conformational Properties of Macromolecules*, Academic Press, New York, 1973.

136. S. Karplus and S. Lifson, *Biopolymers* **10**, 1973 (1971).

137. M. Levitt and S. Lifson, *J. Mol. Biol.* **46**, 269 (1969).

138. B. R. Gelin and M. Karplus, *J. Am. Chem. Soc.* **97**, 6996 (1975).

139. M. Bixon and S. Lifson, *Tetrahedron* **23**, 769 (1967).

140. D. A. Brant, *Annu. Rev. Biophys. Bioeng.* **1**, 369 (1972).

141. R. B. Setlow and E. C. Pollard, *Molecular Biophysics*, Addison-Wesley, London, 1962.

142. P. Debye, *Physik. Z.* **21**, 178 (1920).

143. P. Debye, *Physik. Z.* **22**, 302 (1921).

144. J. C. Slater and J. G. Kirkwood, *Phys. Rev.* **37**, 682 (1931).

145. F. A. Momany, H. A. Sheraga, et al., *J. Phys. Chem.* **79**, 2361 (1975).

146. H. A. Scheraga, *Adv. Phys. Org. Chem.* **6**, 103 (1968).

147. H. A. Scheraga, R. A. Scott, G. Vanderkooi, S. J. Leach, K. D. Gibson, and T. Ooi, in G. N. Ramachandran, Ed., *Conformation of Biopolymers*, Vol. 1, Academic Press, New York 1967, p. 43.

148. G. N. Ramachandran, C. Ramakrishan, and V. Sasisekhran, *J. Mol. Biol.* **7**, 95 (1963).

149. S. J. Leach, G. Nemethy, and H. A. Scheraga, *Biopolymers* **4**, 369 (1966).

150. S. J. Leach, G. Nemethy, and H. A. Scheraga, *Biopolymers* **4**, 887 (1966).

151. S. Tanaka and H. A. Scheraga, *Proc. Natl. Acad. Sci. USA* **74**, 1320 (1977).

152. D. R. Ferro and J. Hermans, Jr., in J. F. Johnson and R. S. Porter, Eds., *Liquid Crystals and Ordered Fluids*, Plenum Press, New York, 1970, p. 259.

153. A. T. Hagler, E. Huler, and S. Lifson, *J. Am. Chem. Soc.* **96**, 5319 (1974).

154. A. Warshel and M. Levitt, *J. Mol. Biol.* **103**, 227 (1976).

155. F. A. Momany, L. M. Carruthers, R. F. McGuire, and H. A. Sheraga, *J. Phys. Chem.* **78**, 1595 (1974).

156. D. A. Brant and P. J. Flory, *J. Am. Chem. Soc.* **87**, 2788 (1965).

157. A. Warshel and M. Karplus, *J. Am. Chem. Soc.* **94**, 5612 (1972).

158. R. A. Scott and H. A. Scheraga, *J. Chem. Phys.* **42**, 2209 (1965).

159. M. E. Nuss, F. J. Marsh, and P. A. Kollman, *J. Am. Chem. Soc.* **101**, 825 (1979).

160. D. E. Williams, *J. Chem. Phys.* **45**, 3770 (1966).

161. A. I. Kitaygorodsky, *Tetrahedron* **14**, 230 (1961).

162. A. I. Kitaygorodsky, *Tetrahedron* **9**, 183 (1960).

163. C. M. Venkatachalam and G. N. Ramachandran, in G. N. Ramachandran, Ed., *Conformation of Biopolymers*, Vol. 1, Academic Press, New York, 167, p. 83.

164. I. H. Hillier and B. Robson, *J. Theor. Biol.* **76**, 83 (1979).

165. A. T. Hagler, P. S. Stern, R. Sharon, J. M. Becker, and F. Naider, *J. Am. Chem. Soc.* **101**, 6842 (1979).

166. A. T. Hagler and S. Lifson, *Acta. Crystallogr.* **830**, 1336 (1974).

167. A. T. Hagler and S. Lifson, *J. Am. Chem. Soc.* **96**, 5327 (1974).

168. G. C. Pimentel and A. L. McClellan, *Annu. Rev. Phys. Chem.* **22**, 347 (1971).

169. G. C. Pimentel and A. L. McClellan, *The Hydrogen Bond*, W. H. Freeman, San Francisco, Calif., 1960.

170. P. A. Kollman and L. C. Allen, *Chem. Rev.* **72**, 283 (1972).

171. P. De Santis, E. Giglio, A. M. Liquori, and A. Ripamonti, *Nature (London)* **206**, 456 (1965).

172. D. A. Brant, *Macromolecules* **1**, 291 (1968).

173. V. Magnasco, G. Gay and C. Nicora, *Nuovo Cimento* **34**, 1263 (1964).

174. P. M. Morse, *Phys. Rev.* **34**, 57 (1929).

175. W. G. Moulton and R. A. Kromhout, *J. Chem. Phys.* **25**, 34 (1956).

176. E. R. Lippincott and R. Schroeder, *J. Chem. Phys.* **23**, 1099 (1955).

177. L. C. Allen, *J. Am. Chem. Soc.* **97**, 6921 (1975).

178. G. Nemethy and H. A. Scheraga, *J. Chem. Phys.* **36**, 3382 (1962).

179. G. Nemethy and H. A. Scheraga, *J. Chem. Phys.* **36**, 3401 (1962).

180. G. Nemethy and H. A. Scheraga, *J. Phys. Chem.* **66**, 1773 (1962).

181. C. Chothia and J. Janin, *Nature (London)* **256**, 705 (1975).

182. S. Krimm and C. M. Venkatachalam, *Proc. Natl. Acad. Sci. USA* **68**, 2468 (1971).

183. K. D. Gibson and H. A. Scheraga, *Proc. Natl. Acad. Sci. USA* **58**, 420 (1967).

184. A. J. Hopfinger, *Macromolecules* **4**, 731 (1971).

185. K. H. Forsythe and A. J. Hopfinger, *Macromolecules* **6**, 423 (1973).

186. E. A. Moelwyn-Hughs, *Physical Chemistry*, Pergamon Press, Oxford, 1957.

187. C. Chothia, *Nature* **248**, 338 (1974).

188. Y. Nozaki and C. Tanford, *J. Biol. Chem.* **216**, 2211 (1971).

189. B. Lee and F. M. Richards, *J. Mol. Biol.* **55**, 379 (1971).

190. J. L. Finney, *J. Mol. Biol.* **119**, 415 (1978).

191. R. E. Gates, *J. Mol. Biol.* **127**, 345 (1979).

192. E. Ralston and R. L. Samorjai, in R. Walter, and J. Meienhofer, Eds., *Peptides: Chemistry, Structure and Biology*, Ann Arbor Science, Ann Arbor, Michigan, 1975, p. 271.

193. D. A. Greenberg, C. D. Barry, and G. R. Marshall, *J. Am. Chem. Soc.* **100**, 4020 (1978).

194. S. Lifson and M. Levitt, *Comput. Chem.* **3**, 49 (1979).

195. G. Nemethy and H. A. Scheraga, *Q. Rev. Biophys.* **10**, 239 (1977).

196. E. Katchalski, in E. R. Blout, F. A. Bovey, M. Goodman, and N. Lotan, Eds., *Peptides Polypeptides and Proteins*, Wiley, New York, 1974, p. 1.

197. C. B. Anfinsen and H. A. Scheraga, *Adv. Protein Chem.*, **29**, 205 (1975).

198. G. N. Ramachandran, in E. R. Blout, F. A. Bovey, M. Goodman, and N. Lotan, Eds., *Peptides Polypeptides and Proteins*, Wiley, New York, 1974, p. 15.

199. H. A. Scheraga, in E. R. Blout, F. A. Bovey, M. Goodman, and N. Lotan, Eds., *Peptides Polypeptides and Proteins*, Wiley, New York, 1974, p. 49.

200. H. A. Scheraga, in M. Goodman and H. Meienhofer, Eds., *Peptides*, Wiley, New York, 1972, p. 246.

201. G. R. Marshall, H. E. Bosshard, N. C. Eilers and P. Needleman, in J. Meienhofer, Ed., *Chemistry and Biology of Peptides*, Ann Arbor Science Publishers, Ann Arbor, 1972, p. 571.

202. F. M. Pohl, *Nature (London) New Biol.* **234**, 277 (1971).

203. B. Pullman and B. Maigret, in E. D. Bergmann and B. Pullman, Eds., *Conformation of Biological Molecules and Polymers*, The Israel Acadamy of Sciences and Humanities, Jerusalem, 1973, p. 13.

204. B. Lotz, F. Colonna-Cesari, H. Heitz, and G. Spach, *J. Mol. Biol.* **106**, 915 (1976).

205. F. A. Momany, R. F. McGuire, J. F. Yan, and H. A. Scheraga, *J. Phys. Chem.* **75**, 2286 (1971).

206. F. A. Momany, L. M. Carruthers, and H. A. Scheraga, *J. Phys. Chem.* **78**, 1621 (1974).

207. C. V. Gurskaya, *Molecular Structure of Amino Acids*, Consultants Bureau, New York, 1968.

208. R. E. Marsh and J. Donohue, *Adv. Protein Chem.* **22**, 234 (1967).

209. G. Nemethy and H. A. Scheraga, *Biopolymers* **3**, 155 (1965).

210. M. Levitt and A. Warshel, *Nature (London)* **253**, 694 (1975).

211. M. Levitt, *J. Mol. Biol.* **104**, 59 (1976).

212. B. Robson and D. J. Osguthorpe, *J. Mol. Biol.* **132**, 19 (1979).

213. P. J. Flory, *Statistical Mechanics of Chain Molecules*, Wiley, New York, 1969.

214. P. K. Ponnuswamy, P. K. Warme, and H. A. Scheraga, *Proc. Natl. Acad. Sci. USA* **70**, 830 (1973).

215. M. Levitt, *J. Mol. Biol.* **82**, 393 (1974).

216. M. Levitt, *Ph.D. Thesis*, Cambridge University, 1972.

217. P. K. Warme and H. A. Scheraga, *Biochemistry* **13**, 757 (1974).

218. P. K. Warme, F. A. Momany, S. V. Rumball, R. W. Tuttle, and H. A. Scheraga, *Biochemistry* **13**, 768 (1974).

219. D. Rasse, P. K. Warme, and H. A. Scheraga, *Proc. Natl. Acad. Sci. USA* **71**, 3736 (1974).

220. J. Hermans, Jr. and J. E. McQueen, Jr., *Acta Crystallogr.* **A30**, 730 (1974).

221. D. R. Ferro, J. E. McQueen, Jr., J. T. McCowan, and J. Hermans, Jr., *J. Mol. Biol.* **136**, 1 (1980).

222. W. Bode and P. Schwager, *J. Mol. Biol.* **98**, 693 (1975).

223. R. Huber, D. Kukla, A. Ruhlmann, and W. Steigemann, *Cold Spring Harbor Symp. Quant. Biol.* **36**, 141 (1971).

224. R. Huber, D. Kukla, W. Bode, P. Schwager, K. Bartels, J. Deisenhofer, and W. Steigemann, *J. Mol. Biol.* **89**, 73 (1974).

225. T. E. Creighton, *Prog. Biophys. Mol. Biol.* **33**, 231 (1978).

226. A. W. Burgess and H. A. Scheraga, *Proc. Natl. Acad. Sci. USA* **72**, 1221 (1975).

227. A. T. Hagler and B. Honig, *Proc. Natl. Acad. Sci. USA* **75**, 554 (1978).

228. A. M. Warshel and M. Levitt, *J. Mol. Biol.* **106**, 421 (1976).

229. I. D. Kuntz, G. M. Crippen, P. A. Kollman, and D. Kimelman, *J. Mol. Biol.* **106**, 983 (1976).

230. A. T. Hagler, B. Honig, and R. Sharon, in M. Goodman and J. Meienhofer, Eds., *Peptides*, Wiley, New York, 1972, p. 280.

231. P. Y. Chou and G. D. Fasman, *Annu. Rev. Biochem.* **47**, 251 (1978).

232. P. Y. Chou and G. D. Fasman, *Biochemistry* **13**, 211 (1974).

233. J. A. Lenstra, *Biophys. Biochem. Acta* **491**, 333 (1977).

234. P. Argos, J. Schwarz, and J. Schwarz, *Biophys. Biochem. Acta* **439**, 261 (1976).

235. B. W. Matthews, *Biophys. Biochem. Acta* **405**, 442 (1975).

236. G. E. Schultz, C. D. Barry, J. Friedman, P. Y. Chou, G. D. Fasman, A. V. Finkelstein, V. I. Lim, O. B. Ptitsyn, E. A. Kabat, T. T. Wu, M. Levitt, B. Robson, and K. Nagano, *Nature* **250** 140 (1974).

237. W. J. Browne, A. C. T. North, D. C. Phillips, K. Brew, T. C. Vanaman, and R. L. Hill, *J. Mol. Biol.* **42**, 65 (1969).

238. E. A. Kabat and T. T. Wu, *Proc. Natl. Acad. Sci. USA* **69**, 960 (1972).

239. D. Gabel, D. Rasse, and H. Scheraga, *Int. J. Pept. Protein Res.* **8**, 237 (1976).

240. S. Tanaka and H. Scheraga, *Macromolecules* **10**, 305 (1977).

241. R. H. Kretsinger and C. D. Barry, *Biophys. Biochem. Acta* **405**, 40 (1975).

242. N. Metropolis, A. W. Rosenbluth, M. N. Rosenbluth, A. H. Teller, and E. Teller, *J. Chem. Phys.* **21**, 1087 (1953).

243. M. V. Volkenstein, *Configurational Statics of Polymeric Chains*, translated by S. N. Timasheff and M. T. Timasheff, Interscience, Wiley, New York, 1963.

244. D. Polland and H. A. Scheraga, *Theory of Helix-Coil Transitions in Biopolymers*, Academic Press, New York, 1970.

245. N. Lotan, A. Berger, and E. Katchalski, *Annu. Rev. Bio.* **41**, 869 (1972).

246. C. Tanford, *Adv. Protein Chem.* **23**, 121 (1968).

247. C. Tanford, *Adv. Protein Chem.* **24**, 1 (1970).

248. W. Kauzmann, *Adv. Protein Chem.* **14**, (1959).

249. J. Hermans, Jr., D. Lohr, and D. Ferro, *Adv. Polym. Sci.* **9**, 230 (1972).

250. B. H. Zimm and J. K. Bragg, *J. Chem. Phys.* **31**, 526 (1959).

251. G. M. Crippen, *Macromolecules* **10**, 21 (1977).

252. G. M. Crippen, *Macromolecules* **10**, 25 (1977).

253a. H. E. Warvari and R. A. Scott, *J. Chem. Phys.* **57**, 1154 (1972).

253b. H. E. Warvari and R. A. Scott, *J. Chem. Phys.* **57**, 1146 (1972).

253c. H. E. Warvari and K. K. Knaell, and R. A. Scott, *J. Chem. Phys.* **55**, 2020 (1971).

254. S. Premilat and J. Hermans, Jr., *J. Chem. Phys.* **59**, 2602 (1973).

255. F. T. Hesselink, *Biophys. Chem.* **2**, 76 (1974).

256. S. Premilat and B. Maigret, *J. Chem. Phys.* **66**, 3418 (1977).

257. A. Cooper, *Proc. Natl. Acad. Sci. USA* **73**, 2740 (1976).

258. G. Wagner and K. Wuthrich, *J. Mol. Biol.* **134**, 75 (1979).

259. M. J. E. Sternberg, D. E. P. Grace, and D. C. Phillips, *J. Mol. Biol.* **130**, 231 (1979).

260. Y. Ueda, H. Takeomi, and N. Go, *Biopolymers* **17**, 1531 (1978).

261. H. Takeomi, Y. Ueda, and N. Go, *Int. J. Pept. Protein Res.* **7**, 445 (1975).

262. C. D. Barry, *Ph.D. Thesis*, Manchester University, 1965.

263. N. Go and H. Takeomi, *Proc. Natl. Acad. Sci. USA* **75**, 559 (1978).

264. N. Go and H. Takeomi, *Int. J. Pep. Prot. Res.* **13**, 235 (1979).

265. N. Go and H. Takeomi, *Int. J. Pep. Prot. Res.* **13**, 447 (1979).

266. S. Tanaka and H. A. Scheraga, *Proc. Natl. Acad. Sci. USA* **72**, 3802 (1975).

267. S. Tanaka and H. A. Scheraga, *Macromolecules* **9**, 945 (1976).

268. C. N. Pace, *CRC Crit. Rev. Biochem.* **May**, 1 (1975).

269. G. S. Manning, *Q. Rev. Biophys.* **11**, 179 (1978).

270. F. T. Hesselink and H. A. Scheraga, *Macromolecules* **6**, 541 (1973).

271. C. B. Anfinsen, *Science* **181**, 223 (1973).

272. I. D. Campbell, C. M. Dobson, and R. J. P. Williams, *Proc. R. Soc. London* **189**, 503 (1975).

273. I. D. Campbell, C. M. Dobson and R. J. P. Williams, *Proc. R. Soc. London* **189**, 485 (1975).

274. C. Levinthal, *J. Chim. Phys.* **69**, 44 (1968).

275. B. Honig, A. Ray, and C. Levinthal, *Proc. Natl. Acad. Sci. USA* **73**, 1974 (1976).

276. A. W. Burgess and H. A. Scheraga, *J. Theor. Biol.* **52**, 403 (1975).

277. R. R. Matheson, Jr. and H. A. Scheraga, *Macromolecules* **11**, 819 (1978).

278. R. L. Baldwin, *Annu. Rev. Biochem.* **44**, 453 (1975).

279. K. Nagano, *J. Mol. Biol.* **84**, 337 (1974).

280. O. B. Ptitsyn and A. A. Rashin, *Biophys. Chem.* **3**, 1 (1974).

281. R. E. Dickerson, in H. Neurath, Ed., *The Proteins*, Vol. II, 2nd ed., Academic Press, New York, 1964, p. 603.

282. G. N. Ramachandran, C. M. Venkatachalam, and S. Krimm, *Biophys. J.* **6**, 849 (1966).

283. D. W. Weatherford and F. R. Salemme, *Proc. Natl. Acad. Sci. USA* **76**, 19 (1979).

284. C. H. Chothia and J. Janin, *Nature (London)* **256**, 705 (1975).

285. C. H. Chothia, *Nature (London)* **248**, 338 (1974).

286. C. H. Chothia, *Nature (London)* **254**, 304 (1975).

287. M. Karplus and D. L. Weaver, *Biopolymers* **18**, 1421 (1979).

CHAPTER **3**

Mass Migration Methods

D. J. WINZOR

Mass migration procedures such as electrophoresis, chromatography, and sedimentation velocity are almost invariably used either for the fractionation of biological millieus, or for testing the efficacy of protein fractionations. Consequently these techniques have played a fundamental role in the detection of many protein interactions, particularly those involving self-association of a protein moiety. In many instances the association equilibrium is rapidly established, and hence adjustment of species concentrations occurs continually during the experiment to counter departure from equilibrium caused by differential migration of the polymeric species. It has therefore been necessary to develop methods of study that take due cognizance of this reequilibration phenomenon.

Interactions between dissimilar molecules are also amenable to study by mass migration methods. For example, moving boundary electrophoresis has been used to study antigen-antibody and protein-protein interactions as well as the association of buffer constituents with proteins. Gel chromatography has also been employed to investigate protein-protein interactions in addition to those involving a protein and a small ligand. Such studies of ligand binding by gel chromatography and also by sedimentation velocity are considered in Chapter 9. It should also be borne in mind that affinity chromatography is a mass migration procedure capable of providing insight into quantitative aspects of heterogeneous association equilibria.

The above introduction sets the pattern of this review inasmuch as considerations of the study of reversibly polymerizing systems by mass migration procedures precede those concerned with investigations of equilibria involving dissimilar molecules. However, before commencing any discussion of either type of interacting system it is pertinent to comment briefly on the three major mass migration procedures, namely, electrophoresis, sedimentation velocity, and chromatography, in terms of the specific requirements imposed by their application to studies of interacting systems.

3.1   GENERAL EXPERIMENTAL ASPECTS

3.1.1   Zonal and Frontal Analysis

Electrophoresis, sedimentation, and chromatography have the ability to impart characteristic migration rates to solutes and hence, under favorable conditions, to provide an analysis of a noninteracting mixture of solutes. Early forms of sedimentation velocity (1), electrophoresis (2), and chromatography (3) entailed the migration of an initially sharp boundary between solvent and solution, a plateau of original composition being preserved throughout the experiment. In these frontal mass migration methods a mixture of solutes was thus detected by resolution of the initially sharp boundary into several boundaries, and indeed the composition could be estimated from the relative sizes of these boundaries. Despite their introduction for analytical purposes the techniques of electrophoresis, chromatography, and sedimentation velocity have all been modified to increase their versatility as preparative procedures. This change in emphasis has led to the development of zonal mass migration methods, particularly in electrophoresis and chromatography, where the zonal procedures have virtually eliminated their frontal forerunners. Classical sedimentation velocity still retains popularity but is under challenge from the zonal technique employing an isokinetic sucrose gradient (4).

In zonal analysis, which entails the migration of a small zone of solute stabilized by a supporting phase or density gradient, a noninteracting mixture becomes resolved into several zones, one for each component. The change-over to zonal techniques is thus readily understood, since they provide not only an analysis of a mixture but also a means of obtaining each resolved component in pure form. However, zonal techniques are at a decided disadvantage in the study of interacting solutes because of the dilution that occurs during zonal migration, a factor clearly evident in Figure 1a, which traces the migration of a zone down a gel chromatography column (5). If, for example, the solute were to have been undergoing rapid, reversible association, such dilution would have favored the monomeric form at the expense of polymer, and hence a continual change in migration rate would have ensued. Figure 1b, which summarizes the results of calculations (6) to simulate zonal migration of ovalbumin on Sephadex G-100, emphasizes the likely extent of this dilution and hence the relative insensitivity and unsuitability of zonal migration methods for the study of rapid association equilibria. It is therefore necessary to revert to the frontal mass migration methods, where retention of

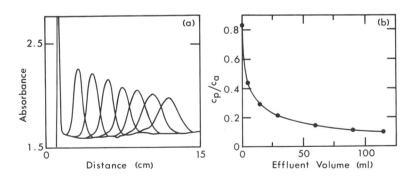

FIGURE 1

Extent of dilution occurring in zonal gel chromatography. (a) Direct optical scans of a zone of potassium chromate migrating down a column of Sephadex G-100. (Adapted from ref. 5 with permission. Copyright by American Society of Biological Chemists, Inc.) (b) Theoretical variation of the peak concentration (c_p), expressed relative to the applied concentration (c_a), during elution of an ovalbumin zone from a column of Sephadex G-100. (Adapted from ref. 6 with permission. Copyright by Biochemical Society.)

the plateau of original composition greatly facilitates the detection and quantitative study of rapid, reversible interactions.

3.1.2 Measurement of Migration in Gel Chromatography

In sedimentation velocity and moving boundary electrophoresis the relevant migration parameters are deduced from optical records of the time dependence of the solute distribution throughout the cell. A series of such $(c-x)_t$ distributions at fixed times may also be used to define migration in gel chromatographic studies provided that a direct optical scanning device (5) is fitted to the column. However, although optical scanning has been used successfully with Sephadex gels (5, 7–9), it is not amenable to general application because of the adverse light scattering characteristics of molecular-sieving media such as Sepharose and porous glass beads (10). A more conventional gel chromatographic record is an elution profile, which represents the distribution of solute in the mobile phase as a function of time taken by solute to migrate the length of the column (11). From the interrelation between such $(c-t)_x$ and the corresponding $(c-x)_t$ distributions for noninteracting solutes it is evident (12) that one distribution should be symmetrical and that the other should deviate, though only marginally, from Gaussian form. By conventional random walk theories of chromatography (13–15) the concentration-distance distribution at fixed time is Gaussian; but an alternative and equally plausible version of the random walk theory can be developed (12), which leads to the opposite prediction, namely, that the elution profile, $(c-t)_x$, is the Gaussian distribution. Attempts to identify the relevant random walk theory from experimental results have been indecisive in that no asymmetry of frontal elution profiles has been detected (12, 15), whereas departure from Gaussian shape has been observed in zonal studies (15). Such asymmetry could have been generated by the chromatographic process (15) or by the process of creating the initial zone, which entails the formation of two perfectly sharp boundaries in very quick succession. The only occasion that this inability to determine unequivocally the correct random walk theory is likely to become a limitation in the interpretation of gel chromatographic studies of interacting protein systems is in the comparison of the detailed experimental boundary shape ($c-x$ distribution or elution profile) with that predicted by computer simulation (see Chapter 4). Furthermore, the magnitude of any uncertainty in the predicted shape introduced by use of the incorrect random walk theory is likely to be insignificant compared with that arising from incorrect allowance for nonuniform packing of the gel column, a phenomenon clearly evident in optical scans of frontal gel chromatographic experiments (5, 7, 16, 17). In many investigations quantitative appraisal of an interaction can be based on the mean migration rate of a boundary. A suitable parameter is readily evaluated from either form of experimental chromatographic record, the elution profile providing the cheaper and more general method of obtaining such information (an elution volume).

3.1.3 Comparison of Conjugate Sides: Concept of Nonenantiography

The means by which rapid equilibria may be detected by the three frontal mass migration procedures will now be demonstrated. Figure 2 presents the elution profile obtained in a gel chromatographic study (18) of a mixture of ovalbumin and lysozyme on Sephadex G-100. In the frontal technique of gel chromatography, which differs from its zonal counterpart only in regard to the volume of solute applied, the column is eluted with mixture until the composition of the column eluate matches that of the solution being applied: the solid line in Figure 2a presents this advancing (or ascending) elution profile. At that stage elution of the column with buffer is commenced to generate the trailing (or descending) elution profile (the solid line in Figure 2b). The volume scale for the trailing profile clearly has as its origin the effluent volume at which this elution with buffer is commenced. The broken lines in Figure 2 indicate the advancing and trailing elution profiles for a noninteracting mixture with the same ovalbumin and lysozyme content. There is clearly disparity between these and the experimental patterns in regard not only to the positions but also the sizes of boundaries. Such nonequivalence of the advancing and trailing profiles as that observed in the experimental profiles is referred to as nonenantiography, a characteristic by which the existence of rapid equilibria may be diagnosed. The origin of the term nonenantiography is best explained by referring to analysis of mixtures by moving boundary electrophoresis, where, because of the U-tube cell assembly, the two boundary systems migrate in opposite directions. Figure 3a presents the schlieren patterns (concentration gradient distributions) obtained

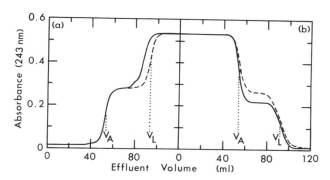

FIGURE 2

Frontal gel chromatography of a mixture of ovalbumin (9.6 μM) and lysozyme (9.7 μM) on a 2.0×32 cm column of Sephadex G-100 equilibrated with 0.02 I phosphate, pH 6.8: (a) advancing elution profile; (b) trailing elution profile. The solid lines represent the experimental profiles and the broken lines the corresponding patterns for a noninteracting mixture with the same composition. V_A and V_L denote the elution volumes of ovalbumin and lysozyme, respectively. (Adapted from ref. 18 with permission. Copyright 1964 American Chemical Society.)

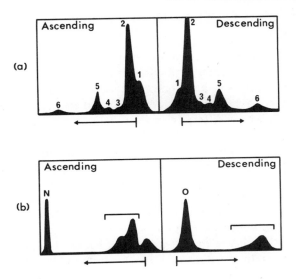

FIGURE 3

Nonenantiography in moving boundary electrophoresis as a criterion for the existence of rapid, reversible interaction. (*a*) Electrophoretic patterns obtained for egg-white in 0.1 I acetate, pH 4.45. (Adapted from ref. 19 with permission. Copyright 1940 American Chemical Society.) (*b*) Patterns obtained for a mixture containing 8.7 g/liter of ovomucoid (O) and 5.5 g/liter of yeast nucleic acid (N) in 0.1 I acetate, pH 4.63. (Adapted from ref. 20 with permission. Copyright by Academic Press.) Numbers adjacent to boundaries in (*a*) are included to emphasize the correspondence between the ascending and descending patterns for the noninteracting egg-white mixture. Brackets in (*b*) signify the extent of reaction boundaries, and the letters indicate boundaries corresponding to pure reactants.

(19) in moving boundary electrophoresis of eggwhite, a noninteracting mixture. These patterns are regarded as enantiographs (or mirror images) of each other inasmuch as there is a reasonable degree of symmetry about the vertical line separating the ascending and descending patterns. Some degree of nonenantiography is observed even with noninteracting mixtures because of the dilution of buffer ions and consequent pH changes that occur across the δ and ε boundaries (20). On the other hand, the schlieren profiles for a mixture of yeast nucleic acid and ovomucoid (20) are decidedly nonenantiographic (Figure 3*b*), which signifies the existence of a rapid, reversible interaction between these two components.

This ability to compare conjugate ascending and descending patterns does not extend to sedimentation velocity, which only generates the descending boundary system in which solute migrates away from a solvent plateau. Accordingly, the detection of interactions by this technique requires the observation of disparate migration behavior in experiments conducted with different initial concentrations of solute(s). Striking examples of concentra-

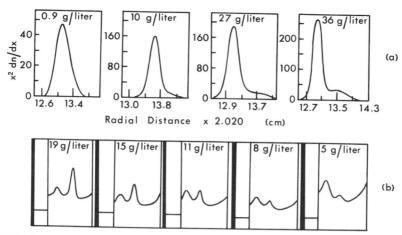

FIGURE 4

Effect of solute concentration on the schlieren patterns obtained in sedimentation velocity of self-associating proteins. (*a*) Human growth hormone. (Adapted from ref. 21 with permission. Copyright 1961 American Chemical Society.) (*b*) Carboxypeptidase A. (Adapted from ref. 22 with permission. Copyright 1965 American Chemical Society.)

tion-dependent changes in sedimentation velocity patterns are presented in Figure 4*a*, *b*, which refer to human growth hormone (21) and carboxypeptidase A (22), respectively: such behavior can only reflect the consequences of the law of mass action on a monomer-polymer equilibrium. In the former case (21) the association was considered to be established sufficiently slowly for the sedimentation velocity pattern to be interpreted classically in terms of the relative amounts of monomeric and polymeric forms present. However, similar identification of boundaries with components in Figure 4*b* would be totally incorrect because the carboxypeptidase A polymers are in rapidly established equilibrium (22). In the event that such concentration-dependent migration behavior is detected for a particular experimental system it is clearly important to establish the interpretation that can be placed on the observed patterns: this is the aim of the next section.

3.2 MIGRATION OF SELF-ASSOCIATING SYSTEMS: THEORETICAL CONSIDERATIONS

The simplest situation to consider is a self-associating system for which the rate of interconversion between oligomers is sufficiently slow for effectively no reequilibration to occur during a mass migration experiment. Under those circumstances the migration behavior in an individual experiment is indistinguishable from that of a noninteracting mixture; but as we have seen in

Figure 4a, the composition is a function of the solute concentration subjected to mass migration. The number of self-associating systems with slow attainment of equilibrium is relatively small, hemerythrin (23,24) being another such example. In most cases, interconversion between polymeric species is sufficiently rapid for the mass migration behavior to be indistinguishable from that for a system in which association equilibrium is established instantaneously. There are, however, a few proteins, such as a lobster hemocyanin (25), for which the polymer interconversion occurs at a rate comparable with that at which they tend to separate. This situation, termed the kinetically controlled case (26), is not given detailed consideration because of (a) the rarity of its occurrence and (b) the excellence of its coverage in a recent review (27). Such systems, which may certainly be recognized by time dependence of the form of the mass-migration pattern, are more amenable to quantitative study by kinetic (T-jump, stopped flow) procedures than by mass migration methods.

Since the discovery (28) that α-chymotrypsin exists as a mixture of polymers in rapidly established association equilibrium, the list of proteins that undergo such association has increased steadily. Examples include the enzymes trypsin (29), papain (30), and thrombin (31), which also have proteolytic function, and α-amylase (32), which is involved in polysaccharide degradation; the oxygen-carrying protein hemoglobin (33–36); the hormone insulin (37–41) and the hormone-carrier protein neurophysin (42). Mass migration procedures have been instrumental in the detection of most of these self-associating systems, and hence it is not surprising that theory has been developed to permit quantitative studies of the association to be made on the basis of the mass migration behavior.

3.2.1 Constituent Quantities and Continuity Equations

Since the theory predicting the migration behavior of rapidly interacting systems has been reviewed extensively elsewhere (e.g., ref. 43), the major emphasis in this review is placed on the application of the theory to the study of experimental systems. This brief theoretical section merely outlines the means adopted for formulating the fundamental expressions required to assess an interacting system on the basis of its migration behavior; reversible association between monomer and a single higher polymer is used to illustrate the approach.

The simplest mass transport system to consider is the migration of a single noninteracting solute with velocity v in a cell of uniform cross section subjected to a homogeneous field. If diffusional spread is neglected, the basic continuity equation describing migration of such a system may be written as

$$u\,dc - d(vc) = 0 \qquad (1)$$

where u denotes the velocity of a lamina of constant composition with weight concentration c (44). A similar approach may also be adopted for the migration of a chemically interacting system provided allowance is made for the existence of the solute in more than one state. For self-associating systems in rapidly (instantaneously) established equilibrium Eq. (1) becomes

$$u \, d\bar{c} - d(\bar{v}\bar{c}) = 0 \tag{2}$$

in which $\bar{c}$ and $\bar{v}$ denote the constituent concentration and constituent velocity, respectively, of solute. If monomer and a single higher polymer are the only species comprising the association equilibrium ($nM \rightleftharpoons P$), these constituent quantities are defined (20, 44, 45) in terms of species concentrations (c_M, c_P) and species velocities (v_M, v_P) as

$$\bar{c} = c_M + c_P \tag{3a}$$

$$\bar{v} = \frac{v_M c_M + v_P c_P}{\bar{c}} \tag{3b}$$

from which it is evident that $\bar{v}$ is also the weight-average velocity. Provided the velocities of individual species are considered to be concentration independent, the law of mass action [Eq. (4)] suffices to interrelate $\bar{v}$ and $\bar{c}$.

$$k = \frac{c_P}{(c_M)^n} \tag{4}$$

Combination of Eqs. (2) and (3) with Eq. (4), differentiated with respect to c_M, yields the continuity equation in explicit form for this system:

$$\left\{ u + un(c_M)^{n-1}k - v_M - v_P n(c_M)^{n-1}k \right\} dc_M = 0 \tag{5}$$

The solution $dc_M = 0$ (and hence $d\bar{c} = 0$) describes a plateau region which is either a solvent plateau ($\bar{c} = 0$) or the plateau of original composition that is maintained in frontal migration experiments. The other solution of Eq. (5) is clearly

$$u = \frac{v_M + v_P n(c_M)^{n-1}k}{1 + n(c_M)^{n-1}k} \tag{6}$$

which indicates that u increases monotonically with $\bar{c}$, and hence that a single reaction boundary separates the solvent and solution plateaus for a solute in rapid association equilibrium. Equation (6) may be used in either of two ways.

3.2.2   The Shape of the Reaction Boundary

One application of Eq. (6) is its use to comment on the shape of the migrating boundary system. By assigning values to n, k, v_M, and v_P, it is obviously possible to calculate values of u [Eq. (6)] and of $\bar{c}$ [Eqs. (3a) and (4)] for selected values of c_M. The plot of $\bar{c}$ vs u is a time-normalized concentration distribution, which is frequently termed the asymptotic, or diffusion-free, shape of the migrating boundary system. Differentiation of Eq. (6) with respect to u followed by similar numerical calculation permits the construction of time-normalized schlieren patterns ($d\bar{c}/du$ vs u). This approach, adopted initially by Gilbert (46, 47), has been used to establish the form of reaction boundaries. For example, it is possible to show that in gel chromatography of a rapidly and reversibly associating solute the profile for the advancing side comprises a hypersharp boundary, that is, a stepwise increase in concentration from $\bar{c} = 0$ to $\bar{c} = \bar{c}^\alpha$, the loading (or plateau) concentration, whereas that for the trailing side is a spread reaction boundary. Moreover, it is also readily shown by this means that such a spread reaction boundary, which would also be observed in sedimentation velocity of the same system, can exhibit bimodality if $n > 2$, even though the polymerization equilibrium is established instantaneously: this situation pertains to the bimodal sedimentation velocity patterns shown in Figure 4b for carboxypeptidase A (22).

One of the major problems associated with these predicted boundary shapes is the fact that diffusional flows in the experimental migration process preclude direct comparison of experimental boundary forms with their asymptotic counterparts. Apart from a few investigations into the possibility of deducing asymptotic boundary shapes from experimental patterns (35, 48) the major thrust in this area has entailed the addition of diffusion terms to the continuity equation (49–55). The resulting expressions, although intractable to analytical solution, may be solved numerically. Detailed considerations of this problem of defining the shapes of reaction boundaries by computer simulation techniques are presented in Chapter 4.

3.2.3 The Median Bisector of the Reaction Boundary

The other means of using Eq. (6) is to disregard the detailed shape of the boundary and to note that $\bar{u}$, the velocity of the median bisector, or centroid (56), is given by (44)

$$\bar{u} = \frac{\int_0^{\bar{c}^\alpha} u\, d\bar{c}}{\int_0^{\bar{c}^\alpha} d\bar{c}} = \frac{v_M c_M^\alpha + v_P k (c_M^\alpha)^n}{c_M^\alpha + k (c_M^\alpha)^n} = \bar{v} \tag{7}$$

Thus the median bisector of the reaction boundary may be identified with the constituent, or weight-average, velocity of solute in the solution plateau region. In moving boundary electrophoresis and frontal gel chromatography experiments, which yield both ascending (advancing) and descending (trailing) migration patterns, $\bar{v}$ is most readily obtained from the hypersharp boundary because of its sharpness and symmetry; but an identical value of $\bar{v}$ should also be obtained by applying Eq. (7) to the spread boundary system on the conjugate side.

Use of Eq. (7) with experimental results requires identification of the experimental parameter corresponding to velocity v, the rate of migration per unit applied field. In moving boundary electrophoresis the electrophoretic mobility should clearly be substituted for velocity. A less obvious conclusion is that application of Eq. (7) to elution profiles requires the direct substitution of elution volumes (not their reciprocals) for velocities (11,33,57): in terms of weight-average elution volume, $\bar{V}$, Eq. (7) thus becomes

$$\bar{V} = \frac{V_M c_M^\alpha + V_P k (c_M^\alpha)^n}{c_M^\alpha + k (c_M^\alpha)^n} \tag{8}$$

where V_M and V_P denote the elution volumes of monomer and polymer, respectively.

In sedimentation velocity, where s, the sedimentation coefficient, is the analog of v, only a spread descending boundary system is observed, and accordingly intregration across the entire boundary is required to obtain the weight-average sedimentation coefficient, $\bar{s}$. However, the sector-shaped cell and nonhomogeneous field operating in ultracentrifugation invalidate the use of the median bisector (first moment) of the boundary to define $\bar{s}$; instead, it is obtained from the square root of the second moment of the reaction boundary (58,59). In an experiment conducted with angular velocity ω, $\bar{s}$ is thus given by

$$\bar{s} = \frac{d \ln \bar{x}/dt}{\omega^2} \qquad \bar{x}^2 = \frac{\int x^2 \, d\bar{c}}{\int d\bar{c}} \tag{9}$$

in which the limits of integration are the solvent and solution plateaus. Another complication is the progressive decrease of the plateau concentration, and accordingly allowance for this radial dilution effect should be made via the expression

$$\bar{c}_{\bar{x}}^\alpha = \bar{c}_0^\alpha \left(\frac{x_m}{\bar{x}} \right)^2 \tag{10}$$

in which $\bar{c}_0^\alpha$ denotes the initial concentration and $\bar{c}_{\bar{x}}^\alpha$ the plateau concentration after the boundary has migrated from the meniscus, x_m, to position $\bar{x}$. Since different values of $\bar{c}_{\bar{x}}^\alpha$ thus pertain to the different photographic exposures used to define $\bar{s}$ [Eq. (9)], an average of these $\bar{c}_{\bar{x}}^\alpha$ values is the most appropriate estimate of $\bar{c}^\alpha$ to be coupled with $\bar{s}$ in the application of Eq. (7).

3.3   MIGRATION OF SELF-ASSOCIATING SYSTEMS: EXPERIMENTAL STUDIES

Most experimental studies of reversibly associating protein systems by mass migration methods have entailed the use of either sedimentation velocity or frontal gel chromatography. The relative absence of electrophoretic studies is not surprising, since association with conservation of charge is likely to yield a mobility for the polymeric species that differs only marginally from that for

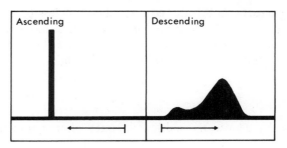

FIGURE 5
Electrophoretic patterns reflecting the self-association of β-lactoglobulin A in 0.1 I
acetate, pH 4.66. (Adapted from ref. 62 with permission. Copyright by Biochemical
Society.)

monomer (60). For moving boundary electrophoresis to be a useful method
for studying an associating protein system the association must therefore
entail either lack of charge conservation or a pronounced change in shape.
The one experimental system that has been detected by moving boundary
electrophoresis is the association of β-lactoglobulin A at pH 4.7 (61–63),
which, in view of the nonenantiography of the ascending and descending
boundaries (Figure 5), is clearly a rapidly equilibrating system: a monomer-
dimer-trimer-tetramer equilibrium ($M_M = 36,600$) has been proposed on the
basis of sedimentation velocity studies (48, 64). Since the spread reaction
boundary is observed in the descending pattern it may be deduced that the
mobilities of polymeric β-lactoglobulin A species are greater than that of
monomer. Quantitative interpretation of Figure 5 in terms of Eq. (7) is
precluded by lack of values (or even estimates) for the mobilities of the
polymeric β-lactoglobulin forms.

3.3.1   Sedimentation Velocity Studies

By far the most common mass migration method used for the detection and
study of self-associating systems is sedimentation velocity. As already mentioned, only a descending boundary system is observed, and accordingly the
interaction must be detected by concentration dependence of $\bar{s}$. Figure 6
summarizes results obtained with two associating systems, both of which yield
the characteristic, initially positive dependence of weight-average sedimentation coefficient $\bar{s}$ upon total concentration $\bar{c}^\alpha$. Figure 6a refers to trypsin in
0.2 I acetate-chloride, pH 3.86 (29) and Figure 6b to β-lactoglobulin in 0.1 M
NaCl-HCl, pH 1.6 (65). A second feature evident with both systems is the
ultimate negative dependence of $\bar{s}$ upon $\bar{c}^\alpha$. This changeover from positive to
negative concentration dependence of $\bar{s}$ reflects the fact that there is a
balance between two interactions with opposing consequences. There is the
physical interaction between any two solute molecules that gives rise to

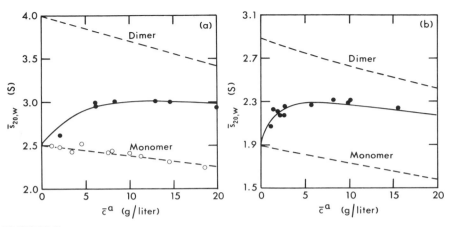

FIGURE 6
Effect of protein concentration on the sedimentation coefficient of self-associating systems (*a*) Trypsin (●) and diisopropylphosphoryl-trypsin (○) in 0.2 I acetate-chloride, pH 3.86. (Adapted from ref. 29 with permission. Copyright by Faraday Society.) (*b*) β-lactoglobulin in 0.1 *M* NaCl-HCl, pH 1.6. (Adapted from ref. 72 with permission. Copyright by Macmillan Journals Ltd.) Broken lines represent the relationships used to describe the dependence of the monomer and dimer sedimentation coefficients upon total concentration $\bar{c}^{\alpha}$. The solid lines denote the theoretical curves predicted on the bases of dimerization constants of 0.13 liter/g and 0.44 liter/g for trypsin and β-lactoglobulin, respectively.

normal, negative dependence of $\bar{s}$ upon $\bar{c}^{\alpha}$; and there is also the chemical association phenomenon that is manifested as positive dependence of $\bar{s}$ upon $\bar{c}^{\alpha}$. The latter is the predominant phenomenon at low $\bar{c}^{\alpha}$, but at higher concentrations the negative dependence due to physical interactions may well outweigh any increase in $\bar{s}$ due to increased self-association. Trypsin and β-lactoglobulin (Figure 6) clearly conform with this general pattern, but bacterial α-amylase is a monomer–dimer system for which neither phenomenon gains the ascendancy in the concentration range 0–12 g/liter (32).

Before quantitative interpretation of $\bar{s}$ vs $\bar{c}^{\alpha}$ data such as those presented in Figure 6 can be attempted via Eq. (7) it is clearly necessary to specify the dependences of the individual species sedimentation coefficients, s_M and s_P, upon $\bar{c}^{\alpha}$. This is usually effected (64, 66) by means of the relationships

$$s_i = s_i^0(1 - g\bar{c}^{\alpha}) \qquad i = \text{M or P} \tag{11a}$$

$$s_P^0 = n^{2/3}\frac{s_M^0}{(f/f_0)_P} \tag{11b}$$

Equation (11a) is an empirical relationship based on that used to describe the corresponding dependence for a noninteracting solute in terms of its limiting sedimentation coefficient, s_i^0, the magnitude of g being in the range 0.005–0.010 liter/g for globular proteins. Equation (11b), which assumes spherical geometry of monomer, interrelates the values of s_M^0 and s_P^0 via the stoichiometry of the association equilibrium, n, and the frictional ratio of polymer, $(f/f_0)_P$. The latter is usually estimated from the Perrin equation (67) for an ellipsoid of revolution with appropriate axial ratio, but means for evaluating the frictional ratio pertinent to other geometries are also available (68–71). This approach, which relies on the availability of a value for either s_M^0 or s_P^0, is illustrated by consideration of the trypsin data in Figure 6a.

A relationship $s_M = 2.5(1 - 0.005\bar{c}^\alpha)$ for monomeric trypsin is inferred from sedimentation velocity experiments on enzyme inhibited with diisopropyl-fluorophosphidate, a covalent modification that suppresses the association (open symbols in Figure 6a). The fact that the reaction boundary is unimodal (Figure 2 of ref. 29), together with the range of $\bar{s}$ observed, suggests a monomer-dimer equilibrium, whereupon $s_P^0 = 4.0$ S on the basis of the value of 2.5 S for s_M^0 and assumed spherical geometry for dimer $[(f/f_0)_P = 1]$. The line drawn through the experimental points is based on Eqs. (4), (7), and (11) with $k = 0.13$ liter/g, an essentially identical result ($k = 0.18$ liter/g) being obtained with $s_P^0 = 3.8$ S, which is the sedimentation coefficient inferred from Eq. (11b) for an ellipsoidal dimer with axial ratio of 2.

The results presented in Figure 6b for β-lactoglobulin at pH 1.6 are also amenable to interpretation in terms of reversible dimerization ($M_M = 18,300$). In this instance the results (65) have been tested (72) for conformity with a monomer-dimer system with $k = 0.44$ liter/g, the value deduced from light scattering studies (65), and estimates of 1.89 and 2.87 S for the respective sedimentation coefficients of monomer and dimer. In the absence of experimental information on the concentration dependence resulting from physical interactions a relationship $s_i = s_i^0/(1 + g\bar{c}^\alpha)$ with $g = 0.010$ liter/g was assumed (72). For small values of the product $g\bar{c}^\alpha$ this earlier manner of describing physical interactions approximates to Eq. (11a) but does introduce slight curvature into the plots of $\bar{s}$ vs $\bar{c}^\alpha$ for the individual oligomers (broken lines in Figure 6b). Lack of a value for the physical interaction parameter, g, is a fairly frequently encountered problem, and it has now become customary (64) to describe nonchemical concentration dependence of species sedimentation coefficients by Eq. (11a) with a compromise value of 0.007–0.008 liter/g for g (35).

The problem of defining the equilibrium constant from sedimentation velocity studies is more difficult for self-associating systems with polymeric species larger than dimer, particularly in instances where the value of n is also being sought from the investigation. Under those circumstances theoretical plots of $\bar{s}$ vs $\bar{c}^\alpha$ must be deduced via Eqs. (7) and (11) for a series of values of n, and the appropriate value of n, and hence of k, selected on the basis of the relative degree to which these theoretical curves describe the experimental data. The method is relatively insensitive as a diagnostic for n, since a reasonable curve-fit can usually be obtained with a range of (n, s_P^0) combinations. There is, of course, also the need (when $n > 2$) to consider whether the weight-average sedimentation coefficient should be described in terms of Eq.

(7) or of the more general expression [Eq. (12)] that takes into account the formation of intermediate polymers.

$$\bar{v} = \frac{\sum_i c_i^\alpha v_i}{\sum_i c_i^\alpha} \tag{12a}$$

$$c_i^\alpha = k_i (c_1^\alpha)^i \qquad k_1 = 1 \tag{12b}$$

Studies of insulin (40) and α-chymotrypsin (73) stress the uncertainties inherent in quantitative interpretation of systems conforming to this more complicated, but also more realistic, association pattern. These investigations (40, 73) also point to a further difficulty, namely, that of deciding upon the most appropriate values for the sedimentation coefficients of polymers, the magnitudes of which become heavily reliant upon the geometrical form that is assumed to describe the polymer (71). The extent of this dilemma is emphasized in Figure 7, which summarizes estimates of polymeric sedimentation coefficients (s_n^0), expressed relative to that (s_1^0) of monomer, as a function of n (71). The line represents the relationship $s_n^0 = n^{2/3} s_1^0$, which is based on spherical geometry for all oligomers, whereas the squares denote values of s_n^0 / s_1^0 deduced for polymers comprising a linear array of spherical monomer units, and the circles refer to results of similar calculations with cyclic,

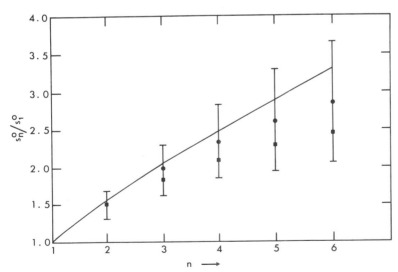

FIGURE 7
Effect of shape on the interrelationship between the sedimentation coefficients of monomeric (s_1^0) and polymeric (s_n^0) species. (———) monomer and polymer both spherical; (■) polymer comprising a rigid, linear array of spherical monomer units; (●) polymer consisting of a cyclic array of spherical monomer units. (Adapted from ref. 71 with permission. Copyright by North-Holland Publishing Co.)

symmetrical arrays of spherical monomer units. Error bars encompass the likely range of s_n^0/s_1^0 values that may be encountered if monomers are allowed to adopt ellipsoidal rather than spherical form.

The above comments clearly indicate that sedimentation velocity studies are unlikely to provide an unequivocal characterization of a self-associating protein system except for the simplest situation involving a monomer-dimer equilibrium. Such a limitation is not unreasonable when it is considered that quantitative assessment is requiring assumptions to be made not only about the nature of species in association equilibrium but also about the magnitudes of their velocities. Despite the severity of this criticism of sedimentation velocity studies, it should be pointed out that the same limitations apply to the use of quasi-elastic light scattering spectroscopy, a method that has been hailed (74–77) as the method of choice for investigating rapid association equilibria. Since laser light scattering merely yields the weight-average diffusion coefficient, $\overline{D}$, this technique is subject to the same general problem inasmuch as it is necessary to assign values to the diffusion coefficient, D_i, of any species postulated to comprise the association equilibrium. As noted by Jullien and Thusius (75), the dependence of D_i upon concentration arising from physical interactions is smaller than the corresponding variation of s_i with $\bar{c}^\alpha$; but this does not justify its neglect, the practice adopted and recommended by Benedek and co-workers (74,76,77). Furthermore, the validity of identifying the basic parameter derived from quasi-elastic light scattering spectroscopy as the weight-average translational diffusion coefficient, $\overline{D}$, has recently been questioned (78).

3.3.2   Gel Chromatographic Studies

The introduction of gel filtration as a method of studying rapid association equilibria (79,80) saw the reemergence of the frontal technique of chromatography and the development of a mass migration procedure that combines the better features of moving boundary electrophoresis and sedimentation velocity. From the viewpoint of detecting self-associating systems, gel chromatography shares with moving boundary electrophoresis the advantage that nonenantiography of advancing and trailing profiles may be used as an index of rapid association equilibrium (Figure 8); and it also shares with sedimentation velocity the advantage that the rate of migration is a function of molecular size. Unlike most chromatographic media, the dextran (Sephadex) and polyacrylamide (Bio-Gel) gels have been eminently suited to studies of concentration-dependent migration in that partition between liquid and gel phases is relatively insensitive to concentration of a noninteracting solute (82). Moreover, the extreme rapidity with which partition equilibrium is attained has meant that equilibrium between mobile and stationary phases can still be maintained at relatively high column flow rates. Consequently, although the detailed shapes of the reaction boundaries observed (Figure 8) in frontal gel chromatography are amenable to interpretation in terms of mass

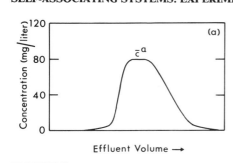 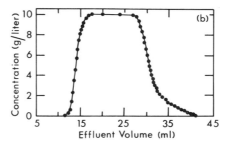

FIGURE 8

Nonenantiography of the advancing and trailing elution profiles in frontal gel chromatography of proteins undergoing rapid, reversible self-association. (a) Carbonmonoxyhemoglobin (80 mg/liter) in 0.2 M phosphate, pH 6.8. (Adapted from ref. 33 with permission.) (b) β-Lactoglobulin A (10 g/liter) in 0.1 I acetate, pH 4.65. (Adapted from ref. 81 with permission. Copyright by American Society of Biological Chemists, Inc.)

migration theory, the weight-average elution volumes are equilibrium parameters (83) that may be accorded the same thermodynamic rigor as results obtained by such techniques as sedimentation equilibrium and light scattering.

In terms of weight-average elution volume the feature that characterizes a self-associating protein system is negative dependence of $\bar{V}$ on concentration $\bar{c}^{\alpha}$. From the viewpoint of studying such concentration-dependent changes in elution volume (migration rate), gel chromatography is, of course, the most versatile of the mass migration procedures inasmuch as the concentration range that can be investigated is dictated solely by the techniques available for assay of the solute. Figure 9 presents gel chromatography results for two enzyme systems that exist in a state of association equilibrium in the concentration range appropriate to enzymic assay. Figure 9a, b, which refer to aryl sulfatase A (84) and alkaline phosphatase (85), respectively, emphasize the low range of concentrations that can be studied quantitatively under favorable circumstances. The curves drawn in Figure 9 are based on Eq. (8) with the indicated values of species elution volumes (V_M and V_P) plus the postulates that aryl sulfatase A is a monomer-tetramer system with $k = 10^{12}$ liter^3/g^3, and that alkaline phosphatase is a monomer-dimer system with $k = 10^4$ liter/g. Although the experimental results thus seemingly conform with the proposed modes of self-association, it should be stressed that such analyses are subject to the same uncertainties as those encountered in sedimentation velocity studies, since magnitudes have had to be ascribed to elution volumes of any postulated species. In this regard the availability of gels with different permeation characteristics may well make possible the selection of a chromatographic medium such that dimer and all higher polymers are excluded from the stationary phase, whereupon the elution

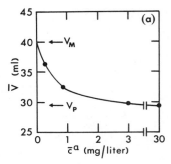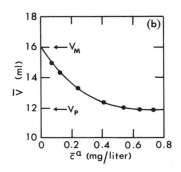

FIGURE 9

Gel chromatographic evidence for the dissociation of enzymes in concentration ranges appropriate to enzymic assay. (*a*) Bovine liver aryl sulfatase. (Adapted from ref. 84 with permission. Copyright 1965 American Chemical Society.) (*b*) *E. coli* alkaline phosphatase. (Adapted from ref. 85 with permission. Copyright by Elsevier Publishing Co.)

volumes of these species may be identified unequivocally with the void volume of the column (86, 87). Under those conditions greater confidence can be placed on analyses in terms of an equilibrium between monomer and single higher polymer, since any uncertainty in the elution volumes of polymeric species is removed.

For gel chromatographic migration governed only by two elution volumes, V_M and V_P, the postulated coexistence of monomer and single higher polymer can be tested by noting in Eq. (8) that the concentration of polymer, $k(c_M^\alpha)^n$, may be replaced by the difference between $\bar{c}^\alpha$, the total concentration in the plateau, and c_M^α, the corresponding monomer concentration. With this substitution it follows that c_M^α may be calculated from Eq. (13) for each $(\bar{c}^\alpha, \bar{V})$ result.

$$c_M^\alpha = \frac{\bar{c}^\alpha (\bar{V} - V_P)}{V_M - V_P} \tag{13}$$

The two-state hypothesis is then most simply checked by expressing the law of mass action for such a system [Eq. (4)] in logarithmic form: in terms of c_M^α and $\bar{c}^\alpha$ this may be written

$$\log(\bar{c}^\alpha - c_M^\alpha) = \log k + n \log c_M^\alpha \tag{14}$$

A plot of $\log (\bar{c}^\alpha - c_M^\alpha)$ vs $\log c_M^\alpha$ should thus be linear, in which case the stoichiometry (n) and equilibrium constant (k) describing the two-state association equilibrium may be determined from the slope and ordinate intercept, respectively. Figure 5 of ref. 88 presents such a plot to verify the existence of α-chymotrypsin as a monomer-dimer system at pH 3.86.

Thus far discussion has been restricted to gel chromatography of self-associating systems for which the variation of $\bar{V}$ with $\bar{c}^\alpha$ reflects solely the chemical equilibrium. However, from Figure 10 it is evident that the form of

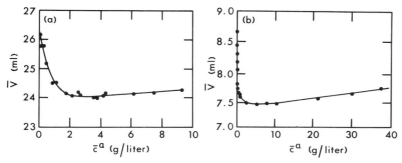

FIGURE 10
Concentration dependence of elution volume in frontal gel chromatography of self-associating proteins. (*a*) α-Chymotrypsin on Sephadex G-100 equilibrated with 0.2 I acetate-chloride, pH 3.86. (Adapted from ref. 80 with permission. Copyright 1964 American Chemical Society.) (*b*) Oxyhemoglobin on Bio-Gel P-100 equilibrated with 0.1 M phosphate-chloride, pH 7.00. (Adapted from ref. 35 with permission. Copyright by American Society of Biological Chemists, Inc.)

the dependence of $\bar{V}$ upon $\bar{c}^\alpha$ exhibited by α-chymotrypsin (80) and oxyhemoglobin (35) is analogous to the situation encountered in sedimentation velocity (Figure 6). Consequently, quantitative interpretation of gel chromatographic studies conducted over greater concentration ranges than those shown in Figure 9 requires specification of the dependences of V_M and V_P upon $\bar{c}^\alpha$. In the first procedures devised to allow for this nonchemical dependence of elution volume upon concentration (35, 89) the analogy with sedimentation velocity was followed in that V_M and V_P were simply considered to be linear functions of $\bar{c}^\alpha$ [cf. Eq. (11a)], an empirical assumption based on the observed gel chromatographic behavior of several noninteracting proteins (79, 90, 91). Although the effects of nonchemical concentration dependence for a noninteracting system may be seemingly similar in sedimentation velocity and gel chromatography, their origins must be entirely different because the variation in s is a consequence of hydrodynamic interactions, whereas the change in V, an equilibrium parameter, must reflect a thermodynamic phenomenon. Indeed, this concentration dependence of elution volume has been traced (92–94) to osmotic shrinkage of the beads comprising the gel column. A more rigorous approach to the problem of allowing for the dependence of V_M and V_P upon $\bar{c}^\alpha$ is therefore available (94).

The shrinkage of gel beads may be interpreted in terms of Eq. (15), which was derived (92) on the basis of the Flory gel swelling theory (95):

$$\left(\frac{\Pi}{RT}\right)_e = (A_2)_s \left\{ \frac{(c_s)^2}{(c_s^0)^2} - \frac{f}{f^0} \right\}(c_s^0)^2 + (A_3)_s \left\{ \frac{(c_s)^3}{(c_s^0)^3} - \frac{f}{f^0} \right\}(c_s^0)^3 \quad (15a)$$

$$f = (\bar{v}_s c_s)^{1/3} - \frac{\bar{v}_s c_s}{2} \qquad f^0 = (\bar{v}_s c_s^0)^{1/3} - \frac{\bar{v}_s c_s^0}{2} \quad (15b)$$

In this expression c_s (g/ml) denotes the internal gel concentration (or reciprocal of the inner volume per gram) under the influence of an external osmotic pressure Π_e at temperature T, and c_s^0 the corresponding concentration in the absence of any external osmotic pressure. $(A_2)_s$ and $(A_3)_s$ are the second and third virial coefficients of the gel matrix, and $\bar{v}_s$ denotes the partial specific volume of the anhydrous gel medium. In the range of osmotic pressures that is likely to be encountered in most gel chromatographic studies of self-associating systems there is theoretical (94) and experimental (93,96) justification for describing this dependence of bead shrinkage on osmotic pressure in the simpler, linear form,

$$\frac{c_s^0}{c_s} = 1 - G\left(\frac{\Pi}{RT}\right)_e \tag{16}$$

where G is a constant whose magnitude must be determined experimentally from measurements of inner volume in the presence of various concentrations of a totally excluded solute with known osmotic characteristics: dextran 500 (92) and dextran 2000 (96) have been used for this purpose. With the proviso that bead shrinkage in a gel chromatographic study of a reversibly associating solute ($nM \rightleftharpoons P$) is describable by Eq. (16), the following set of expressions (94) permit calculations to be made of species elution volumes V_M and V_P, corresponding to total concentration $\bar{c}^\alpha$, whereupon the weight-average elution volume, $\bar{V}$, may be determined from Eq. (8).

$$V_M = V_M^0\left[1 + f_M(\bar{c}^\alpha)\right] \qquad V_P = V_P^0\left[1 + f_P(\bar{c}^\alpha)\right] \tag{17a}$$

$$f_P(\bar{c}^\alpha) = \frac{V_s^0 G(1 - K_P)}{V_P^0 n M_M\left(1 + A^* K_M Gc_s^0 c_M^\alpha + A^* K_P Gc_s^0 c_P^\alpha\right)}$$

$$\times \left\{ nc_M^\alpha\left(1 - K_M - A_M^* M_M K_M c_s^0\right) + c_P\left(1 - K_P - n A_P^* M_M K_P c_s^0\right)\right.$$

$$\left. + 4\left(1 - K_P^2\right)c_P^2 + \left(1 + n^{1/3}\right)^3\left(1 - K_M K_P\right)c_M^\alpha c_P^\alpha \right\} + v_e\left[4n\left(1 - K_M^2\right)c_M^2\right] \tag{17b}$$

$$f_M(\bar{c}^\alpha) = \frac{f_P(\bar{c}^\alpha)V_P^0(1 - K_M)}{V_M^0(1 - K_P)} \tag{17c}$$

V_M^0 and V_P^0 denote the elution volumes of monomer and polymer, respectively, in the absence of any osmotic pressure; K_M and K_P are the partition coefficients (97) corresponding to elution volumes V_M^0 and V_P^0 from a column with stationary phase volume V_s^0, its volume under conditions (zero osmotic pressure) where the internal gel concentration is c_s^0; and M_M is the molecular weight of monomer. Three parameters, namely, v_e, A_M^*, and A_P^*, remain to be defined and considered.

The effective specific volume, v_e, corresponding to the effective radii, r_M and r_P, of the two oligomers, arises in Eq. (17) as the consequence of thermodynamic nonideality due to covolume effects. Its magnitude, considered to be identical for M and P, may be obtained from measurements of the second virial coefficient (see Chapter 1) under conditions where either M or P is essentially the sole form of solute. Alternatively, it could be assumed that the Stokes radius provides a sufficiently accurate estimate of the covolume radius and hence of v_e. The quantities A_M^* and A_P^* are interaction coefficients (82), reflecting covolume effects between solute species and the gel matrix, and require evaluation from the relationships

$$A_M^* = \left(\frac{r_s + r_M}{r_s}\right)^2 \frac{\bar{v}_s}{M_M} \qquad A_P^* = \left(\frac{r_s + r_P}{r_s}\right)^2 \frac{\bar{v}_s}{nM_M} \qquad (18)$$

The radius of the matrix fiber, r_s, may be taken as 0.6 nm for either Sephadex (98, 99) or Bio-Gel (99, 100).

The application of Eq. (17) to obtain a quantitative description of concentration dependence of $\bar{V}$ has been illustrated (96) with gel chromatographic studies of two dimerizing systems, α-chymotrypsin and α-amylase. For α-chymotrypsin on Bio-Gel P-30 equilibrated with 0.2 I acetate-chloride, pH 3.86, failure to consider the consequences of osmotic shrinkage did not affect unduly the conclusion drawn from an earlier experimental study (87) because sufficient results were obtained in a concentration range where the phenomenon could justifiably be neglected. However, the other extreme situation was encountered in gel chromatographic studies on Bio-Gel P-150 of bacterial α-amylase under conditions where the enzyme undergoes a relatively weak dimerization with $k = 0.1$ liter/g (32), consideration of the osmotic phenomenon being required to obtain even a qualitative indication of the existence of the monomer-dimer equilibrium (96).

Although superior to previous approaches (35, 89) to the problem of allowing for nonchemical dependence of elution volume upon concentration of a reversibly associating solute, the above procedure is certainly not devoid of criticism, since no account has been taken of possible variation in the partition coefficients K_M and K_P as the result of (a) changes in porosity due to bead shrinkage or (b) thermodynamic nonideality (86). For studies of concentrated protein solutions, where pronounced osmotic shrinkage of any gel phase is likely to occur, a change of chromatographic medium to porous glass beads (36, 86) is recommended so that complications arising from changes in the void and stationary phase volumes may be avoided.

3.3.3   Exclusion Chromatography on Porous Glass Beads

Previous sections have placed emphasis on systems to which the monomer–single higher polymer model is seemingly appropriate and for which assumed thermodynamic ideality is a reasonable approximation. The latter consideration has necessarily restricted the solute concentration range over which studies could be conducted, a restriction that may well lead to the erroneous classification of a solute undergoing multiple polymerization equilibria as a two-state system. Problems of osmotic shrinkage of the chromatographic medium may be overcome by the choice of controlled-pore glass beads as the stationary phase (86), and hence there is no experimental impediment to an extension of the solute concentration range studied to include the very high levels that some proteins, notably hemoglobin, are found in the biological environment. However, theoretical considerations (86) of the partition behavior of a single nonassociating solute show that the experimentally determined ratio of the concentration in the stationary phase to that in the mobile phase, σ_i (101), which is equivalent to the commonly used distribution coefficient K_D (102), should exhibit concentration dependence according to the expression

$$\sigma_i = \sigma_i^0 \exp\left[\left(\frac{\alpha_{ii}}{M_i}\right)c^\alpha(1-\sigma_i)\right] \tag{19}$$

in which σ_i^0 denotes the value of σ_i at infinite dilution for a solute with molecular weight M_i, c^α the concentration of solute in the elution profile plateau, and α_{ii} the thermodynamic nonideality coefficient reflecting covolume and charge interactions of solute i with itself. Equation (19) is based on the identity of the chemical potentials of solute in the mobile and stationary phases at partition equilibrium, whereupon it is not the ratio of concentrations but rather of thermodynamic activities in the two phases that is constant. Experimental demonstration of such variation in σ_i is presented in Figure 11a, which refers to exclusion chromatography of ovalbumin on CPG-10-75A glass beads equilibrated with 0.156 I phosphate-chloride, pH 7.4. (86), the theoretical curve being based on Eq. (19) and the expression (103)

$$\alpha_{ii} = U_{ii} + \frac{z_i^2(1+2\kappa r_i)}{2\,I(1+\kappa r_i)^2} - M_i\bar{v}_i \tag{20}$$

for the nonideality coefficient α_{ii}. The covolume, U_{ii}, was taken as 500 liter/mol, the molecular weight, M_i, as 45,000, the effective radius, r_i, as 2.92 nm, and the partial specific volume, $\bar{v}_i$, as 0.000748 liter/g (all from ref. 104): a value of -16 was used for the net charge, z_i, on ovalbumin (86) and an estimate of the Debye–Hückel parameter (105) obtained from the expression $\kappa = 3.27 \times 10^7 \sqrt{I}$, which applies to a 1:1 electrolyte at 25°C.

In studies of systems undergoing multiple polymerization equilibria the weight-average elution volume, $\bar{V}$, obtained in exclusion chromatography may be converted to the corresponding weight-average partition coefficient, $\bar{\sigma}$, which is related to the composition of the plateau in the elution profile by

$$\bar{\sigma} = \frac{\sum(\sigma_i c_i^\alpha)}{\bar{c}^\alpha} \qquad \bar{c}^\alpha = \sum c_i^\alpha \tag{21}$$

which in the general case requires specification of σ_i for each oligomeric species (35, 101). However, considerable simplification is introduced (86) if a

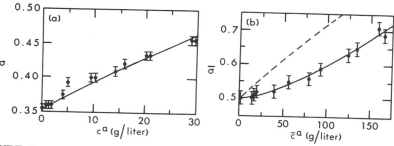

FIGURE 11

Exclusion chromatography of proteins on porous glass beads equilibrated with 0.156 I phosphate-chloride, pH 7.4. (a) Ovalbumin on CPG-10-75A [experimental data from ref. 86 and the line calculated from Eqs. (19) and (20)]: the glass beads were incorrectly described as CPG-10-120A in ref. 86. (b) Bovine (■) and human (●) oxyhemoglobin on CPG-10-120A: the broken line is the theoretical curve predicted for a noninteracting $\alpha_2\beta_2$ species, whereas the solid line is predicted on the basis that it undergoes isodesmic indefinite self-association. (Adapted from ref. 36 with permission. Copyright by North-Holland Publishing Co.)

chromatographic medium can be selected such that dimers and all higher polymers are excluded from the stationary phase ($\sigma_i = 0$ for $i > 1$): under those circumstances $\bar{\sigma}$ is given by the simple relationship

$$\bar{\sigma} = \frac{\sigma_1 c_1^\alpha}{\bar{c}^\alpha} \tag{22}$$

where σ_1 is the partition coefficient of monomer in an experiment with plateau concentration $\bar{c}^\alpha$ and monomer concentration c_1^α. Methods of obtaining the magnitude of σ_1 appropriate to each $\bar{c}^\alpha$ via expressions analogous to Eq. (19) have been discussed in relation to studies of glutamate dehydrogenase (86), oxyhemoglobin (36), and lysozyme (103), systems that are seemingly best described by isodesmic indefinite self-association, that is, indefinite self-association with successive steps governed by the same molar association constant. Figure 11b presents results for bovine and human oxyhemoglobin (36), together with theoretical curves predicted on the bases that the $\alpha_2\beta_2$ species is a noninteracting entity and that it undergoes isodesmic indefinite self-association. Despite the virtual acceptance of the former postulate (106, 107), the results clearly favor the latter concept.

3.3.4 Differential Migration Techniques

Differential migration techniques, in which velocity differences rather than absolute migration rates are measured, are of particular use in the comparison of very similar migration rates or elution volumes. For example, an experimenter may wish to compare the association behavior of (say) hemoglobin from different species, or to examine the effect of reversible ligand binding on the molecular state of an enzyme. The former situation may be examined either by the layering gel chromatographic technique of Gilbert (83) or by the differential sedimentation method of Richards and Schachman (108) in which two solutions with identical protein concentrations are placed in separate compartments of a double-sectored cell. In the layering technique of gel chromatography (83) a solution of one solute is applied to a column pre-equilibrated with an identical concentration of the other solute. Figure 12*a* illustrates a difference in the degree of dissociation of lactate dehydrogenases from beef heart and rabbit muscle at pH 5 (109). Since the muscle enzyme, with which the column of Sephadex G-200 was first equilibrated, moves slower than its beef heart counterpart, there is a net buildup of solute at the junction of the two protein solutions, the area of this hump being given by $\bar{c}^{\alpha}(\bar{V}_{RM} - \bar{V}_{BH})$, where $\bar{V}_{RM}$ and $\bar{V}_{BH}$ denote the weight-average elution volumes of muscle and heart enzymes, respectively. From this layering experiment the elution volumes of beef heart and rabbit muscle lactate dehydrogenases at pH 5.0 were found to differ by 3.0 ml (110).

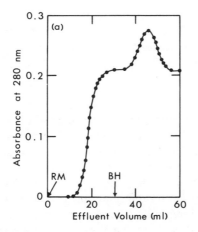
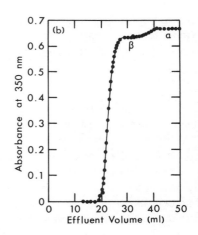

FIGURE 12
Use of difference techniques for quantitative evaluation of small differences between the gel chromatographic behavior of enzymes in different environments. (*a*) Comparison of the elution volumes of rabbit muscle (RM) and beef heart (BH) lactate dehydrogenases in 0.2 I acetate-chloride, pH 5.0, by the layering technique (83): arrows denote effluent volumes at which elution of the Sephadex G-200 column with the appropriate enzyme solution was commenced (adapted from ref. 109 with permission). (*b*) Use of differential gel chromatography (111) to establish the displacement of the monomer–dimer equilibrium caused by preferential binding of phenylpropiolate to monomeric α-chymotrypsin: a solution of enzyme (5 g/liter) in 0.28 I phosphate, pH 7.8, containing 0.02 *M* phenylpropiolate was applied to a Sephadex G-75 column equilibrated with the phosphate buffer. (Adapted from ref. 112 with permission. Copyright 1972 American Chemical Society.)

The use of differential chromatography (111) to demonstrate displacement of a self-association equilibrium by preferential binding of a ligand to one polymeric form is presented in Figure 12b, which shows the elution profile obtained (112) on applying a solution of α-chymotrypsin in 0.28 I phosphate buffer, pH 7.8, containing the competitive inhibitor phenylpropiolate (0.02 M) to a column of Sephadex G-75 preequilibrated with the phosphate buffer. The existence of an initial plateau region (β) in which the concentration ($\bar{c}^\beta$) is less than that ($\bar{c}^\alpha$) in the plateau of original composition implies slower migration of the enzyme in the presence of inhibitor ($\bar{V}^\alpha > \bar{V}^\beta$), the relevant expression of mass conservation being (111, 113),

$$\frac{\bar{c}^\alpha}{\bar{c}^\beta} = \frac{V' - \bar{V}^\beta}{V' - \bar{V}^\alpha} \tag{23a}$$

in which V' denotes the elution volume of the boundary separating the α and β phases. Thus the preferential binding of phenylpropiolate to the monomeric form of α-chymotrypsin is established unequivocally ($\bar{V}^\beta = 22.7$ ml, $\bar{V}^\alpha = 23.5$ ml).

In difference sedimentation velocity experiments (108, 114) solutions with identical concentrations ($\bar{c}^\alpha$) of either two solutes or the same solute in two different environments are placed in the separate sectors of a double-sectored cell, both of which are filled to exactly the same level. Initially the protein concentrations are clearly identical at comparable levels in the two sectors, and hence the Rayleigh interferogram comprises a series of straight fringes, a situation that pertains throughout the sedimentation velocity experiment if migration rates are the same for both systems. A faster migration rate in one sector is detected by the development of curved Rayleigh fringes reflecting the concentration difference $\Delta\bar{c}$ in Figure 13a: the quantitative description of this change is (115)

$$\bar{x}^2 \int_{x_m}^{x_p} \Delta\bar{c}\, x\, dx = \bar{c}^\alpha x_p^2 x_m^2 \left(\ln \frac{\bar{x}}{x_m} \right) \frac{\Delta\bar{s}}{\bar{s}_{av}} \tag{23b}$$

where x_m refers to the position of the meniscus, x_p to the position at which $\Delta\bar{c}$ reassumes a value of zero, and $\bar{x}$ is the mean boundary position. A plot of the left-hand side of Eq. (23) against $\bar{c}^\alpha x_p^2 x_m^2 \ln(x/x_m)$ thus yields a straight line with slope $\Delta\bar{s}/\bar{s}_{av}$, the difference between the weight-average sedimentation coefficients expressed as a fraction of their mean. The greater accuracy with which small changes in $\bar{s}$ may be detected by the difference technique is emphasized in Figure 13b, where the circles, referring to the effect of succinate binding on the sedimentation coefficient of the catalytic subunit of aspartate transcarbamylase (116) clearly show less scatter than the squares, which represent estimates of $\Delta\bar{s}$ based on measurements of $\bar{s}$ in separate experiments on the whole enzyme in the presence and absence of succinate (117). Detailed considerations of the use of difference sedimentation velocity for the quantitative study of such ligand-mediated changes in the state of a self-interacting protein (isomerizing or polymerizing) are presented in refs. 118 and 119.

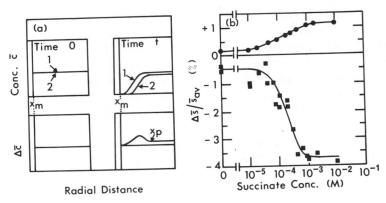

FIGURE 13

Difference sedimentation velocity as a means of measuring small variations in $\bar{s}$. (a) Concentration distributions and concentration difference (Δc) distributions arising from faster migration of solute molecules in sector 2 than in sector 1. (Adapted from ref. 114 with permission. Copyright 1971 American Chemical Society.) (b) The effect of succinate on $\bar{s}$ of aspartate transcarbamylase ($\blacksquare$) and its catalytic subunit ($\bullet$), the latter data having been obtained by the difference technique. (Adapted from ref. 116 with permission. Copyright 1971 American Chemical Society.)

3.3.5   Active Enzyme Centrifugation

In the preceding section emphasis has been placed on the detection and quantitative study of the displacement of equilibria between polymeric states that may result from preferential binding of a ligand to one polymeric form of enzyme. Situations in which the ligand is a competitive inhibitor and an allosteric modifier have been considered so far; but clearly there still remains the problem of examining the macromolecular state of a self-interacting enzyme in the presence of substrate(s), a situation that also has obvious biological relevance. Active enzyme centrifugation (120–123), which certainly provides qualitative information on this point, entails the layering of a small zone of enzyme sample over a much larger volume of substrate solution in a rotating centrifuge cell. The enzyme then sediments as a thin zone into the substrate(s) and catalyzes the formation of product(s). Migration of the enzyme zone is then followed by monitoring optically either the appearance of a product or the disappearance of a substrate. Figure 14a presents densitometer traces of a series of photographs (absorption optics) taken (121) during active enzyme sedimentation of glutamate dehydrogenase layered onto buffer containing glutamate, NAD^+, and ADP. The positions of the enzyme zone are usually identified either as the midpoints of the leading edges of the zones (123) or as the radial distances corresponding to the maxima in the difference curves obtained by subtracting successive densitometer traces (Figure 14b). Although the latter method has the advantage of greater theoretical justification (120), numerical calculations (124) indicate that no

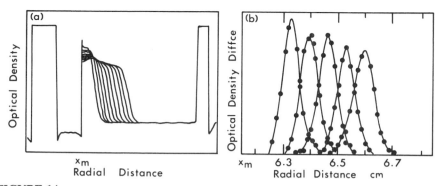

FIGURE 14

Active enzyme sedimentation of a zone (15 μliter) of glutamate dehydrogenase layered onto substrate in 0.15 M phosphate, pH 7.5: (*a*) densitometer traces of exposures taken at 2-min intervals during centrifugation at 59,780 rpm; (*b*) difference distributions reflecting the change in solute concentration between successive exposures. (Adapted from ref. 121 with permission. Copyright by Federation of European Biochemical Societies.)

serious error is introduced by resort to the midpoint procedure, which thus provides a quicker and simpler method of obtaining a value for the sedimentation coefficient of an enzyme in its biologically functional state. However, if the enzyme sample comprises a mixture of polymeric species in rapid association equilibrium, the value so obtained would tend to underestimate $\bar{s}$ because of the dilution of the protein zone during active enzyme centrifugation (124). To overcome this deficiency Llewellyn and Smith (124) have suggested a frontal counterpart of conventional active enzyme sedimentation and verified its ability to yield the correct $\bar{s}$ from computer-simulated patterns. However, its viability as an experimental procedure remains to be tested, since factors such as substrate depletion, immeasurably high absorbance readings, and the necessity to achieve density stabilization, also need to be considered.

Similar information on the macromolecular state of a biologically functioning enzyme is also obtained from a gel chromatography experiment in which a zone of enzyme is applied to a column preequilibrated with substrate, and its migration followed by direct optical scanning of the column (125). In addition to these experimental studies (125), computer simulation has been used (126) to explore the potential of active enzyme gel chromatography, which should not be so susceptible to convective disturbances arising from density inversions.

3.4 INTERACTIONS BETWEEN DISSIMILAR MOLECULES

Mass migration procedures have also been used to study chemical equilibria involving dissimilar molecules because of the biological abundance of these types of interaction, which form the molecular bases of phenomena such as enzyme regulation, gene expression and repression, hormone action, and the immune response. In regard to equilibria involving dissimilar macromolecules, mass migration methods have been used to investigate antigen-antibody reactions (127–132), the specific interactions of proteolytic enzymes with protein substrates (133) and inhibitors (134–136), and also the electrostatic interactions of proteins with nucleic acids (20, 26, 137–139) and other proteins (18, 91, 140–144). Studies of interactions between proteins and small molecules are considered in Chapter 9, and accordingly the emphasis here is on the former type of system. This section concludes with a discussion of the use of affinity chromatography for the quantitative study of equilibria involving dissimilar reactants, large or small (145–152).

3.4.1   Electrophoretic Studies of Macromolecular Interactions

The migration behavior of mixtures comprising two reactants (A and B) in association equilibrium with a 1 : 1 complex, AB ($\equiv$C), has been the subject of extensive theoretical study (44, 153) in terms of the possible asymptotic (diffusion-free) patterns that may pertain to such systems. The logic by which these theoretical profiles are derived has been reviewed in considerable detail (43), and accordingly the present text is restricted to statements of findings that seem to be of direct relevance to particular experimental studies: pertinent proofs may be found in the original articles (44, 153) or in the above-

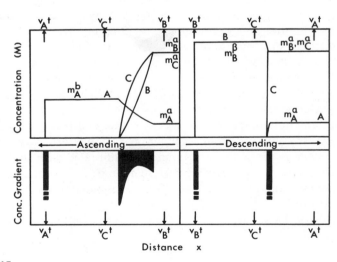

FIGURE 15

Representative patterns for the migration of a rapidly interacting system, $A + B \rightleftharpoons C$, for which $v_A > v_C > v_B$. The upper profile illustrates the concentration distribution, the lower pattern being the corresponding concentration gradient distribution. (Adapted from ref. 153 with permission. Copyright by the Royal Society.)

mentioned review (43). In the context of electrophoretic studies, for example, it seems realistic on the basis of charge requirements to consider only the asymptotic solutions for situations in which the complex C migrates with a velocity intermediate between those of reactants A and B. Salient features of the theoretical patterns (Figure 15) are (*a*) the existence of a region corresponding to pure fast reactant, A, in the ascending profile; (*b*) the existence of a region of pure slow reactant, B, on the descending side; and (*c*) the failure of either of these concentrations (m_A^b, m_B^β) to provide a direct measure of the concentration of reactant in the equilibrium mixture (m_A^α, m_B^α) subjected to electrophoresis. The first two points are confirmed experimentally (Figure 16) by electrophoretic studies of an antigen-antibody mixture (131) and of the interaction of the proteolytic enzyme pepsin with bovine serum albumin (133). Boundaries corresponding to pure reactants are designated accordingly in Figure 16, whereas regions encompassing the reaction boundaries, in which the concentrations of A, B, and C all change concertedly, are bracketed. The third point, namely, that the boundaries of pure reactants overestimate the corresponding equilibrium concentration in the plateau region, was recognized by both research groups.

Cann and Klapper (133) proceeded a stage further by employing the concepts of constituent concentrations and constituent velocities, defined by

$$\bar{v}_A^\alpha = \frac{v_A^\alpha m_A^\alpha + v_C^\alpha m_C^\alpha}{\bar{m}_A^\alpha} \qquad \bar{m}_A^\alpha = m_A^\alpha + m_C^\alpha \qquad (24a)$$

$$\bar{v}_B^\alpha = \frac{v_B^\alpha m_B^\alpha + v_C^\alpha m_C^\alpha}{\bar{m}_B^\alpha} \qquad \bar{m}_B^\alpha = m_B^\alpha + m_C^\alpha \qquad (24b)$$

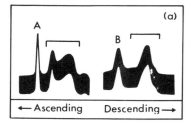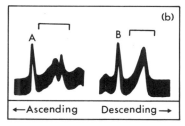

FIGURE 16

Electrophoretic patterns obtained with two interacting systems conforming with the case $v_A > v_C > v_B$. (*a*) A mixture of univalent protein antigen BSA-S-R (A) and its specific antibody (B) in 0.1 I diethylbarbiturate, pH 8.7, the antigen being a derivative of bovine mercaptalbumin formed by covalent attachment of the benzenearsonate residue to the single thiol group. (Adapted from ref. 131 with permission. Copyright 1959 American Chemical Society.) (*b*) A mixture of pepsin (A) and bovine serum albumin (B) in 0.1 I phosphate, pH 5.35. (Adapted from ref. 133 with permission. Copyright by American Society of Biological Chemists, Inc.) Brackets denote the extents of reaction boundaries, and letters adjacent to boundaries signify pure reactant boundaries.

The equilibrium concentration of fast reactant (enzyme), m_A^α, was then obtained by the following adaptation of the moving boundary equation proposed by Longsworth (20):

$$m_A^\alpha(v_A^\alpha - v_B^\alpha) = \overline{m}_A^\alpha(\overline{v}_A^\alpha - v_B^\alpha) - \overline{m}_B^\alpha(\overline{v}_A^\alpha - v_B^\alpha) + m_B^\beta(\overline{v}_A^\alpha - v_B^\alpha) \qquad (25)$$

It followed that the association equilibrium constant, K, could be calculated from

$$K = \frac{m_C^\alpha}{m_A^\alpha m_B^\alpha} = \frac{\overline{m}_A^\alpha - m_A^\alpha}{m_A^\alpha(\overline{m}_B^\alpha - \overline{m}_A^\alpha + m_A^\alpha)} \qquad (26)$$

Subsequent considerations of mass conservation (44, 154) have revealed deficiencies in Eq. (25), which should be written (44)

$$m_A^\alpha(v_A^\alpha - v_B^\alpha) = \overline{m}_A^\alpha(\overline{v}_A^\alpha - v_B^\alpha) - \overline{m}_B^\alpha(v' - v_B^\alpha) + m_B^\beta(v' - v_B^\beta) \qquad (27)$$

where $\overline{v}_A^\alpha$ denotes the median bisector of the concentration gradient in A constituent and v' that of the B constituent in the region of the descending reaction boundary. Although the assumed identity of these two parameters in Eq. (25) is not necessarily valid (91), there seems to be no alternative to this approximation in experiments with refractometric recording of the summed gradients in the two constituents. The substitution of v_B^α for v_B^β in the final term of Eq. (25) implies the absence of any significant Johnston–Ogston effect (113), an assumption that is common to other quantitative electrophoretic studies of interactions between dissimilar proteins (141, 143, 144).

A problem encountered in the application of Eq. (27) or Eq. (25) to schlieren patterns such as those presented in Figure 16 is the lack of precision in the area measurements required for the evaluation of m_B^β. This difficulty may be obviated by noting that the median bisector of the reaction boundary in the conjugate ascending limb provides an estimate of the constituent velocity $\overline{v}_B^\alpha$, which is, of course, subject to the same limitations as those that apply to the value of $\overline{v}_A^\alpha$. Since Eqs. (24a) and (24b) may be rearranged to give

$$m_A^\alpha(v_A^\alpha - v_B^\alpha) = \overline{m}_A^\alpha(\overline{v}_A^\alpha - v_B^\alpha) - \overline{m}_B^\alpha(\overline{v}_B^\alpha - v_B^\alpha) \qquad (28)$$

it follows that m_A^α and hence K may be evaluated without recourse to area measurements. This approach, used to investigate the electrostatic interaction of lysozyme with bovine serum albumin (143), clearly implies the formation of a 1 : 1 complex, an assumption that was justified in the experimental study by observed constancy of the values of K [Eq. (26)] and v_C^α [Eq. (24)] from experiments with a range of mixing concentrations $\overline{m}_A^\alpha$ and $\overline{m}_B^\alpha$. A modified approach has been required in an investigation of the interaction between aldolase and troponin (144) to take into account the multiple binding of this skeletal muscle protein by the glycolytic enzyme.

If the interaction between dissimilar molecules is of the form $AB_{i-1} + B \rightleftarrows AB_i$ there exist in solution the species $AB, AB_2, \ldots, AB_p$ and the free reactants A and B. Specification of the constituent velocities $\overline{v}_A^\alpha$ and $\overline{v}_B^\alpha$ thus requires the assignment of magnitudes to the velocity of each complex species, a formidable task experimentally unless some simplifying assumption can be made (155). In the electrophoretic study of the aldolase-troponin interaction the Smith and Briggs suggestion (156) was adopted that successive additions of B lead to constant incremental changes, Δ, in the velocity of A, that is, $v_{AB_i}^\alpha = v_A^\alpha + i\Delta$. With this assumption, plus the concept of B binding to p equivalent and independent sites on A (157), the expression analogous to Eq. (28) but written in terms of B is (156)

$$m_B^\alpha = \frac{\overline{m}_B^\alpha \{ \bar{v}_A^\alpha - \bar{v}_B^\alpha - (1/p)(\bar{v}_A^\alpha - v_A^\alpha) \} + \overline{m}_A^\alpha (\bar{v}_A^\alpha - v_A^\alpha)}{\bar{v}_A^\alpha - v_B^\alpha - (1/p)(\bar{v}_A^\alpha - v_A^\alpha)} \tag{29}$$

which, provided p is known, yields a value of m_B^α and hence of the molar intrinsic association constant k_A (157) from the expression

$$\frac{\overline{m}_B^\alpha - m_B^\alpha}{\overline{m}_A^\alpha} = \frac{pk_A m_B^\alpha}{1 + k_A m_B^\alpha} \tag{30}$$

In the event that p is also a parameter to be evaluated, then apparent values of m_B^α and k_A must be obtained from Eqs. (29) and (30) for several values of p, the correct stoichiometry and equilibrium constant being deduced from the degree of constancy of k_A values from migration experiments with different total concentrations and mixing ratios of the two reactants. Such treatment of electrophoretic mobility data has been used (144) to show that troponin binds to at least three (probably four) sites on aldolase. It is of interest that electron microscope studies of thin filaments have shown that addition of aldolase causes the production of three-dimensional networks through the formation of cross-links between troponin molecules on adjacent actin filaments (158). This is consistent with the electrophoretic finding that aldolase is a multivalent acceptor but raises the question whether the migration patterns should be reinvestigated in terms of a possible cross-linking scheme (Chapters 1, 5, and 9).

3.4.2 Sedimentation Velocity and Exclusion Chromatography Studies

With interacting systems involving dissimilar reactants there are three velocity combinations that are likely to be encountered in mass migration experiments where the velocities of species are governed largely by their sizes. First, there is the possibility that the two reactants differ in size, whereupon it is relevant to consider the case $v_C > v_A > v_B$. Second, the two reactants may be of similar size, a situation to which the relationship $v_C > v_A = v_B$ may well pertain. Third, there is the case $v_C = v_A > v_B$, which describes the situation in sedimentation velocity studies of interactions between proteins and small ligands (Chapter 9). The latter case also describes the situation in studies of protein-protein interactions by exclusion chromatography if the molecular-sieve medium (gel or porous glass) is chosen such that the larger reactant and hence complex(es) are excluded from the stationary phase (18). Despite the sparsity of quantitative studies of interactions between dissimilar reactants, there is, fortunately, at least one such study to illustrate the treatment of results for systems conforming to each of the three categories.

3.4.2.1 $v_C > v_A > v_B$

Theoretical considerations of mass migration (43, 44, 153) show that in this situation a reaction boundary and a boundary corresponding to either pure A or pure B are generated in sedimentation velocity or in the trailing elution profile in exclusion chromatography. As in electrophoresis ($v_A > v_C > v_B$), measurement of the concentration of the pure solute phase does not give its equilibrium concentration in the plateau region, but in this case it is an underestimate. From the quantitative viewpoint the equilibrium concentration of A continues to be given by Eq. (27) if the experimental conditions (mixing ratios and concentrations) are such that the pure solute boundary corresponds to B: if the pure solute phase is A, the A and B subscripts in Eq. (27) must be interchanged systematically, whereupon m_B^α may be obtained. The limitations and criticisms inherent in the application of Eq. (27) to sedimentation velocity or exclusion chromatography data are basically the same as those already discussed in relation to electrophoretic studies; but to those can be added the uncertainties introduced by the "rectangular" approximation in ultracentrifuge studies.

Figure 17 shows representative schlieren patterns obtained (18) in a sedimentation velocity study of the electrostatic interaction between ovalbumin (A) and lysozyme (B) in 0.02 I phosphate, pH 6.8. Patterns (a) and (b) refer to the individual reactants A and B, respectively, whereas patterns (c) and (d) refer to mixtures of the two reactants. In Figure 17c a lysozyme boundary and a reaction boundary are clearly resolved, and consequently a value of 3×10^4 M^{-1} may be obtained from Eqs. (25) and (26) on the basis that s_A^α

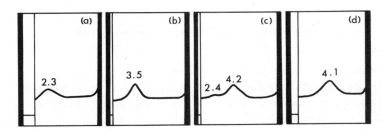

FIGURE 17
Sedimentation velocity patterns for ovalbumin (A), lysozyme (B), and mixtures thereof in 0.02 I phosphate, pH 6.8: (a) lysozyme; (b) ovalbumin; (c) mixture containing 2.05×10^{-4} M lysozyme and 1.33×10^{-4} M ovalbumin; (d) mixture containing 1.37×10^{-4} M lysozyme and 1.56×10^{-4} M ovalbumin. (Adapted from ref. 18 with permission. Copyright 1964 American Chemical Society.) Numbers adjacent to peaks denote sedimentation coefficients ($s_{25,b}$).

and s_B^α are given by the sedimentation coefficients of the pure reactants. No resolution is observed in Figure 17d, which refers to a mixture with a fourfold excess (weight scale) of free ovalbumin over free lysozyme, a situation calculated (44, 153) to give a migration pattern with ovalbumin as the slower boundary. Failure to observe any resolution of boundaries in Figure 17d does not indicate a breakdown of mass migration theory (44, 153) but rather the close proximity of $\bar{s}_A^\alpha$ (4.1 S) to s_A^α (3.5 S): certainly the absence of any lysozyme boundary in Figure 17d is consistent with the predicted switchover from B to A as the pure solute phase. Implicit in the quantitative interpretation of Figure 17c via Eqs. (25) and (26) is the assumption that the electrostatic interaction between ovalbumin and lysozyme is restricted to the formation of a $1:1$ complex. Subsequent sedimentation equilibrium and exclusion chromatography studies have in fact shown that this is merely the first step of a more complex association mechanism that may well lead to a large array of cross-linked ovalbumin-lysozyme complexes (159).

3.4.2.2 $v_C > v_A = v_B$

The situation in which two interacting species migrate with identical velocities is certainly a specialized case, but one which arises, for example, in sedimentation velocity (135) and gel chromatography (136) of mixtures of trypsin and soybean trypsin inhibitor. For this combination of velocities the sedimentation velocity pattern or trailing gel chromatography elution profile is similar to that for systems with $v_C > v_A > v_B$ inasmuch as it comprises a reaction boundary and a more slowly migrating boundary corresponding to pure A or pure B. However, the concentration of this pure solute phase merely reflects the difference between $\bar{m}_A^\alpha$ and $\bar{m}_B^\alpha$ (43, 44, 136, 153). Quantitative information on the heterogeneous association equilibrium is available from the advancing profile in frontal chromatography. Theoretical considerations (44, 153) show that the ascending pattern comprises two reaction boundaries, a hypersharp boundary with velocity $\bar{v}$ intermediate between v_C and $v_A = v_B$, and a second boundary with velocity $v_A = v_B$. The use of flux equations (153) leads to the conclusion that

$$(Z - Z^2) + K(Z\bar{m}_A^\alpha + Z\bar{m}_B^\alpha) - K^2 \bar{m}_A^\alpha \bar{m}_B^\alpha = 0 \qquad (31a)$$

where

$$Z = \left(\frac{v_A - \bar{v}}{\bar{v} - v_C} \right)^2 \qquad (31b)$$

This quadratic equation in K may obviously be solved for experimental systems provided that estimates of $v_A = v_B$ and v_C are available. Furthermore, only one solution is acceptable, since physical reasoning precludes the second mathematical solution that m_C^α is greater than either $\bar{m}_A^\alpha$ or $\bar{m}_B^\alpha$ (136). The feasibility of using Eq. (31) to obtain K from gel chromatographic studies of the interaction between trypsin and soybean trypsin inhibitor has been demonstrated (136) by comparing values so obtained with those inferred from potentiometric measurements (160). As noted by Gilbert (57), the agreement is even better when the correct analog of velocity, namely, the elution volume [not its reciprocal (136)] is used in Eq. (31b).

3.4.2.3 $v_C = v_A > v_B$

The solute distribution generated by migration of a system in which complex and faster reactant comigrate is qualitatively similar to that shown in Figure 15 in that the ascending (advancing) profile exhibits a reaction boundary plus a boundary of pure A, whereas the descending (trailing) pattern contains a reaction boundary and a boundary of pure B. However, in this case the pure solute phase in the ascending pattern corresponds to the total concentration of faster-migrating reactant in the plateau region ($\bar{m}_A^\alpha$), a factor that permits ready identification of an experimental system conforming to this velocity combination (18). Of more interest from the quantitative viewpoint is the fact that the concentration of pure B in the descending pattern reflects its equilibrium concentration, m_B^α, in the mixture being studied, a situation that is evident from Eq. (25) after making the substitution $\bar{v}_A^\alpha = v_A^\alpha$ (18): a rigorous proof of this identity between the magnitudes of m_B^α and m_B^β is to be found in refs. 43 and 44. The important conclusion is thus reached that migration experiments designed to yield this combination of velocities are of the greatest use to an experimenter inasmuch as the equilibrium concentration of slow reactant is measured directly without any assumptions about the nature or the geometry of complexes resulting from the interaction between A and B. Furthermore, the required combination of velocities can frequently be achieved because the availability of gels and porous glass beads with a wide range of permeation characteristics allows chromatographic studies a great deal of flexibility in this regard. The only examples of protein-protein interactions being investigated by this simple and rigorous procedure are gel chromatographic studies of the ovalbumin-lysozyme system on Sephadex G-100 (18) and G-75 (159). In the earlier investigation (18) the particular combination of velocities was not selected but was recognized by the fact that the concentration of A in the advancing profile was consistently the total ovalbumin concentration in the mixture applied to the column. This combination of velocities is, of course, readily attained in studies of equilibria involving proteins and small ligands by either sedimentation velocity or gel chromatography, systems which are considered in Chapter 9.

3.4.3   The Johnston–Ogston Effect

In all of the applications of Eqs. (25) and (27) that have been discussed thus far it has been assumed that the velocities v_A^α and v_B^α may be obtained from experiments with pure A and pure B, respectively. Indeed, the interpretation has relied upon the additional assumption that $v_B^\alpha = v_B^\beta$. As noted initially by

Johnston and Ogston (113), the velocities of species in mixtures are functions not only of their own concentration but also of the overall macromolecular composition. In the present context this observation may be expressed as

$$v_A^\alpha = v_A^0 \{ 1 + f_1(\overline{m}_A^\alpha, \overline{m}_B^\alpha) \} \tag{32a}$$

$$v_B^\alpha = v_B^0 \{ 1 + f_2(\overline{m}_A^\alpha, \overline{m}_B^\alpha) \} \tag{32b}$$

where v_A^0 and v_B^0 refer to the respective limiting velocities of A and B at infinite dilution, and $f_1(\overline{m}_A^\alpha, \overline{m}_B^\alpha)$, $f_2(\overline{m}_A^\alpha, \overline{m}_B^\alpha)$ are unspecified functions expressing the dependence of species velocities on the composition of the mixture subjected to mass migration. In the only instances where any account has been taken of the composition dependence of species velocities (91, 142), one approach has been to simplify Eq. (32) to

$$v_A^\alpha = v_A^0 (1 - g_A \overline{c}_p^\alpha) \tag{33a}$$

$$v_B^\alpha = v_B^0 (1 - g_B \overline{c}_p^\alpha) \tag{33b}$$

where $\overline{c}_p^\alpha$ denotes the total weight concentration of macromolecular solute, $(\overline{m}_A^\alpha M_A + \overline{m}_B^\alpha M_B)$, and g_A, g_B are the coefficients describing the concentration dependence of the velocities of the respective pure components. The validity of this empirical approach was questioned in the earlier (142) of these two studies, and an alternative empirical approach adopted to obtain a second "quantitative" assessment of the results. In retrospect much of the empiricism in both of these gel chromatographic studies (91, 142) could now be avoided, since allowance for gel shrinkage, the source of the concentration dependence (92, 93), is amenable to more rigorous thermodynamic treatment (94).

The above methods of analyzing results thus assume migration under conditions that are met only imperfectly in actual mass migration experiments, the "rectangular" approximation in sedimentation velocity reflecting one such deficiency to which reference has already been made. Although a second complicating factor, the Johnston–Ogston effect, has now been added, it is emphasized that the consequences of these phenomena are usually second order effects, and that any reasonable procedure adopted to take them into account, albeit empirical, is a justifiable approximation. In this connection the commonest approach is to neglect completely these complicating factors, an empirical procedure that is unlikely to be a major source of error in the great majority of instances. However, an awareness of the existence of these factors is clearly desirable if only to enable an experimenter to recognize the occasional situation where consideration of the complicating factor assumes major importance in the quantitative interpretation of mass migration results. A classical example of such a situation occurs in electrophoresis of the hyaluronic acid–bovine serum albumin system (161, 162) for which the consequences of composition-dependent migration resulting from physical interactions between the two constituents are sufficiently great to disguise the consequences of any reversible complex formation (163).

3.4.4 Quantitative Affinity Chromatography

The introduction of affinity chromatography as a means of studying protein-ligand interactions (145–152) has certainly added to the versatility of chromatography as a mass migration method for quantitative studies of heterogeneous association equilibria. Basically the technique entails immobilization of a biospecific reactant group X on an inert chromatographic matrix (usually Sepharose), and measurement of the weight-average elution volume, $\overline{V}_A$, of the protein (A) in a series of chromatography experiments in which the protein migrates in the presence of a range of concentrations of a second solute, B, that also interacts specifically with A or X. In some instances the resultant variation in $\overline{V}_A$ reflects competition between soluble and immobilized reactants for the same protein site(s) (146–148, 150–152): in others it reflects the interaction of immobilized reactant, X, with the binary complex AB formed between protein and soluble ligand (145, 149). Quantitative interpretation of this variation in $\overline{V}_A$ requires the consideration of the various operative equilibria and the realization that any protein complex containing X has zero velocity. From a theoretical viewpoint, frontal chromatography experiments are clearly to be preferred in this context as in others.

A comprehensive investigation of the frontal chromatographic behavior of affinity systems in which protein A possessed at most a single site for each of X and B (147) considered the following equilibria to represent the possible interactions.

$$A + B \rightleftharpoons AB \qquad m_{AB} = K_{AB} m_A m_B$$
$$A + X \rightleftharpoons AX \qquad m_{AX} = K_{AX} m_A m_X$$
$$B + X \rightleftharpoons BX \qquad m_{BX} = K_{BX} m_B m_X$$
$$B + AX \rightleftharpoons BAX \qquad m_{BAX} = K_1 K_{AX} m_A m_B m_X$$
$$A + BX \rightleftharpoons ABX \qquad m_{ABX} = K_2 K_{AX} m_A m_B m_X$$
$$X + AB \rightleftharpoons XAB \qquad m_{XAB} = K_3 K_{AB} m_A m_B m_X \qquad (34)$$

In these expressions the molar concentration of a species is assumed to be the same in all regions of the column that are accessible to that species, X being considered to be uniformly distributed throughout the same volume as A. From a general relationship encompassing affinity chromatography of a system in which all equilibria are operative, a series of expressions has been derived (147) for experimentally realistic systems in which four of the six equilibrium constants are zero. In these relationships, summarized in Table 1, V_A^* denotes the elution volume of A in an experiment with no protein–matrix interaction. If A interacts with X, this unretarded volume V_A^* may be obtained from an experiment with a saturating concentration of competing ligand B, or from an experiment on an equivalent column of matrix material (usually Sepharose) devoid of X groups (146). Several points may be noted in relation to Table 1. First, cases 1 and 2 describe affinity chromatography systems in which $\overline{V}_A$ increases with increasing concentration of B, whereas

TABLE 1
Affinity Chromatography Systems for Which the Weight-Average Elution Volume of the Protein A Is Affected by Introduction of a Ligand B

Case	Operative Equilibrium Constants[a]	Quantitative Dependence of $\bar{V}_A$ on m_B^α
1	K_{AB}, K_3	$\dfrac{1}{\bar{V}_A - V_A^*} = \dfrac{1}{V_s \bar{m}_X K_3 K_{AB} m_B^\alpha} + \dfrac{1 + K_3 \bar{m}_A^\alpha}{V_s \bar{m}_X K_3}$
2	K_{BX}, K_2	$\dfrac{1}{\bar{V}_A - V_A^*} = \dfrac{1}{V_s \bar{m}_X K_2 K_{BX} m_B^\alpha} + \dfrac{1 + K_2 \bar{m}_A^\alpha}{V_s \bar{m}_X K_2}$
3	K_{AB}, K_{AX}	$\dfrac{1}{\bar{V}_A - V_A^*} = \dfrac{K_{AB} m_B^\alpha}{V_s \bar{m}_X K_{AX}} + \dfrac{1 + K_{AX} \bar{m}_A^\alpha}{V_s \bar{m}_X K_{AX}}$
4	K_{AX}, K_{BX}	$\dfrac{1}{\bar{V}_A - V_A^*} = \dfrac{K_{BX} m_B^\alpha}{V_s \bar{m}_X K_{AX}} + \dfrac{1 + K_{AX} \bar{m}_A^\alpha}{V_s \bar{m}_X K_{AX}}$

[a] Defined in Eq. (34).

cases 3 and 4 refer to competitive situations that result in a decrease in $\bar{V}_A$ with increasing m_B^α. Second, unique identification of the relevant case is possible provided the concentration dependence of the migration behavior of the separate reactants A and B is also investigated. The suggested plots [$1/(\bar{V}_A - V_A^*)$ vs $1/m_B^\alpha$ (cases 1 and 2) or m_B^α (cases 3 and 4)] may thus be used to provide values of the two operative equilibrium constants. Third, the expressions involve m_B^α, whereas the experimentally available quantity is $\bar{m}_B^\alpha$ in a frontal experiment. This difficulty, which only arises in cases 1 and 3, may be overcome by an iterative procedure based on $\bar{m}_B^\alpha$ as an initial estimate of m_B^α (149). Fourth, all relationships contain $\bar{m}_A^\alpha$, a quantity that presents no problem in frontal chromatography but one that is of unknown and varying magnitude in zonal studies. However, as noted in ref. 147, if $\bar{m}_A^\alpha$ in the applied zone is sufficiently small then there may be circumstances in which no serious error would be introduced by neglecting the relevant term (Table 1) in $\bar{m}_A^\alpha$. For example, in a zonal study of the interaction between lactose synthetase-N-acetylglucosamine complex and immobilized α-lactalbumin (case 1), the intercept/slope ratio of the double-reciprocal plot (Figure 18 a) was taken as measuring K_{AB} (145) instead of $K_{AB}(1 + K_3 \bar{m}_A^\alpha)$. The consequent error in K_{AB}, estimated (147) to be less than 1%, was clearly insignificant for that particular system.

Despite the theoretical necessity of employing the frontal method for the correct quantitative elucidation of interactions by affinity chromatography, its use seems to have been very restricted (147, 149, 164–166), presumably because of the larger amount of A that is required to generate the plateau region. Most of the zonal studies have entailed the use of affinity chromatography to study equilibria involving enzymes and modifiers, inhibitors, or substrates (145, 146, 148, 150, 167, 168), but the method has recently been applied to a protein-drug interaction (152) and to an antigen-antibody system

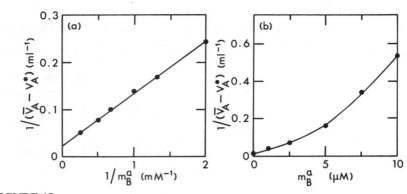

FIGURE 18

Effects of ligand concentration in quantitative affinity chromatography. (*a*) Double-reciprocal plot showing the retardation of lactose synthetase on a Sepharose-α-lactalbumin column as a function of N-acetylglucosamine concentration. (Adapted from ref. 145 with permission. Copyright by Biochemical Society.) (*b*) Plot showing the competition between soluble and immobilized phosphorylcholine in affinity chromatography studies of the interaction between this antigen and its antibody, immunoglobulin A. (Adapted from ref. 151 with permission. Copyright 1979 American Chemical Society.)

(151). The antigen phosphorylcholine was first immobilized on Sepharose and then chromatography of radioactively labeled immunoglobulin A conducted on the affinity column preequilibrated with various concentrations of phosphorylcholine (B). The resulting plot of $1/(\bar{V}_A - V_A^*)$ vs m_B^α (Figure 18*b*) is decidedly curvilinear, reflecting bivalency of the antibody (A) and the consequent formation of the species X-A-X. Chaiken and co-workers (169) have derived a quantitative expression to take into account this phenomenon, which only occurs if the concentration of immobilized antigen (X) is sufficiently high to permit the simultaneous binding of A to two such groups. With low values of $\bar{m}_X^\alpha$ single attachment of A to the matrix despite multivalency of A is a more likely situation, in which case treatment of the consequently linear plot of $1/(\bar{V}_A - V_A^*)$ vs m_B^α yields the intrinsic association constant (157) for the binding of ligand to a protein with several independent and equivalent sites (147, 149, 151, 152). Persistence of curvilinearity of such plots in experiments with very low concentrations of immobilized reactant would imply (*a*) nonequivalence of multiple binding sites, (*b*) the existence of cooperative interactions, or (*c*) complications introduced by the use of zonal rather than frontal techniques. As noted by Chaiken (170), the potential use of affinity chromatography for quantitative studies of ligand binding to interacting protein systems requires further exploration.

3.5 CONCLUDING REMARKS

This review of the mass migration behavior of interacting protein systems differs from its predecessors (e.g., refs. 43 and 171) in that the usual degree of prominence has not been accorded to the shapes of reaction boundaries, which are considered in Chapter 4. Certainly the shape of a reaction boundary holds a great deal of fascination for an experimenter because it is frequently the mass migration characteristic that provides the first indication that a solute being studied is in fact an interacting system. However, detailed analysis of the shape of a reaction boundary by computer simulation (see Chapter 4) is facilitated greatly by preliminary identification of the interacting system. Consequently, the recommended experimental approach is (a) to obtain a quantitative assessment of the system from analysis of weight-average migration rates of boundaries, and (b) then to refine the interaction parameters on the basis of detailed considerations of reaction boundary shapes.

From the viewpoint of quantitative studies of protein self-association it cannot be denied that direct measurement of molecular weight by techniques such as light scattering, sedimentation equilibrium, and osmometry has the obvious advantage over mass migration methods that there is no ambiguity about the magnitude of the parameter to be ascribed to any postulated polymeric species; but in this regard such ambiguity can sometimes be avoided in exclusion chromatography by choosing a chromatographic medium such that dimer and all higher polymers are confined to the mobile phase (36, 86). The use of mass migration methods for preliminary quantitative assessment of interacting protein systems will undoubtedly continue to flourish, if only because a sedimentation equilibrium study can be designed much more effectively when preliminary estimates of the interaction parameters are available. However, expression of this opinion is not intended to convey the impression that mass migration methods are necessarily relegated to the position of being the poor cousins of the equilibrium methods. Sedimentation velocity experiments have played a decisive role in the delineation of the polymerization pattern for α-chymotrypsin from sedimentation equilibrium studies at low ionic strength in the vicinity of the pH optimum (73). Further evidence of the harmonious relationship that can, and should, exist between mass migration and equilibrium studies is the recent investigation (103) of the self-association of lysozyme, where frontal exclusion chromatography of very concentrated lysozyme solutions was required to obtain positive identification of the system as an isodesmic indefinite association, a polymerization pattern that was not defined unequivocally by sedimentation equilibrium studies.

In the past decade there have been four major developments in the study of interacting systems by mass migration methods. (a) The recognition of nonchemical concentration dependence of elution volume in gel chromatography as a consequence of osmotic shrinkage has meant that studies of self-associating systems by this technique can be accorded greater thermodynamic rigor (94). (b) The realization that the polymerization of many proteins involves multiple association equilibria has led to advances in methodology to handle these more complicated systems (36, 103). (c) To that end the availability of porous glass beads as a chromatographic medium has made possible the study of concentrated protein solutions, conditions that favor self-association and hence delineation of the correct polymerization pattern (36, 86, 103). (d) The past decade has seen the emergence of quantitative affinity chromatography (145–147) as a method for studying protein interactions involving dissimilar reactants. This method, which is still in its relative infancy, has the undeniable attraction that specificity of the interaction with the immobilized reactant makes possible the quantitative evaluation of equilibria occurring within biological milieus, a factor demonstrated by studies of the interaction between NADH and the various lactate dehydrogenase isoenzymes in a crude tissue extract (149).

REFERENCES

1. T. Svedberg and H. Rinde, *J. Am. Chem. Soc.* **46**, 2677 (1924).

2. A. Tiselius, *Trans. Faraday Soc.* **33**, 524 (1937).

3. S. Claesson, *Ark. Kemi Mineral. Geol.* **24A**, No. 7 (1946).

4. R. G. Martin and B. N. Ames, *J. Biol. Chem.* **236**, 1372 (1961).

5. E. E. Brumbaugh and G. K. Ackers, *J. Biol. Chem.* **243**, 6315 (1968).

6. D. J. Winzor, *Biochem. J.* **101**, 30C (1966).

7. E. E. Brumbaugh and G. K. Ackers, *Anal. Biochem.* **42**, 405 (1971).

8. G. K. Ackers, E. E. Brumbaugh, S. H. C. Ip, and H. R. Halvorson, *Biophys. Chem.* **4**, 171 (1976).

9. M. M. Jones, G. A. Harvey, and G. K. Ackers, *Biophys. Chem.* **5**, 327 (1976).

10. L. C. Davis, *Biophys. Chem.* **10**, 55 (1979).

11. L. W. Nichol, A. G. Ogston, and D. J. Winzor, *J. Phys. Chem.* **71**, 726 (1967).

12. G. E. Hibberd, A. G. Ogston, and D. J. Winzor, *J. Chromatogr.* **48**, 393 (1970).

13. M. J. Beran, *J. Chem. Phys.* **27**, 270 (1957).

14. G. Houghton, *J. Phys. Chem.* **67**, 84 (1963).

15. H. R. Halvorson and G. K. Ackers, *J. Polym. Sci. A-2* **9**, 245 (1971).

16. G. H. Weiss and G. K. Ackers, *Anal. Biochem.* **57**, 569 (1974).

17. J. K. Zimmerman and G. K. Ackers, *Anal. Biochem.* **57**, 578 (1974).

18. L. W. Nichol and D. J. Winzor, *J. Phys. Chem.* **68**, 2455 (1964).

19. L. G. Longsworth, R. K. Cannan, and D. A. MacInnes, *J. Am. Chem. Soc.* **62**, 2580 (1940).

20. L. G. Longsworth, in M. Bier, Ed., *Electrophoresis, Theory, Methods, and Applications,* Academic Press, New York, 1959, p. 91.

21. P. G. Squire and K. O. Pedersen, *J. Am. Chem. Soc.* **83**, 476 (1961).

22. J. L. Bethune, *Biochemistry* **4**, 2698 (1965).

23. M. H. Klapper, G. H. Barlow, and I. M. Klotz, *Biochem. Biophys. Res. Commun.* **25**, 116 (1966).

24. N. R. Langerman and I. M. Klotz, *Biochemistry* **8**, 4746 (1969).

25. K. Morimoto and G. Kegeles, *Arch. Biochem. Biophys.* **142**, 247 (1971).

26. L. G. Longsworth and D. A. MacInnes, *J. Gen. Physiol.* **25**, 507, (1942).

27. G. Kegeles and J. R. Cann, *Methods Enzymol.* **48**, 248 (1978).

28. G. W. Schwert, *J. Biol. Chem.* **179**, 655 (1949).

29. L. W. Cunningham, F. Tietze, N. M. Green, and H. Neurath, *Discuss. Faraday Soc.* **13**, 58 (1953).

30. E. L. Smith, J. R. Kimmel, and D. M. Brown, *J. Biol. Chem.* **207**, 533 (1954).

31. M. A. Cohly and H. A. Scheraga, *Arch. Biochem. Biophys.* **95**, 428 (1961).

32. R. Tellam, D. J. Winzor, and L. W. Nichol, *Biochem. J.* **173**, 185 (1978).

33. G. K. Ackers and T. E. Thompson, *Proc. Natl. Acad. Sci. USA* **53**, 342 (1965).

34. H. K. Schachman and S. J. Edelstein, *Biochemistry* **5**, 2681 (1966).

35. E. Chiancone, L. M. Gilbert, G. A. Gilbert, and G. L. Kellett, *J. Biol. Chem.* **243**, 1212 (1968).

36. L. W. Nichol, R. J. Siezen, and D. J. Winzor, *Biophys. Chem.* **10**, 17 (1979).

37. E. Fredericq and H. Neurath, *J. Am. Chem. Soc.* **72**, 2684 (1950).

38. R. F. Steiner, *Arch. Biochem. Biophys.* **39**, 333 (1952).

39. A. H. Pekar and B. H. Frank, *Biochemistry* **11**, 4013 (1972).

40. P. D. Jeffrey, B. K. Milthorpe, and L. W. Nichol, *Biochemistry* **15**, 4660 (1976).

41. B. K. Milthorpe, L. W. Nichol, and P. D. Jeffrey, *Biochim. Biophys. Acta* **495**, 195 (1977).

42. P. Nicolas, M. Camier, P. Dessen, and P. Cohen, *J. Biol. Chem.* **251**, 3965 (1976).

43. L. W. Nichol and D. J. Winzor, *Migration of Interacting Systems*, Clarendon Press, Oxford, 1972.

44. L. W. Nichol and A. G. Ogston, *Proc. R. Soc. London, Ser. B* **163**, 343 (1965).

45. A. Tiselius, *Nova Acta Regiae Soc. Sci. Ups.* [4] **7**, No. 4 (1930).

46. G. A. Gilbert, *Discuss. Faraday Soc.* **20**, 68 (1955).

47. G. A. Gilbert, *Proc. R. Soc. London, Ser. A* **250**, 377 (1959).

48. D. J. Winzor, R. Tellam, and L. W. Nichol, *Arch. Biochem. Biophys.* **178**, 327 (1977).

49. J. R. Cann and W. B. Goad, *J. Biol. Chem.* **240**, 148 (1965).

50. M. Dishon, G. H. Weiss, and D. A. Yphantis, *Biopolymers* **4**, 449 (1966).

51. M. Dishon, G. H. Weiss, and D. A. Yphantis, *Biopolymers* **5**, 697 (1967).

52. D. J. Cox, *Arch. Biochem. Biophys.* **119**, 230 (1967).

53. D. J. Cox, *Arch. Biochem. Biophys.* **129**, 106 (1969).

54. J.-M. Claverie, H. Dreux, and R. Cohen, *Biopolymers* **14**, 1685 (1975).

55. R. Cohen and J.-M. Claverie, *Biopolymers* **14**, 1701 (1975).

56. L. G. Longsworth, *J. Am. Chem. Soc.* **65**, 1755 (1943).

57. G. A. Gilbert, *Nature (London)* **210**, 299 (1966).

58. R. J. Goldberg, *J. Phys. Chem.* **57**, 194 (1953).

59. R. Trautman and V. N. Schumaker, *J. Chem. Phys.* **22**, 551 (1954).

60. J. M. Creeth and L. W. Nichol, *Biochem. J.* **77**, 230 (1960).

61. A. G. Ogston and J. M. A. Tilley, *Biochem. J.* **59**, 644 (1955).

62. M. P. Tombs, *Biochem. J.* **67**, 517 (1957).

63. S. N. Timasheff and R. Townend, *J. Am. Chem. Soc.* **82**, 3157 (1960).

64. L. M. Gilbert and G. A. Gilbert, *Methods Enzymol.* **27**, 273 (1973).

65. R. Townend, L. Weinberger, and S. N. Timasheff, *J. Am. Chem. Soc.* **82**, 3175 (1960).

66. L. M. Gilbert and G. A. Gilbert, *Nature (London)* **194**, 1173 (1962).

67. F. Perrin, *J. Phys. Radium* **7**, 1 (1936).

68. V. Bloomfield, W. O. Dalton, and K. E. Van Holde, *Biopolymers* **5**, 135 (1967).

69. V. Bloomfield, W. O. Dalton, and K. E. Van Holde, *Biopolymers* **5**, 149 (1967).

70. P. R. Andrews and P. D. Jeffrey, *Biophys. Chem* **4**, 93 (1976).

71. P. R. Andrews and P. D. Jeffrey, *Biophys. Chem.* **11**, 49 (1980).

72. L. M. Gilbert and G. A. Gilbert, *Nature (London)* **192**, 1181 (1961).

73. R. Tellam and D. J. Winzor, *Biochem. J.* **161**, 687 (1977).

74. R. J. Cohen, J. A. Jedziniak, and G. B. Benedek, *Proc. R. Soc. London, Ser. A* **345**, 73 (1975).

75. M. Jullien and D. Thusius, *J. Mol. Biol.* **101**, 397 (1976).

76. R. J. Cohen and G. B. Benedek, *J. Mol. Biol.* **108**, 151 (1976).

77. R. J. Cohen, J. A. Jedziniak, and G. B. Benedek, *J. Mol. Biol.* **108**, 179 (1976).

78. P. R. Wills, *J. Chem. Phys.* **70**, 5865 (1979).

79. D. J. Winzor and H. A. Scheraga, *Biochemistry* **2**, 1263 (1963).

80. D. J. Winzor and H. A. Scheraga, *J. Phys. Chem.* **68**, 338 (1964).

81. P. A. Baghurst, L. W. Nichol, and W. H. Sawyer, *J. Biol. Chem.* **247**, 3199 (1972).

82. A. G. Ogston and P. Silpananta, *Biochem. J.* **116**, 171 (1970).

83. G. A. Gilbert, *Nature (London)* **212**, 296 (1966).

84. L. W. Nichol and A. B. Roy, *Biochemistry* **4**, 386 (1965).

85. D. J. Winzor, *Biochim. Biophys. Acta* **200**, 423 (1970).

86. L. W. Nichol, R. J. Siezen, and D. J. Winzor, *Biophys. Chem.* **9**, 47 (1978).

87. R. Tellam, J. de Jersey, and D. J. Winzor, *Biochemistry* **18**, 5316 (1979).

88. D. J. Winzor, J. P. Loke, and L. W. Nichol, *J. Phys. Chem.* **71**, 4492 (1967).

89. G. K. Ackers, *J. Biol. Chem.* **242**, 3026 (1967).

90. D. J. Winzor and L. W. Nichol, *Biochim. Biophys. Acta* **104**, 1 (1965).

91. G. A. Gilbert and G. L. Kellett, *J. Biol. Chem.* **246**, 6079 (1971).

92. E. Edmond, S. Farquhar, J. R. Dunstone, and A. G. Ogston, *Biochem. J.* **108**, 755 (1968).

93. L. W. Nichol, M. Janado, and D. J. Winzor, *Biochem. J.*, **133**, 15 (1973).

94. P. A. Baghurst, L. W. Nichol, A. G. Ogston, and D. J. Winzor, *Biochem. J.* **147**, 575 (1975).

95. P. J. Flory, *Principles of Polymer Chemistry*, Cornell University Press, Ithaca, N.Y., 1953, pp. 490–540, 577–581.

96. R. Tellam and D. J. Winzor, *Biophys. Chem.*, in press.

97. T. C. Laurent and J. Killander, *J. Chromatogr.* **14**, 317 (1964).

98. L. M. Siegel and K. J. Monty, *Biochim. Biophys. Acta* **112**, 346 (1966).

99. A. G. Ogston, B. N. Preston, and J. D. Wells, *Proc. R. Soc. London, Ser. A* **333**, 297 (1973).

100. J. S. Fawcett and C. J. O. R. Morris, *Sep. Sci.* **1**, 9 (1966).

101. G. K. Ackers, *J. Biol. Chem.* **243**, 2056 (1968).

102. B. Gelotte, *J. Chromatogr.* **3**, 330 (1960).

103. P. R. Wills, L. W. Nichol and R. J. Siezen, *Biophys. Chem.* **11**, 71 (1980).

104. P. D. Jeffrey, L. W. Nichol, D. R. Turner, and D. J. Winzor, *J. Phys. Chem.* **81**, 776 (1976).

105. P. Debye and E. Hückel, *Phys. Z.* **24**, 185 (1923).

106. M. F. Perutz, *Nature (London)* **228**, 726 (1970).

107. A. Arnone, *Nature (London)* **237**, 146 (1972).

108. E. G. Richards and H. K. Schachman, *J. Am Chem. Soc.* **79**, 5324 (1957).

109. S. J. Lovell, Ph.D. Thesis, University of Queensland, 1976.

110. S. J. Lovell and D. J. Winzor, *Biochemistry* **13**, 3527 (1974).

111. P. A. Baghurst, L. W. Nichol, R. J. Richards, and D. J. Winzor, *Nature (London)* **234**, 299 (1971).

112. L. W. Nichol, W. J. H. Jackson, and D. J. Winzor, *Biochemistry* **11**, 585 (1972).

113. J. P. Johnston and A. G. Ogston, *Trans. Faraday Soc.* **42**, 789 (1946).

114. M. W. Kirschner and H. K. Schachman, *Biochemistry* **10**, 1900 (1971).

115. H. K. Schachman, *Ultracentrifugation in Biochemistry*, Academic Press, New York, 1959.

116. M. W. Kirschner and H. K. Schachman, *Biochemistry* **10**, 1919 (1971).

117. J. C. Gerhart and H. K. Schachman, *Biochemistry* **7**, 538 (1968).

118. G. D. Smith and H. K. Schachman, *Biochemistry* **12**, 3789 (1973).

119. G. D. Smith, M. W. Kirschner, and H. K. Schachman, *Biochemistry* **12**, 3801 (1973).

120. R. Cohen, *C.R. Acad. Sci. (Paris)* **256**, 3513 (1963).

121. R. Cohen and M. Mire, *Eur. J. Biochem.* **23**, 267 (1971).

122. R. Cohen and M. Mire, *Eur. J. Biochem.* **23**, 276 (1971).

123. B. Taylor, R. Barden, and M. Utter, *J. Biol. Chem.* **247**, 7383 (1972).

124. D. J. Llewellyn and G. D. Smith, *Arch. Biochem. Biophys.* **190**, 483 (1978).

125. M. M. Jones, J. W. Ogilvie, and G. K. Ackers, *Biophys. Chem.* **5**, 339 (1976).

126. B. B. Brown and J. K. Zimmerman, *Biophys. Chem.* **5**, 351 (1976).

127. S. J. Singer and D. H. Campbell, *J. Am. Chem. Soc.* **74**, 1974 (1952).

128. S. J. Singer and D. H. Campbell, *J. Am. Chem. Soc.* **77**, 4851 (1955).

129. M. C. Baker, D. H. Campbell, S. I. Epstein, and S. J. Singer, *J. Am. Chem. Soc.* **78**, 312 (1958).

130. F. A. Pepe and S. J. Singer, *J. Am. Chem. Soc.* **78**, 4583 (1956).

131. F. A. Pepe and S. J. Singer, *J. Am. Chem. Soc.* **81**, 3878 (1959).

132. S. J. Singer, F. A. Pepe, and D. Ilten, *J. Am. Chem. Soc.* **81**, 3887 (1959).

133. J. R. Cann and J. A. Klapper, Jr., *J. Biol. Chem.* **236**, 2446 (1961).

134. J. S. Ram, L. Terminiello, M. Bier, and F. F. Nord, *Arch. Biochem. Biophys.* **52**, 451 (1954).

135. E. Sheppard and A. D. McLaren, *J. Am. Chem. Soc.* **75**, 2587 (1953).

136. L. W. Nichol and D. J. Winzor, *Biochim. Biophys. Acta* **94**, 591 (1965).

137. E. Goldwasser and F. W. Putnam, *J. Phys. Colloid Chem.* **54**, 79 (1950).

138. S. J. Singer, S. N. Timasheff, and J. G. Kirkwood, *J. Am. Chem. Soc.* **74**, 5985 (1952).

139. E. L. Hess, A. M. Herranen, and S. E. Lagg, *J. Biol. Chem.* **236**, 3020 (1961).

140. S. N. Timasheff and J. G. Kirkwood, *J. Am. Chem. Soc.* **75**, 3124 (1953).

141. S. Ehrenpreis and R. C. Warner, *Arch. Biochem. Biophys.* **61**, 38 (1956).

142. L. W. Nichol, A. G. Ogston, and D. J. Winzor, *Arch. Biochem. Biophys.* **121**, 727 (1967).

143. L. W. Nichol, G. D. Smith, and D. J. Winzor, *J. Phys. Chem.* **77**, 2912 (1973).

144. T. P. Walsh, D. J. Winzor, F. M. Clarke, C. J. Masters, and D. J. Morton, *Biochem. J.* **186**, 89 (1980).

145. P. Andrews, B. J. Kitchen, and D. J. Winzor, *Biochem. J.* **135**, 897 (1973).

146. B. M. Dunn and I. M. Chaiken, *Proc. Natl. Acad. Sci. USA* **71**, 2382 (1974).

147. L. W. Nichol, A. G. Ogston, D. J. Winzor, and W. H. Sawyer, *Biochem. J.* **143**, 435 (1974).

148. B. M. Dunn and I. M. Chaiken, *Biochemistry* **14**, 2343 (1975).

149. R. I. Brinkworth, C. J. Masters, and D. J. Winzor, *Biochem. J.* **151**, 631 (1975).

150. I. M. Chaiken and H. C. Taylor, *J. Biol. Chem.* **251**, 2044 (1976).

151. D. Eilat and I. M. Chaiken, *Biochemistry* **18**, 790 (1979).

152. F. M. Veronese, R. Bevilacqua, and I. M. Chaiken, *Mol. Pharmacol.* **15**, 313 (1979).

153. G. A. Gilbert and R. C. L. Jenkins, *Proc. R. Soc. London, Ser. A* **253**, 420 (1959).

154. L. W. Nichol and A. G. Ogston, *J. Phys. Chem.* **69**, 1754 (1965).

155. R. A. Alberty and H. H. Marvin, Jr., *J. Phys. Colloid Chem.* **54**, 47 (1950).

156. R. F. Smith and D. R. Briggs, *J. Phys. Colloid Chem.* **54**, 33 (1950).

157. I. M. Klotz, *Arch. Biochem.* **9**, 109 (1946).

158. M. Stewart, D. J. Morton, and F. M. Clarke, *Biochem. J.* **186**, 99 (1980).

159. P. D. Jeffrey, L. W. Nichol, and R. D. Teasdale, *Biophys. Chem.* **10**, 379 (1979).

160. J. Lebowitz and M. Laskowski, Jr., *Biochemistry* **1**, 1044 (1962).

161. D. Platt, W. Pigman, H. L. Holley, and F. M. Patton, *Arch. Biochem. Biophys.* **64**, 152 (1956).

162. E. Gramling, W. Niedermeyer, H. L. Holley, and W. Pigman, *Biochim. Biophys. Acta* **69**, 552 (1963).

163. M. Davies, L. W. Nichol, and A. G. Ogston, *Biochim. Biophys. Acta* **75**, 436 (1963).

164. C. R. Lowe, M. J. Harvey, D. B. Craven, and P. G. Dean, *Biochem. J.* **133**, 499 (1973).

165. K. Kasai and S. Ishii, *J. Biochem.* (*Tokyo*) **77**, 261 (1975).

166. M. Nishikata, K. Kasai, and S. Ishii, *J. Biochem.* (*Tokyo*) **82**, 1475 (1977).

167. H. C. Taylor and I. M. Chaiken, *J. Biol. Chem.* **252**, 6991 (1977).

168. J. Danner, J. E. Somerville, J. Turner, and B. M. Dunn, *Biochemistry* **18**, 3039 (1979).

169. I. M. Chaiken, D. Eilat, and W. M. McCormick, *Biochemistry* **18**, 794 (1979).

170. I. M. Chaiken, *Anal. Biochem.* **97**, 302 (1979).

171. L. W. Nichol, J. L. Bethune, G. Kegeles, and E. L. Hess, in H. Neurath, Ed., *The Proteins*, Vol. 2, Academic Press, New York, 1964, p. 305.

CHAPTER 4

Simulation of Transport Experiments for Interacting Systems

DAVID J. COX AND RICHARD S. DALE

4.1   INTRODUCTION

To describe a chemically interacting mixture of macromolecules one wishes to know the stoichiometry and equilibrium constant for each association reaction occurring in the system. This problem is most commonly approached by using one or another equilibrium technique to measure the variation of the average molecular weight of the mixture with the concentration of the constituents. The nature of the reaction is generally inferred by finding the reaction model that best fits all the experimental molecular weights. This protocol often works well, but it sometimes happens that the experimental data can be made to fit more than one reaction scheme. In cases of this kind it is worthwhile to develop complementary experimental information that may assist in resolving the residual ambiguity.

One potential source of additional information on a reacting system is its behavior in a transport (migration) experiment such as velocity sedimentation in the ultracentrifuge or gel chromatography. It has been known since the initial work of Gilbert (1–3) that the shape of the moving boundary formed by a chemically reacting solute during a transport experiment may be a quite distinctive indicator of the nature of the reaction. If the transport behavior of a series of plausible models of the reacting solute mixture can be predicted in detail, it should be possible to identify the particular model (or models) that will accurately mimic real experiments. It is probable that two models that fit equilibrium data equally well can be distinguished by transport experiments or vice versa.

Analytical solutions are not available for the continuity equations that describe the behavior of reacting systems in transport experiments. However, the problem can be addressed by computer simulation, and several numerical methods have been devised to deal with it.

The first technique developed to simulate the sedimentation of reacting macromolecules was the countercurrent analog of Bethune and Kegeles (4,5). This very clever scheme is quite efficient in its use of computing time, and it was used successfully to describe the sedimentation of solutes undergoing self-association or mixed association with rapid or slow reequilibration (6–11). It is, however, difficult to adapt for precise quantitative treatments incorporating the effects of the sector shape of real centrifuge cells or of composition-dependent sedimentation, and it is unable to accept correct diffusion coefficients for systems containing more than two sedimenting species. For these reasons, the countercurrent analog has been largely supplanted by more flexible simulation methods.

The method of Cann and Goad (12,13) proceeds by dividing the centrifuge cell into segments and computing the flow of solute between segments by finite-difference expressions that approximate the flow equation for the transport process. The behavior of chemically reacting systems is addressed by alternating rounds of simulated transport and chemical relaxation. The method has been exploited by Cann and his co-workers to treat a variety of transport problems, not only in sedimentation but also in electrophoresis and isoelectric focusing (14–21). They have placed particular emphasis on self-associating macromolecules with equilibrium constants that vary with the concentration of low molecular weight ligands.

The method of Dishon et al. (22) is a very general and powerful finite-difference method for solving the continuity equation for the ultracentrifuge. It has been applied to the concentration-dependent sedimentation of single constituents and mixtures, to pressure-dependent sedimentation, to sedimentation in a density gradient, and to the effect of varying rotor speed on the approach to sedimentation equilibrium, and it is clearly applicable to a still broader range of systems (23–30). It has the advantage that it includes the correct boundary conditions at the top and bottom of the solution column and so is particularly useful for dealing with sedimenting boundaries that are distorted by reflected diffusion at the meniscus or with the approach to sedimentation equilibrium.

Two additional simulation techniques are available: the distorted-grid model of Cox (31–38), and the finite-element method recently developed by Claverie (39–41). We have selected these latter methods for extended discussion in the remainder of this chapter, with the intention of making them more widely available for practical use. In choosing these methods for closer examination, we are undoubtedly influenced by our familiarity with them, since both have been in use in our laboratory for some time. However, the distorted-grid and finite-element techniques also have the objective advantage that they are unusually efficient. In an application that involves finding a simulated transport result that fits a real one, a number of simulations may be needed, and parsimonious use of computing time is an important advantage in a simulation procedure. Nevertheless, the methods of Cann and Goad, and of Dishon and co-workers, are well adapted to certain problems and both methods have been thoroughly described (refs. 13 and 22). All of the available techniques should be carefully considered before a simulation procedure is selected for a particular application.

4.2 DISTORTED-GRID SIMULATION

4.2.1 Concentration-Dependent Sedimentation of One Constituent

A quite detailed description has appeared elsewhere (38) of the distorted-grid method of simulating the sedimentation of a single constituent whose sedimentation and diffusion coefficients are concentration-dependent. This model is also capable of describing the sedimentation of solutes involved in self-association equilibria, provided that the self-association reaction relaxes toward equilibrium very rapidly. Our primary purpose here is to describe recent developments in the distorted-grid model that have made it capable of dealing with the concentration-dependent sedimentation of two-constituent systems, including solutes involved in rapidly equilibrating mixed association. The details of the one-constituent procedure will not be repeated here; readers whose principal interest is in simulating one-constituent systems should consult the previous article. In what follows we shall restrict the description of the simple model to those features necessary for understanding the procedures used for treating two-constituent systems.

4.2.1.1   General structure of the model

The simulation of the sedimentation of a solute begins by dividing the ultracentrifuge cell into an array of n boxes each Δx deep and describing the initial situation by assigning a mean concentration to the solute in each box. For example, a cell with the meniscus at $x = 6.0$ cm, the cell bottom at 7.0 cm, and a sharp initial boundary at $x = 6.1$ cm could be described as follows:

$$x_1 = 6.0 \text{ cm} \tag{1}$$

$$\Delta x = 0.01 \text{ cm} \tag{2}$$

$$\bar{c}_i = 0 \quad i = 1, \ldots, 10 \tag{3}$$

$$\bar{c}_i = c_0 \quad i = 11, \ldots, 100 \tag{4}$$

Notice that the positions x_i define the boundaries between adjacent boxes. If there are 100 boxes there must be 101 boundaries, and box i will lie between the boundaries at x_i and x_{i+1}. The midpoint of box i, to which weight concentration $\bar{c}_i$ is assigned, is

$$\bar{x}_i = \frac{x_{i+1} + x_i}{2} \tag{5}$$

The simulation proceeds by treating the concentration array alternately with expressions that simulate, first, diffusion without sedimentation for a short time and then sedimentation without diffusion for an equal time. A procedure of this kind does not describe accurately the course of events at the ends of the solution column (32). The method is thus capable of simulating an experiment only from the time the sedimenting boundary leaves the meniscus until the plateau region disappears.

4.2.1.2   Simulation of diffusion

The accumulation or depletion of solute in box i by diffusion during a time interval Δt_D depends on the flow of solute across boundaries i and $i+1$ that enclose the box. The flow of solute *upward* in the array across boundary i is, by Fick's first law,

$$F_i = D_i A_i g_i \Delta t_D \tag{6}$$

where D_i and g_i are the diffusion coefficient and the concentration gradient at boundary i, and A_i is the area of boundary i. The area of boundary i is

$$A_i = b\theta x_i \tag{7}$$

where b is the thickness and θ is the sector angle of the centrifuge cell. In many cases of interest, the local diffusion coefficient is concentration-dependent and so must be computed by an appropriate expression from the concentration at boundary i. The concentration at boundary i is obtained by linear interpolation between the mean concentrations in the boxes on either side.

$$c_i = \bar{c}_{i-1} + \frac{(\bar{c}_i - \bar{c}_{i-1})(x_i - \bar{x}_{i-1})}{\bar{x}_i - \bar{x}_{i-1}} \tag{8}$$

The mean concentration gradient between boxes $i-1$ and i is

$$g_i' = \frac{\bar{c}_i - \bar{c}_{i-1}}{\bar{x}_i - \bar{x}_{i-1}} \tag{9}$$

For many applications g_i' is an adequate approximation for the gradient at boundary i. However, the operation of the sedimentation routine (see below) distorts the array of boundaries so that boundary i does not necessarily lie midway between the midpoints of boxes $i-1$ and i. For this reason, it is preferable to assign the gradient g_i' to the point x_i' equidistant from the midpoints of the flanking boxes:

$$x_i' = \frac{\bar{x}_i + \bar{x}_{i-1}}{2} \tag{10}$$

When complete arrays of g' and x' have been computed the gradient at boundary i is found by interpolation:

$$g_i = g_i' + \frac{(g_{i+1}' - g_i')(x_i - x_i')}{x_{i+1}' - x_1'} \tag{11}$$

The accumulation of solute in box i during time Δt_D is the difference between the flow across boundary $i+1$ into the box and the flow out of the box across boundary i. The change in concentration during time Δt_D is

$$\Delta \bar{c}_i = \frac{F_{i+1} - F_i}{V_i} \tag{12}$$

where V_i, the volume of the box, is

$$V_i = b\theta \bar{x}_i (x_{i+1} - x_i) \tag{12a}$$

Combining Eqs. (6), (7), (12), and (12a) and canceling $b\theta$ gives

$$\Delta \bar{c}_i = \frac{\Delta t_D (D_{i+1} g_{i+1} x_{i+1} - D_i g_i x_i)}{\bar{x}_i (x_{i+1} - x_i)} \tag{13}$$

The simulation of diffusion proceeds as follows: the initial values of $\bar{c}$, $\bar{x}$, and x are used to compute arrays of D and g. These values are inserted into Eq. (13) giving a value of $\Delta \bar{c}$ for each box. Then the $\bar{c}$ array is updated:

$$\bar{c}_i(\text{new}) = \bar{c}_i(\text{old}) + \Delta \bar{c}_i \tag{14}$$

and the procedure is repeated.

The simulation of an experiment lasting t seconds will involve n successive applications of the routine, each step representing Δt_D seconds of real time, so that $n\Delta t_D = t$. It is reasonable to minimize computing time by selecting a relatively long time interval Δt_D, so that the number of computing cycles will be as small as possible. However, if Δt_D is made too long, the computation will produce very serious artifacts that have been described previously (31,42). For that reason, an upper limit is placed on Δt_D:

$$\Delta t_D \leqslant \frac{0.2\,\Delta x_{min}^2}{D_{max}} \tag{15}$$

where Δx_{min} is the smallest interval between boundaries and D_{max} is the largest diffusion coefficient that can occur at any time during the calculation. D_{max} is generally known in advance. The initially uniform boundary interval is distorted by the sedimentation routine, but a lower limit is placed on box size and boxes that are compressed below Δx_{min} are eliminated at each step by the box-splitting routine described below.

4.2.1.3 Simulation of sedimentation

After several rounds of diffusion simulated by Eqs. (13) and (14) sedimentation is simulated by shifting each boundary away from the axis of rotation. If the diffusion routine is applied n_D times before each sedimentation shift, the time interval for one sedimentation shift is $\Delta t_s = n_D\Delta t_D$. In this time interval a boundary initially at x_i will move at a new position $x_i^\dagger$:

$$x_i^\dagger = x_i\exp\left(s_i\omega^2\,\Delta t_s\right) \tag{16}$$

where s_i is the local sedimentation coefficient and ω is the angular velocity of the centrifuge rotor. The local sedimentation coefficient usually depends on the local concentration at the boundary, and so an appropriate expression for the concentration dependence is used with the boundary concentrations, c in Eq. (8), to assemble an array of sedimentation coefficients for use in Eq. (16). If each boundary moves with the local sedimentation coefficient, no boundary will pass or be passed by any of the solute. All of the solute initially between x_i and x_{i+1} will be between $x_i^\dagger$ and $x_{i+1}^\dagger$ after the time interval Δt_s. The boundaries will, however, move at different rates, and so the volume of box i will change and the solute concentration will change in inverse proportion. In a sector-shaped cell the volumes of box i before and after Δt_s are

$$V_i = \frac{b\theta\left(x_{i+1}^2 - x_i^2\right)}{2}$$

$$V_i^\dagger = \frac{b\theta\left(x_{i+1}^{\dagger 2} - x_i^{\dagger 2}\right)}{2} \tag{17}$$

and so the new mean concentration in box i is

$$\bar{c}_i^\dagger = \frac{\bar{c}_i\left(x_{i+1}^2 - x_i^2\right)}{x_{i+1}^{\dagger 2} - x_i^{\dagger 2}} \tag{18}$$

The shift of the boundaries moves all of the boxes outward from the axis of rotation, leaving a gap between the top of the array and the meniscus and moving the lowest boundary beyond the bottom of the cell. This shift of the frame of the calculation relative to the solution column is countered at each step by creating a new box at the top of the array, discarding the lowest box, and reindexing the boxes between. The distorted grid method is applied only to experiments in which the initial solute boundary is well removed from the meniscus (32), and so the concentration is set to zero in the new box between the meniscus at x_m and the top of the shifted array:

$$
\begin{aligned}
x_1 &= x_m \\
\bar{c}_1 &= 0 \\
\bar{c}_i &= \bar{c}_{i-1}^\dagger \qquad i = 2, \ldots \\
x_i &= x_{i-1}^\dagger \qquad i = 2, \ldots
\end{aligned}
\tag{19}
$$

The reindexing procedure requires that Δt_s be chosen so that the new box generated at the top of the solution column will be similar in size to the others in the array. A convenient depth for the new box is Δx, the box size specified for the entire array at the beginning of the simulation. In this case, the sedimentation time interval will be

$$
\Delta t_s = \frac{\ln\left[(x_1 + \Delta x)/x_1\right]}{s_0 \omega^2}.
\tag{20}
$$

The use of s_0, the sedimentation coefficient at infinite dilution, is appropriate, since the method is used only when the concentration is zero at the meniscus throughout the experiment.

For most cases of interest, Δt_s is found to be much greater than the maximum acceptable time interval for diffusion specified by Eq. (15). It is usually necessary, therefore, to repeat the diffusion routine several times, n_D, before each sedimentation shift. Since the total times spent diffusing and sedimenting must be the same, $\Delta t_s = n_D \Delta t_D$, and n_D is made sufficiently large to allow Δt_D and Δt_s to satisfy Eqs. (15) and (20).

4.2.1.4 Box splitting

The independent movement of the boundaries by the sedimentation routine distorts the array of boxes and may make some boxes very much larger or smaller than the original size. This may create a computing problem which is most troublesome if the sedimentation coefficient decreases with increasing solute concentration. Then, wherever there is a steep concentration gradient, each boundary will tend to overtake the one immediately ahead, and the intervening box will be repeatedly compressed. Some boxes will become so shallow that the criterion of Eq. (15) may no longer be met or that small errors in calculating boundary movement may become a substantial fraction of the remaining box size. If the sedimentation coefficient increases with concentration, as it does for self-associating solutes, the boundary array will stretch progressively, and some boxes may become very large. This effect is also undesirable, since the linear interpolations of Eqs. (8) and (11) may become inadequate.

For this reason, the array of boxes is inspected after each sedimentation shift. Boxes larger than $0.8\Delta x$ and smaller than $2\Delta x$ are retained; boxes larger or smaller than these limits are eliminated. The minimum box size, $0.8\Delta x$, is used as Δx_{min} to set the diffusion time interval in Eq. (15). When an oversized box is found it is split at its midpoint into two boxes, and the following members of the array are reindexed; the bottom box in the array is discarded. Undersized boxes are also split, and their contents are assigned to the two boxes on either side. A new box identical to the lowest remaining one is created at the bottom of the array.

When a box is split, the solute it contains must be allocated unequally to the top and bottom halves. The bottom half receives more of the solute than the top half. The concentration gradient at the new boundary between the top and bottom segments is interpolated linearly between the gradients immediately above and below the box to be divided. The interpolated gradient gives the difference between $\bar{c}_t$ and $\bar{c}_b$, the concentrations in the top and bottom segments. The sum of the two concentrations is given by an expression that conserves mass [misprinted in Eq. (49) of ref. 38].

$$\bar{c}_i\left(x_{i+1}^2 - x_i^2\right) = \bar{c}_t\left(\bar{x}_i^2 - x_i^2\right) + \bar{c}_b\left(x_{i+1}^2 - \bar{x}_i^2\right) \tag{21}$$

The box splitting routine is the part of the procedure that is most vulnerable to artifacts arising from the discontinuous nature of the model. These artifacts occur where the concentration gradient shows sharp curvature, that is, where the third derivative of the concentration profile is large. Obvious irregularities near the baseline at the leading or trailing edges of the calculated gradient curves are the usual symptoms. In these unusual cases it is sometimes helpful to use a more elaborate way of calculating the gradient at the midpoint of the box to be divided, in which the second derivative of the concentration profile, rather than the first, is interpolated linearly between the values above and below the split box.

4.2.1.5 Organization of the program

A simulation begins by specifying the sedimentation and diffusion coefficients and their dependence on concentration, selecting a boundary interval and filling the initial arrays [Eqs. (1)–(4)]. The rotor speed is given, and time intervals consistent with Eqs. (15) and (20) are calculated for the diffusion and sedimentation routines. The diffusion routine [Eqs. (6)–(13)] is applied several times: $n_D = \Delta t_s / \Delta t_D$. Then the sedimentation routine [Eqs. (16) and (18)] is applied once; the array is inspected for off-sized boxes, and boxes are split if necessary. The combined procedure—diffusion, sedimentation, and box splitting—is repeated as many times as necessary to simulate the entire experiment. At various times appropriate for comparison with the real experiment, the simulation is interrupted and the calculated concentration and gradient profiles are stored for later examination or plotting.

This general model can be applied immediately to the concentration-dependent sedimentation of a single component. In this simple case it is necessary only to insert an appropriate expression for the local sedimentation coefficient at boundary i into Eq. (16), for example,

$$s_i = s_0(1 - kc_i) \quad \text{or} \quad s_i = \frac{s_0}{1 + k'c_i} \tag{22}$$

The model can be developed in a straightforward way to deal with self-associating solutes in rapid equilibrium and with systems containing two thermodynamically independent constituents.

4.2.2   Self-Associating Solutes in Rapid Equilibrium

A self-associating solute may be described by one or more equilibrium constants, which may be written in weight concentration units:

$$n\mathrm{A} \rightleftharpoons \mathrm{A}_n \qquad K_n = \frac{c_n}{c_1^n} \tag{23}$$

Even if several equilibria operate simultaneously and multiple aggregated species are present, the concentration of every species is fixed once the monomer concentration is specified. The monomer concentration, in turn, is unambiguously related to the total solute concentration, c_T:

$$c_T = \sum_j K_j c_1^j \qquad K_1 = 1 \tag{24}$$

where K_j is the product of successive stoichiometric equilibrium constants. It follows that the total concentration of a self-associating solute is sufficient to determine any average quantity describing the solute: the average molecular weight, for example.

Any transport process perturbs the local solute concentrations in a moving boundary. However, if the relaxation of the chemical equilibrium is very rapid, the solute will remain close to chemical equilibrium everywhere in the system throughout a transport experiment. In that case the local species distribution, and so the local average transport coefficients, will be specified unambiguously by the total solute concentration at every point in the system. The sedimentation of a solute of this kind is a special case of concentration-dependent sedimentation and diffusion (43), which is directly accessible to a variety of simulation procedures, including the distorted-grid method outlined above. The problem reduces itself to finding appropriate values of s and D for insertion into Eqs. (13) and (16).

4.2.2.1 Average transport coefficients

The appropriate expressions for s and D in an ideally sedimenting self-associating solute are (34, 44)

$$\bar{s} = \frac{\sum_j s_j c_j}{\sum_j c_j} = \frac{\sum_j s_j K_j c_1^j}{\sum_j K_j c_1^j} \qquad K_1 = 1 \qquad (25)$$

and

$$\bar{D} = \frac{\sum_j j D_j c_j}{\sum_j j c_j} = \frac{\sum_j j D_j K_j c_1^j}{\sum_j j K_j c_1^j} \qquad K_1 = 1 \qquad (26)$$

Taken in combination with Eq. (24) these expressions yield values of the local average sedimentation and diffusion coefficients as functions of the local total solute concentration. Simulation of the sedimentation of a self-associating solute in rapid equilibrium involves simply inserting these values into the working Eqs. (13) and (16). The composition-dependent sedimentation of such a solute is managed with equal ease by perturbing Eq. (25) appropriately, for example,

$$\bar{s}' = \bar{s}(1 - kc_T) \qquad (27)$$

and using the values of $\bar{s}'$ in Eq. (16).

The use of the weight-average sedimentation coefficient in Eq. (25) is a consequence of the fact that the fraction of the time each monomer spends as part of a j-mer is equal to the weight fraction of j-mer in the total solute. The appropriateness of the average diffusion coefficient in Eq. (26) is less obvious, but the derivation is available elsewhere (34, 38, 44) and will not be repeated here. The most important feature of the derivation is that Eq. (26) is correct only if the equilibrium constants are the same everywhere in the system: $(dK_j/dx = 0)$. In fact if this proviso is not met an average D dependent only on the local solute concentration cannot be written at all, and the solute cannot be treated by the distorted-grid scheme as a single constituent with concentration-dependent s and D. The most important case of this kind in the centrifuge is pressure dependence of the association equilibrium constant (45–47).

The sedimentation and diffusion coefficients appropriate for a given local solute concentration are calculated by first solving Eq. (24) for the monomer concentration and then inserting c_1 into Eqs. (25) and (26). For a monomer–dimer equilibrium Eq. (24) is a quadratic and is easy to solve directly. The solution is more complicated for association equilibria proceeding beyond the dimer and particularly for systems containing more than one aggregated species. For these cases it is generally necessary to use a binary search (38) or an equivalent procedure to find the value of c_1 that fits precisely the given total concentration and the equilibrium constants.

A typical simulation in a 100-box array may involve 50 sedimentation shifts, each preceded by 5–10 diffusion transfers. The calculation will thus require about 5000 values of $\bar{s}$ and 25,000–50,000 values of $\bar{D}$. If the computation of $\bar{s}$ and $\bar{D}$ is at all complicated, the computing time may be prohibitive. This difficulty can be dealt with by assembling tables of $\bar{s}$ and $\bar{D}$ at a few hundred values of c_T before the simulation begins. The values of $\bar{s}$ and $\bar{D}$ needed by the simulation are then extracted from the tables by an interpolation routine that can be made very efficient.

4.2.3   Concentration-Dependent Sedimentation of Two Nonreacting Constituents

The distorted-grid format can be adapted in a straightforward way to deal with mixtures of two constituents which are not chemically reacting. If the two components sedimented independently, simulating the behavior of a mixture would be a trivial problem. One would run two simulations separately and sum the resulting concentration or gradient profiles. In every case of interest, however, the components of a mixture do not sediment independently. The local sedimentation coefficient of each constituent depends not only on its own concentration but also on the local concentration of the other constituent. The resulting distortion of the sedimenting boundary produces the Johnston–Ogston effect.

Simulating the sedimentation of a concentration-dependent mixture can be done conveniently using the distorted-grid model by assigning the two constituents to separate concentration arrays, each described initially by Eqs. (1)–(4), and simulating their sedimentation simultaneously, cross-referring between the two arrays at each sedimentation step. Only the sedimentation routine needs to be changed. Since the diffusion coefficient is commonly assumed to vary negligibly with concentration, cross-reference between the arrays carrying the two constituents is not necessary in the diffusion routine; diffusion is simulated independently in the two arrays. Moreover, the management of box size does not require cross-reference between the two arrays. A box in one array whose history has made it too shallow or too deep can be (and must be) eliminated or divided without regard to the situation in the other array.

4.2.3.1   Cross-reference between arrays

To apply Eq. (16) to the sedimentation of constituent A in the presence of constituent B, a value of $s_{A,i}$ must be found for each boundary in the constituent A array. The sedimentation coefficient $s_{A,i}$ depends on the concentrations of both constituents at boundary i, for example:

$$s_{A,i} = s_{A,0}(1 - k_{AA}c_{A,i} - k_{AB}c_{B,i}) \tag{28}$$

where $c_{A,i}$ and $c_{B,i}$ are the local concentrations of constituents A and B at

$x_{A,i}$, the position of boundary i in the array that carries constituent A. $c_{A,i}$ is found in the usual way from the mean concentrations in the A-array boxes, using Eq. (8). To find $c_{B,i}$, it is necessary to interpolate in the B array. Since the two arrays are generally not in register, it is first necessary to find the two boxes in the B array whose midpoints "bracket" $x_{A,i}$:

$$\bar{x}_{B,j} \leqslant x_{A,i} < \bar{x}_{B,j+1} \tag{29}$$

Then the concentration of constituent B at $x_{A,i}$ is

$$c_{B,i} = \bar{c}_{B,j} + \frac{(\bar{c}_{B,j+1} - \bar{c}_{B,j})(x_{A,i} - \bar{x}_{B,j})}{\bar{x}_{B,j+1} - \bar{x}_{B,j}} \tag{30}$$

The interpolated concentrations $c_{A,i}$ and $c_{B,i}$ can be inserted into Eq. (28) to give a local sedimentation coefficient $s_{A,i}$ at every boundary in the A array. The inverse operation yields the corresponding array s_B.

4.2.3.2 Time averaging

At this point a difficulty arises that does not occur in the one-constituent case. The boundaries in, for example, the A array move along with the sedimenting constituent A, so that the concentration $c_{A,i}$ does not change very much during the sedimentation time interval Δt_s. However, the sedimentation coefficients of the two constituents are generally different, and so the grid points in the two arrays move at different rates. Suppose that constituent A has the higher sedimentation coefficient. Then the boundaries in the A array will move downward through the B array during Δt_s, while the B boundaries will drift upward through the A array. A grid point in one array will sample a range of concentrations in the other. The mean concentrations $\bar{c}$ in Eq. (30) and its mirror image are the concentrations at the beginning of the time interval Δt_s, and the cross-referred concentrations, which should be a time average over Δt_s, will be systematically in error.

In most cases the error, although not negligible, is small, and it can be dealt with in a simple way. The systematically erroneous cross-referred concentration arrays are calculated using the mean concentrations at the beginning of the time interval Δt_s [Eq. (30)]. These concentrations are stored and are also used to find an approximate value of s at each boundary in both arrays, using Eq. (28). The values of s are used in Eq. (16) to make a provisional shift in the boundaries, and a provisional new mean concentration is calculated for each box using Eq. (18). Then the cross-reference of Eq. (30) is repeated. One obtains an approximate value of the concentration of constituent B opposite every grid point in the A array (and vice versa) *after* the time interval Δt_s. Then the "before" and "after" cross-referred concentrations are averaged, the boundaries are returned to their positions before Δt_s, a corrected set of sedimentation coefficients is computed using the time-averaged concentration in Eq. (28), and a final shift of the boundaries is carried out using Eq. (16).

This scheme assumes that the cross-referred concentrations vary linearly with time during Δt_s. Since Δt_s is generally short and the range of cross-referred concentrations is small, this assumption is not damaging.

4.2.3.3 Minor complications

In the one-constituent model Δt_s is selected so that, when the uppermost boundary is assigned the infinite-dilution sedimentation coefficient, it will move a distance Δx during time Δt_s and so will generate a new box of the original size at the top of the array [Eq. (20)]. In the two-constituent model, the same Δt_s must be used in dealing with both arrays, but, since the two sedimentation coefficients are different, a Δt_s that allows the formation of a box Δx deep at the top of one array will produce an off-size box at the top of the other. This problem is managed by allowing the top of one array to "float." The time interval Δt_s is computed using the faster of the two sedimentation coefficients in Eq. (20). After each sedimentation shift, a new box is created at the top of the fast-constituent array and the remaining boxes are reindexed in the usual way. Then the top of the slow-component array is inspected to see whether there is sufficient room for a new box Δx deep between the uppermost boundary and the original meniscus position. If so, the new box is inserted and the remainder of the array is reindexed; if not, the array is passed on without change. The result will be that the top boundary in the slow-component array will oscillate within the original positions of boundaries 1 and 2.

4.2.3.4 Organization of the program

The program begins by specifying two sedimentation coefficients and their concentration dependences, two diffusion coefficients, and the rotor speed. The sedimentation time interval Δt_s is calculated using Eq. (20) and the higher of the two sedimentation coefficients. Diffusion time intervals $\Delta t_D = \Delta t_s / n_D$ consistent with Eq. (15) are calculated for each constituent; the upper limit of Δt_D and so the minimum number of diffusion transfers per sedimentation transfer (n_D) may be different in the two arrays, since the diffusion coefficients are not the same. The two initial arrays of boxes are constructed and filled [Eqs. (1)−(4)]. The diffusion routine [Eqs. (6)−(13)] is applied the appropriate number of times to each array. Then the sedimentation routine is applied to both arrays. The routine consists of interpolating the local concentrations of both constituents at the boundaries in both arrays [Eqs. (8) and (30)], making a provisional shift of all boundaries and calculating the resulting mean concentration in each box [Eqs. (28), (16), and (18)], interpolating the local concentrations again, and making a final sedimentation shift using the time-averaged concentrations. Boxes are added to the top and discarded from the bottom of the arrays when that is appropriate. The two arrays are examined and the box splitting procedure is applied as needed to divided boxes that are too deep or to eliminate boxes that are too shallow. The sequence diffusion, sedimentation, and box splitting is repeated a sufficient number of times to simulate the entire experiment. Representative concentration and gradient profiles for each constituent and for the sum of the two are extracted and stored at appropriate times during the experiment. The concentration and gradient profiles for the two constituents are conveniently summed using interpolation expressions analogous to Eq. (30).

4.2.4 Mixed Associations in Rapid Equilibrium

In a mixed association monomers of two different kinds react to form an aggregate; such a reaction can be described by a weight-scale equilibrium constant:

$$nA + mB \rightleftharpoons A_n B_m \qquad K_{nm} = \frac{c_{nm}}{c_A^n c_B^m} \tag{31}$$

In general, several equilibria may operate simultaneously, producing multiple aggregated species of various compositions. In Eq. (31) and the following discussion c_A and c_B are used to indicate the weight concentration of the *monomeric species* A and B. The weight concentrations of *constituents* A and B will be noted $c_{A,T}$ and $c_{B,T}$. If only one aggregate is present,

$$c_{A,T} = c_A + f_A c_{nm} = c_A + f_A K_{nm} c_A^n c_B^m$$

$$c_{B,T} = c_B + f_B c_{nm} = c_B + f_B K_{nm} c_A^n c_B^m \tag{32}$$

where f_A and f_B are the weight fractions of constituents A and B in species $A_n B_m$,

$$f_A = \frac{n M_A}{M_{A_n B_m}} \qquad f_B = \frac{m M_B}{M_{A_n B_m}} \tag{33}$$

and M is molecular weight. That is, the mass of each constituent is distributed between monomer and aggregate. If multiple equilibria operate, then the second term in Eq. (32) is a sum over all the aggregates present. Once the equilibrium constants are specified, the composition of the system at chemical equilibrium is unambiguously defined *either* by the two monomer concentrations c_A and c_B *or* by the two constituent concentrations $c_{A,T}$ and $c_{B,T}$.

When such a system is subjected to a transport experiment, each monomeric unit will spend part of its time as monomer and part as a member of one or more aggregates. It will move at an average rate that depends on the composition of the system. If the chemical reaction relaxes rapidly to equilibrium after the concentrations are perturbed by the transport experiment, the distribution of each constituent among monomer and aggregates is defined everywhere in the system during the experiment by the constituent concentrations $c_{A,T}$ and $c_{B,T}$. It follows that the local average transport coefficients are unambiguously defined by the two constituent concentrations.

This line of reasoning suggests that the sedimentation and diffusion of a solute involved in a rapidly relaxing mixed association can be simulated by a two-array distorted-grid model of the kind used to deal with nonreacting mixtures, each array carrying one of the two constituents. Two difficulties arise in adapting the two-array model for chemically reacting mixtures. The more obvious problem is that the relation between the local average sedimentation coefficient and the local constituent concentrations will be much more complicated than Eq. (28). The less obvious but more difficult problem is that constituents involved in a mixed association do not diffuse independently. This can be seen qualitatively in a simple way. Consider the simplest mixed association, $A + B \rightleftharpoons AB$, and imagine a system in which the constituent gradient $dc_{A,T}/dx$ is zero, while the constituent gradient $dc_{B,T}/dx$ is not zero. Mass action requires that as $c_{B,T}$ rises at constant $c_{A,T}$, the distribution of *constituent* A must shift from species A toward species AB. The zero gradient in constituent A conceals equal but opposite gradients in species A and in the A-constituent share of species AB: $dc_A/dx = -(M_A/M_{AB})(dc_{AB}/dx)$. Since the diffusion coefficients of species A and AB are certainly different, the equal and opposite gradients will produce a net flow of constituent A. The flow of constituent A in response to a gradient in constituent B when $dc_{A,T}/dx$ is zero implies that the diffusion of a constituent undergoing mixed association must contain a cross-diffusion term:

$$-J_{A,T} = D_{AA}\frac{dc_{A,T}}{dx} + D_{AB}\frac{dc_{B,T}}{dx} \tag{34a}$$

and, by the inverse argument,

$$-J_{B,T} = D_{BB}\frac{dc_{B,T}}{dx} + D_{BA}\frac{dc_{A,T}}{dx} \tag{34b}$$

Simulation by the two-array model of the transport of a mixture undergoing mixed association thus requires cross-reference between the arrays not only in the sedimentation routine but also in the diffusion routine. Moreover, expressions must be found to link the local direct and cross-diffusion coefficients to the local constituent concentrations.

4.2.4.1 Constituent sedimentation coefficients

For a single aggregated species the total constituent weight concentration $c_{A,T}$ is distributed between the monomer c_A and the A-constituent fraction of the aggregate, $f_A c_{nm}$. The time of each A monomer is distributed between the two species in the same proportion, and so constituent A moves with a weight-average sedimentation coefficient defined in terms of the sedimentation coefficients of the species A and $A_n B_m$:

$$s_{A,T} = \frac{s_A c_A + s_{nm} f_A c_{nm}}{c_A + f_A c_{nm}} = \frac{s_A c_A + s_{nm} f_A K_{nm} c_A^n c_B^m}{c_A + f_A K_{nm} c_A^n c_B^m} \tag{35a}$$

Similarly, for constituent B,

$$s_{B,T} = \frac{s_B c_B + s_{nm} f_B c_{nm}}{c_B + f_B c_{nm}} = \frac{s_B c_B + s_{nm} f_B K_{nm} c_A^n c_B^m}{c_B + f_B K_{nm} c_A^n c_B^m} \tag{35b}$$

If several aggregated species are present, the analogous expressions for $s_{A,T}$ and $s_{B,T}$ contain additional terms in the numerator and denominator. The problem of computing constituent sedimentation coefficients for a given pair of values of the constituent concentrations $c_{A,T}$ and $c_{B,T}$ thus reduces itself to solving Eq. (32) for the monomer concentrations. This familiar but not necessarily trivial problem is considered below.

4.2.4.2 Constituent diffusion coefficients

To use Eqs. (34) to describe the diffusion of a mixture involved in a rapid association equilibrium, it is necessary to relate the direct and cross-diffusion coefficients to the constituent concentrations $c_{A,T}$ and $c_{B,T}$. This can be done most conveniently by linking the diffusion coefficients and the constituent concentrations through the *monomer* concentrations c_A and c_B. The algebra required to express the constituent diffusion coefficients in terms of the monomer concentrations is clumsy but straightforward, and the sequence of the steps is the same for any two-constituent system however many aggregates are present. The procedure will be illustrated by the case of a single aggregate, but the extension to more complex systems is simple. The sequence is as follows:

1. Express the constituent flows in terms of the *species* gradients and diffusion coefficients:

$$-J_{A,T} = D_A \frac{dc_A}{dx} + D_{nm} f_A \frac{dc_{nm}}{dx}$$

$$-J_{B,T} = D_B \frac{dc_B}{dx} + D_{nm} f_B \frac{dc_{nm}}{dx} \tag{36}$$

2. Express the aggregate gradient in terms of the monomer gradients:

$$c_{nm} = K_{nm} c_A^n c_B^m \tag{37}$$

$$\frac{dc_{nm}}{dx} = m K_{nm} c_A^n c_B^{m-1} \frac{dc_B}{dx} + n K_{nm} c_A^{n-1} c_B^m \frac{dc_A}{dx} \tag{38}$$

3. Insert Eq. (38) into Eqs. (36) and group terms:

$$-J_{A,T} = d_{AA} \frac{dc_A}{dx} + d_{AB} \frac{dc_B}{dx}$$

$$-J_{B,T} = d_{BB} \frac{dc_B}{dx} + d_{BA} \frac{dc_A}{dx} \tag{39}$$

where

$$d_{AA} = D_A + n D_{nm} f_A K_{nm} c_A^{n-1} c_B^m$$

$$d_{BB} = D_B + m D_{nm} f_B K_{nm} c_A^n c_B^{m-1}$$

$$d_{AB} = m D_{nm} f_A K_{nm} c_A^n c_B^{m-1}$$

$$d_{BA} = n D_{nm} f_B K_{nm} c_A^{n-1} c_B^m$$

4. Differentiate Eqs. (32) to obtain the constituent gradients in terms of the species gradients:

$$\frac{dc_{A,T}}{dx} = \frac{dc_A}{dx} + \frac{f_A dc_{nm}}{dx}$$

$$\frac{dc_{B,T}}{dx} = \frac{dc_B}{dx} + \frac{f_B dc_{nm}}{dx} \tag{40}$$

5. Substitute Eq. (38) into Eqs. (40) and group terms:

$$\frac{dc_{A,T}}{dx} = q_{AA}\frac{dc_A}{dx} + q_{AB}\frac{dc_B}{dx}$$

$$\frac{dc_{B,T}}{dx} = q_{BB}\frac{dc_B}{dx} + q_{BA}\frac{dc_A}{dx} \tag{41}$$

where

$$q_{AA} = 1 + nf_A K_{nm}c_A^{n-1}c_B^m$$

$$q_{BB} = 1 + mf_B K_{nm}c_A^n c_B^{m-1}$$

$$q_{AB} = mf_A K_{nm}c_A^n c_B^{m-1}$$

$$q_{BA} = nf_B K_{nm}c_A^{n-1}c_B^m$$

6. Solve Eqs. (41) to give the monomer gradients in terms of the constituent gradients:

$$\frac{dc_A}{dx} = \frac{q_{BB}\dfrac{dc_{A,T}}{dx} - q_{AB}\dfrac{dc_{B,T}}{dx}}{q_{AA}q_{BB} - q_{AB}q_{BA}}$$

$$\frac{dc_B}{dx} = \frac{q_{AA}\dfrac{dc_{B,T}}{dx} - q_{BA}\dfrac{dc_{A,T}}{dx}}{q_{AA}q_{BB} - q_{AB}q_{BA}} \tag{42}$$

7. Substitute Eqs. (42) into Eqs. (39) and rearrange to give Eq. (34) with:

$$D_{AA} = \frac{d_{AA}q_{BB} - d_{AB}q_{BA}}{q_{AA}q_{BB} - q_{AB}q_{BA}}$$

$$D_{AB} = \frac{d_{AB}q_{AA} - d_{AA}q_{AB}}{q_{AA}q_{BB} - q_{AB}q_{BA}}$$

$$D_{BB} = \frac{d_{BB}q_{AA} - d_{BA}q_{AB}}{q_{AA}q_{BB} - q_{AB}q_{BA}}$$

$$D_{BA} = \frac{d_{BA}q_{BB} - d_{BB}q_{BA}}{q_{AA}q_{BB} - q_{AB}q_{BA}} \tag{43}$$

Equations (43) define the direct and cross-diffusion coefficients for any system undergoing mixed association. If multiple aggregates are present the coefficients q and d defined in Eqs. (39) and (41) contain additional terms, one for each species. The expressions can also deal with systems containing self-associated species in addition to mixed aggregates, for example, A_n. For this species, $f_A = 1$ while m and f_B are zero. A_n will contribute a term $nK_{n,0}c_A^{n-1}$ to q_{AA} and $nD_{n,0}K_{n,0}c_A^{n-1}$ to d_{AA}; it will make no contribution to the other coefficients.

The diffusion coefficients needed for a simulation can be computed efficiently using Eqs. (43) and the expressions for q and d once the monomer concentrations are known. The problem of finding the local diffusion coefficients appropriate for a pair of local constituent concentrations is, like the corresponding calculation of the local sedimentation coefficients, a matter of finding the monomer concentrations specified by the particular values of $c_{A,T}$ and $c_{B,T}$.

4.2.4.3 *Computation of monomer concentrations*

During a simulation the local constituent concentrations at each grid point are used to compute the local sedimentation coefficients using Eqs. (35) and the local diffusion coefficients using Eqs. (43). For either purpose it is necessary to find the monomer species concentrations c_A and c_B corresponding to the known constituent concentrations $c_{A,T}$ and $c_{B,T}$. The difficulty of this calculation depends on the complexity of the system.

The simplest class of systems is the following:

$$A + B \rightleftarrows AB$$
$$AB + B \rightleftarrows AB_2$$
$$\cdots$$

$$AB_{n-1} + B \rightleftarrows AB_n \tag{44}$$

Any number of species may be present, but none contains more than one A subunit. In this case

$$c_{A,T} = c_A + f_{A,1}K_1 c_A c_B + f_{A,2}K_2 c_A c_B^2 + \cdots$$
$$= c_A(1 + f_{A,1}K_1 c_B + f_{A,2}K_2 c_B^2 + \cdots) \tag{45}$$

where

$$f_{A,i} = \frac{M_A}{M_{AB_i}} \quad \text{and} \quad K_i = \frac{c_{AB_i}}{c_A c_B^i}$$

Similarly

$$c_{B,T} = c_B + f_{B,1}K_1 c_A c_B + f_{B,2}K_2 c_A c_B^2 + \cdots$$
$$= c_B + c_A(f_{B,1}K_1 c_B + f_{B,2}K_2 c_B^2 + \cdots) \tag{46}$$

where

$$f_{B,i} = \frac{iM_B}{M_{AB_i}}$$

Solving Eq. (45) for c_A and inserting the result into Eq. (46) gives

$$c_{B,T} = c_B + \frac{c_{A,T}(f_{B,1}K_1 c_B + f_{B,2}K_2 c_B^2 + \cdots)}{(1 + f_{A,1}K_1 c_B + f_{A,2}K_2 c_B^2 + \cdots)} \tag{47}$$

Multiplying Eq. (47) by $(1 + f_{A,1}K_1 c_B + f_{A,2}K_2 c_B^2 + \cdots)$ and rearranging:

$$c_{B,T} + (c_{B,T}f_{A,1}K_1 - c_{A,T}f_{B,1}K_1 - 1)c_B$$
$$+ (c_{B,T}f_{A,2}K_2 - c_{A,T}f_{B,2}K_2 - f_{A,1}K_1)c_B^2 + \cdots = 0 \tag{48}$$

All of the coefficients of the polynomial in c_B are defined once $c_{A,T}$ and $c_{B,T}$ are specified. For the simplest system, $A + B \rightleftarrows AB$, Eq. (48) is a quadratic,

$$c_{B,T} + (c_{B,T} f_{A,1} K_1 - c_{A,T} f_{B,1} K_1 - 1)c_B - f_{A,1} K_1 c_B^2 = 0 \qquad (48a)$$

which can be solved immediately. For any other case the most efficient approach is a binary search for the value of c_B which fits Eq. (48) for the given values of the constituent concentrations. Once c_B has been evaluated, the result is substituted into Eq. (45) and the equation is solved for c_A.

The problem becomes more cumbersome if, in addition to the various species AB_i, there are species containing two A subunits:

$$AB + A \rightleftarrows A_2 B$$
$$AB_2 + A \rightleftarrows A_2 B_2$$
$$\cdots$$
$$AB_n + A \rightleftarrows A_2 B_n \qquad (49)$$

The constituent concentrations are

$$c_{A,T} = c_A + U_{11} c_A c_B + U_{12} c_A c_B^2 + \cdots$$
$$+ U_{21} c_A^2 c_B + U_{22} c_A^2 c_B^2 + \cdots \qquad (50a)$$

$$c_{B,T} = c_B + V_{11} c_A c_B + V_{12} c_A c_B^2 + \cdots$$
$$+ V_{21} c_A^2 c_B + V_{22} c_A^2 c_B^2 + \cdots \qquad (50b)$$

where

$$U_{ij} = \frac{iM_A}{M_{A_i B_j}} K_{ij} \qquad V_{ij} = \frac{jM_B}{M_{A_i B_j}} K_{ij}$$

and

$$K_{ij} = \frac{c_{ij}}{c_A^i c_B^j}$$

Eq. (50a) can be rearranged to give

$$c_{A,T} = Q c_A + P c_A^2 \qquad (51)$$

where Q and P are polynomials in the *monomer species* concentration c_B:

$$Q = 1 + V_{11} c_B + V_{12} c_B^2 + \cdots$$
$$P = V_{21} c_B + V_{22} c_B^2 + \cdots \qquad (52)$$

Equation (51) is a quadratic with one positive solution:

$$c_A = \frac{-Q + (Q^2 + 4P c_{A,T})^{1/2}}{2P} \qquad (53)$$

Equation (50b) can be written:

$$c_{B,T} = c_B (1 + V_{11} c_A + V_{21} c_A^2) + c_B^2 (V_{12} c_A + V_{22} c_A^2) + \cdots \qquad (54)$$

For given values of $c_{B,T}$ and $c_{A,T}$, the monomer concentrations are found by a binary search. c_B is given an initial test value of $c_{B,T}/2$, and the polynomials Q and P in Eq. (52) are computed. Equation (53) is solved for c_A which is inserted along with the test value of c_B into Eq. (54). If the correct value of $c_{B,T}$ is not obtained, c_B is increased or decreased by $c_{B,T}/4$, and the binary search cycles through Eqs. (52–54) until values of c_B and c_A consistent with the given constituent concentrations are found (38).

Methods can be devised for calculating c_A and c_B from $c_{A,T}$ and $c_{B,T}$ when one or more species A_3B_i are present, but, except in some special cases, none is efficient enough to be of practical use in a simulation program, where many such calculations must be done. Since the same problem must arise in one way or another in any simulation scheme, no method is available for modelling these more complex systems without a large investment of computing time. It should be noted that a system that contains self-associated species larger than the dimer A_2 simultaneously with mixed aggregates involving more than two B subunits will present the same difficulty.

4.2.4.4 Table assembly

The operations involved in starting with a pair of constituent concentrations $c_{A,T}$ and $c_{B,T}$, extracting the monomer concentrations, and computing the corresponding sedimentation and diffusion coefficients can be coded quite efficiently. Nevertheless, a simulation that called on such a complex routine many thousand times would be prohibitively expensive. The computing time can be minimized as suggested for self-associating solutes by assembling a table of average sedimentation and diffusion coefficients before the simulation begins. What is required here is a two-dimensional table covering the range of constituent concentrations that may be present, so that a simple interpolation routine can extract the transport coefficients corresponding to any pair of values of $c_{A,T}$ and $c_{B,T}$ that is encountered during the simulation.

We have found that a 40×40 table generally suffices; that is, more finely divided tables do not give significantly different results. That is fortunate, since even this modest table produces 1600 pairs of constituent concentrations, each requiring the calculation of two monomer concentrations, two sedimentation coefficients, and four diffusion coefficients. The table assembly requires about a twentieth of the computing time needed for the complete simulation; in simulations of self-associating solutes, table assembly occupies a still smaller fraction of the computing time.

4.2.4.5 Organization of the program

The program begins by assembling a two-dimensional table of transport coefficients at various constituent concentrations. To do this the monomer concentrations c_A and c_B are found which correspond to each pair of constituent concentrations (Section 4.2.4.4). The species sedimentation and diffusion coefficients are defined and are inserted, with c_A and c_B, into Eqs. (35) and (43) to compute the constituent transport coefficients. The rotor speed is defined and the time intervals Δt_D and Δt_s are selected. The higher of the two monomer sedimentation coefficients is used to define Δt_s using Eq. (20), and the monomer diffusion coefficients define the upper limit of Δt_D [Eq. (15)] and so the lower limit of n_D for each array. The two arrays are constructed and filled with the two constituents, using Eqs. (1)–(4), and the simulation begins to cycle through the diffusion, sedimentation, and box-splitting routines.

The diffusion routine is the principal point of difference between the simulations for mixed associations and for nonreacting mixtures, since cross-reference between the arrays is required for the reacting system. The routine proceeds as follows:

1. The constituent gradients g' and points x' midway between pairs of boxes in both arrays are calculated (Eq. 9).

2. The gradient of each constituent at each boundary in its own array is found using Eq. (11).

3. Each boundary position x_i in both arrays is located between two positions x' in the opposite array: $x'_{B,j} \leqslant x_{A,i} < x'_{B,j+1}$ and a cross-referred gradient is calculated, for example,

$$g_{B,i} = g'_{B,j} + \frac{(g'_{B,j+1} - g'_{B,j})(x_{A,i} - x'_{B,j})}{x'_{B,j+1} - x'_{B,j}} \tag{55}$$

where $g_{B,i}$ is the gradient of constituent B at position $x_{A,i}$ in the constituent A array.

4. The concentrations of both constituents at each boundary in both arrays are computed, using the interpolation expression in Eq. (8) and the cross-reference procedure of Eqs. (29) and (30).

5. The direct and cross-diffusion coefficients corresponding to the local constituent concentrations are extracted by interpolation from the table.

6. The flow of each constituent at every boundary in its own array is calculated. For example, the mass of constituent A that moves *upward* across boundary $i+1$ and enters box i in the A array during time Δt_D is

$$F_{A,i+1} = \Delta t_D b \theta x_{A,i+1}(D_{AA,i+1} g_{A,i+1} + D_{AB,i+1} g_{B,i+1}) \tag{56}$$

7. The change in the constituent concentration in each box during time Δt_D is computed using Eqs. (12).

8. The sequence is repeated n_D times.

After one set of diffusion calculations is complete, a shift of the boundaries is carried out to simulate sedimentation. The concentrations of both constituents at every boundary in both arrays are found by interpolation [Eqs. (8), (29), and (30)]. The corresponding local sedimentation coefficients are extracted from the table and inserted into Eq. (16), and the new array of constituent concentrations is computed using Eq. (18). Time-averaging of the cross-referred concentrations is managed by carrying out a provisional shift of the boundaries as described for nonreacting mixtures in Section 4.2.3.2. The arrays are reindexed and off-size boxes are eliminated as described for the simpler models in Sections 4.2.3.3 and 4.2.1.4.

4.2.5 General Considerations

The simulation procedures for concentration-dependent mixtures and for mixed associations appear formidably complicated and might be expected to demand unreasonable amounts of computing time. In practice, however, the problem is not too serious. A concentration-dependent mixture must require a minimum of twice the computing time of a comparable single constituent, since two arrays are treated instead of one. In fact, because cross-reference between the arrays and time-averaging of the sedimentation routine are needed, the time for a mixture is about three times that for a single species. The mixed association introduces the further task of assembling a two-dimensional table of transport coefficients and cross-referring between the arrays during the diffusion routine. These programs typically require about six times as much computing time as the simulation of a single constituent or twice that needed for a nonreacting mixture. Nevertheless, the times are not prohibitive. For example, using the FORTRAN-H compiler in an IBM 370/158 central processing unit, a fairly complex solute containing species A, B, AB, and A_2B_2 can be simulated in approximately one minute using 100-box arrays and a 40×40 table of transport coefficients.

The distorted-grid model is evidently capable of dealing efficiently with a broad range of problems, but there are several things that it cannot do, and these shortcomings may be significant on some occasions:

1.   The distorted-grid model does not correctly describe the course of events at the ends of the solution column. It is thus suited for simulating only the interval during the experiment between the time the sedimenting boundary leaves the meniscus and the time the plateau region disappears. This limitation is serious if one wishes to describe the sedimentation of small molecules for which reflected diffusion continues at the meniscus for some time. It is particularly troublesome for *mixtures* of small molecules, in which the constituents begin to separate appreciably before the boundary leaves the meniscus.

2.   The model is not well adapted to treat chemically reacting systems in which the relaxation to chemical equilibrium is neither very fast nor extremely slow: that is, where the local changes in species concentration due to the chemical reaction and to the transport process occur at comparable rates. Variants of the model have been used for this purpose (48, 49), but they are relatively inefficient. A separate array must be assigned to each *species*. Moreover, solute must be passed from one array to another to simulate

chemical reaction; this is difficult to do without generating artifacts when the arrays are out of register, as they generally are in the distorted-grid scheme.

3. The model will not deal with reacting systems in which the equilibrium constant is not uniform throughout the cell; pressure dependence is the most conspicuous example of this problem. As a practical matter, the failure of this particular model to manage pressure dependence may not be a serious deficiency. This is not to say that real reacting solutes do not show pressure dependence, since many systems do (46, 47). Rather, pressure dependence very commonly produces inverse concentration gradients and so convective disturbances that cannot be simulated plausibly by any model.

4.3 FINITE ELEMENT SIMULATION (CLAVERIE METHOD)

The methods of Cann and Goad (13) and of Dishon et al. (22) can describe the transport of solutes involved in slowly relaxing or pressure-dependent equilibria, and the technique of Dishon and co-workers also describes the ends of the solution column properly. Both of these procedures, however, demand considerably more computing time than the distorted-grid model; if it is necessary to carry out a number of simulations to match a real experiment, the expense may be prohibitive. Claverie has recently described (39–41) a novel approach to simulating the transport of chemically reacting solutes that appears to be as efficient as the distorted-grid scheme in many applications and to be as broadly applicable as the methods of Cann and Goad and of Dishon and co-workers. It is already clear that it can deal with important cases that are inaccessible to the distorted-grid model. It has not yet been used to treat the entire range of simulation problems, but it may well ultimately replace all previous simulation procedures.

4.3.1 Mathematical Background

The Claverie method differs fundamentally from earlier approaches to the problem. Each of the earlier models is, in general, a finite difference procedure. The Claverie model is based on a finite element treatment, and it is this structural difference that gives the method its remarkable efficiency. The mathematical structure has been developed rigorously in Claverie's publications (39), and an outline will suffice here.

The distribution of solute in the centrifuge cell at any time during a sedimentation experiment can be represented by a function $c_{(x,t)}$. This function is usually finite and continuous everywhere in the cell between the meniscus x_m and the bottom of the cell x_b. If this is true, then the solute concentration, its derivatives, and the flow of solute are members of a "function space" that can be treated mathematically as a vector space. The general continuity equation in a sector shaped cell, the Lamm equation, can be written:

$$x\frac{dc}{dt} = -\frac{d(xJ)}{dx} \tag{57}$$

where J is the function describing the flow of mass at each point in the cell. The significant point is that the two sides of Eq. (57) are functions that lie in the same vector space. That being so, if any other function v in the same vector space is selected arbitrarily and the scalar products of v with both sides of Eq. (57) are formed, the scalar products are equal:

$$\int_{x_m}^{x_b}\frac{dc}{dt}vx\,dx = -\int_{x_m}^{x_b}\frac{d(xJ)}{dx}v\,dx \tag{58}$$

At this point, Claverie introduces the boundary conditions, $J_m = J_b = 0$, in an ingenious way. Since $d(xJv) = v\,d(xJ) + xJ\,dv$,

$$\int_{x_m}^{x_b}d(xJv) = \int_{x_m}^{x_b}v\,d(xJ) + \int_{x_m}^{x_b}xJ\,dv \tag{59}$$

The integral on the left is $x_bJ_bv_b - x_mJ_mv_m$, and, since v is finite everywhere and no solute crosses the ends of the solution column, this expression must equal zero. If follows, from Eqs. (58) and (59), that

$$\int_{x_m}^{x_b}\frac{dc}{dt}vx\,dx = \int_{x_m}^{x_b}xJ\frac{dv}{dx}\,dx \tag{60}$$

The important result is that Eq. (60) and any expressions derived from it will be true if and only if $J_m = J_b = 0$, which is the case of interest in the centrifuge.

For the centrifuge specifically, the flow of solute is

$$J = s\omega^2xc - D\frac{dc}{dx} \tag{61}$$

Substituting this expression into Eq. (60) gives

$$\int_{x_m}^{x_b}\frac{dc}{dt}vx\,dx - \int_{x_m}^{x_b}s\omega^2xc\frac{dv}{dx}x\,dx + \int_{x_m}^{x_b}D\frac{dc}{dx}\frac{dv}{dx}x\,dx = 0 \tag{62}$$

To construct expressions suitable for a simulation, it is now necessary to replace the continuous functions c and v with members of a finite element vector space. A number of basis sets might be chosen, but Claverie selects the particularly convenient one shown in Fig. 1d. The n elements of the basis set are spaced at equal intervals Δx between x_m and x_b:

$$\Delta x = \frac{x_b - x_m}{n-1} \tag{63}$$

Each element P_i is a "hat function," which rises linearly from zero to unity between x_{i-1} and x_i and falls linearly to zero between x_i and x_{i+1}. When each element of this basis set is multiplied by an appropriate scalar coefficient $C^*_{i(t)}$(Fig. 1c) and the result is summed, the sum (Fig. 1b) is a piecewise linear

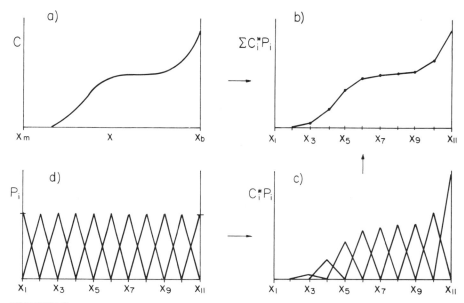

FIGURE 1

Finite-element representation of $c_{(x,t)}$. The continuous function $c_{(x,t)}$ (a) can be approximated by a piecewise linear function (b). The piecewise approximation can be constructed by selecting a set of basic functions (d), applying an appropriate weight C_i^* to each member P_i of the basis set (c), and summing the results.

approximation to the continuous function $c_{(x,t)}$ (Fig. 1a).

$$c_{(x,t)} \cong \sum_{i=1}^{n} C_{i(t)}^* P_i \qquad (64)$$

It is important to note that the coefficients C^* are scalars. At a given time, each C_i^* is invariant with x. On the other hand, the basis functions P_i are invariant with time. Thus, in the finite-element approximation for $c_{(x,t)}$ of Eq. (64), the variation with x is entirely in the basis elements P, while the variation with time is entirely in the coefficients C^*. The derivatives with x and t, are

$$\frac{dc_{(x,t)}}{dx} = \sum_{i=1}^{n} C_{i(t)}^* \frac{dP_i}{dx} \quad \text{and} \quad \frac{dc_{(x,t)}}{dt} = \sum_{i=1}^{n} P_i \frac{dC_i^*}{dt} \qquad (65)$$

The operation analogous to Eq. (62) can now be carried out using for v any vector in the finite-element vector space. Each one of the basis elements P_i is itself a member of the vector space, with the coefficient C_i^* equal to unity and the other coefficients equal to zero. Selecting one element P_j as v and inserting Eqs. (64) and (65) into Eq. (62), one obtains

$$\sum_{i=1}^{n} \frac{dC_i^*}{dt} \int_{x_m}^{x_b} P_i P_j x \, dx - s\omega^2 \sum_{i=1}^{n} C_i^* \int_{x_m}^{x_b} P_i \frac{dP_j}{dx} x^2 \, dx$$

$$+ D \sum_{i=1}^{n} C_i^* \int_{x_m}^{x_b} \frac{dP_i}{dx} \frac{dP_j}{dx} x \, dx = 0 \qquad (66)$$

for the simplest case in which the transport coefficients are independent of x and so of concentration. The coefficients C^* move outside the integrals because they are independent of x.

Equation (66) is true whichever of the n basis elements is selected for P_j; that is, Eq. (66) is in fact a set of n simultaneous equations, one for each element P_j of the basis set. This set of simultaneous equations is conveniently summarized in matrix notation:

$$\mathbf{B} \frac{d\mathbf{C}^*}{dt} - s\omega^2 \mathbf{A}_2 \mathbf{C}^* + D\mathbf{A}_1 \mathbf{C}^* = 0 \qquad (67)$$

where $\mathbf{C}^*$ is a vector of the coefficients C_i^* and $d\mathbf{C}^*/dt$ is a vector of the time derivatives of the coefficients. $\mathbf{B}$, $\mathbf{A}_1$, and $\mathbf{A}_2$ are $n \times n$ matrices whose elements are

$$B_{ji} = \int_{x_m}^{x_b} P_i P_j x \, dx \qquad (68a)$$

$$A_{1,ji} = \int_{x_m}^{x_b} \frac{dP_i}{dx} \frac{dP_j}{dx} x \, dx \qquad (68b)$$

$$A_{2,ji} = \int_{x_m}^{x_b} P_i \frac{dP_j}{dx} x^2 \, dx \qquad (68c)$$

Over a short time interval, the time derivatives of the coefficients C_i^* can be approximated by $dC_i^*/dt = (C_{i,+}^* - C_{i,-}^*)/\Delta t$, where $C_{i,-}^*$ and $C_{i,+}^*$ are the values of the coefficients before and after the time interval Δt. In vector notation

$$\frac{d\mathbf{C}^*}{dt} = \frac{\mathbf{C}_+^* - \mathbf{C}_-^*}{\Delta t} \qquad (69)$$

Substituting Eq. (69) into Eq. (67) and rearranging gives

$$\mathbf{B}\mathbf{C}_+^* - \mathbf{B}\mathbf{C}_-^* + \Delta t \mathbf{A}\mathbf{C}_+^* = 0 \qquad (70)$$

where

$$A_{ji} = DA_{1,ji} - s\omega^2 A_{2,ji}$$

The choice between $\mathbf{C}_+^*$ and $\mathbf{C}_-^*$ in the transport term $\Delta t \mathbf{A}\mathbf{C}^*$ is arbitrary; the "correct" values are between the two. However, the use of $\mathbf{C}_+^*$ makes Eq. (70) an *implicit* solution of the problem and so preferable for greater computational stability.

Rearranging Eq. (70) gives the final result:

$$\mathbf{G}\mathbf{C}_+^* = \mathbf{B}\mathbf{C}_-^*$$

where

$$G_{ji} = B_{ji} + \Delta t A_{ji} \tag{71}$$

4.3.2 Solution of the Matrix Equation

The general structure of a simulation by the Claverie method involves the repeated solution of Eq. (71). The elements of the matrices G and B are computed and the initial distribution of the solute is represented by the vector C^*_-; for example, if the solute concentration is initially uniform throughout the cell, $C^*_{i,-} = c_0$; $i = 1, \ldots, n$. Equation (71) is solved for C^*_+ to give the solute distribution after time Δt. The new concentration distribution becomes C^*_-, and the cycle is repeated a sufficient number of times to simulate the entire experiment. Since the sedimenting boundary sweeps past the fixed grid points, the consistent use of C^*_+ (or C^*_-) in Eq. (70) will produce serious errors unless Δt is kept quite short—generally a few seconds. The problem appears to be quite formidable, involving many operations with $n \times n$ matrices, where n must be large if the piecewise linear representation (Fig. 1b) is to be a good approximation of the continuous function $c_{(x,t)}$.

In fact, however, the matrices are much simpler than they appear to be, and the solutions of Eq. (71) can be found very rapidly. The evaluation of the matrix elements is considered below, but one feature of the matrices can be seen at once. For any element of the basis set P_i and its derivatives are zero outside the range between x_{i-1} and x_{i+1}. The elements of the matrices B, A_1, and A_2 contain the products $P_i P_j$, $(dP_i/dx)(dP_j/dx)$, and $P_i(dP_j/dx)$. Unless j is equal to $i-1$, i, or $i+1$, elements P_i and P_j do not overlap, and these products are zero everywhere. It follows that the matrices, B, A_1, and A_2 and so the matrix G are tridiagonal. That is, the first and last rows contain only two nonzero elements, and the intermediate rows contain only three. This fact has two important effects. First, the computer needs to store only $3n$ elements rather than n^2 for each matrix—for example, 600 instead of 40,000 elements if $n = 200$. Secondly, and even more important, the set of n simultaneous equations represented by Eq. (71) can be solved extremely rapidly in the following way.

First, the right-hand side of Eq. (71) is evaluated to give the intermediate vector Z:

$$Z = BC^*_- \tag{72a}$$

Writing only the nonzero elements of B, the elements of Z are

$$B_{11}C^*_{1,-} + B_{12}C^*_{2,-} = Z_1 \tag{72b}$$

$$B_{21}C^*_{1,-} + B_{22}C^*_{2,-} + B_{23}C^*_{3,-} = Z_2 \tag{72c}$$

$$\cdots$$

$$B_{i,i-1}C^*_{i-1,-} + B_{i,i}C^*_{i,-} + B_{i,i+1}C^*_{i+1,-} = Z_i \tag{72d}$$

$$\cdots$$

$$B_{n-1,n-2}C^*_{n-2,-} + B_{n-1,n-1}C^*_{n-1,-} + B_{n-1,n}C^*_{n,-} = Z_{n-1} \tag{72e}$$

$$B_{n,n-1}C^*_{n-1,-} + B_{n,n}C^*_{n,-} = Z_n \tag{72f}$$

The simplified matrix equation $\mathbf{GC}_+^* = \mathbf{Z}$ now represents the following family of n simultaneous equations:

$$G_{11}C_{1,+}^* + G_{12}C_{2,+}^* = Z_1 \tag{73a}$$

$$G_{21}C_{1,+}^* + G_{22}C_{2,+}^* + G_{23}C_{3,+}^* + Z_2 \tag{73b}$$

$$\cdots$$

$$G_{i,i-1}C_{i-1,+}^* + G_{i,i}C_{i,+}^* + G_{i,i+1}C_{i+1,+}^* = Z_i \tag{73c}$$

$$\cdots$$

$$G_{n-1,n-2}C_{n-2,+}^* + G_{n-1,n-1}C_{n-1,+}^* + G_{n-1,n}C_{n,+}^* = Z_{n-1} \tag{73d}$$

$$G_{n,n-1}C_{n-1,+}^* + G_{n,n}C_{n,+}^* = Z_n \tag{73e}$$

This family of equations is easy to solve efficiently. When the first equation is solved for $C_{1,+}^*$, the result is

$$C_{1,+}^* = Y_1 - X_1 C_{2,+}^* \tag{74a}$$

where

$$Y_1 = \frac{Z_1}{G_{11}} \quad \text{and} \quad X_1 = \frac{G_{12}}{G_{11}} \tag{74b}$$

Since $C_{2,+}^*$ is not yet known, $C_{1,+}^*$ cannot be evaluated, but X_1 and Y_1 can be computed and stored. When Eq. (74a) is substituted into Eq. (73b), the result can be rearranged to give

$$C_{2,+}^* = Y_2 - X_2 C_{3,+}^* \tag{75a}$$

where

$$Y_2 = \frac{Z_2 - G_{21}Y_1}{G_{22} - G_{21}X_1} \quad \text{and} \quad X_2 = \frac{G_{23}}{G_{22} - G_{21}X_1} \tag{75b}$$

Here again, $C_{3,+}^*$ is not yet available, but X_2 and Y_2 are computed and stored. This result is inserted into the next equation of the set and the process is continued, computing values of X_i and Y_i at each stage:

$$C_{i,+}^* = Y_i - X_i C_{i+1,+}^* \tag{76a}$$

where

$$Y_i = \frac{Z_i - G_{i,i-1}Y_{i-1}}{G_{i,i} - G_{i,i-1}X_{i-1}} \quad \text{and} \quad X_i = \frac{G_{i,i+1}}{G_{i,i} - G_{i,i-1}X_{i-1}} \tag{76b}$$

Ultimately one obtains the values of the coefficients X_{n-1} and Y_{n-1} in the equation

$$C_{n-1,+}^* = Y_{n-1} - X_{n-1}C_{n,+}^* \tag{77}$$

When this equation is substituted into Eq. (73e), the result can be solved explicitly for $C_{n,+}^*$:

$$C_{n,+}^* = \frac{Z_n - G_{n,n-1}Y_{n-1}}{G_{n,n} - G_{n,n-1}X_{n-1}} \tag{78}$$

With a value of $C_{n,+}^*$ in hand the stored coefficients X_{n-1} and Y_{n-1} can be used with Eq. (77) to compute $C_{n-1,+}^*$. This result is used to find $C_{n-2,+}^*$ and so forth until the entire vector $\mathbf{C}_+^*$ has been computed.

The solution of Eq. (71) thus consists of one pass "downward" through the n equations to find the coefficients X and Y and one pass "upward" to find the elements of $\mathbf{C}^*_+$.

4.3.3 Evaluation of the Matrix Elements

The integrals [Eq. (68)] in the *diagonal elements* B_{ii}, $A_{1,ii}$, and $A_{2,ii}$ are confined to the region between x_{i-1} and x_{i+1} (Fig. 2a). The integration is done separately over the rising limb of P_i from x_{i-1} to x_i and over the descending limb from x_i to x_{i+1} and then the two results are summed. It is convenient to do the integrations in terms of a normalized radial coordinate X. In the rising limb of P_i,

$$X \equiv \frac{(x - x_{i-1})}{\Delta x}$$
$$x = x_{i-1} + X\Delta x = x_i - \Delta x + X\Delta x$$
$$P_i = X \tag{79}$$
$$\frac{dP_i}{dx} = \frac{1}{\Delta x}$$
$$dx = \Delta x \, dX$$

In the descending limb

$$X \equiv \frac{(x - x_i)}{\Delta x}$$
$$x = x_i + X\Delta x \tag{80}$$
$$P_i = 1 - X$$
$$\frac{dP_i}{dx} = -\frac{1}{\Delta x}$$
$$dx = \Delta x \, dX$$

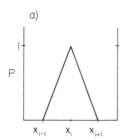
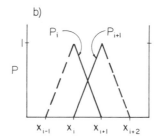

FIGURE 2

(a) Element P_i of the basis set. The products $P_i P_i$, $P_i(dP_i/dx)$, and $(dP_i/dx)(dP_i/dx)$ are nonzero everywhere between x_{i-1} and x_{i+1}. (b) Two adjacent basis elements. The products $P_i P_{i+1}$, $P_i(dP_{i+1}/dx)$, $P_{i+1}(dP_i/dx)$, and $(dP_i/dx)(dP_{i+1}/dx)$ are nonzero only in the region indicated by solid lines where P_i and P_{i+1} overlap.

These expressions for x, P_i, dP_i/dx, and dx are substituted into Eqs. (68) to give integrals in terms of X, and the integrations are performed over the range $X=0$ to $X=1$. Notice that P_1 contains only the descending limb between x_1 and x_2, while P_n contains only the rising limb between x_{n-1} and x_n.

The integrals in the *off-diagonal elements* i, $i+1$ and $i+1$, i are restricted to the region between x_i and x_{i+1}, where P_i and P_{i+1} overlap. In this region (Fig. 2b)

$$X \equiv \frac{(x-x_i)}{\Delta x}$$

$$x = x_i + X\Delta x$$

$$P_i = 1 - X \qquad P_{i+1} = X \tag{81}$$

$$\frac{dP_i}{dx} = -\frac{1}{\Delta x} \qquad \frac{dP_{i+1}}{dx} = \frac{1}{\Delta x}$$

$$dx = \Delta x \, dX$$

TABLE 1
Matrix Elements for Claverie Simulation

	Cylindrical Coordinates	Rectangular Coordinates
$B_{ii} i \neq 1, n$	$\dfrac{2x_i \Delta x}{3}$	$\dfrac{2\Delta x}{3}$
B_{11}	$\dfrac{\Delta x}{3}\left(x_1 + \dfrac{\Delta x}{4}\right)$	$\dfrac{\Delta x}{3}$
B_{nn}	$\dfrac{\Delta x}{3}\left(x_n - \dfrac{\Delta x}{4}\right)$	$\dfrac{\Delta x}{3}$
$B_{i,i+1} = B_{i+1,i}$	$\dfrac{\Delta x}{6}\left(x_i + \dfrac{\Delta x}{2}\right) = \dfrac{\Delta x}{6}\left(x_{i+1} - \dfrac{\Delta x}{2}\right)$	$\dfrac{\Delta x}{6}$
$A_{1,ii} i \neq 1, n$	$\dfrac{2x_i}{\Delta x}$	$\dfrac{2}{\Delta x}$
$A_{1,11}$	$\dfrac{1}{\Delta x}\left(x_1 + \dfrac{\Delta x}{2}\right)$	$\dfrac{1}{\Delta x}$
$A_{1,nn}$	$\dfrac{1}{\Delta x}\left(x_n - \dfrac{\Delta x}{2}\right)$	$\dfrac{1}{\Delta x}$
$A_{1,i,i+1} = A_{1,i+1,i}$	$-\dfrac{1}{\Delta x}\left(x_i + \dfrac{\Delta x}{2}\right) = -\dfrac{1}{\Delta x}(x_{i+1} - \dfrac{\Delta x}{2})$	$-\dfrac{1}{\Delta x}$
$A_{2,ii} i \neq 1, n$	$-\dfrac{2x_i \Delta x}{3}$	0
$A_{2,11}$	$-\left(\dfrac{x_1^2}{2} + \dfrac{x_1 \Delta x}{3} + \dfrac{\Delta x^2}{12}\right)$	$-\dfrac{1}{2}$
$A_{2,nn}$	$\dfrac{x_n^2}{2} - \dfrac{x_n \Delta x}{3} + \dfrac{\Delta x^2}{12}$	$\dfrac{1}{2}$
$A_{2,i,i+1}$	$-\left(\dfrac{x_i^2}{2} + \dfrac{2x_i \Delta x}{3} + \dfrac{\Delta x^2}{4}\right) = -\left(\dfrac{x_{i+1}^2}{2} - \dfrac{x_{i+1} \Delta x}{3} + \dfrac{\Delta x^2}{12}\right)$	$-\dfrac{1}{2}$
$A_{2,i+1,i}$	$\dfrac{x_i^2}{2} + \dfrac{x_i \Delta x}{3} + \dfrac{\Delta x^2}{12} = \dfrac{x_{i+1}^2}{2} - \dfrac{2x_{i+1} \Delta x}{3} + \dfrac{\Delta x^2}{4}$	$\dfrac{1}{2}$

The appropriate substitutions are made in Eqs. (68) and the integrations are carried out from $X=0$ to $X=1$.

The resulting matrix elements are given in the first column of Table 1. Notice that, since the integrals in $B_{i,i+1}$ and $A_{1,i,i+1}$ contain the products $P_i \cdot P_{i+1}$ and $(dP_i/dx)(dP_{i+1}/dx)$, **B** and **A**$_1$ are symmetrical; that is, the $i, i+1$ and $i+1, i$ elements are identical. In the matrix **A**$_2$, however, the $i, i+1$ and $i+1, i$ elements are not identical, as would be expected, since this matrix represents the directed transport (sedimentation) of the solute.

Claverie has shown (41) that the finite element method, like the distorted-grid model, can be adapted very easily to simulate transport of a solute with uniform velocity in a system of constant cross section. The result is the rectangular approximation, which is of limited interest for the centrifuge, but which can also be used to simulate gel chromatography or electrophoresis. If V is the uniform velocity of the solute, the flow equation is

$$J = Vc - D\frac{dc}{dx} \tag{82}$$

and the continuity equation is

$$\frac{dc}{dt} = -\frac{dJ}{dx} \tag{83}$$

Using these equations in place of Eqs. (61) and (57) and following the development of Section 4.3.1, one obtains

$$\mathbf{G}'\mathbf{C}^*_+ = \mathbf{B}'\mathbf{C}^*_- \qquad \mathbf{G}' = \mathbf{B}' + \Delta t(D\mathbf{A}'_1 - V\mathbf{A}'_2) \tag{84}$$

where the matrix elements are

$$B'_{ji} = \int_{x_m}^{x_b} P_i P_j \, dx \qquad A'_{1,ji} = \int_{x_m}^{x_b} \frac{dP_i}{dx}\frac{dP_j}{dx} \, dx \qquad A'_{2,ji} = \int_{x_m}^{x_b} P_i \frac{dP_j}{dx} \, dx \tag{85}$$

Integration of these expressions gives the remarkably simple results shown in the second column of Table 1.

4.3.4 Organization of the Program for Concentration-Independent Sedimentation

The program begins by specifying the number of finite elements in the basis set, the radial interval Δx, and the radial positions of the basis elements. The elements of **B**, **A**$_1$, and **A**$_2$ are computed using the expressions in Table 1. The transport coefficients, the rotor speed, and the time interval Δt are specified and combined with the matrices to give the working matrix **G** [Eq. (71)]. Appropriate values are inserted into **C**$^*_-$ to describe the initial solute distribution.

The elements of the vector **Z** are computed [Eq. (72)], and these values are used with the elements of **G** to compute the complete array of coefficients X and Y [Eqs. (73)–(76)] and the value of $C^*_{n,+}$. The stored coefficients are then used to compute the remainder of the values in the vector **C**$^*_+$. The new concentration vector replaces C_-^* in Eq. (72), and the process is repeated a sufficient number of times to simulate the entire experiment. Concentration profiles are extracted and stored during the simulation at times appropriate for comparison with experimental records. Concentration gradient profiles can also be constructed to simulate experimental schlieren patterns:

$$\left(\frac{dc}{dx}\right)_{\bar{x}_i} = \frac{C_{+,i+1}^* - C_{+,i}^*}{\Delta x} \tag{86a}$$

$$\bar{x}_i = \frac{x_{i+1} + x_i}{2} \tag{86b}$$

The coding for the Claverie procedure is exceptionally simple. The entire program, including input and output routines, can be written in about 60 FORTRAN statements. Since the grid points remain fixed and do not drift with the sedimenting solute, the method must use much shorter time intervals and so many more repetitions of the working routines than the distorted-grid scheme. Nevertheless, the matrix formulation is so very efficient that the computing times are comparable for the two techniques. From the argument in Eqs. (59) and (60), it follows that the Claverie model has the significant advantage of describing the ends of the solution column properly.

4.3.5 Concentration-Dependent Sedimentation

The procedure described to this point is designed to deal with concentration-independent sedimentation. The model can, however, be adapted without difficulty to treat concentration-dependent sedimentation, which is of greater experimental interest. There are at least two ways to approach the problem. Claverie points out (41) that the concentration dependence of s can be treated by perturbing the Z vector [Eq. (72)] at each stage of the computation before proceeding to solve the set of simultaneous equations represented by Eq. (71). This procedure is feasible if the dependence of s on concentration is a polynomial, but it has some disadvantages. A linear concentration dependence of s and many polynomial expressions will usually produce negative sedimentation coefficients in the region of high concentration near the bottom of the cell. The resulting artifacts are not serious from a practical point of view, since experimental profiles are not legible near the bottom of the cell. The problem is nevertheless irritating, and it can be eliminated by selecting an inverse concentration dependence of the sedimentation coefficient: $s = s_0/(1 + kc)$. However, the perturbation scheme of Claverie can not be formulated for this case.

For this reason we prefer to treat the problem by perturbing the matrix operator A_2 instead of the concentration vector at each step. Indeed, this alternative approach is suggested by a passing comment of Claverie on p. 1694 of ref. 39. A local sedimentation coefficient is computed corresponding to each element in the C_-^* vector: $s_i = s_0(1 - kC_{i,-}^*)$, or $s_i = s_0/(1 + kC_{i,-}^*)$, or whatever other relation is desired. Then the elements of the matrix A_2 are treated to give an appropriate perturbed operator A_3:

$$A_{3,ij} = A_{2,ij} s_j \tag{87}$$

That is, each element in column j of the sedimentation operator is multiplied by the local sedimentation coefficient s_j. The matrix A in Eq. (70) is

$$A = D A_1 - \omega^2 A_3 \tag{88}$$

The elements of the matrix G are computed in the usual way [Eq. (71)] and the solution proceeds as before, updating the matrix operator at each step.

The two procedures are comparable in efficiency and give the same result for linear or polynomial concentration dependence. In fact, programs incorporating the two schemes call for precisely the same arithmetic operations in slightly different order.

Claverie has also shown that linear concentration dependence of the diffusion coefficient can be incorporated into the model by a procedure that involves perturbing the concentration vector. This change makes the matrix expression a good deal more complex, and it seems probable that an alternative procedure involving repeated updating of the A_1 matrix would be superior.

It is particularly important to note that the adjustment of the matrix operators illustrated in Eq. (87) will also allow the treatment of situations in which s and/or D varies with position for some reason other than concentration dependence. The most interesting case of this kind is density gradient centrifugation. The scheme will also deal with pressure dependence arising from a difference between the compressibilities of the solute and the solvent.

The concentration-dependent sedimentation of a mixture is easily simulated by the Claverie method; the modifications needed in the finite-element model are closely analogous to those that allow the distorted-grid model to deal with the same problem. The two (or more) constituents are carried in separate arrays; that is, the distribution of the solute is defined by two vectors C_A^* and C_B^*. The procedure suggested by Claverie, perturbing the concentration vectors at each step of the calculation, can be used, but the alternative method, updating the A_2 matrix before each round of simulated transport, is especially straightforward for this case. The local sedimentation coefficients of both constituents are computed for each position x_i, using whatever expression is appropriate for the concentration dependence, for example,

$$s_{A,i} = s_{A,0}(1 - k_{AA} C_{A,i}^* - k_{AB} C_{B,i}^*)$$

$$s_{B,i} = s_{B,0}(1 - k_{BB} C_{B,i}^* - k_{BA} C_{A,i}^*) \tag{89}$$

In the finite-element method, the grid points do not move as they do in the distorted-grid model; as a result, the two grids remain in register and so interpolation is not necessary to pass values of the concentrations between the two arrays. Each set of sedimentation coefficients is combined with the matrix A_2 using Eq. (87) to obtain two adjusted matrices $A_{3,A}$ and $A_{3,B}$. Two working matrices are computed:

$$\mathbf{G}_A = \mathbf{B} + \Delta t \left(D\mathbf{A}_1 - \omega^2 \mathbf{A}_{3,A} \right)$$

$$\mathbf{G}_B = \mathbf{B} + \Delta t \left(D_B \mathbf{A}_1 - \omega^2 \mathbf{A}_{3,B} \right) \tag{90}$$

The sets of simultaneous equations represented by

$$\mathbf{G}_A \mathbf{C}^*_{A,+} = \mathbf{B} \mathbf{C}^*_{A,-}$$

$$\mathbf{G}_B \mathbf{C}^*_{B,+} = \mathbf{B} \mathbf{C}^*_{B,-} \tag{91}$$

are formed and solved separately by the method outlined in Section 4.3.2. The calculation cycles as usual, computing two new sets of sedimentation coefficients and updating both working matrices at each step.

4.3.6 Chemically Reacting Solutes

The finite-element procedure is very well suited to simulate the behavior of solutes that undergo chemical reaction during a transport experiment. Like the distorted-grid model, it can treat systems that relax rapidly to chemical equilibrium. In addition, however, it can deal with solutes that react so slowly that local chemical equilibrium is not maintained during the transport process. In fact, the procedure was originally developed by Claverie to simulate active-enzyme sedimentation (40, 53) which is a special case of the transport of reacting solutes that do not relax rapidly to chemical equilibrium, and he has subsequently applied it to a slowly dimerizing solute (54). Zimmerman (48, 49, 55) has used a modified distorted-grid model to examine the same problems.

The rigorous mathematical justification of the technique developed by Claverie for this application is fairly complicated, but the practical result is entirely straightforward (53). Each *species* in the reacting system is assigned to a separate concentration vector. For example, a simple dimerization $2A \rightleftharpoons A_2$ will require two arrays, one for the monomer and the other for the dimer. The simplest mixed association $A + B \rightleftharpoons AB$ uses three arrays for the species A, B, and AB. The appropriate sedimentation-diffusion operators $\mathbf{G}$ are constructed for each species; the transport of the various species is treated independently, with cross-reference between the arrays, if necessary, to reflect the mutual concentration dependence of the transport coefficients, exactly as is done for any concentration-dependent mixture (Section 4.3.5).

The effect of the chemical reaction is simulated by perturbing the concentration vectors after each cycle of simulated transport. This scheme, alternating simulated rounds of transport and chemical reaction, is essentially identical to the structure used for this problem by Cann and Goad (13) and it resembles the modified distorted-grid model devised by Zimmerman (48) for slowly reacting solutes. The reaction may be rapid enough that the species distribution relaxes to equilibrium at every point in the cell within the time interval Δt. In these cases the species concentrations emerging as $\mathbf{C}^*_+$ vectors from the transport calculations are appropriately summed to give the constituent concentrations at each grid point. In a self-association there is only one constituent, and its local concentration is the sum of all the species concentrations. For a mixed association the constituent concentrations are the weighted sums given by Eq. (32). The *equilibrium* species distributions corresponding to the new local constituent concentrations are calculated by solving Eq. (24) for self-associations and by the procedures discussed in Section 4.2.4.3 for mixed associations. Pressure dependence of the chemical equilibrium can be dealt with by assigning different values to the equilibrium constant used to calculate the species concentrations at the various points in the array. The equilibrium concentrations are distributed to the $\mathbf{C^*}$ vectors for the various species, and the next cycle of simulated transport is carried out using Eqs. (91).

If, at any point in the cell, the reaction is too slow to relax to equilibrium during the time interval Δt, then appropriate kinetic equations must be solved at every grid point. For the simplest self-association

$$2A \underset{k_{-1}}{\overset{k_1}{\rightleftharpoons}} A_2 \tag{92a}$$

the rate equation is most conveniently expressed in terms of weight concentrations:

$$\frac{dc_{A_2}}{dt} = k_1 c_A^2 - k_{-1} c_{A_2} \tag{92b}$$

and conservation of mass requires

$$\frac{dc_A}{dt} = -\frac{dc_{A_2}}{dt} \tag{92c}$$

For the simplest mixed association,

$$A + B \underset{k_{-1}}{\overset{k_1}{\rightleftharpoons}} AB \tag{93a}$$

the rate expression is

$$\frac{dc_{AB}}{dt} = k_1 c_A c_B - k_{-1} c_{AB} \tag{93b}$$

and the conservation expressions are

$$\frac{dc_A}{dt} = -f_A \frac{dc_{AB}}{dt} \quad \text{and} \quad \frac{dc_B}{dt} = -f_B \frac{dc_{AB}}{dt} \tag{93c}$$

where the weight fractions f are defined in Eq. (33).

If the extent of reaction during the time interval Δt is small enough that *none* of the species concentrations changes greatly, then linear approximations to Eqs. (92b) or (93b) will be adequate.

$$\Delta c_{A_2} = \Delta t \left(k_1 c_A^2 - k_{-1} c_{A_2} \right) = -\Delta c_A \tag{94a}$$

$$\Delta c_{AB} = \Delta t (k_1 c_A c_B - k_{-1} c_{AB}) = -\frac{\Delta c_A}{f_A} = -\frac{\Delta c_B}{f_B} \tag{94b}$$

The perturbations Δc are applied to the concentration vectors, and the adjusted vectors are submitted to another cycle of simulated transport.

If the change in concentration is an appreciable fraction of *any* of the species concentrations, then the perturbations must be found by integrating the rate equation. It is not clear in the literature whether this more difficult problem has been treated by the finite-element method and, if so, whether the computing times are acceptable. Dealing with moderate extents of reaction in complex systems containing the products of a sequence of bimolecular associations may, perhaps, be particularly troublesome in this respect.

4.4 POSSIBLE HYBRID MODELS

The most important use of computer simulated transport of interacting systems is in surveying various possible models of an interacting system in order to find those whose behavior resembles that of the real system within an acceptable experimental error. In each application of this kind, a sizeable number of simulations will be necessary, and so it is important to use simulation procedures of the greatest possible efficiency to minimize computing costs. Both the distorted-grid and the finite-element methods are now capable of describing the transport of a wide variety of interacting systems in adequately short computing times. Nevertheless, it is likely that methods combining certain features of the two models will be more efficient than either alone.

The development of hybrid models seems particularly worthwhile for solutes involved in rapidly relaxing association reactions. A possible hybrid approach to the problem for self-association is suggested by the modest modification of the Claverie method for concentration-dependent sedimentation described in Section 4.3.5, which uses local sedimentation coefficients to adjust the sedimentation operator [Eq. (89)] at each step of the calculation. This alternative procedure has very little effect on computing time for simple concentration dependence, but it might be quite helpful with rapid self-associations. The calculation would begin by computing tables of average sedimentation and diffusion coefficients over an appropriate range of total solute concentrations [Eqs. (24)–(26) and ref. 38]. Then a finite-element simulation begins, carrying the *total* solute in a *single* concentration vector instead of distributing the solute species into separate arrays. At each step, the local sedimentation and diffusion coefficients corresponding to each point in the C^*_- vector are extracted from the table. The A_2 matrix is adjusted according to Eq. (87) and the A_1 matrix is similarly perturbed:

$$A_{4,ij} = A_{1,ij} \overline{D}_j \tag{95}$$

The working matrix is constructed,

$$\mathbf{G} = \mathbf{B} + \Delta t (\mathbf{A}_4 - \omega^2 \mathbf{A}_3) \tag{96}$$

and the computation continues as usual through the next cycle of simulated transport. This procedure would have two advantages over the usual Claverie approach to these systems. First, the calculation would carry only one concentration array rather than one for each species; this advantage would be substantial if several aggregated species were present and particularly so in the case of isodesmic associations (37). Second, the table assembly and subsequent interpolation would greatly reduce the number of reequilibration calculations, which may be quite time-consuming in systems of any complexity. The only obvious difficulty is in extending the tables to the very high concentrations found near the bottom of the cell, but this problem can probably be evaded by assigning dummy transport coefficients to the part of the cell below the plateau region, which is of little experimental interest in any case.

The analogous use of constituent concentration arrays with the Claverie model to manage rapid mixed associations is an attractive idea, but it presents certain difficulties. Expressions analogous to Eq. (67) can be formulated for each constituent, but they must contain cross-diffusion terms, and so, for two constituents, both constituent concentration vectors occur in both matrix equations. There appear to be a few possible ways to solve the two families of simultaneous equations represented by these matrix expressions, but it is not yet clear that the available approaches will be accurate and efficient enough to be useful.

The prior assembly of two-dimensional tables of the species concentrations corresponding to various pairs of constituent concentrations (Section 4.2.4.3) may be useful in finite-element simulations even if it proves inconvenient to treat rapid mixed associations directly in terms of constituent concentrations. The Claverie model for this problem carries out a reequilibration calculation at every point in the concentration grids after every cycle of simulated transport. Since the method requires finely divided space grids and very short time intervals, the number of such calculations is large, and the routines to be used can be fairly complicated. If a table of limited size were constructed at the beginning of the simulation, extracting the species concentrations corresponding to any pair of constituent concentrations arising during the simulation would involve only interpolation in the table. The saving in computing time would certainly be worthwhile. It is worth noting that table assembly routines could be equally useful in applications of the Cann and Goad model to rapid associations.

In treating either self-associations or mixed associations, the use of tables of transport coefficients saves computing time at the expense of storage space. This is an advantage if the programs are being run on a large computer. On the other hand, if the programs are adapted for an in-house minicomputer, as has been done for the Cann and Goad model by Davis and Chen (56), then core size rather than time is likely to be limiting. In this case, ad hoc calculation of the transport coefficients may be preferred over table storage.

ACKNOWLEDGMENTS

We are indebted to Jean-Michel Claverie for his very helpful instruction in the use of the finite-element model. The work described here was supported by a grant GM-22243 from the National Institutes of Health and by funds from the Kansas Agricultural Experiment Station. This is publication number b80-216 from the Department of Biochemistry, Kansas Agricultural Experiment Station.

REFERENCES

1. G. A. Gilbert, *Discuss. Faraday Soc.* **20**, 68 (1955).

2. G. A. Gilbert, *Proc. R. Soc.* **A250**, 377 (1959).

3. G. A. Gilbert and R. C. Jenkins, *Proc. R. Soc.* **A253**, 420 (1959).

4. J. L. Bethune and G. Kegeles, *J. Phys. Chem.* **65**, 1761 (1961).

5. J. L. Bethune, *J. Phys. Chem.* **74**, 3837 (1970).

6. J. L. Bethune and P. J. Grillo, *Biochemistry* **6**, 796 (1967).

7. B. J. McNeil, L. W. Nichol, and J. L. Bethune, *J. Phys. Chem.* **74**, 3846 (1970).

8. D. F. Oberhauser, J. L. Bethune, and G. Kegeles, *Biochemistry* **4**, 1878 (1965).

9. G. Kegeles, L. Rhodes, and J. L. Bethune, *Proc. Natl. Acad. Sci. USA* **58**, 45 (1967).

10. G. Kegeles and M. L. Johnson, *Arch. Biochem. Biophys.* **141**, 59 (1970).

11. G. Kegeles and M. L. Johnson, *Arch. Biochem. Biophys.* **141**, 63 (1970).

12. J. R. Cann and W. B. Goad, *J. Biol. Chem.* **240**, 148 (1965).

13. J. R. Cann, *Interacting Macromolecules*, Academic Press, New York, 1970.

14. W. B. Goad and J. R. Cann, *Ann. N.Y. Acad. Sci.* **164**, 172 (1969).

15. J. R. Cann and W. B. Goad, *J. Biol. Chem.* **240**, 1162 (1965).

16. J. R. Cann, *Biophys. Chem.* **1**, 1 (1973).

17. J. R. Cann and N. D. Hinman, *Biochemistry* **15**, 4614 (1976).

18. J. R. Cann and D. I. Stimpson, *Biophys. Chem.* **7**, 103 (1977).

19. J. R. Cann and G. Kegeles, *Biochemistry* **13**, 1868 (1974).

20. D. I. Stimpson and J. R. Cann, *Biophys. Chem.* **7**, 115 (1977).

21. J. R. Cann and K. J. Gardiner, *Biophys. Chem.* **10**, 211 (1979).

22. M. Dishon, G. H. Weiss, and D. A. Yphantis, *Biopolymers* **4**, 449 (1966).

23. M. Dishon, G. H. Weiss, and D. A. Yphantis, *Biopolymers* **4**, 457 (1966).

24. I. H. Billick, M. Dishon, M. Schulz, G. H. Weiss, and D. A. Yphantis, *Proc. Natl. Acad. Sci. USA* **56**, 399 (1966).

25. I. H. Billick, M. Dishon, G. H. Weiss, and D. A. Yphantis, *Biopolymers* **5**, 1021 (1967).

26. M. Dishon, G. H. Weiss, and D. A. Yphantis, *Biopolymers* **5**, 697 (1967).

27. M. Dishon, G. H. Weiss, and D. A. Yphantis, *Biopolymers* **10**, 2095 (1971).

28. W. K. Sartory, H. B. Halsell, and J. P. Breillat, *Biophys. Chem.* **5**, 107 (1976).

29. M. L. Johnson, D. A. Yphantis, and G. H. Weiss, *Biopolymers* **12**, 2477 (1973).

30. J. J. Correia, M. L. Johnson, G. H. Weiss, and D. A. Yphantis, *Biophys. Chem.* **5**, 255 (1976).

31. D. J. Cox, *Arch. Biochem. Biophys.* **112**, 249 (1965).

32. D. J. Cox, *Arch. Biochem. Biophys.* **112**, 259 (1965).

33. D. J. Cox, *Arch. Biochem. Biophys.* **119**, 230 (1967).

34. D. J. Cox, *Arch. Biochem. Biophys.* **129**, 106 (1969).

35. D. J. Cox, *Arch. Biochem. Biophys.* **142**, 514 (1971).

36. D. J. Cox, *Arch. Biochem. Biophys.* **146**, 181 (1971).

37. R. R. Holloway and D. J. Cox, *Arch. Biochem. Biophys.* **160**, 595 (1974).

38. D. J. Cox, *Methods Enzymol.* **48**, 212 (1978).

39. J.-M. Claverie, H. Dreux, and R. Cohen, *Biopolymers* **14**, 1685 (1975).

40. R. Cohen and J.-M. Claverie, *Biopolymers* **14**, 1701 (1975).

41. J.-M. Claverie, *Biopolymers* **15**, 843 (1976).

42. H. Vink, *Acta Chem. Scand.* **18**, 409 (1964).

43. H. Fujita, *Mathematical Theory of Sedimentation Analysis*, Academic Press, New York, 1962.

44. R. F. Steiner, *Arch. Biochem. Biophys.* **49**, 400 (1954).

45. L. F. Ten Eyck and W. Kauzmann, *Proc. Natl. Acad. Sci. USA* **58**, 888 (1967).

46. R. Josephs and W. F. Harrington, *Proc. Natl. Acad. Sci. USA* **58**, 1587 (1967).

47. W. F. Harrington and G. Kegeles, *Methods Enzymol.* **27**, 306 (1973).

48. J. K. Zimmerman, *Biochemistry* **13**, 384 (1974).

49. J. K. Zimmerman, *Biophys. Chem.* **3**, 339 (1975).

50. J. K. Zimmerman and G. K. Ackers, *J. Biol. Chem.* **246**, 1078 (1971).

51. J. K. Zimmerman and G. K. Ackers, *J. Biol. Chem.* **246**, 7298 (1971).

52. J. K. Zimmerman, D. J. Cox, and G. K. Ackers, *J. Biol. Chem.* **246**, 4242 (1971).

53. R. Cohen, B. Girault, and A. Messiah, *Biopolymers* **5**, 203 (1967).

54. M. Huet and J.-M. Claverie, *Biochemistry* **17**, 236 (1978).

55. B. B. Brown and J. K. Zimmerman, *Biophys. Chem.* **5**, 351 (1976).

56. L. C. Davis and M. S. Chen, *Arch. Biochem. Biophys.* **194**, 34 (1979).

CHAPTER 5

Equilibrium Methods

P. D. JEFFREY

The "equilibrium methods" of the title are taken to be the classical ones for studying solutions of macromolecules, namely, osmometry, light scattering, and equilibrium sedimentation. Small-angle X-ray scattering is conveniently included because of the close relationship it bears to light scattering. These techniques are discussed in relation to the elucidation of interactions, between proteins in solution, whose state of chemical equilibrium is not disturbed by their application. The field of study thus defined is very large and inevitably not all of it can be explored in depth in a chapter of this length. Fortunately, the methods and their applications to the behavior of proteins in solution have been notably well served by review articles and books. Only the most recent reviews will be given here, since an exhaustive survey would require a chapter in itself, but those listed and others will be referred to frequently in the following discussion and provide references to earlier articles if further information is sought.

In osmotic pressure measurement, the book by Tombs and Peacocke (1) and the more recent article by Adams and co-workers (2) between them give basic theory, detailed explanations of instruments and experimental techniques, and a wide-ranging discussion of methods of analysis of protein interactions. In light scattering the most recent sources of this kind of information may be found in the reviews by Timasheff and Townend (3) and Pittz and others (4), while for small-angle X-ray scattering the works of Timasheff (5,6) and Pessen and colleagues (7) could be consulted. Equilibrium sedimentation, the most widely used of these techniques, has received a commensurate degree of attention by reviewers. For the basic theory the books of Svedberg and Pedersen (8), Schachman (9), Fujita (10), and Williams (11) are available and for more details of the analysis of protein interactions, the review articles of Adams (12), Teller (13), van Holde (14), and Kim and co-workers (15). Finally, for a lucid exposition of the application of multicomponent system theory in the application of equilibrium methods to protein solutions the recent book by Eisenberg (16) is indispensable.

The methods under consideration, all being thermodynamically based, have much in common, and to make the discussion in the present chapter useful, as well as tractable, the aim is to concentrate on these common elements, giving particular emphasis to potential difficulties and to newer developments in methods of analysis. Thus the first section states the basic equations for all of the methods for both three-component and multicomponent systems of macromolecules, special attention being paid to the problems associated with the definition of a charged macrocomponent in a multicomponent system and to how thermodynamic nonideality can be taken into account in the description of interactions between proteins. The next section is concerned with the evaluation of the concentration of the smallest macromolecular reactant in the system as a function of total protein concentration. The molecular weight of this unit is of unique importance, and, since it is required in the determination of monomer concentration as a function of total concentration by all techniques, its measurement receives attention first. Well-established methods for determining monomer concentration as a function of total concentration are discussed next and the section concludes with a description of a recently developed technique (utilizing the "Ω function"), which can be applied to equilibrium sedimentation concentration distributions.

Various types of protein-protein interactions and some representative methods for their analysis are described in the third major section. These include methods based on molecular weight averages, because they are relevant to all of the equilibrium methods, and those based on concentration distribution data obtainable only from equilibrium sedimentation experiments, because it is believed these are likely to be used increasingly in the future. Finally, examples are given of the application of several different methods of analysis to some specific protein-protein interactions. These are selected with a view to illustrating, in a more concrete way, several aspects of the preceding discussion. Each of the equilibrium methods is represented and the systems discussed range from a simple monomer-dimer reaction to complex indefinite associations; the description includes the evaluation of thermodynamic nonideality terms in both situations.

5.1 BASIC EQUATIONS AND THERMODYNAMIC NONIDEALITY

5.1.1 Thermodynamically Nonideal Systems of Three Components

In this section the aim is simply to state the basic equations for osmotic pressure, equilibrium sedimentation, light scattering and small-angle X-ray scattering measurements so that they may be compared on a common basis. The system of three components, normally water, buffer, and macromolecule, coresponds to that generally used in studies of protein interactions. In the first instance, component 2 will be viewed as a single noninteracting protein to allow the significant considerations in such studies to be illustrated without the complications of macromolecular heterogeneity. This is introduced in the following section. Truncation of the equations at the term linear in concentration produces a useful simplification also in that it provides for inclusion of all the types of terms contributing to thermodynamic nonideality without introducing unnecessary complexities. Extension to include higher virial coefficients is possible in principle and is sometimes necessary, as is indicated later.

The treatment is largely that of Eisenberg (16), and the details of derivations, which are not given here, may usually be found in his book. In several instances the equations given below are not presented explicitly by Eisenberg but in these cases the algebraic manipulations involved to derive them are straightforward. The well-known formalism devised by Scatchard and his colleagues (17–19) is employed. The principal solvent, almost always water in studies of proteins, is denoted component 1 and the low molecular weight diffusible salt, having one ion in common with the electrostatically charged macromolecule, is denoted component 3. The macromolecular component, a protein in this work, is denoted component 2. Throughout, unless specifically indicated otherwise, M_i denotes the molecular weight of species i, m_i its molal concentration in moles of species i per kilogram of principal solvent component, c_i its weight concentration in grams of species i per unit volume of solution, and C_i its molar concentration in moles of component i per liter of solution.

5.1.1.1   Osmotic pressure equations

In these terms the basic osmotic pressure equation can be written in differential form as

$$\frac{V_m^0}{RT}\left(\frac{\partial P}{\partial m_2}\right)_{T,\mu_1,\mu_3} \simeq 1 + \left(\sum_i \frac{\nu_{i2}^2}{m_i} + \beta_{22} - \frac{a_{23}^2}{a_{33}}\right)m_2 \tag{1}$$

where R is the gas constant, T the absolute temperature, P the pressure, and μ is the chemical potential. V_m^0 is the limiting volume (in ml) of the solution containing 1000 g of the solvent and ν_{i2} is the number of moles of diffusible species i included in 1 mole of component 2 and whose value depends on the definition adopted for the macromolecular component (1). In addition,

$$\beta_{J,K} \equiv \left(\frac{\partial \ln \gamma_J}{\partial m_K}\right)_{T,P,m} \qquad \beta_{22} = \left(\frac{\partial \ln \gamma_2}{\partial m_2}\right)_{T,P,m} \tag{2a}$$

$$a_{J,K} \equiv \left(\frac{\partial \ln a_J}{\partial m_K}\right)_{T,P,m} \qquad \begin{cases} a_{23} = \sum_i \dfrac{\nu_{i2}\nu_{i3}}{m_i} + \beta_{23} \\[2mm] a_{33} = \sum_i \dfrac{\nu_{i3}^2}{m_i} + \beta_{33} \end{cases} \tag{2b}$$

where γ, the activity coefficient on the molal scale is defined by $\mu_J = \mu_J^0 + RT\ln\gamma_J m_J$ and the subscript m signifies constant molality of all constituents of the solution except component 2. The approximation sign in Eq. (1) means only that inconsequential terms involving the partial volume of component 3 and the solution compressibility have been omitted. They will be left out of subsequent equations, which will appear with normal equality signs, since they are negligible in comparison with the other terms (16).

Equation (1) can be converted to the weight concentration scale (g/ml) and integrated to give

$$\frac{\pi}{c_2} = RT\left[\frac{1}{M_2} + \frac{V_m^0}{2M_2^2}\left(\sum_i \frac{\nu_{2i}^2}{m_i} + \beta_{22} - \frac{a_{23}^2}{a_{33}}\right)c_2\right] \tag{3}$$

where π is the equilibrium osmotic pressure as usually measured.

5.1.1.2 Equilibrium sedimentation equations

Beginning, for example, from Eq. 5.15 of ref. 16 one can derive the equation that is the analog of Eq. (1), as

$$\frac{\omega^2}{2RT}\left(\frac{d\ln m_2}{dx^2}\right)^{-1}\left(\frac{\partial\rho}{\partial m_2}\right)_{T,P,\mu_3} = 1 + \left(\sum_i \frac{\nu_{i2}^2}{m_i} + \beta_{22} - \frac{a_{23}^2}{a_{33}}\right)m_2 \tag{4}$$

where ω is the angular velocity of the sedimentation equilibrium experiment, x is the distance from the axis of rotation, and $(\partial\rho/\partial m_2)_{T,P,\mu_3}$ is the density increment of the macromolecular solution on the molal scale measured at constant chemical potential of component 3. On the weight concentration scale (g/ml) Eq. (4) becomes

$$\frac{\omega^2}{2}\left(\frac{d\ln c_2}{dx^2}\right)^{-1}\left(\frac{\partial\rho}{\partial c_2}\right)_{T,P,\mu_3} = RT\left[\frac{1}{M_2} + \frac{V_m^0}{M_2^2}\left(\sum_i \frac{\nu_{i2}^2}{m_i} + \beta_{22} - \frac{a_{23}^2}{a_{33}}\right)c_2\right] \tag{5}$$

5.1.1.3 Light scattering equations

The analogous relation to Eqs. (1) and (4) can be derived, for example, from Eq. 4.38 of ref. 16, as

$$\frac{KV_m m_2}{\Delta R(O)}\left(\frac{\partial n}{\partial m_2}\right)_{T,P,\mu_3}^2 = 1 + \left(\sum_i \frac{\nu_{i2}^2}{m_i} + \beta_{22} - \frac{a_{23}^2}{a_{33}}\right)m_2 \tag{6}$$

where $K = 4\pi^2 n^2/N\lambda^4$, n is the refractive index of the solution, V_m is the volume of solution (in ml) containing 1 kg of principal solvent, N is Avogadro's number, λ is the wavelength of the light in vacuum and $\Delta R(O)$ is the difference between Rayleigh factors for solution and solvent (component 1 plus component 3) extrapolated to zero scattering angle (3). On the weight concentration scale (g/ml)

$$\frac{K}{\Delta R(O)}c_2\left(\frac{\partial n}{\partial c_2}\right)_{T,P,\mu_3}^2 = \frac{1}{M_2} + \frac{V_m^0}{M_2^2}\left(\sum_i \frac{\nu_{2i}^2}{m_i} + \beta_{22} - \frac{a_{23}^2}{a_{33}}\right)c_2 \tag{7}$$

5.1.1.4 Small-angle X-ray scattering equations

By similar steps to those used in the derivation of the light scattering equations it may be shown that

$$\frac{I_{e1}P(q)V_m}{\Delta I(q)N}m_2\left(\frac{\partial\rho_{e1}}{\partial m_2}\right)_{T,P,\mu_3}^2 = 1 + \left(\sum_i \frac{\nu_{i2}^2}{m_i} + \beta_{22} - \frac{a_{23}^2}{a_{33}}\right)m_2 \tag{8}$$

where $q = (4\pi n/\lambda)\sin(\theta/2)$, θ being the angle at which the intensity of scattering is measured, I_{e1} is the intensity of radiation scattered by an electron, $\Delta I(q)$ indicates that correction for the scattering due to solvent has been made and $P(q)$ is a function introduced to account for the angular dependence of the scattered intensity. More details about how these quantities are evaluated can be obtained from recent articles discussing the technique (7, 16). For example, the electron density increment is the direct analog of the refractive index increment. The equation corresponding to Eq. (7), again written on the g/ml concentration scale, is

$$\frac{I_{el}}{N}\frac{P(q)}{\Delta I(q)}c_2\left(\frac{\partial\rho_{el}}{\partial c_2}\right)^2_{T,P,\mu_3} = \frac{1}{M_2} + \frac{V^0_m}{M^2_2}\left(\sum_i\frac{\nu^2_{i2}}{m_i} + \beta_{22} - \frac{a^2_{23}}{a_{33}}\right)c_2 \qquad (9)$$

5.1.1.5   General comments

Equations (1)–(9) have much in common. In particular, they include quantities that are to be evaluated at constant chemical potential of the solvent components. The vital conclusion, as has often been pointed out (1, 16, 20, 21), is that in all of the techniques the correct molecular weight of the macromolecular component is obtained on extrapolation of the measured experimental quantity to infinite dilution, provided this condition is fulfilled. The macromolecular component whose molecular weight is thus evaluated in the limit as $c_2 \rightarrow 0$ is that defined by the concentration used in the quantities appearing in the equations. Thus, for example, in a light scattering experiment if one substituted in Eq. (7) the refractive index increment measured by comparing solution and solvent equilibrated by dialysis and using for c_2 the number of grams of dry protein per milliliter of solution, M_2 would be obtained as the molecular weight of this anhydrous entity.

The solution and solvent used in the experiments should also be those that have been previously equilibrated by dialysis with a membrane impermeable to the macromolecular component, but it is useful to note that this requirement may often be relaxed if experimental contingencies make it difficult to obey. At low concentration of the macromolecule in a system consisting predominantly of component 1 and a moderate concentration of component 3, say 0.1 M, only insignificant errors would result from not using dialyzed solutions (16). The theoretical demand for substitution of increments measured at constant chemical potential of solvent in the equations can also often be relaxed under similar conditions. At moderate concentration of component 3 and low charge density of protein usually only small errors in the molecular weight result from using instead, say, the value measured at constant molality of solvent components (16, 22). However, quite unacceptable errors are likely if the correct quantities are not used in experiments involving high concentrations of salt, 8 M urea, 6 M GuHCl, or other components such as organic solvents (16, 20).

In the osmotic pressure, equilibrium sedimentation, light scattering, and small-angle X-ray scattering equations presented it is seen that the coefficients of the concentration term contain the same contributions, the three latter coefficients being just twice that obtaining in osmotic pressure experiments. The three terms in the bracket are discussed in some detail by Tombs and Peacocke (1), for example, but for the purposes of the present treatment the following simplifications will be made. First, the so-called "Donnan term," $\sum\nu^2_{i2}/m_i$, is assumed to be insignificant with respect to β_{22}, a condition in aqueous solutions of proteins requiring only a moderate concentration of diffusible electrolyte, for example, 0.1 M sodium chloride (1). Second, the term a_{23}^2/a_{33} is also considered to be effectively equal to zero. Indeed, the macromolecular component may be defined as suggested by Casassa and Eisenberg (20) so that the term actually is set equal to zero. This definition is equivalent to the statement that addition of the macromolecular component so-defined to a system at dialysis equilibrium produces no redistribution of the diffusible ions across the membrane. The term is usually small for proteins in any event (e.g., ref. 1) and it will be omitted in future with the mental note that in so doing the macromolecular component is, in effect, defined as suggested by Casassa and Eisenberg and in some experimental designs it might be necessary to take this into account. In the remainder of the chapter then, thermodynamic nonideality will be treated as arising solely from the β_{22} term. As defined in Eq. (2a) this term accounts for the dependence of the macromolecular component 2 on its own concentration. Its elaboration then is required to define the major contribution to thermodynamic nonideality in situations where component 2 comprises a set of interacting macromolecular species.

5.1.2 Systems Heterogeneous in the Macromolecular Component

Two basic types of macromolecular association are considered, self-association of the protein and mixed associations. The "monomer," of molecular weight M_1, in a protein self-association is regarded as the smallest entity which can be produced by dissociation of a quaternary structure without cleavage of covalent bonds (23). Another concept, occasionally useful, is that of the "protomer," the smallest-sized subunit in a given reaction whose aggregation gives rise to the oligomeric structures being studied. Thus a protomer can be identical with the monomer or it may consist of a number of monomers, which varies with the experimental conditions. In reactions between dissimilar protein molecules A and B, referred to here as "mixed associations," the concept of a monomer is not applicable, but it is sometimes possible to describe reactions in terms of a protomer such as AB. In mixed associations, monomeric B will be taken as the smallest macromolecular species present in solution. In protein self-associations subscripts are numbers, thus M_1 the molecular weight of the monomer, M_2 that of the dimer and so on; in mixed associations they are letters, M_B, M_{AB}, for example.

Theoreticians have found it convenient to visualize systems, termed thermodynamically ideal, where the contributions of terms such as β_{22} are set equal to zero. While in strict terms this is never correct for real systems the notion retains usefulness, especially as conditions may be found where the contributions are indeed negligible. For such systems heterogeneous in the macromolecular component it is readily shown that the molecular weight evaluated from $\pi/c_2 RT$ in an osmotic pressure experiment is a number average $\overline{M}_n(1,2)$. For light scattering, equilibrium sedimentation, and small-angle X-ray scattering, evaluation of the left-hand sides of Eqs. (5), (7), and

(9), respectively (divided by RT where indicated) yields the weight average molecular weight, $\overline{M}_w$ in a heterogeneous ideal system (7, 10, 16). These averages are defined below together with the z-average molecular weight $\overline{M}_z$, which will be referred to later.

$$\overline{M}_n = \frac{\sum c_i}{\sum c_i / M_i}$$

$$\overline{M}_w = \frac{\sum c_i M_i}{\sum c_i} \qquad (10)$$

$$\overline{M}_z = \frac{\sum c_i M_i^2}{\sum c_i M_i}$$

When nonideality effects of significant magnitude are encountered it is necessary to refer to an "apparent" average molecular weight defined as the quantity measured experimentally and the relevant equations are then,

$$\frac{\pi}{RT\bar{c}} = \frac{1}{\overline{M}_{n,a}} = \frac{1}{\overline{M}_n} + A\bar{c} \qquad (11)$$

$$\frac{\omega^2}{2RT}\left(\frac{d\ln\bar{c}}{dx^2}\right)^{-1}\left(\frac{\partial\rho}{\partial\bar{c}}\right)_{TP,\mu_3} = \frac{1}{\overline{M}_{w,a}} = \frac{1}{\overline{M}_w} + 2A\bar{c} \qquad (12)$$

$$\frac{K}{\Delta R(O)}\bar{c}\left(\frac{\partial n}{\partial\bar{c}}\right)^2_{T,P,\mu_3} = \frac{1}{\overline{M}_{w,a}} = \frac{1}{\overline{M}_w} + 2A\bar{c} \qquad (13)$$

$$\frac{I_{el}}{N}\frac{P(q)}{\Delta I(q)}\bar{c}\left(\frac{\partial\rho_{el}}{\partial\bar{c}}\right)^2_{T,P,\mu_3} = \frac{1}{\overline{M}_{w,a}} = \frac{1}{\overline{M}_w} + 2A\bar{c} \qquad (14)$$

where $\bar{c}$ is the total concentration of macromolecular component.

If the heterogeneity arises from the presence of nonreacting macromolecular components, the average molecular weights of undisturbed solutions are not functions of total concentration insofar as they reflect the original composition of the solution, and the same can be said of the virial coefficients. In equilibrium sedimentation experiments, in contrast to the other techniques, the composition of such solutions is disturbed by the application of the centrifugal field and the weight average molecular weight is therefore a function of radial position. In this work we are not concerned with such heterogeneity but rather with that arising from the association behavior of a single protein, or the reaction between different proteins. The average molecular weights measured by all of the techniques are then functions of the total concentration or composition, since the operation of the law of mass action ensures a change in the proportion of reactants and products as the total concentration is changed. Strictly speaking then, the average molecular weights in the equations should be labeled in some way to signify this fact but to avoid unnecessarily cumbersome notation such indications are omitted, the concentration dependence of all average molecular weights being implied throughout the discussion.

It follows that equilibrium sedimentation is again a special case because of the redistribution of macromolecular components in the centrifugal field producing dependence of average molecular weight upon radial position, x, through the variation of the concentration of each species with x. In later sections where the treatment requires explicit consideration of the radial dependence of some quantities it will be necessary to introduce appropriate nomenclature. It is easily shown that in interacting protein systems the requirements of sedimentation equilibrium and chemical equilibrium are satisfied at each level in the ultracentrifuge cell (8, 24, 25) and therefore that the weight average molecular weight measured at a particular total concentration is the same (in the absence of pressure effects) as it would be in a light scattering experiment for example. This applies also to apparent molecular weights measured under conditions where thermodynamic nonideality is appreciable. It remains to investigate the significance of thermodynamic nonideality as reflected in the virial coefficients of Eqs. (11)–(14) in interacting protein systems.

As defined by these equations the second virial coefficient for osmotic pressure, A, and that for the other techniques, $2A$, are empirical quantities that can be evaluated experimentally. It is instructive to inquire how they are related to nonideality terms like β_{22} in the equations for single macromolecular solutes and how they might be related to the properties of the individual constituents of the system.

The logarithm of the activity coefficient on the weight concentration scale can be written as a Taylor's series expansion (13),

$$\ln y_i = M_i \sum_k B_{ik} c_k + O c_i c_k \tag{15}$$

and then the osmotic pressure equation, for example, for a heterogeneous system is

$$\frac{\pi}{\bar{c}RT} = \frac{1}{M_n} + \frac{1}{2\bar{c}} \sum_i \sum_k B_{ik} c_i c_k + \frac{\bar{v}\bar{c}}{2\overline{M}_n} \tag{16}$$

if the partial specific volumes of all macromolecular components are assumed to be equal, with the value $\bar{v}$.

The same equation results from writing Eq. (3) on the g/liter scale separately for each macromolecular component, neglecting the terms referred to before, and making the identity

$$\beta_{ik} \equiv M_i M_k B_{ik} + M_k \bar{v} \tag{17}$$

It is evident by comparing Eqs. (11) and (16) that the virial coefficient defined in Eqs. (11)–(14) is actually equivalent to

$$2A = \sum_i \sum_k B_{ik} \frac{c_i c_k}{\bar{c}^2} + \frac{\bar{v}}{\overline{M}_n} \tag{18}$$

In the next sections the application of these equations to the evaluation of second virial coefficients in interacting protein systems is considered.

5.1.3   Nonideality in Interacting Systems—The "Adams–Fujita Approach"

Solutions of self-interacting proteins may contain a large number of macro-molecular species, and it is obvious from Eq. (18) that the nonideality term in the experimental Eqs. (11)–(14) will then be extremely complex. To simplify the analysis of self-interacting systems the relationship referred to here as the "Adams–Fujita assumption"(25) is often used (2, 13, 15, 16). This is stated as

$$\ln y_i = iM_1 B\bar{c} \tag{19a}$$

and in this form Eq. (19a) actually embodies two assumptions. The first is that

$$\ln y_i = i \ln y_1 \tag{19b}$$

The logarithms of the activity coefficients of oligomers can then be written with the aid of Eq. (15) as

$$\ln y_i = iM_1 (B_{i1} c_1 + B_{i2} c_2 + B_{i3} c_3 + \cdots)$$

which on combination with Eq. (19b) yields

$$\ln y_i = iM_1 (B_{11} c_1 + B_{12} c_2 + B_{13} c_3 + \cdots)$$

This formulation is seen to be consistent with Eq. (19a) if B is regarded as a weight-average quantity,

$$B = \frac{\sum B_{ik} c_k}{\sum c_k} \tag{19c}$$

However, in an interacting system B would still be a function of total concentration, and therefore the second assumption required for practical application of Eq. (19a) is that all the B_{ik}'s are identical and set equal to B. This allows equations for the apparent molecular weights to be written as

$$\frac{1}{\overline{M}_{n,a}} = \frac{1}{\overline{M}_n} + \frac{B}{2}\bar{c} \tag{20a}$$

$$\frac{1}{\overline{M}_{w,a}} = \frac{1}{\overline{M}_w} + B\bar{c} \tag{20b}$$

The advantages of such a formulation are twofold. First, it allows the nonideality term to be evaluated empirically as a second virial coefficient independent of total concentration. Second, that equilibrium constants for reactions between protein molecules, which may be evaluated as appropriate ratios of concentrations after the thermodynamic nonideality has been corrected for, are equivalent to thermodynamic constants evaluated via ratios of activities because the consequence of Eq. (19a) is that the relevant ratio of activity coefficients is unity,

$$\frac{(y_1)^i}{y_i} = 1 \tag{21}$$

In mixed associations between protein molecules A and B Adams and co-workers (26) advocate a similar approach. The simplifying assumptions are that the activity coefficients may be expressed in terms of constituent concentrations, so that

$$\ln y_A = M_A B_{AA} c_A^0 + M_A B_{AB} c_B^0 \tag{22a}$$

$$\ln y_B = M_B B_{BB} c_A^0 + M_B B_{BB} c_B^0 \tag{22b}$$

where c^0 denotes the initial concentration, and

$$\ln y_{AB} = \ln y_A + \ln y_B; \qquad \frac{y_{AB}}{y_A y_B} = 1 \tag{22c}$$

These equations lead to the ability to write for the osmotic pressure equation, for example (2),

$$\frac{\bar{c}}{\overline{M}_{n,a}} = \frac{\bar{c}}{\overline{M}_n} + \frac{1}{2} \sum_i \sum_k B_{ik} c_i^0 c_k^0$$

$$= \frac{\bar{c}}{\overline{M}_n} + \frac{1}{2} \left\{ B_{AA} (c_A^0)^2 B_{BB} (c_B^0)^2 \right\} + B_{AB} c_A^0 c_B^0 \tag{23}$$

The parameters B_{AA} and B_{BB} can be measured in separate experiments with A and B alone and substituted in Eq. (23) to allow B_{AB} to be evaluated from the experimental data on the reaction mixture.

It would of course be valuable to know how good the assumptions embodied in Eqs. (19a) and (22) are likely to be in the practical analysis of protein-protein interactions by equilibrium methods. Ogston and Winzor (27) have investigated this by calculating osmotic pressure curves, including nonideal terms for some simple model interacting systems in which the equivalent of the B_{ik} in Eq. (18) were evaluated as the covolumes of uncharged spheres of the appropriate radius. Second virial coefficients were then obtained on the basis of the equivalent equations to Eq. (20a) and used to recalculate the equilibrium constants, which were compared with the values originally used to generate the data. Monomer-dimer, monomer-tetramer, and monomer-octamer systems were analyzed over realistic concentration ranges and with different equilibrium constants. The general conclusion was that reasonably reliable values of equilibrium constants were likely to result from the "Adams

Fujita" approach. It was pointed out, however, that this was in part due to cancelation of errors and that more serious errors are likely in the application of equilibrium constants so-obtained to the calculation of the composition of a solution of interacting protein molecules. The authors also noted the possibility of using calculated interaction constants based on size and shape information derived from dynamic methods, in conjunction with analysis of data from equilibrium methods, to obtain better estimates of monomer and polymer concentrations in associating protein systems. A discussion of how this might be undertaken is given in the following section.

5.1.4 Calculation of Thermodynamic Nonideality Terms

There are basically three ways, in the analysis of protein-protein interactions, of dealing with the contribution of thermodynamic nonideality to the measured quantities. It may be possible to work under such conditions, especially at low concentrations of macromolecule, that its effect is negligible; the "Adams–Fujita assumption" may be applied and quantities manipulated accordingly; the nonideal interaction terms may be calculated explicitly. In this section a rationale for calculation, largely following that suggested in a recent article (28), is presented. Later, the application of the three approaches in practice will be illustrated.

The quantities which are to be estimated are the terms B_{ik}. With a knowledge of these, or their equivalent, the nonideality can be allowed for in the elucidation of the specific protein interactions of interest. It will be remembered that the only significant contributions to nonideality in the solutions we are dealing with are regarded as being due to macromolecular interactions (Section 5.1.1). Thus, the factors involved are the electrostatic charge and the finite size and particular shape of the particles. These are treated in terms of an "excluded volume" which cannot be occupied by two particles at once. It is conveniently regarded as being made up of a geometrically determined "covolume" plus a contribution due to like electrostatic charges, which, giving rise to a repulsion, effectively increases the excluded volume. A molar interaction parameter, α_{ik}, is defined which is related to that on the g/liter scale previously used in this work, by

$$\frac{\alpha_{ik}}{M_i M_k} = B_{ik} \tag{24a}$$

In the nomenclature used (28), α_{ik} is related to the osmotic virial coefficient on the molar scale, A_{ik}, by

$$\alpha_{ik} = 2 A_{ik} - M_k \bar{v} \tag{24b}$$

where, as before, $\bar{v}$ is the partial specific volume in liter/g assumed identical for all oligomeric species.

By making use of available statistical mechanical (29–31) and electrostatic theory (32) it was shown (28) that if all oligomeric species are treated as impenetrable spheres with radii r and bearing net charge z on their surfaces

$$2A_{ik} = \frac{4\pi N(r_i + r_k)^3}{3} + \frac{z_i z_k (1 + \kappa r_i + \kappa r_k)}{2I(1 + \kappa r_i)(1 + \kappa r_k)} \tag{24c}$$

where $\kappa = (8\pi N e^2 I / 1000 \varepsilon k T)^{1/2}$, e is the electronic charge, I is the molar ionic strength, ε is the dielectric constant of the medium, and k is Boltzmann's constant. The first term of Eq. (24c) is the geometric covolume of two hard spheres (27) and expressions for other geometric shapes such as ellipsoids and cylinders are available (27,30) if required. When κr_i and κr_k are small compared to unity the electrostatic term in Eq. (24c) reduces to $z_i z_k / 2I$, the term conventionally added to the geometrical covolume as the electrostatic contribution (17,27,33,34). It was noted that this approximation may often overestimate the electrostatic term for proteins in buffers of moderate ionic strength, and so the term as written in Eq. (24c) should be used in preference. This second term relies on the fact that the electrostatic energy be very small in comparison to kT for particle separation distances greater than the sum of their radii. If this condition is not obeyed, a more elaborate procedure for its evaluation, requiring numerical integration, is recommended (28).

It is perhaps arguable whether the acceptance of some reasonable assumptions as to particle shape and charge distribution to calculate a virial coefficient on the above basis is preferable to the ambiguity in the choice of a model which can result from some curve-fitting procedures based on the application of Eq. (19a) with B a constant to be determined. However, the method based on statistical mechanical equations seems to the present author to provide the most rational approach to the problem available at present. At the very least it might be used to check whether values of B determined empirically are physically reasonable. It is true, of course, that a large number of interaction coefficients have to be evaluated even in comparatively simple reactions between proteins. For example, in a monomer-dimer association B_{11}, $B_{12} (\equiv B_{21})$ and B_{22} are required but there is no barrier in principle on this score as the preceding equations indicate. The full equation or an approximate version of it have already been utilized in the analysis of some complex interactions between like (28,33,35) and unlike (34) molecules. Some such applications are discussed more fully in Sections 5.4.2 and 5.4.3. The previous work (28) also described how terms corresponding to third virial coefficients may be calculated if required. In experiments with lysozyme (28), the concentration range employed did in fact warrant the inclusion of such terms.

5.2   EVALUATION OF THE MONOMER CONCENTRATION

Many methods of analysis of self-association reactions between protein molecules are based on a knowledge of the concentration of the monomer as a function of total concentration. In the case of a mixed association the analogous quantities are the concentrations of species A and B as a function of total concentration. The information is obtained either by analysis of experimental data in the form of average molecular weight versus concentration as obtained by osmometry, equilibrium sedimentation, light scattering or small-angle X-ray scattering, or total concentration as a function of radial distance, a form only available from equilibrium sedimentation. In the former case the original analysis was devised by Steiner (36), later extended to non-ideal systems by Adams and Williams (37) and has been used widely (38–41). The second method, using the so-called "Ω function" was published only recently (42) and has so far been applied to only a limited number of systems (33,43,44). In both procedures the molecular weight of the monomer is required. Initially, therefore, it is necessary to pay some attention to the accuracy with which this quantity can be determined.

5.2.1 The Molecular Weight of the Monomer

In self-associating systems the mass action law applies and progressive dilution increases the proportion of monomer in solution until, in the limit of zero concentration of macromolecule, the system contains only monomer as the macromolecular component. Extrapolation to infinite dilution, of curves of average molecular weight vs concentration obtained via Eqs. (11)–(14), yield the monomer molecular weight. In practice the extrapolation can be difficult to perform accurately because a high association constant generates a steeply rising curve. Another potential source of error in extrapolation is exemplified in Figure 1, which shows that for certain systems weight average molecular weight curves can be sigmoidal. The most effective way to minimize these errors is to carry the molecular weight measurements to as low

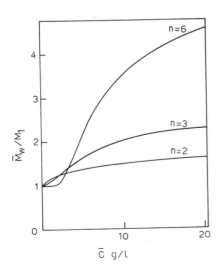

FIGURE 1
Differences in form of weight average molecular weight vs concentration curves for three monomer–n-mer systems. The curves were calculated for association constants of $2\,dl/g$ ($n=2$); $4\,dl^2/g^2$ ($n=3$); $32\,dl^5/g^5$ ($n=6$). (Adapted from ref. 45.)

concentrations as possible. The method of choice for measuring molecular weights for the purpose of determining an accurate monomer value is, therefore, the so-called "meniscus depletion" method developed by Yphantis (46). Here, sedimentation equilibrium experiments carried out at high speeds allow weight-average molecular weights to be evaluated with reasonable precision with Rayleigh optics at concentrations as low as 0.1g/liter.

In a recent review (15) it was concluded that the error in $\overline{M}_{w,a}$ measured by equilibrium sedimentation was likely to be rather more than 2% at low concentration and, of course, this would be reflected in the monomer molecular weight obtained by extrapolation. Fortunately in many, probably most, cases the protein is already well characterized before detailed analysis of its interaction behavior in solution is undertaken. Then the molecular weight of the monomer can be specified with much greater precision than is inherent in the equilibrium method. The low concentration measurements function to define the protomer in the association as illustrated in Figure 2. There is no question that the protomer undergoing association here is the true insulin monomer, consisting of one A and one B chain, and hence M_1 can be specified with the accuracy allowed by the amino acid sequence data. The same considerations apply to mixed associations, except that the molecular

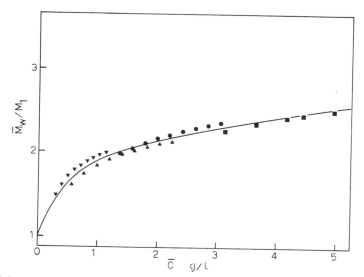

FIGURE 2

Weight average molecular weight vs concentration curves measured by equilibrium sedimentation for bovine insulin at pH 2.0, $I = 0.1$, 25°C. Data derived from different experiments are denoted by different symbols. The solid line, drawn by eye as an attempt to smooth the data, was extrapolated to the known monomer molecular weight of 5734. (Reprinted with permission from ref. 39. Copyright by the American Chemical Society.)

weights of interest are M_A and M_B, which may be measured in separate experiments. The extrapolation problem does not arise, only the precision with which one can determine the molecular weight of a single solute. This is likely to be about $\pm 2-3\%$ (15) by sedimentation equilibrium.

As was pointed out in Section 5.1.1 the molecular weights determined by Eqs. (3), (5), (7), and (9) in three-component systems or Eqs. (11)–(14) in solutions heterogeneous in the macromolecular component are defined by the way the concentration has been measured in evaluating the appropriate increment at constant chemical potential. In the case of equilibrium sedimentation the increment required is $(\partial\rho/\partial c)_\mu$ [Eqs. (5) and (12)] but in analogy with two-component system nomenclature this is usually written as $(1-\phi'\rho^0)$ where ρ^0 is the solvent-mixture density and is effectively constant in the equilibrium sedimentation experiment. Then in the limit of vanishing solute concentration, $\bar{c}$, Eq. (12) can be written

$$M = \frac{2RT}{\omega^2(1-\phi'\rho^0)}\left(\frac{d\ln\bar{c}}{dx^2}\right) \tag{25}$$

The use of the apparent specific volume, ϕ', evaluated from density increments between dialyzed solution and solvent and the concentration of dry isoionic protein would then yield the molecular weight of this same component. In the event, as is often the case, that the true partial specific volume, $\bar{v}$, is the parameter used to evaluate the molecular weight of the monomer, a different molecular weight $M^* = M\Lambda$ is obtained. The magnitude of Λ, which is defined by Eisenberg (16), depends on the composition of the solution as reflected in the interaction term between macromolecule and supporting electrolyte and their concentrations and partial specific volumes. It suffices to say that under the conditions of the equilibrium sedimentation experiments we are considering (aqueous solutions containing low concentrations of protein and moderate concentrations of low molecular weight electrolytes) the use of $\bar{v}$ instead of ϕ' leads to errors of the order of 0.5% (16, 22).

Finally in this section it is relevant to ask what is the likely error introduced in the molecular weight by possible systematic error in $\bar{v}$ (or ϕ') used in its evaluation. First, it can be noted, since the $(1-\bar{v}\rho)$ term in aqueous protein solutions is about 0.3, $\bar{v}$ being about 0.7 ml/g, that a 1% error in the partial specific volume appears as a 3% error in the molecular weight. It appears that it is possible with reasonable care to measure the partial specific volumes of proteins in aqueous solution with a precision of about ± 0.002 ml/g (47), implying an error of less than 1% in the corresponding molecular weight determined in a sedimentation equilibrium experiment. Comparison by Woods (47) of measured partial specific volumes with those calculated from amino acid composition suggests that the error might often be of the same order if the means of values calculated on the basis of available data (48, 49) are used. In the latter publication the greatest discrepancy between a measured and a calculated partial specific volume, for a protein in aqueous solution, was found to be 0.02 ml/g leading to a maximum error of 7% in molecular weight.

Admittedly this is too large to be tolerated usually and therefore $\bar{v}$ (or preferably ϕ') should be measured if possible. In solutions containing high concentrations of GuHCl or urea the situation is more critical. Here it is mandatory to measure ϕ' because of the much higher preferential interaction term. Even then somewhat larger errors can be expected because of the difficulty of carrying out accurate measurements in these solutions containing a high concentration of a third component (47).

5.2.2 Methods for Determining Weight Fraction of Monomer Based on Molecular Weight Averages

These are all elaborations of an ingenious approach devised by Steiner (36) to extract the weight fraction of the monomer as a function of total concentration from weight average molecular weight data obtained by a light scattering study of an interacting protein system. For an ideal polymerizing protein, denoted P, the total weight concentration, $\bar{c}$, is defined by

$$\bar{c} = \sum_i c_i = M_1 \sum_i i K_i^* C_1^i \tag{26}$$

where C_1 is the molarity of the monomer P_1, and K_i^* is the product of the successive molar equilibrium constants required for the formation of P_i. For ideal systems K_i^* may also be defined as the ratio of the molarity of P_i to the ith power of the monomer molarity,

$$K_i^* = \prod_{l=2}^{i} (K_l)_{l-1,1} = \frac{C_i}{C_1^i} \tag{27}$$

$(K_l)_{l-1,1}$ is the molar equilibrium constant for the formation of P_l from P_{l-1} and P_1 and is usually abbreviated to K_l. For example, in a system consisting of monomer, dimer, and trimer in equilibrium the relevant equilibrium constants on a molar basis would be $(K_2)_{1,1}$ and $(K_3)_{2,1}$, written as K_2 and K_3, respectively, and $K_3^* = C_3/C_1^3 = K_2 K_3$.

Differentiation of Eq. (26) with respect to C_1 gives

$$\frac{d\bar{c}}{dC_1} = M_1 \sum_i i^2 K_i^* C_1^{i-1} \tag{28}$$

It also follows on combination of Eqs. (10) and (27) on noting the relation $C_i = c_i/iM_1$ that

$$\frac{\overline{M_w}}{M_1} = M_1 \sum_i i^2 K_i^* \frac{C_1^i}{\bar{c}} \tag{29}$$

Combination of Eqs. (28) and (29) yields

$$\frac{\overline{M_w}}{M_1} = \frac{d\ln \bar{c}}{d\ln C_1} \tag{30}$$

The weight fraction of monomer f_1 is defined as

$$f_1 = \frac{c_1}{\bar{c}} = \frac{M_1 C_1}{\bar{c}}$$ (31)

and may be substituted into Eq. (30) to give

$$d\ln f_1 = \eta_w d\bar{c}$$ (32)

where

$$\eta_w = \frac{\left\{\left[(M_1/\overline{M}_w) - 1\right]\right\}}{\bar{c}}$$

Integration of Eq. (32) from $c = 0$ where $f_1 = 1$ to any other $\bar{c}$ gives

$$\ln f_1 = \int_0^{\bar{c}} \eta_w \, d\bar{c}$$ (33)

the expression obtained by Steiner (36).

Experimentally, in a light scattering or equilibrium sedimentation study, η_w is not available down to $\bar{c} = 0$ but only to some finite low concentration. Accordingly a plot of η_w vs $\bar{c}$ must be extrapolated to $\bar{c} = 0$ so that the integration in Eq. (33) may be carried out numerically to yield f_1, and thereby c_1, as a function of the total concentration $\bar{c}$.

Adams and Williams (37) showed that for nonideal solutions an apparent weight fraction of monomer, $f_{1,a}$ could be evaluated. This function is defined by

$$\ln f_{1,a} = \int_0^{\bar{c}} \eta_{w,a} \, d\bar{c} = \ln f_1 + B M_1 \bar{c}$$ (34)

where

$$\eta_{w,a} = \frac{\left\{(M_1/\overline{M}_{w,a}) - 1\right\}}{\bar{c}}$$

Steiner (50) has defined the number fraction of monomer as $f_n = C_1/C$ where $C = \bar{c}/\overline{M}_n$ and derived the following relation:

$$\ln f_n = \int_0^{\bar{c}} \left\{\left(\frac{M_1}{\overline{M}_n}\right) - 1\right\} d\ln C$$ (35)

Following the work of Steiner (50), Adams (51), and Adams and co-workers (2) have shown that one can obtain the *weight* fraction of monomer from osmotic pressure experiments. Thus for an ideal system

$$\ln f_1 = \int_0^{\bar{c}} \eta_n \, d\bar{c} + \frac{M_1}{M_n} - 1 \qquad \eta_n = \frac{\left\{(M_1/\overline{M}_n) - 1\right\}}{\bar{c}}$$ (36)

and for a nonideal system

$$\ln f_{1,a} = \int_0^{\bar{c}} \eta_{n,a} \, d\bar{c} + \frac{M_1}{M_{n,a}} - 1 \qquad \eta_{n,a} = \frac{\left\{(M_1/\overline{M}_{n,a}) - 1\right\}}{\bar{c}}$$ (37)

5.2.3 The "Ω Function"

A recently published method for finding the concentration or thermodynamic activity of the monomer, in a self-associating system (42), or of the species of lowest effective molecular weight, in a mixed association (52), as a function of total concentration, is now to be discussed. The procedure applies only to sedimentation equilibrium experiments and relies on the definition of the Ω function as a ratio of activity fractions of monomer at two different total concentrations. Thus

$$\Omega(x) = \frac{a_1(x_F)\bar{c}(x)}{\bar{c}(x_F)a_1(x)} \tag{38}$$

where $a_1(x) = y_1(x)c_1(x)$ and the notation (x), is included to show that the quantities so labeled are functions of the radial distance, x, from the axis of rotation in a sedimentation equilibrium experiment. The position x_F is a reference radius arbitrarily selected by the experimenter, as will become clear shortly.

The integrated form of Eq. (5) can be written as (8)

$$a_i(x) = a_i(x_F)\exp\{M_i\phi_i(x^2 - x_F^2)\} \tag{39}$$

where ϕ_i can be considered to be evaluated as $\omega^2(1 - \bar{v}_i\rho)/2RT$ remembering what was said earlier about the buoyancy term. A number of assumptions are implied in the expression and customary application of Eq. (39). They are conveniently listed by Eisenberg (16) as (a) the solution is incompressible; (b) all activity coefficients are independent of pressure; (c) interaction parameters between diffusible components and macromolecule are independent of the concentration of macromolecule; and (d) no redistribution of diffusible components occurs in the absence of macromolecule. These conditions are considered to be effectively fulfilled in equilibrium sedimentation experiments with proteins in aqueous solutions containing moderate concentrations of low molecular weight buffers.

From Eq. (39) $a_1(x_F)/a_1(x) = \exp\{M_1\phi_1(x_F^2 - x^2)\}$ and thus Eq. (38) may be written

$$\Omega(x) = \frac{\bar{c}(x)\exp\{M_1\phi_1(x_F^2 - x^2)\}}{\bar{c}(x_F)} \tag{40}$$

Equation (40) allows experimental evaluation of $\Omega(x)$ as a function of $\bar{c}(x)$ from the equilibrium sedimentation concentration distribution, providing $M_1\phi_1$ is known, since it only requires selection of a reference concentration $\bar{c}(x_F)$ at a reference radius x_F and then application of the equation to the measured $(\bar{c}(x), x)$ points.

Several properties of the Ω function may now be mentioned. First, it can be shown rigorously (42) that

$$\lim_{\bar{c}(x) \to 0} \Omega(x) = \frac{a_1(x_F)}{\bar{c}(x_F)} \tag{41}$$

hence extrapolation of a plot of $\Omega(x)$ vs $\bar{c}(x)$ to $\bar{c}=0$ yields the activity of the monomer at a specified radial position, x_F, and Eq. (39) then allows calculation of $a_1(x)$ as a function of total concentration, $\bar{c}(x)$. In an ideal system $y_1 = 1$, and then Eq. (41) yields $c_1(x_F)$ allowing generation of c_1, the concentration of monomer, as a function of $\bar{c}$. This is the same information as derived by the Steiner treatment but the present approach offers the advantage, with respect to sedimentation equilibrium data, of not requiring a differentiation step to obtain $\overline{M_w}$ as a function of $\bar{c}$ and a subsequent integration to obtain the weight fraction of monomer. Second, the $\Omega(x)$ function has no critical points and, provided experiments are carried to low enough concentrations, poses no difficulties in extrapolation, as will be seen later. This may be contrasted with the behavior of the Steiner parameter η, which has been shown to have critical points in certain systems (42). Third, it is possible to combine data from several experiments in a single plot of $\Omega(x)$ vs $\bar{c}(x)$ by selecting a suitable reference point in experiments spanning adjacent concentration ranges, namely, one that corresponds to the same total concentration value in each experiment (42,53). This process offers the possibility of detecting any volume changes accompanying protein interactions, since these, if they occur, will lead to the dependence of the equilibrium constant for the reaction on x and nonsuperposition of plots based upon different x_F positions. Finally, it is important to note that the determination of $a_1(x)$ as a function of $\bar{c}(x)$ does not depend on the selection of any particular model for the interaction being elucidated. This is of course also true of the Steiner technique but not of other methods of analysis, which do not begin with a knowledge of the activity or concentration of the monomer as a function of $\bar{c}$.

5.2.4   Mixed Associations

It is convenient for purposes of illustration to consider two methods for obtaining the analogous quantities to the concentration of monomer in a self-interacting system with reference to the simple mixed association $A + B \rightleftarrows AB$. The first method to be discussed was devised by Steiner (54) for analyzing data from a colligative method such as osmotic pressure measurements. For a thermodynamically ideal solution Steiner's equation is

$$\ln f_A + \beta \ln f_B = (1+\beta)\int_0^m (\alpha_n^{-1} - 1)\frac{dm}{m} + \ln\left(\frac{1}{1+\beta}\right) + \beta\ln\left(\frac{\beta}{1+\beta}\right)$$

(42)

The quantity m, the equilibrium molarity is equal to $\bar{c}/\overline{M_n}$ and the quantities f_A and f_B are the mole fractions of A and B, respectively, defined by

$$f_A = \frac{C_A}{C} = \frac{C_A \overline{M_n}}{\bar{c}}$$

(43a)

$$f_B = \frac{C_B}{C} = \frac{C_B \overline{M_n}}{\bar{c}}$$

(43b)

where C_A and C_B are the molar concentrations of free A and B, C is the total molar concentration of all species ($= \Sigma c_i / M_i$) and it is stressed that $\overline{M}_n$ the number average molecular weight is a function of total concentration. β is the ratio of the initial molar concentrations of A and B, that is, $\beta = (c_B^0 / M_B)/(c_A^0 / M_A)$ and is held constant during experiments in which the total weight concentration is varied, and α_n the number average degree of association is given by $\overline{M}_n / \overline{M}_n^0$, $\overline{M}_n^0$ being the number average molecular weight in the absence of interaction.

Equation (42) is the analog of Eq. (36) for a self-interaction, and its use may be illustrated as follows. For the example above, $C_A = (C - C_B^0)$ and $f_A = (C - C_B^0)/\bar{c}$, where C_B^0 is the total (initial) concentration of B and is known so that substitution of f_A into Eq. (42) allows f_B to be evaluated. Knowledge of f_A and f_B as a function of total concentration leads immediately to C_A and C_B, or c_A and c_B, as functions of total concentration via Eq. (43). In his original article (54) and a subsequent one (55), Steiner shows how more complicated ideal mixed associations may be analyzed by this method. It is also possible to extend the analysis to nonideal systems (2), although it is suggested by the authors that it may be preferable to proceed by evaluating the nonideality term first, convert the apparent number average molecular weights to their ideal form, and then follow the procedure for ideal systems as indicated above.

An alternative method (52) for finding the concentration of B (and in favorable cases of A also) as a function of total concentration in a mixed association between A and B, is based upon the use of the Ω function described in Section 5.2.3 and is, of course, relevant only to sedimentation equilibrium experiments. The functions $\Omega_A(x)$ and $\Omega_B(x)$ are defined as

$$\Omega_A(x) = \frac{\bar{c}(x) \exp\{ M_A \phi_A (x_F^2 - x^2)\}}{\bar{c}(x_F)} \tag{44a}$$

$$\Omega_B(x) = \frac{\bar{c}(x) \exp\{ M_B \phi_B (x_F^2 - x^2)\}}{\bar{c}(x_F)} \tag{44b}$$

and it can be shown rigorously (52) that

$$\lim_{\bar{c}(x) \to 0} \Omega_B(x) = \frac{a_B(x_F)}{\bar{c}(x_F)} \qquad \phi_A M_A > \phi_B M_B \tag{45a}$$

$$= +\infty \qquad \phi_A M_A < \phi_B M_B \tag{45b}$$

$$= \frac{a_A(x_F) + a_B(x_F)}{\bar{c}(x_F)} \qquad \phi_A M_A = \phi_B M_B \tag{45c}$$

Equation (45c) may be viewed in terms of a system containing a single polymerizing solute where $\phi_A = \phi_B$, $M_A = M_B$ and $a_A(x_F) = a_B(x_F)$. In this case the limit becomes $2a_A(x_F)/\bar{c}(x_F)$ which agrees with that specified in Eq. (41) for such systems: indeed the extrapolation yields the total activity of the monomer at x_F, represented here by reason of nomenclature as $2a_A(x_F)$.

Since in the mixed association discussed in the present work we have defined B as the smaller reactant ($\phi_B M_B < \phi_A M_A$) Eq. (45a) is the important expression in the present context. It is the analogue of Eq. (41) for a self-interacting system and indicates that extrapolation of a plot of $\Omega_B(x)$ vs $\bar{c}(x)$ to infinite dilution will give the activity of reactant B at the reference position x_F. Application of Eq. (39) then allows evaluation of the activity, or in an ideal system the concentration, of B as a function of total concentration, $\bar{c}$. As before, it can be shown that the function $\Omega_B(x)$ is not complicated by the existence of critical points and thus that the extrapolation is quite straightforward. An example is shown in Figure 3.

Examination of Eq. (45b) leads to the conclusion that a plot of the Ω function for the larger of the two reactants in the interaction is not useful, since its intercept with the vertical axis is at infinity. However, a useful plot

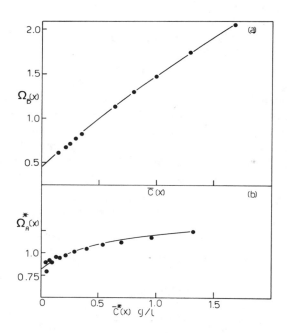

FIGURE 3

Plots of the "Ω function" for a mixture of lysozyme, B, of initial concentration 0.244 g/liter, and ovalbumin, A, of initial concentration 0.36 g/liter, in a sedimentation equilibrium experiment at 20,000 rpm, pH 6.80, $I = 0.02$, 25°C. (a) A plot of $\Omega_B(x)$ as defined in Eq. (44b) vs the total solute concentration $\bar{c}(x)$. The reference point, x_F, was 7.0318 cm from the axis of rotation and $\bar{c}(x_F)$ was 0.521 g/liter. (b) The corresponding plot of $\Omega_A^*(x)$ defined in Eq. (46a) vs $\bar{c}^*(x) = \bar{c}(x) - c_B(x)$. Solid lines show the extrapolations to obtain the limiting values of $\Omega_B(x)$ and $\Omega_A^*(x)$ required for evaluation of the thermodynamic activities of B and A, respectively, as functions of $\bar{c}(x)$. (Adapted from ref. 44 with permission of the North-Holland Publishing Company.)

may be constructed by defining

$$\Omega_A^{\star}(x) = \frac{\bar{c}^*(x)\exp\{M_A\phi_A(x_F^2 - x^2)\}}{\bar{c}^*(x_F)} \tag{46a}$$

$$= \frac{\bar{c}^*(x)}{\bar{c}^*(x_F)}\frac{a_A(x_F)}{a_A(x)} \tag{46b}$$

where

$$\bar{c}^*(x) = \bar{c}(x) - c_B(x) \tag{46c}$$

It follows that

$$\lim_{\bar{c}^*(x)\to 0} \Omega_A^{\star}(x) = \frac{a_A(x_F)}{\bar{c}^*(x_F)} \tag{46d}$$

The plot of $\Omega_A^{\star}(x)$ contains no critical points and evidently, evaluation of $a_A(x_F)$ from its intercept at $\bar{c}^*(x)=0$, via Eq. (46d), provides a means of determining the thermodynamic activity or concentration of reactant A as a function of total concentration once the relevant data for B are available by application of Eqs. (45a) and (39). In the original presentation (52) a cautious note was sounded on the use of $\Omega_A^{\star}$, on the grounds that the required extrapolation seemed likely to be difficult on account of the steepness of the $\Omega_A^{\star}$ vs $\bar{c}^*$ plot. This view was based on the behavior of a numerical example and more recent experience with a real protein interaction (44) suggests that it may be unduly pessimistic. As Figure 3b illustrates, although there is the scatter of points expected to be associated with a difference method, the extrapolation is not difficult.

5.3 THE ANALYSIS OF INTERACTIONS

In the final two sections some methods of analysis of protein-protein interactions that make use of the data available from equilibrium techniques will be illustrated, first, by outlining some procedures, and then (in Section 5.4), by discussing some specific cases. The process of analysis as defined here is aimed essentially at discovering the stoichiometries of the interactions and the values of the equilibrium constants that govern them. A comprehensive survey can not be attempted, but it is hoped that the description of a few representative approaches and some recent developments will supply a useful set of basic techniques. For more inclusive coverage the reader is referred to several recent articles (2, 12, 13, 15, 56) reviewing most of the many methods now available to facilitate this process, nicely described by Eisenberg (16) as "a delicate undertaking entailing ambiguities which are not always easily avoided."

5.3.1 Types of Protein – Protein Interaction

Chapter 1 has given a description of the types of interaction encountered in practice. The following section provides a summary of those particular interactions which have been studied by equilibrium methods.

5.3.1.1 Self-associations

These are of three basic types. First, systems are encountered where a monomer exists in equilibrium with essentially one higher polymer, interactions of this type being described by

$$nP_1 \overset{K_n}{\rightleftharpoons} P_n \qquad (n \text{ assumes a single value}) \qquad (47a)$$

Second, situations arise where monomer coexists in equilibrium with a series of polymers, according to

$$P_1 + P_{i-1} \overset{K_i}{\rightleftharpoons} P_i \qquad (47b)$$

In the latter situation, a limited series of polymers may exist $(i = 1, 2 \cdots n)$ terminating with the polymer P_n of definite size and the self-association is termed definite or discrete. Alternatively, the series of polymers may interact such that $(i = 1, 2 \cdots \infty)$ and an indefinite self-association is encountered. The equilibrium constants K_n and K_i are taken to be association constants on the molar scale as defined in Eqs. (26) and (27). This implies either that nonideality effects are negligible or that the "Adams–Fujita assumption" is applicable so that $y_i / y_{i-1} y_1 = 1$. The molar equilibrium constants may be expressed on the g/liter scale as k_n or k_i using the standard relations,

$$K_n = k_n \left(\frac{M_1}{n} \right)^{n-1} \qquad K_i = k_i \left(\frac{M_1}{i} \right)^{i-1} \qquad (48)$$

The limited series and the indefinite series may be divided into further categories depending on the relative magnitudes of the equilibrium constants. In the former, a fairly common category is described by K_3, K_5, and so on $= 0$ so that, after the dimerization step, the system consists essentially of tetramer, hexamer, up to some finite aggregate. An example is bovine insulin at pH 2 (39). In the indefinite series a recent review (2) lists explicitly the following four subcategories: (a) all species are present, all K_i are equal; (b) the odd-numbered species are absent, but all K_i are equal, that is, $K_2 = K_4$, and so on; (c) the dimerization constant is different from all the others that are equal, a variant of (a); (d) all odd-numbered species are absent, and the dimerization constant is different from all the others which are equal, a variant of (b). The case of an indefinite series where all the equilibrium constants on a molar basis are equal is called "isodesmic" and seems to represent, at least to a close enough approximation, a number of real systems (28, 33). The reason is that it describes the situation where the sequential addition of protomers to a growing aggregate involves the same standard free energy increment. The existence of such a situation allows a considerable simplification in the expression for the total concentration (57). Thus for an isodesmic indefinite association where all $K_i = K_1$,

$$\bar{c} = \frac{M_1 C_1}{(1 - K_1 C_1)^2} \qquad K_1 C_1 < 1 \qquad (49a)$$

Alternatively, an equilibrium constant on a weight concentration basis can be determined as $k = K_1 / M_1$, whereupon

$$\bar{c} = \frac{c_1}{(1 - kc_1)^2} \qquad kc_1 < 1 \qquad (49b)$$

The constant, k, has dimensions of liter/g but must not be confused with k_i defined in Eq. (48), since the latter are not equal for an isodesmic association. It is relevant to note, in connection with Eq. (49) that Eisenberg (16) has shown using probability arguments that the requirement that $kc_1 < 1$ is always true. Equations (49a) and (49b) embody the possibility of evaluating equilibrium constants in indefinite protein associations when the monomer concentration is known as a function of total concentration $\bar{c}$. It has been shown (33,58) that closed solutions of similar form to those in Eqs. (49) can be written also for more complicated indefinite associations such as those listed (a) to (d) above.

5.3.1.2 Mixed associations

A set of categories similar to those used for self-associations may be formulated. Examples are formation of a single complex,

$$n A + m B \rightleftharpoons A_n B_m \qquad (50a)$$

or a limited series of complexes analogous to multiple binding of a small ligand to an acceptor,

$$A \quad + B \rightleftharpoons AB$$

$$AB \quad + B \rightleftharpoons AB_2 \qquad (50b)$$

$$\vdots \qquad \vdots$$

$$AB_{n-1} + B \rightleftharpoons AB_n$$

The formation of an indefinite series of compounds could be envisaged in two ways. First, Steiner (54) has considered situations where both A and B self-associate, and an array of complexes is formed between the various polymers: later he extended the concept in relation to systems comprising more than two reactants (55). Second, an infinite array of complexes was visualized in the scheme of Calvert and co-workers (59) who considered the case of multifunctional A with f equivalent and independent sites reacting with bivalent B to produce A_iB_j, where $i = 1, 2 \cdots \infty$; $j = (i-1), i, (i+1) \cdots i(f-1)+1)$. In specific terms this array may be formulated as

$$A_iB_j$$

$i=1$	:	A	AB	AB_2	$\cdots$	AB_f	
$i=2$	:	A_2B	A_2B_2	A_2B_3	$\cdots$	A_2B_{2f-1}	(50c)

Even for systems like these it is possible to write equations for the molar concentration of any complex in terms of the free concentrations of A and B (54, 59). The examples quoted are sufficient to show that analysis is feasible of systems as complex as any likely to be encountered in practice. In Section 5.4.3 the application of equilibrium sedimentation to one such system is discussed to illustrate how the analysis might proceed.

5.3.2   Methods Using Molecular Weight Averages

The first step in most analysis procedures is to decide on a model, or set of models, to be tested and some aspects of the selection process often seem more like an art than a science. Sometimes guidance as to a likely model may be obtained from the appearance of the average molecular weight vs concentration plot. Certainly, this usually defines the molecular weight of the protomer in the reaction as described earlier (in Section 5.2.1) and it may also indicate the molecular weight of the largest oligomer. Unfortunately, the relative magnitudes of equilibrium constants and of contributions of thermodynamic nonideality can frequently obscure this information. Figure 4 shows the influence of the value of the equilibrium constant, and Figure 5 that of nonideality on weight average molecular weights in two types of dissociating protein systems. Certain "diagnostic plots" (15) utilizing either combinations of weight, number and z-average molecular weight (61–63) or concentration distribution data (37) are available for systems containing two or three species and may be applied if such a reaction is suspected.

In an interesting treatment of the problem of defining the stoichiometry of protein self-associations under thermodynamically ideal conditions, Teller (13) finds that the *optimum* information is available when the weight fraction of monomer has a value of 0.24. This value supplies some guidance as to an adequate concentration range for investigating a particular association but it may be impractical under the initially chosen set of conditions. Experiments under a more favorable set of conditions should then be considered. Teller's deliberations also indicate that there are quite well-defined differences in the value of the "saturation function" (defined as the ratio of polymer concentration to total concentration), which need to be attained to allow a decision about stoichiometry when different molecular weight averages are measured. To distinguish between the examples he chose, a monomer-dimer and an

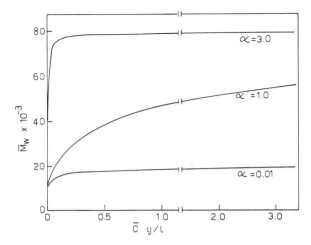

FIGURE 4

Variation of weight average molecular weight with concentration for the association of a monomer of molecular weight 10,000 to form octamer. The association constant for dimer formation, K_2, [defined by Eq. (27)] was given the value 1×10^5. The "cooperativity parameter," α, (defined by $\alpha = K_{i+1}/K_i$) provides a convenient way of varying the relative magnitudes of successive equilibrium constants. The values selected in this example illustrate the difficulties that can arise in specifying a model from the appearance of the average molecular weight vs concentration curves of associating protein systems. (Taken from ref. 23.)

indefinite self-association, Teller found the saturation function would need to be about 0.5 for $\overline{M}_n$ data, about 0.45 for $\overline{M}_w$ data, and 0.4 for $\overline{M}_z$ data. No distinction seemed possible unless the saturation function was greater than about 0.35. For thermodynamically nonideal systems and more complex stoichiometries even higher fractional saturations would have to be reached.

In general analysis of protein interactions proceeds by trial and error, likely models are tested first, and in the process the experimenter develops a "feel" for what modifications and extensions are necessary. The broad-ranging review by Kim et al. (15) of investigation of self-associations by equilibrium sedimentation suggests three general categories of analyzing average molecular weight versus concentration data, "derivative procedures," "general curve-fitting procedures," and "combinations of molecular weight averages." These are appropriate to average molecular weight data from any of the equilibrium methods considered and one example under each heading is given here briefly to indicate the scope of the techniques.

A classic "derivative procedure" is based on the formulation by Steiner (36), who wrote for a self-associating system,

$$\bar{c}\overline{M}_w / M_1 = f_1\bar{c} + 2k_2^*(f_1\bar{c})^2 + 3k_3^*(f_1\bar{c})^3 + \cdots \tag{51a}$$

where f_1 is the weight fraction of monomer as defined in Eq. (31) and k_i^* is

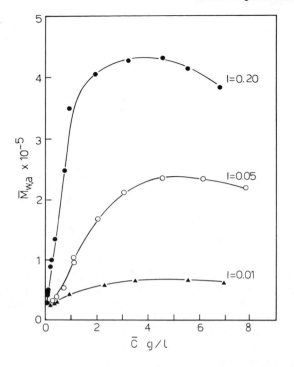

FIGURE 5
Concentration dependence of the apparent weight average molecular weight of β-casein measured by light scattering at pH 7.0, 21°C and three ionic strengths. Thermodynamic nonideality is evident from the appearance of maxima in the curves and, indeed, it was estimated that the true molecular weight at the maximum of the curve for $I=0.2$, for example, is 7.25×10^5. (Adapted from ref. 60.)

the equilibrium constant on the weight concentration scale equivalent to that defined on the molar scale in Eq. (27). Thus $k_i^* = k_2 \, k_3 \cdots k_i = c_i / c_1^i$, where the k_i are defined in Eq. (48). Kim et al. (15) point out that a similar relationship to Eq. (51a) can be written for number average molecular weight data as

$$\frac{\bar{c} M_1}{\overline{M}_n} = f_1 \bar{c} + k_2^* \frac{(f_1 \bar{c})^2}{2} + k_3^* \frac{(f_1 \bar{c})^3}{3} + \cdots \qquad (51b)$$

Knowledge of the weight fraction of monomer as a function of total concentration, obtained as described in Section 5.2, allows evaluation of the coefficients of the polynomial either by manual plots and drawing tangents at the origin (36) or by curve-fitting, for example, by the method of least squares (39). A drawback of the method is the accumulation of errors in successive equilibrium constants because of the need to use preceding constants in their evaluation. Another example of an equation suitable for a "curve-fitting procedure" is that for a nonideal monomer–n-mer system, $nP_1 \rightleftharpoons P_n$,

$$\frac{M_1}{\overline{M}_{w,a}} = \left\{ n + (1-n)f_{1,a}\exp(-BM_1\bar{c}) \right\}^{-1} + BM_1\bar{c} \qquad (52)$$

The apparent weight fraction of monomer, $f_{1,a}$, can be evaluated as described earlier (Section 5.2) leaving B as the only unknown in the equation. This is therefore suitable for curve-fitting to obtain B and hence f_1 via Eq. (34) and k_n^* via the equation for an ideal monomer–n-mer system $(1/f_1) - 1 = k_n^*(\bar{c}f_1)^{n-1}$ (64).

For systems involving more species in equilibrium, or those in which the number of species is unknown, the procedure employing "combination of molecular weight averages" as described in detail in particular by Adams (12) is more appropriate. Once the $\overline{M}_{n,a}$ and $\overline{M}_{w,a}$ have been measured as a function of total concentration and f_a evaluated, Adams suggests the following protocol. (a) Decide on the association model to be tested. (b) Write down $n+1$ starting equations, one for each of the n species and one for the nonideality term, employing the "Adams–Fujita assumption" (Section 5.1.3). (c) Successively eliminate the highest term by combining equations suitably until one equation in the two unknown c_1 and BM_1 is obtained. (d) The relationship $c_1 = \bar{c}f_{1,a}\exp(-BM_1\bar{c})$ [Eq. (34)] is used to write an equation in one unknown, B. This is solved by successive approximations and then one works backwards to obtain c_1 and the equilibrium constants.

When weight or number average molecular weights are measured as a function of concentration they exhibit scatter as a result of experimental error (see Figure 2, for example) and it is usually recommended (13) that some smoothing procedure be applied before attempting further analysis. An extremely sophisticated example is the use of polynomials of degree 10 by Derechin (65) to fit data that were to be successively differentiated in the application of the multinomial theory. Another point that merits comment in the use of molecular weights is the combination of different averages obtained from the same set of data. It is possible to obtain, for example, number average molecular weight from equilibrium sedimentation data (46) or weight averages from osmotic pressure experiments (2). A more satisfactory approach, if methods using combinations are to be applied, is to obtain independent estimates of the required quantities by applying different techniques (15).

5.3.3 Methods Using Concentration Distribution Data

Information in this form is available only from equilibrium sedimentation experiments and is obtained either by the use of the Rayleigh optical system or the absorbance system of the ultracentrifuge. In the former case it is usually assumed that all macromolecular species in the system have the same specific refractive index increments and that there is a linear relationship between the number of Rayleigh interference fringes and concentration on the weight per volume scale; in the latter that at the wavelength employed all macromolecular species have the same extinction coefficient. It is also assumed in what follows that all $\phi_i = \phi$ so that the reactions do not involve volume changes. Although this possibility can be included in the equations (45,66), and should be kept in mind in experimental studies, it introduces an unnecessary complication in the present context. Thus in considering the primary datum from any equilibrium sedimentation experiment, a plot of total concentration, $\bar{c}(x)$, vs radial distance, x, from the axis of rotation, it will be assumed that the composition of the solution at any given total concentration is the same regardless of what radial position it occurs at in different experiments.

For an ideal system Eq. (39) can be written as

$$c_i(x) = c_i(x_F)\exp\left\{M_i\phi\left(x^2 - x_F^2\right)\right\} \tag{53}$$

Then for a discrete polymerization, terminating in n-mer, a set of simultaneous equations may be derived using Eqs. (53) and (26), which relate the total concentration at several different radial positions, x_j, to that at x_F (37,67,68).

$$\bar{c}(x_j) = \sum_i c_i(x_F)\exp\left\{iM_1\phi\left(x_j^2 - x_F^2\right)\right\} \qquad i = 1, 2, \ldots, n \tag{54}$$

This equation may be used directly to determine $c_i(x_F)$ and $M_1\phi$ by any matrix technique that will solve a set of nonlinear simultaneous equations involving the sum of exponentials. Alternatively if $M_1\phi$ is known, as it usually will be (see Section 5.2.1), Eq. (54) becomes linear with respect to the unknowns $c_i(x_F)$ and is much more easily solved, for example by the method of least squares. Once the values of $c_i(x_F)$ are known the equilibrium constants follow immediately. Haschemeyer and Bowers (68) point out that with realistic errors in measurement, five parameters, equilibrium constants or exponents can be determined reasonably by such an approach. It will be appreciated that a model for the interaction must be specified initially so that the required equations can be written.

The nonideal analog of Eq. (53) embodying the "Adams–Fujita assumption" is

$$c_i(x) = c_i(x_F)\exp\left\{iM_1\left[\phi\left(x^2 - x_F^2\right) - B(\bar{c}(x) - \bar{c}(x_F))\right]\right\} \tag{55}$$

In principle this can be summed to give $\bar{c}(x)$ as in Eq. (54) and the resulting set of equations solved for $M_1\phi$, BM_1, and k_i once a model has been assumed for the system. The set of equations is, however, nonlinear even when $M_1\phi$ is known and requires numerical techniques for its solution unless the value of B is known. Even less equilibrium constants can be reliably evaluated in this event.

It is readily appreciated that analysis is considerably simplified if the molecular weight of the protomer, its activity as a function of total concentration, and the magnitudes of thermodynamic nonideality terms are known.

The evaluation of these quantities is feasible and has been described in Sections 5.1.4 and 5.2. In nonideal systems use of the Ω function allows specification of the thermodynamic activity of the monomer (or species of lowest effective mass in the system) as a function of total concentration via Eqs. (41), (45), and (39). Up to that point it is not required that any particular model for the interaction be designated; but to proceed further it is necessary to formulate a model and to form first estimates of the relevant equilibrium constants. The factors involved in model selection were discussed in Section 5.3.2, and it is now timely to explore the question of how equilibrium constants can be evaluated in a thermodynamically nonideal system when the experimenter is in possession of the information referred to above. In this aim the approach recently suggested by Wills and co-workers (28) is followed.

It is convenient to combine Eq. (26) and (27) and to write them in a form appropriate to equilibrium sedimentation as

$$\bar{c}(x) = \sum_i c_i(x) = M_1 \sum_i i \left\{ \prod_{l=1}^{l=i} K_l \right\} \frac{a_1^i(x)}{y_i(x)} \tag{56}$$

where $a_1(x)$ is the thermodynamic activity of the monomer referred to the molar concentration scale at radial position x and $y_i(x)$ is the corresponding activity coefficient of species i. The successive molar equilibrium constants, K_l, are those defined in Eq. (27). On the molar concentration scale Eq. (15) is

$$\ln y_i(x) = \sum_k \alpha_{ik} C_k(x) \tag{57}$$

and the relationship of the α_{ik} to interaction parameters on other scales and their evaluation has been described in Eqs. (24a)–(24c). Since use of the Ω function allows evaluation of $a_1(x)$ as a function of $\bar{c}(x)$, availability of the corresponding values of $y_i(x)$ would allow solution of Eq. (56) in terms of the equilibrium constants for a chosen model. It has been suggested (28) that a suitable first estimate of $y_i(x)$ be obtained by setting $\ln y_i(x) = \alpha_{ii} \bar{c}(x) / iM_1$. Equation (56) is then solved for the model under investigation and the equilibrium constants so obtained are used to calculate the relevant $a_i(x)$. In turn, these are divided by the first estimates of $y_i(x)$ and substituted in Eq. (57) to give improved $y_i(x)$, and the process continued until they converge. The resulting values of $y_i(x)$ are then used in Eq. (56) to obtain a better fit to the experimental data and improved values of the equilibrium constants. The process can be iterated until a desired tolerance is achieved.

Part of the art of elucidating the details of interactions between proteins lies in selecting a method suited to the example under investigation. If the study can be made under conditions where contributions from thermodynamic nonideality are negligible, for example at low protein concentrations, the Ω analysis gives the concentration of monomer, rather than its thermodynamic activity, and equations like Eq. (56), being greatly simplified are much more easily solved for the equilibrium constants. It may be possible to deploy more specialized techniques as well, such as the Laplace transform analysis which has been shown to be useful in conjunction with the Ω function in estimating equilibrium constants in the rather complicated indefinite self-association of bovine insulin at pH 7 (33). Models defined under quasi-ideal conditions then supply an excellent starting point for the application of the more complex equations required at high concentration which may be of interest for reasons of biological relevance (69) or to distinguish between competing models (28,33). Some examples of the application of different equilibrium methods and analysis techniques to specific protein-protein interactions are given in the following section.

5.4   APPLICATIONS OF EQUILIBRIUM METHODS TO SPECIFIC INTERACTIONS

5.4.1   Osmotic Pressure Studies

As we have seen, a great deal of theory is available that is applicable to osmotic pressure studies of protein interactions but there are comparatively few experimental studies in the literature. Here, two studies are discussed briefly, the self-association of a soybean proteinase inhibitor (70) and of the histone F2b (1, 71).

The Bowman–Birk trypsin inhibitor was studied at 25°C with a high speed membrane osmometer at several values of pH and two ionic strengths. Solutions were assumed to be thermodynamically ideal and number average molecular weights were evaluated from the ideal form of Eq. (11), $\overline{M}_n = RT\bar{c}/\pi$. A typical result is shown in Figure 6. The equilibrium constant was computed by first evaluating the number fraction of monomer using Eq. (35). A monomer molecular weight of 8000 based on a comparison of the extrapolated value of $\overline{M}_n$ vs $\bar{c}$ (Figure 6) and the minimum 7975 calculated from the amino acid analysis was employed. Having found the molar concentration of monomer C_1, as a function of total molar concentration, $C(=\bar{c}/\overline{M}_n)$, consecutive association constants were evaluated from $C = C_1 + K_2C_1^2 + K_2K_3C_1^3 + \cdots$ [cf. Eqs. (26) and (27)]. At pH 7.0, $I=0.1$ it was found that plots of C_1 vs C/C_1 were always linear up to a concentration of 10 g/liter showing that the reaction was dimerization with an equilibrium constant of 7.97×10^3 liters/mol.

Peacocke and co-workers (1,71,72) report results on several histones but only the results for F2b at ionic strength 0.1 and several values of pH will be discussed. As Figure 7 shows, measurements of $\pi/\bar{c}$ or $\overline{M}_n$ vs $\bar{c}$ begin by decreasing but then actually pass through a minimum and increase again, providing a classical example, as the authors realized, of the simultaneous operation of association–dissociation equilibria and a large second virial coefficient. The analysis of the system was aided by the independent determination of the molecular weight of the monomer, M_1, in 6 M guanidine hydrochloride as 14,500.

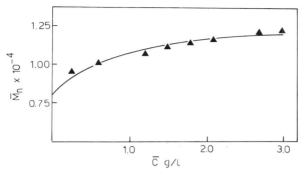

FIGURE 6

Osmotic pressure measurement of the number average molecular weight of Bowman–Birk trypsin inhibitor at pH 7.0, $I=0.1$, 25°C. The data are extrapolated to the value 8000 corresponding to the molecular weight of the monomer. The association was found to be a dimerization. (Reprinted with permission from ref. 70. Copyright by the American Chemical Society.)

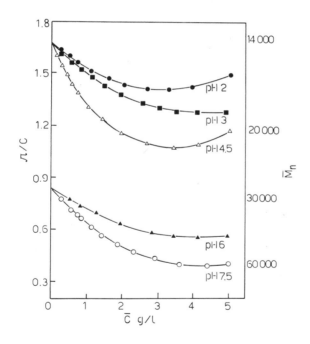

FIGURE 7

π/c and apparent number average molecular weights measured by osmometry for histone F2b at $I=0.1$, 25°C and five values of pH. The shapes of the curves indicate a combination of association behavior and thermodynamic nonideality. In the three upper curves the protomer in the association is the true monomer ($M_1 = 14,500$); in the two lower, the protomer is the dimer of this unit. (Taken from ref. 1.)

The apparent number average molecular weights of histone F2b as a function of $\bar{c}$ as determined by osmometry were combined with apparent weight average molecular weights determined either via the equation, applicable to interacting systems (2),

$$\frac{M_1}{\overline{M}_{w,a}} = \frac{M_1}{\overline{M}_{n,a}} + \frac{d\left(M_1/\overline{M}_{n,a}\right)}{d\ln\bar{c}} \tag{58}$$

or from equilibrium sedimentation experiments (72). Then the procedure of Adams (12) as outlined in section 5.3.2 was followed to obtain BM_1, the stoichiometry and the values of the equilibrium constants. For histone F2b it was found that at all of the pH values studied the association was a dimerization, the protomer being the true monomer (14,500) at pH 2, 3, and 4.5 and the dimer (29,000) at pH 6 and 7.5 as indeed may be deduced from Figure 7. The equilibrium constants ranged from 1.8 dl/g at pH 2 to 29 dl/g at pH 7.5 and the analysis was in agreement with the results of a sedimentation equilibrium study of the same system.

5.4.2 Light and Small-Angle X-ray Scattering Studies

In a light scattering study of the associating milk protein α_{s1}-casein B at pH 6.6 Schmidt and van Markwijk (73) found that nonideality could not be neglected at low ionic strength. Subsequently Schmidt (35) showed how the nonideality could be taken into account in the analysis. As a first approximation, Schmidt treated the system as being thermodynamically ideal and applied Steiner's method (36) to evaluate c_1 as a function of $\bar{c}$ via Eq. (33), using low concentration data, where the assumption was reasonable, and a value of M_1 of 23,000 measured in previous studies. First estimates of association constants $k_2, k_3, \ldots$ could then be evaluated from Eq. (51a) and the concentrations of polymeric forms calculated for use in the estimation of the nonideality terms as follows.

The expression for the apparent weight average molecular weight in a light scattering study is given by Eq. (13), where the second virial coefficient, $2A$, is given by Eq. (18) and the task is, therefore, to evaluate the interaction parameters, B_{ik}. Schmidt made the simplification that monomer and polymer molecules were spherical and that $2B_{ik} = B_{ii} + B_{kk}$. He then evaluated $B_{11}, B_{22} \cdots$ in essentially the same way as described in Section 5.1.4, that is, by taking into account the geometrical covolume terms and the interactions between the electrical double layers of charged spheres using the equations developed by McMillan and Mayer (29) and Verwey and Overbeek (32). Knowledge of the B_{ik} and estimates of the c_i allowed $2A$ to be calculated from Eq. (18) and thus an improved estimate of $\overline{M}_w$ to be obtained from Eq. (13). The process was iterated until the derived k's no longer changed. The final values of the equilibrium constants and virial coefficients were used to calculate the apparent weight average molecular weight versus concentration curve for comparison with experimental data. As Figure 8 shows the method

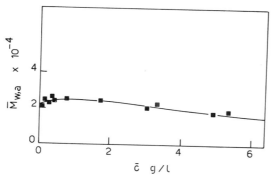

FIGURE 8

Apparent weight average molecular weight of α_{s1}-casein B measured by light scattering at pH 6.6, $I=0.01$, 21°C (points). The line (corrected in accord with ref. 78) is that calculated for a nonideal monomer-dimer association as described in Section 5.4.2. (Adapted from ref. 35.)

was extremely successful. The equilibrium at $I=0.05$ required k_2, k_3, and k_4 for description, that at $I=0.01$ only k_2, and at $I=0.003$ no association was detectable. It is noteworthy that virtually no correction for nonideality was required at protein concentrations below 1 g/liter, validating the initial treatment in terms of ideal behavior at low concentrations.

So far as the author is aware, small-angle X-ray scattering has never been used to elucidate the details of a protein interaction de novo. It would appear that its chief value in this context may be, as Pessen et al. (7) have suggested, to give information about shape and hydration of protein aggregates in solution after the stoichiometry and equilibrium constants have been settled by other studies. A very nice example of the application of small-angle X-ray scattering in this way is provided by a study on the geometry of the β-lactoglobulin A tetramer at pH 4.5 and 3° (74). Apparent weight average molecular weights measured by Eq. (14) were in the range 97,000–99,000 at the concentrations used in the experiments whereas the values calculated from the known tetramerization constant obtained by light scattering were 107,000–119,000 ($M_1 = 36,000$, $M_4 = 146,400$). The difference allows calculation of the virial coefficient, $2A$, from the small-angle X-ray scattering results and the values obtained were in good agreement with that obtained by light scattering in the same concentration range.

Of special interest is the evaluation of the radius of gyration of the β-lactoglobulin A tetramer, which was possible from the average measured by small-angle X-ray scattering because the proportion of monomer and tetramer was calculable from light scattering studies, and the radius of gyration of the monomer was measured in a companion small-angle X-ray scattering study. Various models of the configuration of the tetramer were postulated on the basis of the known size and shape of the monomer and their calculated radii of gyration compared with the experimental value. It was concluded that the β-lactoglobulin A tetramer has the geometric structure of a cubic array of eight spheres. A recent application by the present author of a method of deducing quaternary structure of protein aggregates from their sedimentation coefficients (75), it is gratifying to note, gave the same result. A full presentation of equations relevant to the determination of radius of gyration, hydrated volume, surface to volume ratio and hydration from small-angle X-ray scattering is given in the excellent review by Pessen et al. (7).

5.4.3 Sedimentation Equilibrium Studies

Two examples will be presented; the first illustrates the analysis of a mixed association between two proteins, ovalbumin and lysozyme, the second that of the indefinite association of bovine insulin at pH 7.0 which includes consideration of thermodynamic nonideality.

In their study of the reaction between ovalbumin and lysozyme at pH 6.80, $I = 0.02$ Jeffrey et al. (44) considered two possible models. The system was treated as being thermodynamically ideal, a reasonable assumption in view of the restricted concentration range. The first model referred to as the "cross-linking model" is defined by Eq. (50c), ovalbumin, A, is considered to have f equivalent and independent reaction sites, and lysozyme, B, to be bivalent. Equations can then be written (44, 59) for the total molar concentrations of A and B in terms of reacted site probability functions, P_A and P_B, where P_A is defined as the probability that any given site on an A molecule has reacted with a site on a B molecule. Thus

$$\bar{C}_A = \frac{C_A}{(1 - P_A)^f} \qquad 0 \leqslant P_A < 1 \tag{59a}$$

$$\bar{C}_B = \frac{C_B}{(1 - P_B)^2} \qquad 0 \leqslant P_B < 1 \tag{59b}$$

where $\bar{C}_i$ is the total and C_i the free, molar concentration of species i. A site binding constant, k, is defined as the ratio of the reacted A sites ($f P_A \bar{C}_A$) to the product of unreacted A and B sites so that

$$k = \frac{P_A}{2(1 - P_A)(1 - P_B)\bar{C}_B} \tag{59c}$$

or alternatively,

$$k = \frac{P_B}{f(1 - P_A)(1 - P_B)\bar{C}_A} \tag{59d}$$

At sedimentation equilibrium Eqs. (59a)–(59d) apply at each radial position,

x, and may be combined to give

$$P_B(x) = 1 - \frac{2k[1 - P_A(x)]C_B(x)}{P_A(x)} \tag{60a}$$

$$2fk^2 C_A(x)C_B(x)[1 - P_A(x)]^{2-f}$$
$$- P_A(x)[1 + 2kC_B(x)] + 2kC_B(x) = 0 \tag{60b}$$

It has already been pointed out [Eqs. (45) and (46)] that use of the Ω function in an ideal system allows evaluation of $C_A(x) = c_A(x)/M_A$ and $C_B(x) = c_B(x)/M_B$ as functions of total concentration and the plots required to determine $c_A(x_F)$ and $c_B(x_F)$ for the ovalbumin-lysozyme system are shown in Figure 3. Equations (60a), (60b), (59a), and (59b) were then used together with known values of $C_A(x)$ and $C_B(x)$ to calculate $\overline{C}_B(x)$ and $\overline{C}_A(x)$ for ranges of values of f and k at one particular radial value x. Since,

$$\bar{c}(x) = M_A \overline{C}_A(x) + M_B \overline{C}_B(x) \tag{61}$$

the process can be repeated until values of f and k are found which satisfy Eq. (61) for the known experimental value of $\bar{c}(x)$ at the point selected. These values can then be checked, and refined if necessary, by fitting the entire sedimentation equilibrium distribution and those from other experiments as well. When this was done for two equilibrium sedimentation experiments with mixtures of ovalbumin and lysozyme, it was found possible to fit satisfactorily the results of the experiment covering the lower concentration range with k values in conjunction with value of $f = 2$, 3, or 4. However, when the second experiment over a higher concentration range was included in the analysis only $f = 4$, $k = 0.14 \times 10^4$ liter/mol gave a satisfactory fit.

The second model for the reaction, described as the "multiple binding model" is defined by Eq. (50b). In this case only the complexes $AB, AB_2, AB_3 \cdots$ are formed and the relevant equations are (44)

$$\overline{C}_A(x) = C_A(x)[1 + k_A C_B(x)]^f \tag{62a}$$

$$\overline{C}_B(x) = C_B(x) + f k_A C_A(x)C_B(x)[1 + k_A C_B(x)]^{f-1} \tag{62b}$$

where k_A is the intrinsic binding constant appropriate to f equivalent and independent sites for B on A. Again, knowledge of $C_A(x)$ and $C_B(x)$ allows Eqs. (62) and (61) to be solved for a selected x point for a range of values of f and k and the resultant pairs of values checked and refined against the complete equilibrium sedimentation concentration distributions. With this model a value of $f = 4$ and $k_A = 0.35 \times 10^4$ liter/mol was found to give a satisfactory fit to both equilibrium sedimentation concentration distributions. It was not possible to decide between the models on the basis of equilibrium sedimentation experiments alone, a not uncommon situation in analyses of protein interactions. The authors concluded, on the basis of the combination of the above results with those from binding and precipitin curves, that the favored interpretation was that involving the large array of complexes generated in the cross-linking model.

The polymerization pattern of zinc-free insulin at pH 7.0, $I = 0.2$ and 25°C was analyzed in terms of three different models by Jeffrey et al. (33). All of the models terminated with an isodesmic indefinite association but differed in the protomer involved in this process. Model 1 was originally proposed by Pekar and Frank (76) where the species present were specified by $i = 1, 2, 6, 12, \ldots, \infty$ and the reaction was envisaged as an initial dimerization ($M_1 = 5800$) with molar association constant K_2, a trimerization of the dimer, with association constant, K_6, to form the hexamer and, thereafter, an isodesmic indefinite association of hexamers with equilibrium constant $K_{I,6}$. The closed solution for the weight concentration in such a system is (33)

$$\bar{c}(x) = M_1 \left\{ C_1(x) + 2K_2 C_1^2(x) + \frac{6K_6 K_2^3 C_1^6(x)}{\left[1 - K_{I,6} K_6 K_2^3 C_1^6(x) \right]^2} \right\} \qquad (63a)$$

Model 2, specified by $i = 1, 2, 3, \ldots, \infty$ but with a different equilibrium constant, K_2, for dimerization than that governing the subsequent addition of monomer units, $K_{I,1}$, corresponds to model (c) of ref. 2 as described in Section 5.3.1. For this model

$$\bar{c}(x) = \frac{M_1 C_1(x) \left\{ 1 + 2C_1(x)(K_2 - K_{I,1}) + K_{I,1} C_1^2(x)(K_{I,1} - K_2) \right\}}{\left[1 - K_{I,1} C_1(x) \right]^2} \qquad (63b)$$

Model 3, specified by $i = 1, 2, 4, 6, \ldots, \infty$ envisaged a dimerization with equilibrium constant, K_2, followed by isodesmic indefinite addition of dimer units with association constant $K_{I,2}$, and corresponds to model (b) of ref. 2. In this instance

$$\bar{c}(x) = \frac{M_1 C_1(x) \left\{ \left[1 - K_2 K_{I,2} C_1^2(x) \right]^2 + 2K_2 C_1(x) \right\}}{\left[1 - K_2 K_{I,2} C_1^2(x) \right]^2} \qquad (63c)$$

The analysis started by treating the results of two equilibrium sedimentation experiments at low concentration, (below 0.7 g/liter) where ideal solution behavior was assumed. Thus $c_1(x)$ was obtained as a function of $\bar{c}(x)$ by the use of the Ω function and employed in Eqs. (63a), (63b), and (63c) to calculate the complete sedimentation equilibrium distribution for each model for selected values of the relevant equilibrium constants. These were chosen in the following way. For Model 1, the values quoted by Pekar and Frank (76) were used; for Model 2, starting values were obtained by use of the Laplace transform method (77) and refined successively; for Model 3, a range of values between the two previous sets was searched until a satisfactory fit to the experimental $\bar{c}(x)$ vs x distribution for the two experiments was found.

It was possible to fit the experimental data to the desired tolerance with all three models when these two low concentration range experiments were considered. Accordingly the analysis was continued by carrying out three further experiments, which extended the concentration range up to approximately 4 g/liter. Thermodynamic nonideality then had to be taken into account and this was done by evaluating activity coefficients via Eq. (57) and a simplified version of Eq. (24c) in which the charge term was approximated by $z_i z_k / 2I$.

Use of the Ω function in the high concentration range leads to the activity of the monomer as a function of x. The activities of all other relevant species as a function of x may then be calculated by using the equilibrium constants found appropriate to the models in the low concentration range analysis. The activities so determined were used as first estimates of the $C_k(x)$ in Eq. (57) together with the calculated values of α_{ik}, the summation being taken over all species contributing significantly to the total concentration. This gave first estimates of the species activity coefficients, $y_i(x)$, which were divided into the $a_i(x)$ to give improved estimates of $c_i(x)$. Repetition of the process until the values converged yielded final values of $c_i(x)$ which could be summed and compared with the total observed $\bar{c}(x)$. A typical example of the values

TABLE 1

Illustration of the Determination of Activity Coefficients and Species Concentrations for Bovine Insulin at pH 7.0, $I=0.1$, 25°.[a]

Species	$a_i(x)$[b]	Est. Activity Coefficient[c], $y_i(x)$			$c_i(x)$
i		1	2	3	(g/liter)
1	0.102	1.0122	1.0117	1.0117	0.101
2	0.392	1.0191	1.0183	1.0183	0.385
4	0.464	1.0319	1.0304	1.0305	0.450
6	0.411	1.0442	1.0422	1.0422	0.394
8	0.324	1.0562	1.0536	1.0537	0.307
10	0.239	1.0682	1.0650	1.0651	0.224
12	0.169	1.0801	1.0763	1.0765	0.157
14	0.117	1.0920	1.0877	1.0879	0.108
16	0.079	1.1040	1.0990	1.0993	0.072
18	0.052	1.1160	1.1104	1.1107	0.047
20	0.034	1.1281	1.1219	1.1222	0.030
22	0.022	1.1402	1.1334	1.1337	0.019
24	0.014	1.1525	1.1450	1.1453	0.012

[a] The calculation applies to Model 3 and results are shown for species up to 24-mer only; in practice the calculations were extended to include species up to 50-mer at each point. The example is from a sedimentation equilibrium experiment at 14,000 rpm and applies to a point where $\bar{c}(x)=2.359$ g/liter, $x=7.1172$ cm from the axis of rotation.
[b] Determined with $a_1(x)$ from the experimental $\Omega(x)$ plot, Eqs. (41) and (39) and $K_2 = 11 \times 10^4 M^{-1}$, $K_{1,2} = 1.7 \times 10^4 M^{-1}$.
[c] Determined by iteration as described in Section 5.4.3. Reprinted with permission from ref. 33. Copyright by the American Chemical Society.

of the activity coefficients and $c_i(x)$ obtained in the iteration process at one particular x value in one experiment is shown for 13 species in Table 1. The convergence is rapid but the large number of data points required the use of a computer.

The final result of the analysis was that only Model 3 adequately described all of the experimental results when the composition-dependent activity coefficients were taken into account. Thus the extension to higher concentrations and the concomitant need to take thermodynamic nonideality into account resulted, in this example, in the ability to distinguish between three models which were equally good descriptions of the reaction in a more restricted concentration range.

5.4.4   Concluding Remarks

Equilibrium sedimentation has been easily the most heavily utilized of the methods discussed for the study of protein-protein interactions and seems likely to remain so because it is technically the easiest to use and yields most information for the amount of time invested. Traditionally methods of analysis relying on molecular weight averages have been the most popular; in future the emphasis is likely to swing toward those employing sedimentation equilibrium concentration distributions. Moreover, it should become routine to make allowance for composition-dependent thermodynamic nonideality in the treatment of experimental results.

The other equilibrium methods have special contributions to make. Thus osmometry supplies an independent estimate of a different molecular weight average and has the advantage of not relying on assumptions of equal refractive index increments and partial specific volumes (except in a trivial way). Its use is indicated when complications from these sources are expected in the application of the other techniques. Light scattering, being a static technique, is more suitable than equilibrium sedimentation when it is desirable to avoid problems arising from pressure gradients or for monitoring such techniques as temperature jump kinetics. Small-angle X-ray scattering, as we have seen, can give information about protein shape and hydration not available from the other methods.

In many ways, then, these equilibrium methods can be regarded as complementary. This is exemplified in Figure 9, which shows for a particular system how the concentration range most appropriate to each technique for measuring molecular weights extends from equilibrium sedimentation at the low end to small-angle X-ray scattering at the high. It should not be inferred that these methods are advocated to the exclusion of others. Evidently there are problems in the detection of interactions, in the selection of models, and in discriminating between them. The "mass migration" or "transport" methods discussed in preceding chapters provide the obvious supplementary techniques in these areas, but it can be expected that, as in the past, the satisfactory description of interactions between proteins in solution will rely

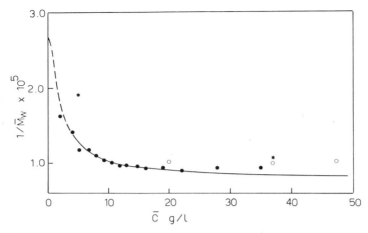

FIGURE 9
Comparison of concentration ranges covered by the equilibrium methods as exemplified in the association of β-lactoglobulin A at pH 4.5, $I=0.1$, 3°C. Equilibrium sedimentation (---), light scattering (●), small-angle X-ray scattering (○). (Adapted from ref. 7.) The concentration range appropriate to osmotic pressure measurements on this system and the apparent number average molecular weights at its extremes (★) were calculated by the present author as follows. Apparent number average molecular weights were calculated using $M_1 = 36,600$, $M_4 = 146,400$, and the association constant for tetramer formation and second virial coefficient determined by Witz et al. (74). The concentration range over which osmotic pressure measurements could reasonably be made with this system was calculated by assuming that 1 cm and 10 cm of water are the lower and upper pressure limits, respectively, usable by the experimenter, in terms of acceptable error and limitations of commercial high-speed membrane osmometers.

on the ingenious deployment of an arsenal of techniques. It is hoped that the discussion has demonstrated that in this endeavor the equilibrium methods provide the experimenter with some of his most powerful weapons.

REFERENCES

1. M. P. Tombs and A. R. Peacocke, *The Osmotic Pressure of Biological Macromolecules*, Oxford University Press, London and New York, 1974.

2. E. T. Adams, Jr., P. J. Wan, and E. F. Crawford, "Membrane and Vapor Pressure Osmometry," *Methods Enzymol.* **48**, 69 (1978).

3. S. N. Timasheff and R. Townend, "Light Scattering," in S. J. Leach, Ed., *Physical Principles and Techniques of Protein Chemistry, Part B*, Academic Press, New York, 1970, p. 147.

4. E. P. Pittz, J. C. Lee, B. Bablouzian, R. Townend, and S. N. Timasheff, "Light Scattering and Differential Refractometry," *Methods Enzymol.* **27**, 209 (1973).

5. S. N. Timasheff, "The Application of Light Scattering and Small-Angle X-ray Scattering to Interacting Biological Systems," in M. Kerker, Ed., *Electromagnetic Scattering (Interdisciplinary Conference on Electromagnetic Scattering)*, Pergamon Press, Oxford, 1963, p. 337.

6. S. N. Timasheff, *Adv. Chem. Ser.* **125**, 327 (1971).

7. H. Pessen, T. F. Kumosinski, and S. N. Timasheff, "Small-Angle X-ray Scattering," *Methods Enzymol.* **27**, 151 (1973).

8. T. Svedberg and K. O. Pedersen, *The Ultracentrifuge*, Clarendon Press, Oxford, 1940.

9. H. K. Schachman, *Ultracentrifugation in Biochemistry*, Academic Press, New York, 1959.

10. H. Fujita, *Mathematical Theory of Sedimentation Analysis*, Academic Press, New York, 1962.

11. J. W. Williams, *Ultracentrifugation of Macromolecules*, Academic Press, New York, 1972.

12. E. T. Adams, Jr., "Self-Associating Systems," in *Fractions Number 3 (Feature Article)*, Spinco Division of Beckman Instruments, 1967.

13. D. C. Teller, "Characterization of Proteins by Sedimentation Equilibrium in the Ultracentrifuge," *Methods Enzymol.* **27**, 346 (1973).

14. K. E. van Holde, "Sedimentation Analysis of Proteins," in H. Neurath, and R. L. Hill, Eds., *The Proteins*, 3rd ed., Vol. 1, Academic Press, New York, 1975, p. 225.

15. H. Kim, R. C. Deonier, and J. W. Williams, *Chem. Rev.* **77**, 659 (1977).

16. H. Eisenberg, *Biological Macromolecules and Polyelectrolytes in Solution*, Clarendon Press, Oxford, 1976.

17. G. Scatchard, *J. Am. Chem. Soc.* **68**, 2315 (1946).

18. G. Scatchard, A. C. Batchelder, and A. Brown, *J. Am. Chem. Soc.*, **68**, 2320 (1946).

19. G. Scatchard, "The Osmotic Pressure, Light Scattering and Ultracentrifuge Equilibrium of Polyelectrolyte Solutions," in B. E. Conway and R. G. Barradas, Eds., *Chemical Physics of Ionic Solutions*, Wiley, New York, 1966, p. 347.

20. E. F. Casassa and H. Eisenberg, "Thermodynamic Analysis of Multicomponent Solutions," *Adv. Protein Chem.* **19**, 287 (1964).

21. J. M. Creeth and R. H. Pain, "The Determination of Molecular Weights of Biological Macromolecules by Ultracentrifuge Methods," *Prog. Biophys. Mol. Biol.* **17**, 217 (1967).

22. E. F. Casassa and H. Eisenberg, *J. Phys. Chem.* **65**, 427 (1961).

23. I. M. Klotz, D. W. Darnall, and N. R. Langerman, "Quaternary Structure of Proteins," in H. Neurath and R. L. Hill, Eds., *The Proteins*, 3rd ed., Vol. 1, Academic Press, New York, 1975, p. 293.

24. L. W. Nichol and A. G. Ogston, *J. Phys. Chem.* **69**, 4365 (1965).

25. E. T. Adams, Jr. and H. Fujita, "Sedimentation Equilibrium in Reacting Systems," in J. W. Williams, Ed., *Ultracentrifugal Analysis in Theory and Experiment*, Academic Press, New York, 1963, p. 119.

26. E. T. Adams, Jr., A. H. Pekar, D. A. Soucek, L. H. Tang, G. Barlow, and J. L. Armstrong, *Biopolymers* **7**, 5 (1969).

27. A. G. Ogston and D. J. Winzor, *J. Phys. Chem.* **79**, 2496 (1975).

28. P. R. Wills, L. W. Nichol and R. J. Siezen, *Biophys. Chem.* **11**, 71 (1980).

29. W. G. McMillan, Jr., and J. E. Mayer, *J. Chem. Phys.* **13**, 276 (1945).

30. J. O. Hirschfelder, C. F. Curtiss and R. B. Bird, *Molecular Theory of Gases and Liquids*, Wiley, New York, 1954.

31. T. L. Hill, *Discuss. Faraday Soc.* **21**, 31 (1956).

32. E. J. W. Verwey and J. Th. G. Overbeek, *Theory of the Stability of Lyophobic Colloids*, Elsevier, New York, 1948.

33. P. D. Jeffrey, B. K. Milthorpe, and L. W. Nichol, *Biochemistry* **15**, 4660 (1976).

34. L. W. Nichol and D. J. Winzor, *J. Phys. Chem.* **80**, 1980 (1976).

35. D. G. Schmidt, *Biochim. Biophys. Acta* **207**, 130 (1970).

36. R. F. Steiner, *Arch. Biochem. Biophys.* **39**, 333 (1952).

37. E. T. Adams, Jr. and J. W. Williams, *J. Am. Chem. Soc.* **86**, 3454 (1964).

38. P. G. Squire and C. H. Li, *J. Am. Chem. Soc.* **83**, 3521 (1961).

39. P. D. Jeffrey and J. H. Coates, *Biochemistry* **5**, 489 (1966).

40. D. A. Albright and J. W. Williams, *Biochemistry* **7**, 67 (1968).

41. T. A. J. Payens and D. G. Schmidt, *Biochim. Biophys. Acta* **109**, 214 (1965).

42. B. K. Milthorpe, P. D. Jeffrey, and L. W. Nichol, *Biophys. Chem.* **3**, 169 (1975).

43. B. K. Milthorpe, L. W. Nichol, and P. D. Jeffrey, *Biochim. Biophys. Acta* **495**, 195 (1977).

44. P. D. Jeffrey, L. W. Nichol, and R. D. Teasdale, *Biophys. Chem.* **10**, 379 (1979).

45. G. J. Howlett, *The Sedimentation Equilibrium of Chemically Interacting Systems with Special Reference to Studies on Lysozyme*, Ph.D. Thesis, University of Melbourne, 1972.

46. D. A. Yphantis, *Biochemistry* **3**, 297 (1964).

47. E. F. Woods, *Aust. J. Biol. Sci.* **32**, 423 (1979).

48. E. J. Cohn and J. T. Edsall, *Proteins, Amino Acids and Peptides*, Reinhold, New York, 1943, Chapters 7 and 16.

49. A. A. Zamyatnin, "Protein volume in Solution," in J. A. V. Butler and D. Noble, Eds., *Prog. Biophys. Mol. Biol.* **24**, 107 (1972).

50. R. F. Steiner, *Arch. Biochem. Biophys.* **49**, 400 (1954).

51. E. T. Adams, Jr., *Biochemistry* **4**, 1655 (1965).

52. L. W. Nichol, P. D. Jeffrey, and B. K. Milthorpe, *Biophys. Chem.* **4**, 259 (1976).

53. B. K. Milthorpe, *Sedimentation Equilibrium Studies on Associating Systems*, Ph.D. Thesis, Australian National University, 1977.

54. R. F. Steiner, *Biochemistry* **7**, 2201 (1968).

55. R. F. Steiner, *Biochemistry* **9**, 1375 (1970).

56. M. E. Magar, *Data Analysis in Biochemistry and Biophysics*, Academic Press, New York, 1972.

57. E. T. Adams, Jr. and M. S. Lewis, *Biochemistry* **7**, 1044 (1968).

58. G. J. Howlett, L. W. Nichol, and P. R. Andrews, *J. Phys. Chem.* **77**, 2907 (1973).

59. P. D. Calvert, L. W. Nichol, and W. H. Sawyer, *J. Theor. Biol.* **80**, 233 (1979).

60. T. A. J. Payens, J. A. Brinkuis, and B. W. van Markwijk, *Biochim. Biophys. Acta* **175**, 434 (1969).

61. D. E. Roark and D. A. Yphantis, *Ann. N.Y. Acad. Sci.* **164**, 245 (1969).

62. D. C. Teller, T. A. Horbett, E. G. Richards, and H. K. Schachman, *Ann. N.Y. Acad. Sci.* **164**, 66 (1969).

63. P. W. Chun and S. J. Kim, *Biochemistry* **9**, 1957 (1970).

64. P. W. Chun, S. J. Kim, J. D. Williams, W. T. Cope, L. H. Tang, and E. T. Adams, Jr., *Biopolymers* **11**, 197 (1972).

65. M. Derechin, *Biochemistry* **10**, 4981 (1971).

66. G. J. Howlett, P. D. Jeffrey, and L. W. Nichol, *J. Phys. Chem.* **74**, 3607 (1970).

67. P. W. Chun and S. J. Kim, *J. Phys. Chem.* **74**, 899 (1970).

68. R. H. Haschemeyer and W. F. Bowers, *Biochemistry* **9**, 435 (1970).

69. L. W. Nichol, R. J. Siezen, and D. J. Winzor, *Biophys. Chem.* **9**, 47 (1978).

70. J. B. Harry and R. F. Steiner, *Biochemistry* **8**, 5060 (1969).

71. J. H. Diggle and A. R. Peacocke, *FEBS Lett.* **1**, 329 (1968).

72. J. H. Diggle, J. D. McVittie, and A. R. Peacocke, *Eur. J. Biochem.* **56**, 173 (1975).

73. D. G. Schmidt and B. W. van Markwijk, *Biochim. Biophys. Acta* **154**, 613 (1968).

74. J. Witz, S. N. Timasheff, and V. Luzzati, *J. Am. Chem. Soc.* **86**, 168 (1964).

75. P. D. Jeffrey and P. R. Andrews, *Biophys. Chem.* **11**, 49 (1980).

76. A. H. Pekar and B. H. Frank, *Biochemistry* **11**, 4013 (1972).

77. L. W. Nichol, P. D. Jeffrey, and B. K. Milthorpe, *J. Phys. Chem.* **80**, 1071 (1976).

78. D. G. Schmidt and T. A. J. Payens, "Micellar Aspects of Casein," *Surf. Colloid Sci.* **9**, 165 (1976).

CHAPTER **6**

Fluorescence Methods

GORDON G. HAMMES

6.1   INTRODUCTION

Fluorescence is a standard tool for studying proteins. It has the virtues of great sensitivity and great specificity. With substances possessing quantum yields of 10^{-2} or greater, micromolar concentrations are readily detectable, and detection of nanomolar concentrations is possible. Since only a few amino acids possess observable fluorescence, the intrinsic protein fluorescence provides a fairly specific and sometimes very sensitive indicator of protein structure and interactions. Chemical modification of proteins with fluorescent molecules is not difficult and also provides specific and sensitive indicators in many protein systems. In this chapter some aspects of fluorescence that are particularly useful for elucidating interacting systems are discussed, with particular emphasis on fluorescence anisotropy and singlet-singlet resonance energy transfer. These techniques permit the study of protein-protein and ligand–protein interactions. In addition, model membranes and cell surfaces can be probed, and structural maps of complex biological structures can be developed. A few specific applications are discussed for illustrative purposes, but an encyclopedic coverage of the literature is not intended as many excellent reviews are available (cf. refs. 1–3).

6.2   FLUORESCENCE: BASIC DEFINITIONS AND PHENOMENA

In simplistic terms fluorescence is the light emitted when a molecule returns from an excited singlet electronic state to its ground singlet electronic state. This is illustrated in Figure 1. The absorption of light excites the molecule from the lowest vibrational level of the singlet ground state to various vibrational levels of excited singlet states in about 10^{-15} sec. For molecules in solution the excess vibrational energy is lost in about 10^{-12} sec through collisions with the solvent. Fluorescence emission occurs when the molecule returns from the first excited singlet state to one of the vibrational levels of the ground electronic state. Again the excess vibrational energy is rapidly lost through thermal exchange with the solvent.

The frequency of light emitted in fluorescence, ν, is given by the equation

$$\nu = \frac{\Delta E}{h}$$

where ΔE is the energy change associated with the emission and h is Planck's constant. Because of the nonradiative losses of vibrational energy, fluorescence obviously must occur at a longer wavelength (shorter frequency) than absorbance. The fine structure of the fluorescence emission is due to the multiplicity of vibrational levels in the ground state since fluorescence always occurs from the same energy level.

In some cases a triplet state lies just below the excited singlet electronic state, and a rapid conversion to the triplet state can occur. Because triplet-singlet transitions are quantum mechanically forbidden, the decay from the

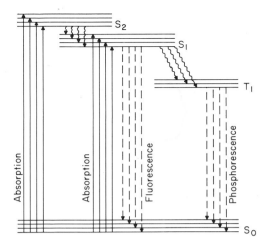

FIGURE 1
Schematic representation of the transition of a molecule from a ground level singlet state (S_0) to excited singlet (S_1, S_2) and triplet (T_1) states and subsequent fluorescence and phosphorescence. The solid lines represent absorption of light, the dashed lines represent radiative transitions, and the wavy lines represent nonradiative transitions. Some vibrational fine structure is shown.

triplet to the ground state is very slow. The emission observed is *phosphorescence* and can occur on the time scale of seconds, whereas fluorescence typically occurs in nanoseconds or less.

The quantum yield Q of fluorescence is defined as

$$Q = \frac{F}{A} \tag{1}$$

where F and A are the number of quanta of emitted and absorbed light, respectively. The quantum yield is not equal to unity because nonradiative processes, for example, interactions with solvent, are available to dissipate some of the energy absorbed. A simple kinetic scheme for fluorescence can be written as

$$D + h\nu \rightarrow D^*$$
$$D^* \xrightarrow{k_f} h\nu' + D \tag{2}$$
$$D^* \xrightarrow{k_{nr}} D$$

where the first step represents the excitation process, the second step represents fluorescence, and the third step represents all nonradiative deactivation processes. The decay process then is described by

$$\frac{d(D^*)}{dt} = (k_f + k_{nr})(D^*)$$

or

$$(D^*) = (D^*)_0 e^{-t/\tau} \tag{3}$$

where τ is the fluorescence lifetime, $1/(k_f + k_{nr})$, and $(D^*)_0$ is the initial concentration of the excited state. The rate constant k_f is the spontaneous transition probability, and $1/k_f$ is termed the "natural" lifetime, τ_0. The natural lifetime can be calculated from the spectral properties of the fluorescent species (4, 5). The quantum yield is related to the fluorescence lifetimes through

$$Q = \frac{k_f}{k_f + k_{nr}} = \frac{\tau}{\tau_0} \tag{4}$$

since the flux of light emitted is $(k_f + k_{nr})(D^*)$ and would be $k_f(D^*)$ in the absence of any radiationless deactivation. Typical fluorescence lifetimes are in the range of nanoseconds to picoseconds.

Absolute measurements of quantum yields are exceedingly difficult to make. In practice quantum yields are usually determined by comparison of the fluorescence emission of the species of interest with a standard having a known quantum yield. Fluorescent species are characterized by their *excitation* and *emission* spectra. In the former case the emission is viewed at constant wavelength and the excitation wavelength is varied, while in the latter case excitation is at a constant wavelength and the wavelength for viewing emission is varied. With most spectrofluorimeters, only *apparent* excitation and emission spectra are measured; the true spectra must be obtained by correcting for the wavelength dependent intensity of the light source and for the wavelength dependent variation of the detector response. These corrections are normally made by comparison with the known corrected spectrum of a standard [e.g., quinine in sulfuric acid (6, 7)]. The corrected excitation and emission spectra for NADH are shown in Figure 2.

The observed intensity of fluorescence, I, is

$$I = I_0 Q (1 - 10^{-\varepsilon cd}) \tag{5}$$

where I_0 is the incident light intensity, ε is the extinction coefficient, c is the concentration, and d is the path length. When $\varepsilon cd \ll 1$, that is, for solutions with low absorbance,

$$I = I_0 Q 2.303 (\varepsilon cd) \tag{6}$$

Thus only at low absorbancies is the fluorescence proportional to the concentration; at high absorbancies the solution acts as an optical filter causing the excitation to vary with the path length of the light. For corrected spectra of two fluorescent species, 1 and 2,

$$\frac{Q_1}{Q_2} = \frac{(I/I_0)_1}{(I/I_0)_2} \frac{A_2}{A_1} \tag{7}$$

where A_i is the absorbance and $(I/I_0)_i$ is the area under the corrected emission spectrum of the ith species. [If the emission is strongly polarized a

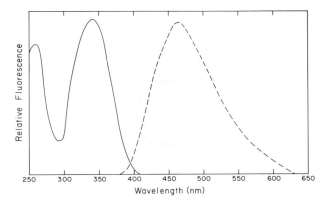

FIGURE 2
Corrected excitation and emission spectra of NADH. The excitation spectrum was obtained by observing emission at 460 nm; the emission spectrum was obtained with excitation at 340 nm. [Adapted from R. F. Chen and J. E. Hayes, Jr., *Anal. Biochem.* **13**, 523 (1965).]

small ($< 10\%$) correction to this equation should be made (8).] Relative quantum yields can be conveniently measured by use of Eq. (7). Relative fluorescence lifetimes also can be determined from quantum yield measurements, since according to Eq. (4),

$$\frac{Q_1}{Q_2} = \frac{\tau_1}{\tau_2} \tag{8}$$

Thus far a very simple model of a fluorescent species has been utilized. Often the decay of fluorescence cannot be described by a single first-order rate process because two or more species are present with different lifetimes. In this case the quantum yield still can be determined from the corrected emission spectrum, but the relationship between the quantum yield and the fluorescence lifetimes is complex. In general the time dependence of the fluorescence decay can be written as

$$F(t) = \sum A_i e^{-t/\tau_i} \tag{9}$$

where $F(t)$ is the fluorescence, the A_i are amplitude parameters, and the τ_i are relaxation times. Unfortunately no method exists for uniquely determining how many relaxation times are actually of importance in a given relaxation process. More often than not, a one exponential decay is assumed, and if this is not adequate, a two exponential decay is used. Very rarely are the data sufficiently precise to require more than two relaxation times for an adequate analysis. Since the relaxation times may only be curve-fitting parameters rather than molecular parameters of fundamental significance, a multiexponential decay curve can be usefully characterized in terms of an average relaxation time, τ_{AV}, defined as

$$\tau_{AV} = \frac{\sum A_i \tau_i}{\sum A_i} \qquad (10)$$

While this definition of an average relaxation time is arbitrary, it has the significance of being the normalized area under the decay curve and, therefore, can be regarded as a relative quantum yield. This correspondence can be shown by noting that the steady-state fluorescence, $\overline{F}$, is

$$\overline{F} = \int_0^\infty F(t)\, dt$$

$$= \int_0^\infty \sum A_i e^{-t/\tau_i}\, dt \qquad (11)$$

$$= \sum A_i \tau_i$$

(Since experimental measurements generally yield a signal proportional to the fluorescence, the normalization $\sum A_i = 1$ is used.)

The excited-state lifetime can in principle be determined by measurement of the quantum yield and calculating τ_0 from the spectral properties of the fluorescent species. However, only approximate values of τ can be obtained with this approach. Two methods are available for directly measuring τ. In one method, the fluorescent species is irradiated with a modulated beam of light, and the phase shift due to the finite lifetime of the excited state is measured (cf. refs. 9 and 10). This method is convenient and rapid but is difficult to use when multiple relaxation processes occur. Variation of the modulating frequency alleviates this problem somewhat, and success has been obtained in describing fluorescence decay in terms of two exponential functions. In the second method the fluorescence is excited by a single pulse of light and the decay of fluorescence is observed directly (cf. refs. 3 and 11). Usually the light is pulsed at kilocycle frequencies and single photon counting with a multichannel analyzer is used to accumulate the decay curve. Since the entire decay curve is determined, it can be analyzed in terms of multiexponentials, although in practice more than a two-exponential analysis is seldom used. The pulse method can be used for times shorter than about 1 nsec only if sophisticated and very expensive pulsed lasers are used (12).

6.3 FLUORESCENCE POLARIZATION

A simple model for fluorescence is to consider two linear dipole oscillators held together at a fixed angle with one of the oscillators corresponding to absorption and the other to emission. The degree of polarization of fluorescence at right angles to the incident beam is determined by the value of the angle between the direction of the absorption oscillator when absorption occurs and the direction of the emission oscillator when emission occurs. For

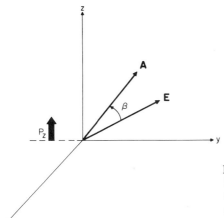

FIGURE 3
Schematic representation of the absorption (**A**) and emission (**E**) transition moments at a fixed angle β interacting with light polarized in the z direction.

a collection of such oscillator pairs the average value of the angle determines the polarization. If, as shown in Figure 3, the light is polarized in the z direction (vertical polarization), the fluorescence emission will be polarized. The degree of polarization, P, is defined as (13)

$$P = \frac{I_v - I_h}{I_v + I_h} \tag{12}$$

where I_v and I_h are the intensities of the vertically and horizontally polarized components of the emission, and the exciting beam either is polarized in the z (vertical) direction or is unpolarized. The extent of polarization depends on the average angle discussed above, which, of course, depends on how rapidly the fluorescent species rotates. If no appreciable rotation occurs during the excited state lifetime, such as in very viscous media, the emission has its maximum polarization, P_0, which depends on the fixed angle, β, between the absorption and emission dipoles. For vertically polarized excitation (14)

$$P_0 = \frac{3\cos^2\beta - 1}{3 + \cos^2\beta} \tag{13}$$

so that the maximum value of $P_0 = 0.5$. The other extreme value of the polarization occurs when the period of molecular rotation is short relative to the fluorescence lifetime. In this case the emission dipole loses all memory of the excitation polarization and $P = 0$. When the fluorescence lifetime and rotational period are comparable, the polarization will have values intermediate between 0 and P_0.

A somewhat more useful measure of the polarization of fluorescence is the emission anisotropy, r, which is defined as (15)

$$r = \frac{I_v - I_h}{I_v + 2I_h} \qquad \text{(vertically polarized excitation)} \tag{14}$$

or

$$r_n = \frac{I_v - I_h}{2I_v + I_h} \qquad \text{(natural excitation)} \qquad (15)$$

The emission anisotropy and degree of polarization are, of course, simply related by

$$r = \frac{2P}{3 - P} \qquad (16)$$

The physical interpretation of the emission anisotropy is similar to that of the degree of polarization. The advantage of the former is that its time dependence is determined only by the rotational motion of the fluorescent species, whereas the time dependence of the degree of polarization is determined both by the fluorescence lifetime and the rotational motion (3, 16). The maximum value of r is (16)

$$r_0 = \frac{0.4(3\cos^2\beta - 1)}{2} \qquad (17)$$

so that the maximum value of r_0 is 0.4.

For a rigid spherical molecule, the decay of anisotropy is given by (17)

$$r(t) = r_0 e^{-t/\phi} \qquad (18)$$

where ϕ, the rotational correlation time, is

$$\phi = \frac{V\eta}{kT} = \frac{1}{6D} \qquad (19)$$

In Eq. (19), V is the hydrated volume of the spherical molecule, η is the solvent viscosity, k is the Boltzmann constant, and D is the rotational diffusion coefficient; thus ϕ is a measure of how fast the molecule rotates. For interacting systems of macromolecules, V (and therefore ϕ) can undergo marked changes, which reflect alterations in molecular weight.

For nonspherical molecules the time dependence of the anisotropy is characterized by a sum of exponential terms. For example, for a symmetrical ellipsoid (3, 16),

$$r(t) = \sum_{i=1}^{3} A_i e^{-t/\theta_i} \qquad (20)$$

where the correlation times, θ_i, are functions of the rotational diffusion constants about the major and minor axes (D_1 and D_2), and the amplitudes, A_i, are functions of the absorption and emission transition moment tensors $[\phi_1 = 1/(6D_2); \; \phi_2 = 1/(5D_2 + D_1); \; \phi_3 = 1/(2D_2 + 4D_1)]$. For a small value of t/θ_i, the anisotropy can be approximated as (16)

$$r = r_0 e^{-t/\theta_h} \qquad (21)$$

where θ_h is a harmonic average defined by

$$\frac{1}{\theta_h} = \frac{1}{3} \sum \frac{A_i}{\theta_i} \qquad (22)$$

If the fluorescence emission of a macromolecule is due to a small aromatic chromophore bound to the macromolecule, the chromophore may rotate locally as well as with the macromolecule. For the case where the chromophore rotates freely around its connection to the macromolecule (18)

$$r(t) = e^{-t/\theta}\left(A_1 e^{-2t/\theta_i} + A_2 e^{-t/6\theta_i} + A_3\right) \tag{23}$$

where θ and θ_i are the correlation times of the macromolecule and of the chromophore, respectively. In a qualitative sense, whenever local motion of the fluorescent species or a flexibility of the macromolecule is present that is more rapid than the overall rotation of the macromolecule, a more rapid decay of the anisotropy will be seen in addition to the decay associated with the rigid macromolecule. Of course, to determine $r(t)$ at all, θ and τ must be comparable.

Even if polarizers are not present, the fluorescence emission may be polarized, since the electric vector of unpolarized light vibrates only in the plane perpendicular to the direction of propagation. If the excited light is polarized along the z axis and the detection polarizer is oriented at 54.74° with respect to the z axis, the decay of fluorescence is only dependent on τ (3). In principle fluorescence lifetimes should be determined under such conditions, but in practice this is seldom done.

The steady-state anisotropy, $\bar{r}$, can be calculated from the time-dependent fluorescence and emission anisotropy with the relationship

$$\bar{r} = \frac{\int_0^\infty r(t) F(t)\, dt}{\int_0^\infty F(t)\, dt} \tag{24}$$

For a rigid sphere and a decay of fluorescence characterized by a single relaxation time

$$\bar{r} = \frac{\int_0^\infty r_0 e^{-t/\tau} e^{-t/\theta}\, dt}{\int_0^\infty e^{-t/\tau}\, dt}$$

$$= \frac{r_0}{1 + (\tau/\theta)} \tag{25}$$

A similar result can be obtained for a rigid ellipsoid: three terms identical in form to the rigid sphere case are obtained, except that each term has a different θ_i. These results are the same as obtained by Perrin (19) in terms of the degree of polarization:

$$\frac{1/P \pm 1/3}{1/P_0 \pm 1/3} = 1 + 2\tau \sum \theta_i \tag{26}$$

where the positive sign is for unpolarized excitation and the negative sign is for polarized excitation in the z direction. For a rigid sphere Eq. (26) can be written as

$$\frac{1/P \pm 1/3}{1/P_0 \pm 1/3} = 1 + \frac{RT\tau}{\eta V} \tag{27}$$

and P_0 (or r_0) is usually obtained by plotting $1/P$ vs T/η. If several different species are responsible for the polarization, the emission anisotropy can be written as

$$r = \sum f_i r_i \tag{28}$$

where f_i is the fraction of the total intensity contributed by the ith species. The corresponding expression for the degree of polarization is (13)

$$\frac{1}{P} \pm \frac{1}{3} = \left[\sum_i \frac{f_i}{(1/P_i) \pm 1/3} \right]^{-1} \tag{29}$$

Fluorescent polarization techniques can be used to monitor the binding of small molecules to macromolecules, to study conformational changes in macromolecules, and to study the self-association of macromolecules.

6.4   RESONANCE ENERGY TRANSFER

One of the mechanisms for nonradiative deactivation of the excited state is the transfer of the energy for fluorescent molecules in the excited state to a second molecule in the ground state. If the second molecule also is fluorescent, the transferred energy can be emitted as a fluorescence characteristic of the second molecule. If the second molecule is not fluorescent, the energy is lost through equilibration with solvent. The conditions for energy transfer to occur are that the fluorescence emission of the fluorescent energy donor overlap the absorption spectrum of the energy acceptor, as shown schematically in Figure 4, and that the energy donor and acceptor are sufficiently close and favorably oriented. A quantitative theory for singlet-singlet energy transfer has been developed assuming the transfer occurs through dipole-dipole interactions of donor and acceptor (20, 21). This theory is not valid when the donor and acceptor are very close because multipole and electron exchange interactions also can result in energy transfer.

Energy transfer to an acceptor A can be included in the decay mechanism for an excited fluorescent species by addition of the following processes to Eq. (2):

$$D^* + A \xrightarrow{k_t} A^* + D \qquad \text{(transfer)}$$

$$A^* \rightarrow A + h\nu'' \qquad \text{(emission)} \tag{30}$$

or

$$A^* \rightarrow A \qquad \text{(radiationless)}$$

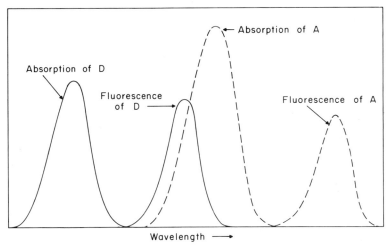

FIGURE 4

Schematic representation of the spectral overlap necessary for resonance energy transfer between an energy donor D and an energy acceptor A. A need not be fluorescent.

The theory of Forster shows that k_t can be written as

$$k_t = \frac{(R_0/R)^6}{\tau_D} \tag{31}$$

where R is the distance between the energy acceptor and donor, τ_D is the donor excited-state lifetime (previously written as $1/\tau = k_f + k_{nr}$) and R_0, the distance at which half of the fluorescence decay is due to energy transfer, is

$$R_0 = 9.79 \times 10^3 (\kappa^2 J Q_D n^{-4})^{1/6} \mathring{A} \tag{32}$$

where n is the refractive index of the medium, Q_D is the quantum yield of the energy donor, J is the overlap integral (which is a measure of the spectral overlap of the fluorescence emission of the donor and the absorption spectrum of the acceptor), and κ^2 is the orientation factor for dipole-dipole coupling. The overlap integral is defined as

$$J = \frac{\int \overline{F}(\lambda)\varepsilon(\lambda)\lambda^4\,d\lambda}{\int \overline{F}(\lambda)\,d\lambda} \tag{33}$$

where ε is the extinction coefficient of the acceptor, $\overline{F}$ is the corrected fluorescence emission spectrum of the donor, and λ is the wavelength; this integral can be calculated from readily accessible experimental data. The orientation factor arises because the donor and acceptor transition moment

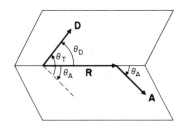

FIGURE 5
Geometry of the donor-acceptor transition moment vector that is used to define the dipole-dipole orientation factor κ^2.

vectors can have different orientations, as shown in Figure 5. This factor can be written in terms of the angles in Figure 5 as

$$\kappa^2 = (\cos\theta_T - 3\cos\theta_D \cos\theta_A)^2 \tag{34}$$

and can vary from 0 to 4. The orientation factor cannot be experimentally determined although upper and lower bounds can be calculated from measurements of the fluorescence polarization (22, 23). If the donor and acceptor rotate rapidly relative to the fluorescence lifetime and the relative orientations of D and A are random, $\kappa^2 = \frac{2}{3}$. This value is often used in calculating R_0, and normally will not cause an appreciable error in R_0 because the sixth root of κ^2 appears in Eq. (32). The uncertainty in κ^2 is discussed further below.

The efficiency of energy transfer is

$$E = \frac{k_t}{k_f + k_{nr} + k_t}$$

$$= 1 - \frac{\tau_{DA}}{\tau_D} = 1 - \frac{Q_{DA}}{Q_D} \tag{35}$$

where $1/\tau_D = k_f + k_{nr}$ and $1/\tau_{DA} = k_f + k_{nr} + k_t$. Thus the efficiency can be readily determined through measurements of the quantum yields or fluorescence lifetimes of the donor in the presence or absence of the acceptor. The efficiency of energy transfer also can be obtained by measuring the induced fluorescence of the acceptor (if it is fluorescent). In this case the excitation spectrum of the acceptor has an additional contribution due to energy transfer. At a given wavelength the magnitude of the excitation spectrum, $\bar{F}$, is given by

$$\bar{F} = \varepsilon_A + E\varepsilon_D \tag{36}$$

where ε_A and ε_D are the extinction coefficients of the acceptor and donor, respectively.

The efficiency can be written in terms of R_0 and R by substitution of Eq. (31) into Eq. (35) to give

$$E = \frac{(R_0/R)^6}{1 + (R_0/R)^6} \tag{37}$$

For a single donor-acceptor pair, the distance between the donor and acceptor can be calculated from experimentally determined values of E and R_0. The validity of this theory has been elegantly demonstrated with a series of polyproline oligomers having a donor at one end and an acceptor at the other end (24). The distances determined with energy transfer measurements corresponded well with those derived from molecular models. Since values of R_0 typically range from 15 to 45 Å, distances from about 10 to 65 Å can be measured with this technique. As previously mentioned, the major uncertainty in the calculation of R is that κ^2 cannot be directly measured. This problem has been discussed often and exhaustively: the conclusion drawn by most investigators is that this is unlikely to be a major problem (25–27). Upper and lower bounds for κ^2 can be established from polarization measurements (22, 23). For typical examples in the literature, this gives maximum uncertainties in R of ± 10–20%. If multiple electronic transitions are of importance, which is usually the case, this uncertainty is further reduced (28). Furthermore, probability distributions for R can be calculated, and they usually are sharply peaked (26). Finally, experiments can be done with different donor-acceptor pairs: if the same value of R is obtained assuming $\kappa^2 = \frac{2}{3}$, the assumption is very likely close to correct. Obviously every possible effort should be made to delineate the bounds on κ^2, but in practice using $\kappa^2 = \frac{2}{3}$ will rarely yield a value of R seriously in error.

The use of energy transfer measurements to obtain structural maps of complex biological structures is a well established area of research (cf. 24, 25, 29). The primary difficulty usually is placing the energy donor and acceptor specifically at known sites. This involves nontrivial protein chemistry! In addition the finite size of the probes and the occurrence of multiple donors and acceptors on the same macromolecule can create difficulties in the establishment of structural maps. If multiple identical donors are present, the efficiency can be written as

$$E = \frac{1}{n} \sum_{i=1}^{n} \frac{(R_0/R_i)^6}{1+(R_0/R_i)^6} \tag{38}$$

where n is the number of donors and each term in the sum corresponds to a donor-acceptor pair separated by a distance R_i. If multiple identical acceptors are present

$$E = \frac{\sum_{j=1}^{m} (R_0/R_j)^6}{1+\sum_{j=1}^{m} (R_0/R_j)^6} \tag{39}$$

where m is the number of acceptors and R_j again is the separation of the donor-acceptor pair. If both multiple donors and acceptors are present

$$E = \frac{1}{n} \sum_{i=1} \frac{\sum_{j=1} (R_0/R_{ij})^6}{1 + \sum_{j=1} (R_0/R_{ij})^6} \tag{40}$$

If all of the donors or all of the acceptors do not have identical spectral properties, more complex equations are generated, since each donor–acceptor pair will have a different R_0. (The value of κ^2 is assumed to be the same, i.e., $\frac{2}{3}$, in all cases.) Obviously such complex equations only can be used if simplifying assumptions can be made; this usually requires invoking symmetry or known relationships among the R_{ij}. If the numbers of donors and/or acceptors can be varied, additional information about the R_{ij} may be obtained. Any practical type of quantitative analysis is restricted to the cases where only a few donors or acceptors are present, or at the other extreme where large numbers of acceptors and donors are present so that uniform distributions can be assumed (see below).

The experimental determination of the energy transfer efficiency is not altered by the presence of multiple donors and/or acceptors. However, interpretation of the measured efficiency can be difficult, and both quantum yields and fluorescence lifetimes should be studied. These two approaches can lead to different efficiencies: for example, if essentially complete quenching occurs for a fraction of the donors, this would be seen with quantum yield measurements but might be missed with lifetime measurements, since no signal would be observed from the quenched donors. The occurrence of multiexponential decay curves is commonplace, and no general theory exists for handling the energy transfer for such a case. The use of an average relaxation time [Eq. (10)] seems to be the best procedure at the present time.

Two cases where uniform distributions of acceptors and donors are present merit special mention for their potential usefulness in studying interacting systems. One is the situation where energy donors and acceptors are distributed uniformly on the surface of a sphere, such as on a cell or a phospholipid vesicle, and the other is the case where one sphere is uniformly labeled with donors and another sphere is uniformly labeled with acceptors, such as might occur for two polypeptide chains within an oligomeric protein. In the initial treatment presented here, the following assumptions are made: (a) donor-donor interactions can be neglected; (b) the same R_0 exists for all donor-acceptor pairs, that is, all donors and all acceptors have identical spectral properties and $\kappa^2 = \frac{2}{3}$; (c) movement of donors and acceptors during the excited state lifetime can be neglected; and (d) each donor is in an identical position with respect to the potential acceptors (this is equivalent to assuming a dilute system in which the donors and acceptors do not approach too closely). This last assumption must be modified for many cases of practical importance, including interacting spheres, as is discussed later. Subject to the above assumptions, the rate equation for the excited state decay of the donors can be written as

$$-\frac{d(\mathrm{D}^*)}{dt} = (k_\mathrm{f} + k_\mathrm{nr})(\mathrm{D}^*) + \sum_i k_{ti}(\mathrm{D}^*) \tag{41}$$

where the sum of energy transfer rate constants is over all acceptors. The decay process is described by a single first-order rate constant equal to $k_\mathrm{f} + k_\mathrm{nr} + \Sigma k_{ti}$. The simplest case to consider is a uniform distribution of donors and acceptors in an infinite plane as shown in Figure 6A. In this case

$$k_{ti} = \frac{1}{\tau_\mathrm{D}} \left(\frac{R_0}{R_i} \right)^6$$

The summation can be replaced by an integral, and the probability of finding an acceptor between R and $R + dR$ is $\sigma 2\pi R\, dR$, where σ is the surface density of acceptors. Therefore

$$\sum_i k_{ti} \simeq \int_L^\infty \frac{\sigma}{\tau_\mathrm{D}} \left(\frac{R_0}{R} \right)^6 2\pi R\, dR$$

$$= \frac{\pi R_0^6 \sigma}{2\tau_\mathrm{D} L^4} \tag{42}$$

where L is the distance of closest approach between an energy donor and an acceptor. In terms of the measurable experimental quantities, the quantum

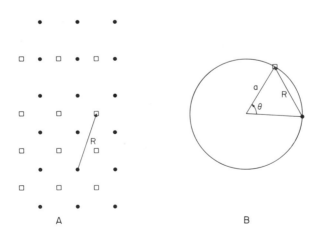

A   B

FIGURE 6
A. Schematic representation of an infinite plane with a uniform distribution of energy donors (●) and acceptors (□). R is the distance between a donor and acceptor. B. Schematic representation of a sphere of radius a with energy donors (●) and acceptors (□) uniformly distributed on the surface. R is the distance between a donor and acceptor.

yields and excited state lifetimes,

$$\frac{\tau_D}{\tau_{DA}} - 1 = \frac{Q_D}{Q_{DA}} - 1 = \frac{\pi R_0^6 \sigma}{2L^4} \tag{43}$$

or

$$E = \left(1 + \frac{2L^4}{\pi R_0^6 \sigma}\right)^{-1}$$

Thus energy transfer measurements permit determination of the distance of closest approach, and the dependence of energy transfer on the density of acceptors. This result can be readily extended to the case of a sphere uniformly labeled with donors and acceptors by use of Figure 6B. In this case

$$\sum_i k_{ti} \simeq \int_{\theta_L}^{\pi} \frac{\sigma}{\tau_D} \left(\frac{R_0}{R}\right)^6 2\pi a \sin\theta \, d\theta \tag{44}$$

where a is the radius of the sphere and θ_L is the angle of closest approach. From simple geometric considerations

$$R^2 = 2a^2(1 - \cos\theta)$$

$$\cos\theta_L = 1 - \frac{L^2}{2a^2}$$

and integration gives

$$\sum k_{ti} = \frac{\pi R_0^6 \sigma}{2\tau_D L^4}\left[1 - \frac{L^4}{16a^4}\right] \tag{45}$$

$$E = \left[1 + \frac{2L^4}{\pi R_0^6 \sigma}\left(\frac{16a^4}{16a^4 - L^4}\right)\right]^{-1}$$

As expected, this reduces to the infinite plane case as $a \to \infty$.

Before considering the energy transfer between a sphere uniformly labeled with donor on its surface and a sphere uniformly labeled with acceptor, we will look at the simpler case shown in Figure 7A where an infinite plane uniformly labeled with donors interacts with a parallel infinite plane uniformly labeled with acceptors. The calculation of $\sum_i k_{ti}$ proceeds exactly as for the case when the donors and acceptors are on the same plane except that the distance of closest approach now is the distance between the planes. Therefore Eqs. (42) and (43) apply equally well to this case except that L is now the distance between the planes.

The case for two interacting spheres is illustrated in Figure 7B. Now the derivation is more complex because each donor on the surface of the sphere sees a different distribution of acceptors. Therefore $\sum_i k_{ti}$ is different for each donor, and the decay process will be multiexponential. The integration over the acceptor sphere can be carried out in a straightforward manner (see

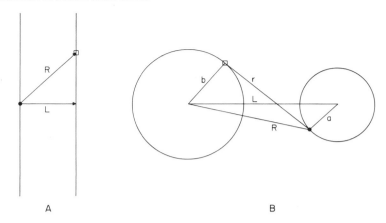

A

B

FIGURE 7
A. Schematic representation of infinite parallel planes with the plane on the left containing a uniform distribution of energy donors and the plane on the right containing a uniform distribution of energy acceptors. R is the distance between a donor and an acceptor and L is the distance between planes. B. Schematic representation of the interaction of two spheres, one containing a uniform distribution of energy acceptors (left), the other containing a uniform distribution of energy donors (right). L is the distance between the centers of the two spheres of radii a and b, r is the distance between a donor and an acceptor, and R is the distance between the center of the sphere of radius b and an energy donor on the surface of the sphere of radius a.

Figure 7B):

$$\sum_i k_{ti} \simeq \frac{N_A R_0^6 \int_0^\pi \frac{1}{r^6} 2\pi b^2 \sin\theta \, d\theta}{\tau_D 4\pi b^2} \tag{46}$$

where $r^2 = R^2 + b^2 - 2bR\cos\theta$ and N_A is the number of uniformly distributed acceptor molecules on a sphere of radius b. Integration gives

$$\sum_i k_{ti} = \frac{N_A R_0^6}{\tau_D}\left[\frac{2b^2}{(R^2-b^2)^4} + \frac{1}{(R^2-b^2)^3}\right] \tag{47}$$

For each donor

$$\frac{d(D_j^*)}{dt} = \mathcal{R}_j - \frac{1}{\tau_j}(D_j^*)$$

where $\mathcal{R}_j$ is the rate of production of the excited state and τ_j is its lifetime. In the steady state $(D_j^*) = \mathcal{R}_j \tau_j$ for each donor, or the total fluorescence observed, is

$$\mathcal{R}k_f\sum_j \tau_j = \mathcal{R}\sum Q_j \tag{48}$$

where $\mathcal{R}_j$ and k_f are assumed to be the same for all donors. The quantum yield is defined as

$$Q_j = \frac{k_f}{k_f + k_{nr} + k_{tj}}$$

where $k_{tj} = \Sigma_i k_{tij}$, that is, the summation over all acceptors already has been done so that

$$\frac{Q_{DA}}{Q_D} = \sum_j \frac{1}{1 + \dfrac{k_{tj}}{k_f + k_{nr}}} = \sum_j \frac{1}{1 + N_A R_0^6 \left[\dfrac{2b^2}{\left(R_j^2 - b^2\right)^4} + \dfrac{1}{\left(R_j^2 - b^2\right)^3} \right]}$$

(49)

This sum can be replaced by an integral over the donor sphere:

$$\frac{Q_{DA}}{Q_D} = \frac{1}{2} \int_0^\pi \frac{\sin\theta \, d\theta}{1 + N_A R_0^6 \left[\dfrac{2b^2}{\left(R^2 - b^2\right)^4} + \dfrac{1}{\left(R^2 - b^2\right)^3} \right]}$$

(50)

with $R^2 = L^2 + a^2 - 2aL\cos\theta$. Unfortunately, this integral must be evaluated numerically for an exact solution. The interpretation of fluorescence lifetimes in terms of this model is complex. However, if the average lifetime as defined in Eq. (10) is used as an *empirical* parameter to describe the fluorescence decay, then since it is proportional to the quantum yield, $Q_{DA}/Q_D = \tau_{AVDA}/\tau_{AVD}$. Thus the above treatment is applicable to both steady-state and transient fluorescence.

Two useful approximations to the numerical integral are possible if the amount of energy transfer is small. If $k_{tj} < (k_f + k_{nr})$, Eq. (49) can be written as

$$\frac{Q_{DA}}{Q_D} = \sum_j \left(1 - \frac{k_{tj}}{k_f + k_{nr}} + \cdots \right)$$

(51)

The integration of the first two terms in this series expansion over the donor sphere can be carried out directly to give

$$E = 1 - \frac{Q_{DA}}{Q_D} = N_A R_0^6$$

$$\times \left\{ \frac{L^6 - L^4(a^2 + b^2) + L^2\left[\frac{8}{3}a^2b^2 - (b^2 - a^2)^2\right] + (b^2 - a^2)^2(a^2 + b^2)}{\left[L^4 - 2L^2(a^2 + b^2) + (b^2 - a^2)^2\right]^3} \right\}$$

(52)

A second approximation is to use the intuitive argument that $1/\tau_{AVDA} - 1/\tau_{AVD} \approx \Sigma k_{tj}$ and to replace the sum by an integral over the donor sphere.

The result is equivalent to Eq. (52) for small amounts of energy transfer:

$$\frac{\tau_{AVD}}{\tau_{AVDA}} - 1 = N_A R_0^6$$

$$\times \left\{ \frac{L^6 - L^4(a^2 + b^2) + L^2\left[\frac{8}{3}a^2b^2 - (b^2 - a^2)^2\right] + (b^2 - a^2)^2(a^2 + b^2)}{\left[L^4 - 2L^2(a^2 + b^2) + (b^2 - a^2)^2\right]^3} \right\}$$

(53)

To illustrate the limited range of validity of the approximations, plots of E vs $L-(a+b)$ are given in Figure 8 for the exact solution [Eq. (50)] and the two approximations [Eqs. (52) and (53)]. Two sets of values of a^2, b^2, N_A, and R_0 are shown.

The primary deficiency thus far in the analysis of energy transfer among distributions of donors and acceptors is that, while the fluorescence decay of each donor follows a single exponential, in molecular systems each donor will be surrounded by a slightly different distribution of acceptors. As a result the fluorescence decay of the entire donor population will be multiexponential, and the analysis becomes quite complex. Only a brief excursion into these more complex theories of energy transfer is given here; more extensive treatments are available elsewhere (30–35). To calculate the fluorescence decay, the average value of D*(t) must be obtained. From Eq. (41) this

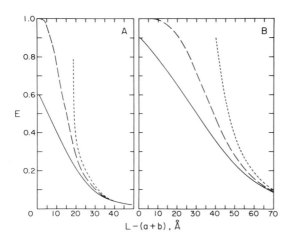

FIGURE 8
Calculation of the energy transfer efficiency between two spheres whose centers are separated by a distance L using Eqs. (50) (———), (52) (---), and (53) (– –). (A) $N_A = 110$, $R_0 = 36$ Å, $a = 21$ Å, $b = 250$ Å; (B) $N_A = 100$, $R_0 = 35$ Å, $a = b = 25$ Å. (See Figure 7 for a schematic representation of the spheres.)

average can be written as

$$\left\langle \frac{D^*(t)}{D^*(0)} \right\rangle = \exp\left[-(k_f + k_{nr})t \right]\left\langle \exp\left[-\sum k_{tj}t \right] \right\rangle \tag{54}$$

where the angle brackets indicate averages. If a random distribution of acceptors and donors on an infinite plane again is considered, the probability of finding an energy acceptor between R and $R + dR$ is $2\pi R\, dR$ for each acceptor and for N acceptors

$$\left\langle \exp\left[-\sum k_{tj}t \right] \right\rangle = \left(\int_L^{r_1} \exp\left[-k_t t \right] \frac{2\pi R\, dR}{A} \right)^N$$

where r_1 is the upper limit of integration, A is the surface area, and $k_t = (R_0/R)^6/\tau_D$. The limit of this expression as r_1, N, and A approach infinity with $\sigma = N/A$ remaining finite is (31)

$$\left\langle \exp\left[-\sum k_{tj}t \right] \right\rangle = \exp\left\{ -\sigma \int_L^\infty (1 - \exp\left[-k_t t \right]) 2\pi R\, dR \right\}$$

Thus the fluorescence decay can be written as

$$\left\langle \frac{D^*(t)}{D^*(0)} \right\rangle = \exp\left[-(k_f + k_{nr})t \right]\exp\left[-\sigma S(t) \right] \tag{55}$$

$$S(t) = \int_L^\infty (1 - \exp\left[-k_t t \right]) 2\pi R\, dR$$

In general, numerical solutions of Eq. (55) are required for data analyses. However, if the exponential term in $S(t)$ is expanded in a series ($e^{-x} \simeq 1 - x$), then

$$S(t) \simeq \int_L^\infty k_t t\, 2\pi R\, dR$$

The resulting equations for both the quenching of fluorescence and shortening of lifetimes due to energy transfer now are identical to those developed previously on a simpler basis [Eqs. (42)–(45)]. This approximation is valid when $(R_0/L)^6$ is small ($< \sim 1$), that is, when the acceptors and donors do not approach too closely. While this analysis has been presented in terms of fluorescence lifetimes, extension to steady-state fluorescence ($\bar{F}$) is straightforward, since

$$\bar{F} \propto \int_0^\infty \left\langle \frac{D^*(t)}{D^*(0)} \right\rangle dt \tag{56}$$

Obviously detailed analyses of energy transfer among multiple energy donors and acceptors can become very difficult, but tractable solutions are available for many systems of practical interest.

Although only singlet-singlet energy transfer is considered in detail here, both triplet-singlet and triplet-triplet energy transfer also are of potential use in the mapping of complex biological structures and have been utilized to a limited extent (36). In the former case, the distance dependence of the transfer process apparently is similar to that of singlet-singlet energy transfer, while in the latter case chromophores must be in very close proximity for energy transfer to occur.

6.5 CHEMICAL KINETICS

Fluorescence changes have been frequently used to monitor kinetic processes. Especially useful is the fact that for systems with a small absorbance, the change in fluorescence light intensity is directly proportional to the concentration [Eq. (6)]. The actual changes in fluorescence can be due to environmental or conformational changes and/or to energy transfer processes. Fluorescence polarization provides a unique method for studying dynamic interactions involving macromolecules, since changes in rotational mobility can be used to follow the extent of reaction (cf. ref. 37). Stopped flow and temperature jump methods can be used to extend the time resolution for kinetic processes to below 10^{-6} sec (cf. refs. 38 and 39). Since the use of fluorescence for chemical kinetics represents the application of principles already discussed, and since recent reviews are available (37–39), further discussion is not given here.

6.6 APPLICATIONS OF FLUORESCENCE METHODS

The primary emphasis in this chapter is on the principles of fluorescence techniques. However, a few illustrative examples are now presented to indicate the type of information which can be obtained. These examples are intended to whet the appetite of the reader for pursuing the many fine studies in the literature.

6.6.1 Antibodies

Antibodies can react specifically with a wide range of different antigens. The overall structure of antibodies has been well established by a variety of different methods (cf. ref. 40), and fluorescence techniques have been used to explore several different aspects of the structure. A schematic diagram of the IgG antibody is shown in Figure 9A. The Y structure contains two arms (labeled Fab), each of which contains an antigen binding site, and a third part (labeled Fc), which is important in aspects of antibody function other than binding of antigen. This structure is made up of four different polypeptide chains, two "heavy" chains and two "light" chains, which are linked through disulfide bonds. The Fc portion of the molecule can be removed by enzymatic digestion with pepsin to give a stable molecule containing the two linked Fab arms (usually designated F(ab')$_2$; Figure 9B), and reduction with

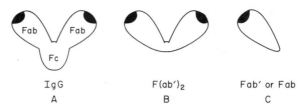

FIGURE 9
Schematic structure of the IgG antibody (A), the $F(ab')_2$ fragment (B) and the Fab' or Fab fragment (C).

cysteine gives separated Fab fragments (usually called Fab'). The Fab arms (Figure 9C) also can be obtained by digestion with papain. The Fab' and Fab fragments differ significantly in that the Fab' fragments contain additional sulfhydryl residues, which can be reoxidized to give $F(ab')_2$.

An important structural question is can the three components of the antibody structure move independently relative to the motion of the overall molecule? The answer to this question was obtained by preparing antibodies that specifically bind ε-dansyl-L-lysine (41). The emission anisotropy of the dansyl bound to intact antibody, to $F(ab')_2$ and to Fab then was measured. The results obtained are shown in Figure 10. Only in the case of the Fab fragment can the data be described by a single rotational correlation time. The data indicate the Fab rotates as a single rigid unit with a rotational correlation time of 33 nsec. Such a long correlation time indicates the Fab fragment is not spherical: the rotational correlation time is consistent with a structure that is a prolate ellipsoid of revolution having an axial ratio of 2. This confirms the nonspherical nature of the Fab structure shown in Figure 9.

The decay of the anisotropy for the intact IgG molecule can be analyzed in terms of two exponential decays, that is, by the equation

$$r(t) = r_0 \left[f_S e^{-t/\phi_S} + f_L e^{-t/\phi_L} \right] \tag{57}$$

Here ϕ_S is the rotational correlation time for the Fab, 33 nsec, and ϕ_L is the rotational correlation time for the IgG molecule, 168 nsec. The fraction of the decay due to segmental motion, f_L, was found to be 0.56. The curve in Figure 10 associated with IgG has been calculated with these parameters and $r_0 = 0.32$. These findings suggest the Fab portion of the molecule can rotate both independently of the overall molecule and with the overall molecule. Again the rotational correlation time of the IgG (168 nsec) is much longer than anticipated for a sphere indicating an asymmetrical structure. Considerable care was taken to show that the multiexponential decay of the anisotropy was not due to the nonspherical structure of the antibody. The results obtained with the dansyl bound to $F(ab')_2$ also indicate considerable flexibility arises from the segmental motion of the Fab's. The hapten itself is bound rigidly to the binding site and undergoes no significant rotation independent of that of the Fab component.

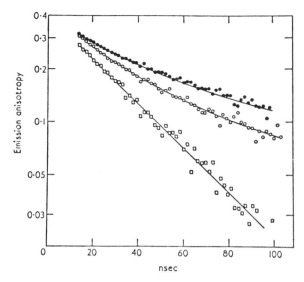

FIGURE 10

Time dependence of the emission anisotropy of dansyl-lysine bound to IgG ($\bullet$), F(ab')$_2$ ($\bigcirc$) and Fab ($\square$). The solid lines are the least squares fits of the observed data to a single exponential (Fab) and to Eq. (57) (IgG) using $\phi_S = 33$ nsec, $\phi_L = 168$ nsec, $f_S = 0.44$, $f_L = 0.56$ and $r_0 = 0.32$. (Taken from ref. 41 with permission.)

The structure of IgG also has been studied using resonance energy transfer (42–45). Three different distances were measured. The minimum distance between the two antigen binding sites within the IgG molecule was determined by preparing a hybrid antibody containing a binding site for dansyl on one Fab arm and a binding site for fluorescein on the other arm. This donor–acceptor pair has an exceptionally large value of R_0, 48 Å, but no energy transfer was observed with the hybrid antibody. This indicates the minimum distance between the two antigen binding sites is $\geqslant 90$ Å. A very open Y structure is required to accommodate this result. Further elucidation of the antibody structure was obtained by labeling a sulfhydryl group near the junction of Fc and the Fab's with fluoresceinthiocarbonyl-D and labeling the binding site with dansyl lysine. The distance between these labels calculated on the basis of energy transfer measurements was 85 Å when the intact antibody was used and 78 Å when the Fab' fragment was used. The difference between these two numbers is within the experimental uncertainties. Thus the structures of the intact antibody and of the Fab' appear to be very similar, namely, quite extended with a minimum length of about 80 Å. A similar experiment was done by labeling a sulfhydryl residue at the end of the Fab fragment (which lacks the sulfhydryl group labeled in the Fab') with the fluorescein derivative: a distance of 64 Å was found between this label and dansyl lysine bound at the antigen site. The measured distances are in good agreement with the results of X-ray crystallography studies.

Because the hapten is immobilized when it binds to the antibody and the hapten is much smaller than the antibody (or the Fab fragment), a large change in fluorescence polarization accompanies the hapten-antibody interaction. This change in polarization has been used to study the kinetics of hapten–antibody reactions (37, 46, 47). Both stopped flow and more conventional techniques have been used. The results obtained using fluorescein as a hapten and a purified antifluorescein are summarized in Table 1. The extent of reaction has been followed with both fluorescence quenching and fluorescence polarization measurements, and good agreement is found between the results obtained with the two techniques. The second-order rate constants are somewhat smaller than would be anticipated for a diffusion controlled process. With both methods slower changes are found to follow the initial combination of hapten and antibody suggesting conformational changes or other processes may be part of the binding event.

The extension of fluorescence measurements to antibodies interacting with more complex systems would be of interest. Moreover, these approaches should be useful with other interacting protein systems.

6.6.2   Chloroplast Coupling Factor

The synthesis of ATP in oxidative- and photophosphorylation involves a complex chain of events involving membrane linked proton and electron transfer. Although the molecular details of the mechanism remain to be established, the chemiosmotic hypothesis provides a unifying foundation (48). In this hypothesis light or oxidation of organic molecules induces a flow of electrons in the membrane, which is accompanied by flow of protons across the membrane, establishing an electrical potential and/or proton gradient across the membrane. The reverse flow of protons and/or reversal of the electrical potential provides the energy for the membrane-bound coupling factor to synthesize ATP. Coupling factor complexes have been isolated from

TABLE 1
Rate and Equilibrium Constants for Hapten-Antibody Reactions[a]

$$H + Ab \underset{k_{-1}}{\overset{k_1}{\rightleftharpoons}} HAb$$

System	Method[b]	$10^{-7} k_1$ $(M^{-1} \sec^{-1})$	$10^4 k_{-1}$ $(\sec^{-1})$	$10^{-11} K$ (M^{-1})
Fluorescein-antifluorescein (Fab)	FP	8.4	8.4	1
Fluorescein-antifluorescein (Fab)	FQ	8.8	8.8	1
Fluorescein-antifluorescein (IgG)	FP	6.0	5.5	1.1
Fluorescein-antifluorescein (IgG)	FQ	7.0	5.8	1.2

[a] Reference 37.
[b] FP, fluorescence polarization; FQ, fluorescence quenching.

a variety of sources (e.g., bacteria, mitochondria, and chloroplasts), and they seem to be quite similar in structure and composition. Only the chloroplast coupling factor is considered here; more general reviews are available (29, 49, 50). As shown schematically in Figure 11, the complex contains two distinct parts. One portion, CF_1, is easily and reversibly dissociated from the membrane without disruption of the phospholipid bilayer structure. The solubilized CF_1 can hydrolyze ATP, but of course cannot synthesize ATP in the absence of a potential and/or pH gradient. The remaining part of the complex, CF_0, is integral to the membrane and mediates proton translocation.

The CF_1 is an approximately spherical molecule with a diameter of about 100 Å and a molecular weight of 325,000 (cf. ref. 29 for a general review of the structure of CF_1 and CF_0). It contains five different polypeptide chains, designated α, β, γ, δ, and ε, of molecular weights 59,000, 56,000, 37,000, 17,500, and 13,000, respectively. The subunit stoichiometry, although still somewhat controversial, is generally accepted as $\alpha_2\beta_2\gamma\delta\varepsilon_2$. The functions of the subunits have not been fully established. However, the α and β subunits contain all of the nucleotide catalytic and regulatory sites, and $\alpha_2\beta_2$ is an active ATPase. The γ subunit apparently plays a role in the regulation of proton transport; the δ subunit attaches CF_1 to CF_0; and the ε subunit, which is an ATPase inhibitor, probably has a regulatory function. The spatial relationships in the intact CF_1 molecule were investigated through the use of chemical cross-linking reagents and two-dimensional sodium dodecyl sulfate electrophoresis (51). The α and β subunits cross-link to each other and to all other subunits; γ and ε subunits cross-link, with evidence for $\gamma\varepsilon_2$; and the δ subunit cross-links only to α and β. A symmetric model consistent with these results is shown in Figure 12A. The subunits are approximated as spheres, although this certainly is an oversimplification, and the δ subunit is not seen because it is assumed to be on the opposite side of the enzyme from γ and ε.

Resonance energy transfer has been used to determine the relative positions of several different sites on soluble CF_1 (52–55), thus providing a structural map of the enzyme. In such experiments, the most difficult experimental aspect is specifically labeling sites with energy donors and acceptors. Also in some cases multiple donors and acceptors are present on the molecule; the distances always were calculated assuming a symmetrical placement of equivalent sites. The specific sites labeled are summarized in Table 2, together with the subunit locations. The reagent 7-chloro-4-nitrobenzo-2-oxa-1, 3-diazole (NBD) specifically labels a single tyrosine residue on a β subunit,

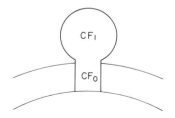

FIGURE 11
Schematic structure of the chloroplast coupling factor, CF_1–CF_0, in the membrane.

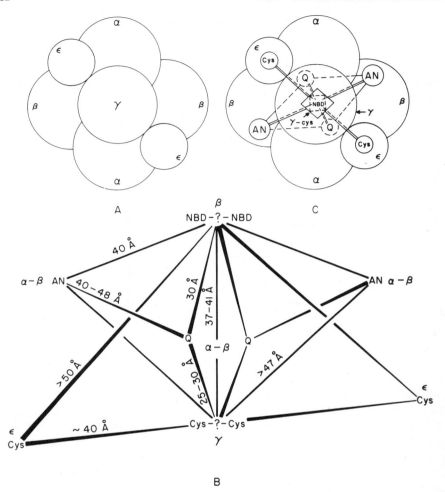

FIGURE 12
Models for the geometrical arrangement of (*A*) subunits and of (*B*) specific sites in solubilized CF$_1$ obtained from chemical cross-linking (*A*) and energy transfer experiments (*B*). In (*C*) the two models are superimposed. The δ subunit, which is not shown, is considered to be on the opposite side of the enzyme from the γ and ε subunits. (Taken from ref. 29 with permission.)

with almost complete inhibition of ATPase activity. A second molecule of the reagent reacts with a tyrosine on the other β subunit at a much slower rate. The tyrosines may be near the interfaces of the β subunits and near the catalytic site, although only circumstantial evidence supports this idea. The fluorescent nucleotide N^6-etheno-ADP binds to two sites on CF$_1$ on the α and β subunits; these sites probably serve an important regulatory function. Quercetin (Q) is a plant biflavenoid which inhibits the ATPase activity; its

TABLE 2
Energy Transfer Probes on CF$_1$

Subunit	Probe and/or Site on CF$_1$ (number)
β	NBD-Tyrosine (1-2)
$\alpha - \beta$	εADP binding (2)
$\alpha - \beta$	Quercetin binding (2)
γ	Maleimide-SH (2)
ε	Maleimide-SH (1)

two binding sites are on either the α or β subunits. Specific sulfhydryl groups on the γ and ε subunits can be labeled with fluorescent maleimides. A summary of the distances measured is given in Figure 12 B. The distances in this structural map are self-consistent and also are consistent with the spatial arrangement of subunits suggested by the cross-linking experiments. The two models are superimposed in Figure 12C.

The entire coupling factor complex can be solubilized and purified (56). This preparation contains the five subunits of CF$_1$, a proteolipid of molecular weight 8000, and three other polypeptides with apparent molecular weights of 17,500, 15,500, and 13,500. The overall molecular weight of the complex is about 405,000. The purified complex can be reconstituted into phospholipid vesicles where it is catalytically active (hydrolytically and synthetically under appropriate conditions). Resonance energy transfer has been used to obtain structural information about the reconstituted enzyme (59). The energy donors were fluorescently labeled monovalent antibody fragments, Fab', specific for the whole CF$_1$ and for the isolated subunits α, β, γ, and ε. Energy acceptors were incorporated into the vesicle bilayer. Stoichiometric amounts of *anti*-CF$_1$-Fab' strongly inhibited the enzyme, and the *anti*-CF$_1$-Fab' sites were found to be greater than 35 Å away from the vesicle surface. (The theory developed in Eqs. (46)–(53) was used for the data analysis.) The Fab' specific to the α, β, γ, and ε subunits did not inhibit and was found to bind 30 Å or further from the vesicle surface. These results, obtained with an active coupling complex, are consistent with the schematic model of Figure 11, in which the CF$_1$ portion of the complex protrudes from the surface of the membrane.

Further energy transfer experiments undoubtedly will provide a more detailed structural map of the chloroplast coupling factor. However, even more important, the general approaches developed (e.g., the use of antibodies as specific labels) are applicable to the elucidation of other complex biological structures.

6.6.3 Phospholipid Vesicles

An important potential use of energy transfer measurements is the determination of distances between molecules on cell surfaces. A good model system is

TABLE 3
Donor-Acceptor Pairs of Phospholipid Analogs

Donor[a]	Acceptor	R_0 (Å)	Ref.
2,6-DPE	2,5-DPE	22.8	34
2,6-DPE	EPE	39.1	34
1,5-DPE	EPE	48.7	34
2,5-DPE	EPE	51.2	34
Anthracene	Perylene	33.5	33

[a] 2,6-DPE, N-(2-dimethylaminonaphthalene-6-sulfonyl)phosphatidylethanolamine; 2,5-DPE, N-(2-dimethylaminonaphthalene-5-sulfonyl)phosphatidylethanolamine; 1,5-DPE, N-(1-dimethylaminonaphthalene-5-sulfonyl)phosphatidylethanolamine; EPE, N-eosin-N'-phosphatidylethanolaminothiourea.

energy transfer measurements between phospholipid analogs on the surface of phospholipid vesicles. Two such studies have recently appeared (33, 34), and the phospholipid analog donors and acceptors are summarized in Table 3, together with the value of R_0 for each donor-acceptor pair calculated from spectral data. In both cases, the vesicles were prepared from phosphatidylcholine.

In the work of Fung and Stryer (34) the extent of energy transfer was measured as a function of the surface density of acceptor for the first four donor-acceptor pairs which have a wide range of R_0 values. The data were found to be in good agreement with Eqs. (55) and (56) assuming a distance of closest approach (L) for the donor and acceptor of 8.4 Å and R_0 values within 2–3 Å of those in Table 3. The approximation of the phospholipid vesicle surface as an infinite plane is quite reasonable in molecular terms. Estep and Thompson (33) used a different theory based on an approximation of the donor-acceptor distribution functions. The results obtained with the fifth donor-acceptor pair in Table 3 were in good accord with the approximate theory which has a single adjustable parameter. If their results are analyzed in terms of the more general theory of Eqs. (55) and (56), only fair agreement between theory and experiment is found: if the distance of closest approach is assumed to be 8.4 Å, the value of R_0 derived from the data is about 44 Å, while that derived from spectral data is 33.5 Å. No difference in experimental results was found between multilamellar vesicles and single bilayer vesicles.

If the energy transfer data are analyzed in terms of the very simple model embodied in Eq. (43) (i.e., an identical distribution of acceptors for each donor), the data conform well to the predicted dependence of the efficiency on the acceptor density, but each donor-acceptor pair is characterized by a different distance of closest approach which is about 0.75 (± 0.04) R_0. While the physical significance of this approach is not clear, it may provide a useful starting point for more exact calculations. More work on these model systems is desirable to establish reliable methodology and theory to handle complex systems.

6.7 CONCLUSION

The study of interacting systems with fluorescence is a productive, thriving endeavor for the investigation of proteins and nucleic acids. The variety of information which can be obtained has been stressed in this chapter, although only a few specific examples have been cited. Future work undoubtedly will extend the use of fluorescence to studies of interacting cells, of interactions on cell surfaces, and of other complex biological processes. Such work, in fact, already is underway. The further development of picosecond laser spectroscopy, single photon counting fluorimeters, and phase difference measurements will provide further impetus to the application of fluorescent methods. Hopefully this review will serve as a useful prelude to the exciting research of the future.

ACKNOWLEDGMENT

The preparation of this chapter was supported by a grant from the National Institutes of Health (GM 13292). I am indebted to Professor A. C. Albrecht for many useful discussions of various aspects of fluorescence.

REFERENCES

1. R. F. Chen, H. Edelhoch, and R. F. Steiner in S. J. Leach, Ed., *Physical Principles and Techniques of Protein Chemistry*, Part A, Academic Press, New York, 1969, p. 171.

2. R. C. Chen and H. Edelhoch, Eds., *Biochemical Fluorescence Concepts*, Vols. 1 and 2, Marcel Dekker, New York, 1975 and 1976.

3. J. Yguerabide, *Methods Enzymol.* **26**, 498 (1972).

4. G. N. Lewis and M. Kasha, *J. Am. Chem. Soc.* **67**, 994 (1945).

5. S. J. Strickler and R. A. Berg, *J. Chem. Phys.* **27**, 814 (1962).

6. W. H. Melhuish, *J. Phys. Chem.* **65**, 229 (1961).

7. T. G. Scott, R. D. Spencer, N. J. Leonard, and G. Weber, *J. Am. Chem. Soc.* **92**, 687 (1970).

8. M. Shinitzky, *J. Chem. Phys.* **56**, 5979 (1972).

9. W. R. Ware, in A. Lamola, Ed. *Creation and Detection of the Excited State*, Vol. 1, Pt. A, Marcel Dekker, New York, 1971, pp. 213–302.

10. R. D. Spencer and G. Weber, *Ann. N.Y. Acad. Sci.* **158**, 361 (1969).

11. A. E. W. Knight and B. K. Selinger, *Aust. J. Chem.* **26**, 1 (1973).

12. G. Porter, E. S. Reid, and C. J. Tredwell, *Chem. Phys. Lett.* **29**, 469 (1974).

13. G. Weber, *Adv. Protein Chem.* **8**, 415 (1953).

14. A. Jablonski, *A. Physik*. **96**, 236 (1935).

15. A. Jablonski, *Bull. Acad. Pol. Sci. Ser. Sci. Math. Astr. Phys.* **8**, 259 (1960).

16. P. Wahl, in R. F. Chen and H. Edelhoch, Eds. *Biochemical Fluorescence Concepts*, Vol. 1, Marcel Dekker, New York, 1975, p. 1.

17. A. Jablonski, *Z. Naturforsch.*, **16a**, 1 (1961).

18. Y. Gottlieb and Ph. Wahl, *J. Chim. Phys.* **60**, 849 (1963).

19. F. Perrin, *J. Phys.* **5**, 497 (1934).

20. Th. Förster, *Ann. Phys.* **2**, 55 (1948).

21. Th. Förster, in O. Sinanoglu, Ed. *Modern Quantum Chemistry*, Part III, Academic Press, New York, 1965, p. 93.

22. R. E. Dale and J. Eisinger in R. F. Chen and H. Edelhoch, Eds. *Biochemical Fluorescence Concepts*, Vol. 1, Marcel Dekker, New York, 1975, p. 115.

23. R. E. Dale, J. Eisinger, and W. E. Blumberg, *Biophys. J.* **26**, 161 (1979).

24. L. Stryer and R. P. Haugland, *Proc. Natl. Acad. Sci. USA* **58**, 719 (1967).

25. S. Matsumoto and G. G. Hammes, *Biochemistry* **14**, 214 (1975).

26. Z. Hillel and C.-W. Wu, *Biochemistry* **15**, 2105 (1976).

27. L. Stryer, *Ann. Rev. Biochem.* **47**, 819 (1978).

28. E. Haas, E. Katchalski-Katzir, and I. Z. Steinberg, *Biochemistry* **17**, 5064 (1978).

29. B. A. Baird and G. G. Hammes, *Biochim. Biophys. Acta* **549**, 37 (1979).

30. Th. Förster, *Z. Naturforsch.* **49**, 321 (1949).

31. N. Shaklai, J. Yguerabide, and H. M. Ranney, *Biochemistry* **16**, 5585 (1977).

32. A. G. Tweet, W. D. Bellamy, and G. L. Gaines, *J. Chem. Phys.* **41**, 2068 (1964).

33. T. N. Estep and T. E. Thompson, *Biophys. J.* **26**, 195 (1979).

34. B. K.-K. Fung and L. Stryer, *Biochemistry* **17**, 5241 (1978).

35. R. B. Gennis and C. R. Cantor, *Biochemistry* **11**, 2509 (1972).

36. L. Stryer, *Science* **162**, 526 (1968).

37. S. A. Levison, in R. F. Chen and H. Edelhoch, Eds. *Biochemical Fluorescence Concepts*, Vol. 1, Marcel Dekker, New York, 1975, p. 375.

38. T. A. Jovin, in R. F. Chen and H. Edelhoch, Eds. *Biochemical Fluorescence Concepts*, Vol. 1, Marcel Dekker, New York, 1975, p. 305.

39. R. Rigler and M. Ehrenberg, *Q. Rev. Biophys.* **6**, 139 (1973).

40. E. A. Kabat, *Structural Concepts in Immunology and Immunochemistry*, 2nd ed., Holt Rinehart and Winston, New York 1976.

41. J. Yguerabide, H. F. Epstein, and L. Stryer, *J. Mol. Biol.* **51**, 573 (1970).

42. R. E. Cathou and J. R. Bunting, in R. F. Chen and H. Edelhoch, Eds. *Biochemical Fluorescence Concepts*, Vol. 2, Marcel Dekker, New York, 1976, p. 845.

43. T. C. Werner, J. R. Bunting, and R. E. Cathou, *Proc. Natl. Acad. Sci. USA* **69**, 705 (1972).

44. J. R. Bunting and R. E. Cathou, *J. Mol. Biol.* **77**, 223 (1973).

45. J. R. Bunting and R. E. Cathou, *J. Mol. Biol.* **87**, 329 (1974).

46. A. J. Portmann, S. A. Levison, and W. B. Dandliker, *Biochem. Biophys. Res. Commun.* **43**, 207 (1971).

47. S. A. Levison, A. J. Portmann, F. Kierszenbaum, and W. B. Dandliker, *Biochem. Biophys. Res. Commun.* **43**, 258 (1971).

48. P. Mitchell, *Biol. Rev. Cambridge Philos. Soc.* **41**, 445 (1966).

49. R. E. McCarty, *Curr. Top. Bioenerg.* **7**, 245 (1978).

50. D. B. Wilson and J. B. Smith in B. P. Rosen, Ed. *Bacterial Transport*, Marcel Dekker, New York, 1977, p. 495.

51. B. A. Baird and G. G. Hammes, *J. Biol. Chem.* **251**, 6953 (1976).

52. L. C. Cantley and G. G. Hammes, *Biochemistry* **14**, 2976 (1975).

53. L. C. Cantley and G. G. Hammes, *Biochemistry* **15**, 1 (1976).

54. L. C. Cantley and G. G. Hammes, *Biochemistry* **15**, 9 (1976).

55. D. A. Holowka and G. G. Hammes, *Biochemistry* **16**, 5538 (1977).

56. U. Pick and E. Racker, *J. Biol. Chem.* **254**, 2793 (1979).

57. B. A. Baird, U. Pick, and G. G. Hammes, *J. Biol. Chem.* **254**, 3818 (1979).

CHAPTER **7**

Approaches That Can Be Used with Enzymes

CARL FRIEDEN

7.1   INTRODUCTION

Much of this book is devoted to physical methods of measuring protein-protein interactions, treating the proteins themselves as if they had no inherently sensitive property that might be useful for such studies. However, a great many of the proteins that do undergo either self-association or associate with other proteins are enzymes (1) and not only may interactions of this sort have important physiological consequences but the enzymatic activity per se might be used as another probe of protein-protein interaction. There are two interrelated questions which are critical when using this particular probe. First, does the association behavior of the enzyme affect its kinetic behavior and, second, does the kinetic behavior of the enzyme reveal useful information about the association reactions? The answer to both of these questions must be affirmative and it is the purpose of this chapter to discuss these issues. It should be pointed out immediately that the enzymatic behavior cannot be definitively used independently of other nonenzymatic methods which measure protein-protein interactions. Rather it is another, albeit quite different, approach for such studies.

In spite of the fact that such studies should provide much useful information, relatively few experimental results have been reported in the literature. This may be a consequence of two problems. One is that studies need to be performed over a wide range of enzyme concentration including rather high enzyme levels where stopped flow methods (or perhaps cryoenzymological methods) must be used to collect the data. The second problem is that rather sophisticated methods of data analysis may be required. The mathematical description of the enzymatic velocity as a function ligand or enzyme concentration can indeed be quite complex and, coupled with problems of rapid substrate depletion, may be difficult to treat. On the other hand, difficulties such as these may be quite simply overcome with computer programs designed for these purposes.

In this chapter we will discuss basic enzyme kinetic properties and analyses which are pertinent for enzymes which undergo association reactions. To give the basis for further discussion, the next two sections (7.2 and 7.3) deal with general kinetic and binding properties for enzymes which do not self-associate.

7.2   KINETIC STUDIES VERSUS LIGAND BINDING STUDIES

The tool that the kineticist has available is the ability to measure the velocity of the reaction under a wide variety of conditions. The velocity may be the initial velocity, those pertinent to the full time course of the reaction or the rate of substrate-product exchange at or near equilibrium. These may be measured as a function of substrate, nonsubstrate ligand or enzyme concentration as well as other variables such as temperature, pH, buffer composition, and so on. For both ligand binding studies and initial velocity studies, it is likely that the behavior will be affected by self-association of the enzyme, but important differences exist between ligand binding and initial velocity experiments. To elucidate this distinction, we will consider in this section the velocity as a function of substrate concentration for a nonassociating enzyme system, and in Section 7.4 turn our attention to self-associating systems.

7.2.1 The Single Substrate (Ligand) Case

It is frequently assumed that a plot of ligand bound vs total ligand concentration is equivalent to that which might be obtained from initial velocity studies. While it is true that the shape of the curves may be the same, the exact equivalence of these two plots involves certain implicit assumptions, even for the case where there is no self-association of the enzyme. Thus only if the enzyme and substrate equilibrate rapidly with the enzyme-substrate complex relative to the conversion of the enzyme-substrate complex to enzyme and product is the Michaelis constant equivalent to a dissociation constant. Another difference is that while direct binding measurements can yield the number of binding sites per mole of enzyme, initial velocity experiments give no information on this point. Unfortunately for a single substrate enzyme it is not possible to carry out substrate binding experiments, since the enzyme will catalyze the reaction of substrate to product. In many ways the situation is less complex for multisubstrate enzymes as discussed in Section 7.2.2.

For the single substrate case and using ligands that are not substrates (i.e., modifiers which are activators or inhibitors), the relation between a direct binding plot and the effect of the modifier on enzymatic activity is clearest with true competitive inhibitors, in which case the inhibition constant is a dissociation constant. For ligands that do not bind at the active site, the situation can be more complex depending on the rate-determining step in the enzymatic reaction and the influence of the substrate concentration on the dissociation constant for the effector. For the mechanism

$$E + A \underset{}{\overset{K_1}{\rightleftharpoons}} EA \overset{k_1}{\rightarrow} E + P$$

$$E + M \underset{}{\overset{K_2}{\rightleftharpoons}} EM$$

$$\left.\begin{array}{l} EA + M \overset{K_3}{\rightleftharpoons} EAM \\ \\ EM + A \overset{K_4}{\rightleftharpoons} EAM \end{array}\right\} \overset{k_2}{\rightarrow} EM + P$$

and assuming that all species equilibrate rapidly, that k_1 and k_2 are rate limiting steps, and that K_1–K_4 are dissociation constants, the initial velocity equation which describes the relation between the substrate and effector concentration is (2)

$$\frac{v_0}{\overline{m}_E} = \frac{k_1[1+k_2 m_M/k_1 K_3]/(1+m_M/K_3)}{1+(K_1/m_A)\{(1+m_M/K_2)/(1+m_M/K_3)\}} \tag{1}$$

where v_0 is the initial velocity, and $\overline{m}_E$ is the total molar concentration of the enzyme and m_A and m_M are the free molar concentrations of substrate and effector, respectively. Thus it should be possible from Eq. (1) and the appropriate kinetic experiments to determine K_2, the dissociation constant for effector in the absence of substrate and compare it directly to the value obtained from direct binding experiments. As implied in this description, one assumes that there is rapid equilibration between enzyme and substrate or enzyme and effector for the kinetic experiments to be equivalent to the ligand binding experiments, the latter, of course, being an equilibrium measurement. It should be noted that it is not always necessary that the rapid equilibrium assumptions hold for the kinetic behavior for the two types of experiments to be equivalent. This issue has been discussed elsewhere (3, 4) and it has been shown that even if a steady state situation holds, there are some conditions under which the results are equivalent to the rapid equilibrium case (2, 5). However, it is not always true that this will be the case and the initial velocity expression may be much more complex than the equivalent binding expression even for the single substrate case. Thus the initial velocity expression could contain square terms in substrate or effector concentration, and therefore the velocity as a function of substrate or modifier concentration may not follow classical Michaelis–Menten behavior, while the binding data would follow a normal saturation isotherm. Some simplification might be obtained if substrate levels are saturating and the velocity measured as a function of the modifier concentration (2) provided the modifier does not compete for the active site. This procedure may yield the dissociation constant for the modifier in the presence of substrate. Extraction of appropriate ligand dissociation constants may also be difficult because there are so many different kinetic mechanisms that give the same complex expressions.

The complexity raised here with respect to initial velocity experiments persists (and will be raised) throughout this whole chapter and there is unfortunately no simple way to deal with it.

7.2.2   The Two (or Multi-) Substrate Case

Comparison of substrate binding curves and initial velocity plots are possible for enzymatic reactions which require more than one substrate for the overall reaction. One can then ask whether the binding curve obtained for one substrate is equivalent to the initial velocity as a function of that substrate in the presence of a constant amount of the second substrate. As before, there is no reason to believe a priori that these curves will be equivalent. In addition to questions of rapid equilibration between enzyme, substrate and enzyme-substrate complexes, there are several reasons why one might expect differences in the two plots. For example, there may be an effect of one substrate on the behavior of the other to either decrease or increase the apparent affinity. In this regard, therefore, it is the binding of one substrate in the presence of the other which should be compared to the initial velocity curve as a function of substrate concentration. This of course is not possible, since the reaction would occur. The kinetic expression for this situation is

$$\frac{v_0}{V_{max}} = \frac{m_A m_B / j K_A K_B}{1 + m_A / K_A + m_B / K_B + m_A m_B / j K_A K_B} \tag{2}$$

where m_A and m_B are the molar concentrations of A and B, and j is a factor which determines how the concentration of one of the substrates A or B influences the apparent Michaelis constant for the other substrate. The V_{max} term includes the number of binding sites, and this value cannot be determined from kinetic experiments. It has been assumed for this derivation, however, that if the enzyme contains multiple active sites the binding of a substrate to one active site does not influence the binding of either substrate to a different active site (i.e., on a different subunit). At a constant concentration of, for example, B, the expression rearranges to

$$\frac{v_0}{V_{max}} = \frac{1/(1 + j K_B / m_B)}{1 + (j K_A / m_A)\{(1 + K_B / m_B)/(1 + j K_B / m_B)\}} \tag{3}$$

which shows that both the apparent maximum velocity and apparent Michaelis constant for substrate A will depend on the concentration of B.

The equivalent binding expression is

$$r_{A(B)} = \frac{p}{1 + (j K_A / m_A)\{(1 + K_B / m_B)/(1 + j K_B / m_B)\}} \tag{4}$$

where $r_{A(B)}$ is the number of moles of A bound per mole of enzyme in the presence of a given amount of B, K_A and K_B are dissociation constants, and p is the total number of binding sites for A. Again, for comparison with Eq. (3), the assumption is made that binding of ligand A at one site does not influence the binding of either A or B on a different subunit. Since substrates A and B must be attached to the same site (on the same subunit) for the catalytic reaction to occur, while no such restriction is present in binding experiments, Eqs. (3) and (4) are similar but not identical. Thus in the kinetic expression the apparent extent of the reaction (the apparent maximum velocity) depends on the concentration of B while, in the binding expression, the total number of moles of A bound per mole of enzyme is independent of the concentration of B. On the other hand the Michaelis constant for A and the dissociation constant for A depend on the concentration of B in exactly the same way.

This discussion has been extended to the situation for (*a*) a multisubunit enzyme which requires two substrates where the enzyme itself may undergo isomerization to a form that differs in kinetic parameters (6) and (*b*) to such an isomerizing protein that can bind two dissimilar ligands to different sites

(7). If the enzyme and substrate(s) are in rapid equilibrium with the enzyme-substrate(s) complex and the two conformational forms equilibrate rapidly, one obtains an equation analogous to that derived by Monod, Wyman, and Changeux (8) to describe allosteric behavior for a single substrate case. However, the equation for the two substrate case can be more complex than that derived by Monod et al. (8) and it is not always permissible to extend the description of Monod et al. to a two substrate enzyme. For example, even if both conformational forms have the same intrinsic catalytic activity, substrate inhibition can occur if one substrate binds preferentially to one conformational form, and the other substrate binds preferentially to the other. Pettigrew and Frieden have given a rather complete description of this system and have shown that comparisons of binding and kinetic data might be useful in distinguishing between certain mechanisms (6). This isomerization model is of interest, since one could consider isomerization to be analogous in some ways to polymerization. However, only in the case of polymerization will there be a dependence of the kinetic behavior on enzyme concentration, and we return to this issue in Section 7.4.

More appropriate experimental comparisons between ligand binding and kinetic experiments might be made for enzymes that can bind a specific effector (activator or inhibitor) in addition to the two substrates. In this case it should be possible to perform direct binding experiments utilizing one substrate and the effector and determine the appropriate dissociation constants from Eq. (4) while using a slight modification of Eq. (1) to determine the appropriate constants from the kinetic experiments. A rather general description for the interaction of effector molecules bound to enzymes containing multiple sites and different conformational forms has been formulated by Whitehead (9).

The above discussion involves assumptions about the kinetic formulation which may not be correct, invalidating any direct comparisons between binding and kinetics. If, for example, the enzyme and substrates are not in equilibrium with the enzyme-substrate(s) complex, the kinetic expression can be, as discussed earlier, more complex than the binding expression and include terms in the substrate concentration squared. Thus the initial velocity as a function of substrate concentration may deviate from normal Michaelis–Menten behavior. Similar to the single substrate–single effector case discussed earlier, some simplification of the kinetic expression may be obtained when one of the substrates is held at a saturating level and the other substrate and the effector concentration are varied. Normal kinetic behavior under these conditions may be one hint that the rapid equilibrium assumption for the kinetic formulation was not correct.

There are certainly other complications when discussing the comparison between kinetic and binding expressions but these may be highly dependent on the mechanism of the reaction, that is, the effect of effector binding to one subunit on the conformation, and therefore binding characteristics, of another subunit. Further descriptions here would not be a particularly useful exercise.

7.3 INITIAL VELOCITY AND FULL TIME COURSE MEASUREMENTS

Experimental measurements of enzyme kinetics are almost always examined in terms of the initial velocity of the reaction. For example, the comparisons described in the previous sections are those of initial velocity and direct ligand binding. However, when a wide range of enzyme concentrations is to be used, as discussed in later sections, the measurement of the initial velocity becomes much more difficult and different techniques are required. For an enzyme for which there is a continuous assay (i.e., absorbancy change), stopped flow measurements are by far the most convenient. For a discontinuous assay a stopped flow quench apparatus might be required, but then the number of experiments that can be done in a given time period is certainly limited. It might be possible to avoid these methods by using a substrate with a very low turnover number or by performing experiments at lower temperatures, particularly at temperatures below 0°C.

Assuming a continuous assay and the availability of a stopped flow device, one can obtain not only the initial velocity but also the full time course of substrate depletion. We have discussed in detail the usefulness of full time courses for enzymes that undergo spontaneous or ligand-induced conformational changes to forms with different kinetic parameters (10, 11). Under such conditions, there is time-dependent behavior which can frequently be described by the expression (10)

$$v_t = v_f + (v_i - v_f)e^{-kt} \tag{5}$$

where v_t is the velocity as a function of time, v_i is the initial velocity, v_f the final (linear) velocity after a lag or burst, and k is the apparent rate constant for the transition. For self-associating enzymes or for heterogeneous interactions between enzymes, such an equation is not only useful but may be required for proper kinetic analysis. For example, if a substrate induces a change in the state of association of the enzyme and thereby a change in kinetic parameters, the velocity of the reaction could show a time-dependent (hysteretic) effect (10). A more complete description of this type of time dependence is discussed later (Section 7.5) where the usefulness of such analyses will be evident. As discussed elsewhere, mathematical analyses of the full time course of a reaction are exceedingly complex if hysteretic effects occur simultaneously with substrate depletion (11). Thus it becomes important to develop computer programs capable of simulating such kinetic data. A review of computer application has been given (12) and iterative programs, such as developed by Bates and Frieden (13), are particularly useful. In this type of program, a specific mechanism is chosen and the time course is computed by solving all the pertinent differential equations for each species. The real data may be superimposed on the simulated data, and the parameters for the mechanism are then varied to obtain the best fit. Two examples of the application of this type of program are the determination of the kinetic parameters of cytoplasmic malate dehydrogenase (14) and the time-dependent inhibition of glutamate dehydrogenase at high NADH levels (15). Programs such as these have not been widely used in enzymology, but there are FORTRAN versions, which should be available to most investigators.

7.4 SELF-ASSOCIATION: RAPIDLY EQUILIBRATING MONOMER–POLYMER REACTIONS

There are a large number of enzymes which undergo association reactions (1). In this section we consider those systems for which, by definition, the monomer and all higher forms are catalytically active. According to the definitions used in this book, the monomer itself may be composed of subunits. Subunit-monomer association reactions are considered separately in Section 7.7. For a monomer-polymer reaction to be kinetically detectable, it is of course necessary that the different molecular weight species have different kinetic parameters. Of the enzymes that do undergo self-association reactions, it is frequently observed that substrate or modifier can influence either the extent or rate of the association (16). Since such an effect ultimately means that the ligand binds preferentially to different molecular weight forms, this is a sufficient difference to suggest that some kinetic properties will vary as a function of enzyme concentration.

7.4.1 The Enzymatic Activity as a Function of Enzyme Concentration at Constant Substrate Concentration

To determine whether polymerization is important in the enzyme activity, the first experiment would be to determine whether the specific activity is a function of enzyme concentration. Concerns about sensitivity of the assay and the ability to measure initial velocity over a wide range of enzyme concentrations have been discussed above, and under the appropriate conditions it is best for the *preliminary* experiments to be made at saturating levels of substrates. Under these conditions, a change in specific activity as a function of enzyme concentration reflects different intrinsic activities for different molecular weight species. For example, let us consider the simplest system of the enzyme undergoing a monomer-dimer reaction,

$$2E \underset{}{\overset{K}{\rightleftharpoons}} E_2 \tag{6}$$

defined by an equilibrium constant, $K = m_{E_2}/(m_E)^2$. We assume that this equilibrium is adjusted rapidly relative to the measurement of enzyme activity. Under these conditions, the specific activity, a, will depend on the total enzyme concentration (17),

$$a = a_D + (a_M - a_D)\frac{\left[-1 + (1 + 8K\overline{m}_E)^{1/2}\right]}{4K\overline{m}_E} \tag{7a}$$

or

$$a = a_M + (a_D - a_M) \left\{ \frac{-1 + (1 + 8K\overline{m}_E)^{1/2}}{8K\overline{m}_E} \right\}^2 \tag{7b}$$

where a_M and a_D are the specific activities for monomer and dimer, respectively, and $\overline{m}_E$ is the total molar concentration of enzyme. Similar to suggestions in the literature (18, 19), it is possible to obtain the equilibrium constant for the dimerization reaction with the expression

$$K = \frac{(a_M - a_D)(a_M - a)}{2\overline{m}_E(a - a_D)^2} \tag{8}$$

if one can determine the specific activity of the monomer and dimer forms. These latter might be equivalent to specific activities extrapolated to infinitely low and high enzyme concentrations. The equation is simplified, of course, if either a_M or a_D is equal to 0.

The above simple example shows that the specific activity will depend on enzyme concentration provided that the specific activity of monomer and dimer differ. Clearly the same argument can be applied to degrees of polymerization greater than dimer. We should include a constant reminder, however, that such calculations determined by enzymatic activity should be compared to other independent methods that measure association reactions as described elsewhere in this book.

7.4.2 The Velocity as a Function of Substrate Concentration

Preliminary experiments as described above (specific activities as a function of enzyme concentration) are best performed at saturating levels of substrate. However, it is quite possible that the association behavior of the enzyme will be affected by the substrate concentration. The literature is replete with examples of enzyme systems where the extent of association is dependent on ligand concentration (16) implying preferential binding to one or another molecular weight form. The type of experiment that might yield useful information is to determine the velocity as a function of substrate concentration at a variety of enzyme concentrations. To describe the results of such experiments for a monomer-dimer case, we start with the assumption that the monomer contains a single active site and the dimer contains two *equivalent* and *independent* active sites (i.e., the dimer alone would give a normal hyperbolic dependence of velocity with substrate concentration). Under these conditions, the specific activity as a function of substrate concentration could be represented as (20)

$$a = \frac{k_2(1-f)}{1 + K_1/m_A} + \frac{k_1 f}{1 + K_2/m_A} \tag{9}$$

where $f = (-1 + (1 + 8K\overline{m}_E)^{1/2})/4K\overline{m}_E$, and therefore is a constant at a given enzyme concentration, k_1 and k_2 are the maximum velocities for monomer and dimer, and K_1 and K_2 are the Michaelis constants for the monomer and dimer, respectively. Equation (9) would not be expected to show hyperbolic behavior under conditions where the enzyme exists as both the dimer and monomer, but rather behavior equivalent to negative cooperativity (21). Thus it might be possible that the kinetic behavior would be normal at very low or very high enzyme concentrations, but negatively cooperative at intermediate enzyme concentrations. As discussed above (and in Chapter 9), ligand binding curves, describing single ligand binding, may be equivalent to the initial velocity curve, although the interpretation may not be the same since the Michaelis constant need not be a dissociation constant.

When the monomer contains several subunits and therefore several active sites, the kinetic behavior may be much more complex, and it has been shown (20–23) that self-association could give rise to positively cooperative kinetic data as well as negative cooperativity. Self-association of enzymes therefore provides another basis for effects of the allosteric type. Ligand binding expressions for this case are described extensively in Chapter 9.

There are some conditions where, for multisite single substrate cases, the appropriate ligand binding equation *is* equivalent to the initial velocity expression as given in Chapter 9 (and references therein). Thus we must assume, as before, that the enzyme and substrate equilibrate rapidly with the enzyme-substrate complex. Further, strict equivalence of the form of the ligand binding equation and the initial velocity expression requires that the specific activity of the different molecular weight species *be the same*.

With the above assumptions and considering only a monomer-dimer association, the initial velocity expression is

$$\frac{v_0}{V_{max}} = \frac{p\alpha(1+\alpha)^{p-1}+2qKm_E d\alpha(1+d\alpha)^{q-1}}{(1+\alpha)^p+2Km_E(1+d\alpha)^q} \tag{10}$$

where p is the number of sites on the monomer, q the number of sites on the dimer, α is the reduced substrate concentration $(=m_A/K_1)$, K is the equilibrium constant for the monomer-dimer reaction, d is the ratio of Michaelis constants for substrate to dimer and monomer, and m_E is the free enzyme concentration defined by

$$m_E = \frac{-(1+\alpha)^p+\left[(1+\alpha)^q+8\overline{m}_E K(1+d\alpha)^q\right]^{1/2}}{4K(1+d\alpha)^q} \tag{11}$$

Equation (10) can give rise to nonhyperbolic kinetic data when the velocity is plotted as a function of substrate concentration, and this behavior will be a function of the enzyme concentration. This latter point is essential to the study of the effect of self-association on the kinetic parameters, since it is well known that nonhyperbolic kinetic data may arise from many different mechanisms which do not involve self-association processes. Obviously, there could be more than one factor involved in nonhyperbolic kinetic behavior for multisite enzymes, that is, isomerization of the enzyme to a form with different kinetic properties, nonequilibration of enzyme, substrate and enzyme-substrate complexes, and so on (see below also). It is beyond the scope of this chapter to delineate and express all the possible kinetic expressions, but it must be noted again that the only way to approach the problem is to carry out such experiments over as wide a range of enzyme concentrations as possible. Questions about the rate of the association or dissociation process are discussed later.

As pointed out earlier, other problems arise when one is dealing with a multisubstrate, multisubunit enzyme relative to a single substrate multisubunit enzyme. In such cases the binding equation and initial velocity equations are not identical unless one of the substrates is held at a saturating concentration.

The same comment must also be made for the substrate-effector case. For any equivalence in the form of the ligand binding equation and initial velocity as a function of substrate concentration, it is necessary that the effector be at a saturating concentration. The kinetic equations to describe the situation where this is not the case become so complex as to be almost useless in any detailed analysis of kinetic behavior. Not only that, but the kinetic description will depend on what mechanism is assumed for the action of the effector. Thus if a model equivalent to that postulated by Monod et al. (8) is assumed correct, effector binding to any of the equivalent subunits will cause a conformational (or self-association) change. If, however, the model is assumed to be more analogous to that postulated by Koshland et al. for the allosteric data (24), the effector binding to the same subunit as the substrate could have a different effect than effector binding to a subunit not containing the substrate. In either case, the kinetic equation will be highly complex. It is possible, however, that computer simulation of the full time course of the enzymatic reaction for a chosen mechanism might circumvent some of these difficulties.

7.4.3 Rates of Association–Dissociation Reactions

Relatively little attention has been paid to the rate at which a monomer-polymer equilibrium is established. Yet this is a very important problem, not only with respect to the kinetic properties of an associating enzyme, but also with respect to some methods, that is, sedimentation velocity, column chromatography, which are utilized in measuring the degree and mode of self-association reactions.

Two relatively simple techniques, light scattering and H^+ changes associated with self-association, are available for such studies and it is surprising how little these methods have been used. A recent survey by Kegeles (25) indicates how relatively infrequently light scattering has been employed in spite of its suggested use a number of years ago. Such studies can, for example, be performed by equilibrium perturbation techniques (Chapter 1) or by stopped flow using either the fluorescence mode or the change in incident light as a measure of turbidity. This latter method has been used in the literature to measure rates of association and dissociation of various enzymes (26, 27). A stopped flow laser light scattering photometer has also been recently described (28), and some data on dissociation rates of rabbit muscle phosphofructokinase have been reported. On the other hand, Koren and Hammes used pH indicators to follow the monomer-dimer interaction of insulin, β-lactoglobulin and α-chymotrypsin (29) and this latter paper also summarizes rate constants which have been obtained with other systems such as trypsin-trypsin inhibitor studies.

Intrinsic fluorescence changes might also be used as a measure of self-association (30), as well as changes in the absorbance or fluorescence of covalently or noncovalently linked fluorescent or chromophoric probes. Fluorescence methods are discussed in detail in Chapter 6.

Examination of the relatively scant literature suggests that, for the most part, the rate of protein-protein interaction is diffusion controlled and will therefore depend on the molecular weight or size of the particular protein system.

A value of the second order rate constant of 10^5-10^6 sec^{-1} mol^{-1} is probably the upper limit for protein-protein interaction and a few simple calculations will illustrate how important this process may be in kinetic experiments. For these calculations, we will oversimplify the situation to emphasize the point. Thus it was discussed earlier that it is important in kinetic studies to examine the kinetic parameters as a function of enzyme concentration. As the enzyme concentration becomes higher, the rate of self-association becomes important. For example, the rate of dimer formation for the process $2E \xrightarrow{k} E_2$ at micromolar concentrations will be

$$\frac{d(m_{E_2})}{dt} = k(m_E)^2 = 10^6(10^{-6})^2 = 10^{-6} \text{ mol/sec}$$

Thus in this simple irreversible case, a 10^{-6} M solution of enzyme will be converted to dimer in about a second. For an enzyme with any reasonable turnover number, a significant portion of the substrate would be depleted during that time at a high enzyme level. If the monomer and polymer are kinetically different, the time course of the reaction will certainly reflect that. For example, if the enzyme exists in the form of an inactive monomer and the dimer is active, there will be a lag covering about a second in product formation. Even if the kinetic difference is not so striking as having one form of the enzyme totally inactive, any kinetic differences between different molecular weight form may be observed as hysteretic effects (see Section 7.5).

The rate of dissociation of polymer to monomer may, by the same argument, give rise to some time-dependent effects. In these cases, however, the rate of dissociation is a unimolecular event and therefore not diffusion-controlled. The rate of dissociation may of course be linked to a conformational change as discussed by Neet (31) with respect to subunit interaction constants, isomerization constants and the apparent dissociation constant.

The analysis of the pH and temperature-dependent dissociation of rabbit muscle phosphofructokinase may serve as a model for this type of system (32–34). In this case, careful analysis of the change in kinetic behavior relative to the rate of dissociation of the active monomer containing four subunits to an inactive form containing two subunits showed that a conformational change, a consequence of proton binding, led to the dissociation. However, all the allosteric properties are related to a conformation change which occurs in the active monomer as a consequence of the same proton binding. The allosteric properties are related, at least in part, to the fact that the substrates and allosteric effectors bind differently to the protonated and unprotonated forms of the enzyme (35, 36). For this case, and perhaps for many others, the dissociation of the enzyme can be a rather slow process, giving rise to at least two forms of metabolic control: (a) a pH-dependent change in the nature of the allosteric properties of the enzyme, and (b) a slower pH-dependent change in the total activity of the enzyme (as a consequence of dissociation to the inactive form).

An extreme case in which the kinetic consequences may be easily discerned are those enzymes which show the characteristics of cold lability accompanied by dissociation of the active monomer into inactive subunits (37, 38). There are a large number of such enzymes and association or dissociation processes may be studied by measuring the loss or return of activity following a shift in temperature.

In any case, the purpose of this section is to show that association-dissociation reactions may be rate limiting in the kinetic behavior of the enzyme under conditions where the monomer and polymer have different kinetic behavior and when the kinetics are studied at sufficiently high enzyme concentration. Further consequences of this situation are discussed in the next section.

7.5 THE EFFECT OF SLOW ASSOCIATION-DISSOCIATION PROCESSES ON THE ENZYMATIC VELOCITY. HYSTERESIS

Given that the monomeric and polymeric forms of an enzyme differ in kinetic properties and that one studies these properties over a wide range of enzyme concentrations, the previous section illustrates that the kinetic behavior will become sensitive to the rate at which the different molecular weight forms interconvert. This may be most noticeable if the different molecular weight forms differ in substrate affinity. One obvious kinetic consequence of these assumptions is that one will observe either lags or bursts in the measurement of substrate disappearance and the observed magnitude of the lags or bursts will depend on the absolute enzyme concentration. For single substrate enzymes with no cooperative interactions between sites, the time-dependent behavior can be described by Eq. (5). Since this equation was used to describe hysteretic behavior due to isomerization of an enzyme, the observed rate constant would not be expected to show any dependence on enzyme concentration (except for artifactual effects—see Section 7.6). However, with the self-associating systems, the rate constant in Eq. (5) would be dependent on total enzyme concentration (10). For the case where an enzyme contains several active sites, Kurganov and co-workers have developed the equations for this situation in considerable detail (20, 39). Kurganov has developed (20) methods which allow one to determine the second order rate constant for association and the first order rate constant for dissociation for the system $2E \rightleftharpoons E_2$ after changing the storage conditions or when the equilibrium is displaced by ligand. These authors have assumed, for simplicity, that the dimer contains twice the number of sites as the monomer, but this assumption, as discussed elsewhere (23), is not essential. Other assumptions involved in these derivations are that the enzymatic reaction is irreversible and not inhibited by the product formed, that the substrate concentration remains constant throughout the activity measurement, that the binding sites are equivalent and independent in the monomer and in the dimer and, finally, that substrate binding is rapid relative to the catalytic reaction. We have discussed the limitations of each of these assumptions earlier in this chapter. Almost certainly the question of substrate depletion becomes of major importance and therefore the rather complex equations derived (20, 40) become even more difficult to handle without utilizing some type of computer simulation analysis. Thus a qualitative examination of the data may be appropriate. This may be accomplished by examination of the apparent rate constant for the hysteretic process as a function of enzyme concentration. Figure 1 illustrates a hypothetical progress curve for product formation as a function of time. Indicated are those portions of the curve from which initial velocity, final velocity and the apparent rate constant may be obtained.

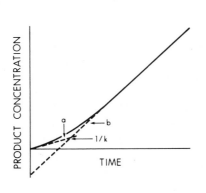

FIGURE 1

A possible time course for an enzymatic reaction showing hysteretic behavior or a coupled enzyme system. For describing hysteretric behavior, which, as in this case, shows a lag, the abscissa value of the intercept of the two lines gives the value of the relaxation time $[= 1/k$ of Eq. (2)]. The extrapolation of the line labeled b [representing v_f in Eq. (2)] to the ordinate yields $(v_f - v_i)/k$. The slope of the line labeled a is v_i. For the case of a coupled enzyme system, extrapolation of the line labeled b to the abscissa is referred to as the transient time and is equal, for the case described, to K_B/V_B. Extrapolation of this line to the ordinate gives the negative value of the steady-state concentration of the intermediate.

Experimentally it is best to obtain such data at high substrate levels (so that it remains relatively constant) and as a function of total enzyme concentration. It should be reemphasized that, while a change in behavior with enzyme concentration is certainly diagnostic for a self-association process, similar results could be generated artifactually due to substrate depletion during the enzymatic reaction due to an isomerization of the enzyme rather than association to a kinetically different form (see Section 7.6).

While the equations describing this type of kinetic behavior are indeed complex, this should not be construed to mean that these effects are not physiologically important. Indeed, it seems likely (as discussed later) that they may be rate controlling processes worthy of considerable study in questions related to metabolic regulation.

7.6 THE EXPERIMENTAL PROCEDURE. A SUMMARY

It might be useful at this point to outline an experimental protocol for investigating the kinetic properties of a self-associating enzyme, summarizing not only the types of experiments that should be done, as detailed earlier, but also indicating some experimental difficulties.

The most obvious first experiment is to measure the velocity of the reaction as a function of enzyme concentration over as wide a range as possible. As indicated earlier, such experiments would be performed best in the first instance at saturating substrate levels. However, since different molecular weight forms of the enzyme may differ in substrate affinity, there could be a question of what a saturating level is and saturation at one enzyme concentration may not be saturation at another. Any deviation from Michaelis–Menten behavior (i.e., substrate inhibition) would certainly complicate the interpretation of this type of experiment. Thus the next step in such an investigation would be to examine the substrate dependence of the velocity over a wide range of enzyme concentrations. This type of experiment is much more difficult to perform than it would appear. One problem is that of substrate depletion where the initial substrate concentration is low. Velocity measurements under these conditions may not be difficult at low enzyme concentrations, but are quite difficult at high enzyme concentration where there will be a considerable depletion of the substrate during the activity measurement. For this reason, it is best to utilize the full time course of substrate depletion. The difficulty here, aside from the fact that it is best to have a continuous assay system, is the analysis of the full time course itself. As indicated earlier, this is best done by computer using a numerical integration of the appropriate differential equations. Such a computer system has to be available to the investigator. While these computer programs may be relatively rare now, it seems likely that various versions of such programs will be available to those interested in this area. Improvements in computer technology are such that data analysis will not be the rate limiting step in studies of this type. A related problem in the experimental procedure, also obviated to some extent by computer simulation, is that of hysteresis which gives rise to lags or bursts of substrate disappearance. This phenomenon should, in theory, be investigated using the full time course of the reaction as a function of both enzyme and substrate concentration, but in practice might be best restricted to a few substrate concentrations over a wide range of enzyme concentrations.

A change in the hysteretic behavior as a function of enzyme concentration would appear to indicate self-association of the enzyme, but a similar result may occur indicating an isomerization process of the enzyme rather than a polymerization process. Thus, suppose an isomerization of the enzyme occurs between two kinetically different forms. In theory, this process should be independent of the enzyme concentration. However, in practice, if one uses the full time course of the reaction, the process may appear to depend on the enzyme concentration and could be misinterpreted to be a consequence of self-association. Suppose, for example, that the isomerization is from a more active to less active form. At low enzyme concentration, the hysteresis appears as a time dependent decrease in enzymatic activity (assuming no product effects or other problems). As the enzyme concentration is increased, complete substrate depletion might occur at a rate faster than the isomerization process and it would appear that the hysteretic effect is lost. Artifacts such as these indicate the importance of using nonkinetic methods to confirm the suspected self-association processes.

7.7   THE SUBUNIT–MONOMER ASSOCIATION

7.7.1   General Considerations

It might be expected that some simplifications in dealing with the kinetic expressions could exist when considering the association of inactive subunits to active monomers. Such behavior is frequently observed for cold labile enzymes (37, 38) and may be slow enough so that it is not necessary to measure product formation during a single run (as in Figure 1) but to measure regain of activity, via initial velocity experiments, as a function of time. The initial velocity is then considered as proportional to the concentration of active polymeric enzyme. For the case

$$2E \underset{k_{-1}}{\overset{k_1}{\rightleftharpoons}} E_2$$

the formation of E_2 as a function of time is (41)

$$m_{E_2}(t) = a \left\{ \frac{1 + b \exp[8ak_1 t]}{1 - b \exp[8ak_1 t]} \right\} + \frac{4\overline{m}_E k_1 - k_{-1}}{8k_1} \tag{12}$$

where

$$a^2 = \left\{ \frac{4\overline{m}_E k_1 + k_{-1}}{8k_1} \right\}^2 - \frac{(\overline{m}_E)^2}{4}$$

$$b = \frac{d_0 - a/4k_1}{d_0 + a/4k_1}$$

and d_0 is the initial value of the expression

$$d = \frac{1}{4k_1} \left\{ m_{E_2} - \frac{4(\overline{m}_E k_1 - k_{-1})}{8k_1} \right\}$$

when $m_{E_2} = 0$.

This is clearly not a simple expression, although perhaps usable. If the mechanism is somewhat more complex, that is

$$2E \rightleftharpoons E_2 \rightleftharpoons E_2'$$

where E_2' is the active form, the full kinetic expressions, if they can be derived (42), would indeed be complex and even the steady-state assumption of $d(m_{E_2})/dt = 0$ does not lead to a simple equation.

Clearly the conclusion here is that for the determination of mechanism or rate constants, it is by far better to attempt to fit experimental results by a numerical computer solution. By such computer simulation procedures, as discussed earlier, one can set up a variety of mechanisms and test each for the ability to fit experimental data, that is, activity recovery as a function of time and total enzyme concentration. While a fit does not prove the mechanism, the possibilities of exploring different mechanisms is much broader than by being constrained by explicit solutions to difficult differential equations. Computer simulation was the procedure used to determine the pH-dependent mechanism for the reassociation of rabbit muscle phosphofructokinase (32) from the inactive form of molecular weight 160,000 to the active form of molecular weight 320,000 (containing 4 subunits). The reassociation was found to be consistent with a mechanism of the type

$$\begin{array}{c} 2E_2' \\ \uparrow\downarrow \\ 2E_2(H^+)_x \rightleftharpoons 2E_2 \rightleftharpoons E_4 \end{array}$$

where only E_4 is active and where the loss of protons from $E_2(H^+)_x$ leads to the reassociation process. It is of course possible that sufficient information for the determination of the mechanism may not be available from the kinetic data alone. For example, the recovery of activity of lactic dehydrogenase from the subunit appears to be a relatively simple process, even though the active enzyme contains four subunits (43). In this case a plot of the log of the initial slope of activity recovery versus log enzyme concentration yielded a slope of 2, indicating that the rate limiting step in the process was an association of two subunits or of two molecules each containing two subunits

(43). At what stage of the process this rate-limiting association occurred, however, is not easily determined from the data.

It is clear from the preceding remarks that the activity measurements should be made in conjunction with other methods which measure different parameters. Thus, molecular weight measurements as a function of time or time dependent conformational changes are important in determination of the mechanism.

7.7.2 Active Enzyme Sedimentation

Some mention should be made here of a technique available that measures the molecular weight of active enzyme species under conditions where the enzyme concentration is quite low (see also Chapter 3). This method has been called active enzyme sedimentation and was originally described several years ago (44). As usually described, the method in essence sediments a band of enzyme through substrate at sufficiently low enzyme concentrations that not all the substrate is utilized during the time it is in contact with the enzyme. An example of the data obtained is given by Figure 14 of Chapter 3. Using the scanning optics of the analytical centrifuge, one can in theory determine the sedimentation coefficient of the molecular weight species which is enzymatically active. A review by Kemper and Everse (45) discusses the applications and possible pitfalls of the method. More recently, Llewellyn and Smith (46) have discussed the merits and potential artifacts in data interpretation. More importantly, however, is that these authors have extended the method to include enzymes which undergo self association or association with other proteins. Self-association of the rat liver pyruvate carboxylase in which different forms are active under different conditions has been explored using active enzyme sedimentation by Taylor et al. (47).

Since low enzyme concentrations are usually used in active enzyme sedimentation, the method has advantages in that other physical methods may not be available. However, it would be advantageous to be able to use this technique over a wide range of enzyme concentrations. Wei and Deal (48) have described both the theoretical and experimental basis for such experiments. In a test of the theory, the authors showed that the sedimentation coefficients obtained by normal schlieren methods and by active enzyme sedimentation were the same for lactate dehydrogenase at levels as high as 1 mg/ml (48). The method might be particularly appropriate for self-associating systems at levels which are too low for conventional centrifugation methods and too high for the usual active enzyme sedimentation methods.

7.8 HETEROGENEOUS INTERACTIONS

Obviously, self-association of enzymes is not the only type of enzyme-macromolecular interaction which may occur. There are numerous examples of interaction of enzymes with, for example, other proteins with either no enzymatic function or an unrelated enzyme function (49). In the latter case, this may involve coupled enzyme systems as discussed in the next section. In addition, enzymes may interact with large macromolecular complexes and such interactions may be physiologically important from the point of view of compartmentalization of metabolic systems. Protein-lipid interaction may also be important in this sense but will not be discussed here.

7.8.1 Enzyme–Protein Interactions

For interactions of enzymes with other proteins in solution, the protein may, in some instances, be simply considered as a direct analog of a small ligand effector. Thus, experimentally, one wants to measure kinetic parameters of the enzyme in the presence and absence of the other protein under conditions where it is known that association occurs. Active enzyme sedimentation, as described in Section 7.7.2 and in Chapter 3, may be quite useful here since the association will change the molecular weight of the enzyme under conditions where the enzyme concentration is low. When the extent of association is relatively small and higher enzyme concentrations are required, it may be necessary to use stopped flow procedures or possibly substrates with low turnover numbers to assure interaction when measuring the kinetic parameters. Provided the kinetic data can be obtained, treatment of the data would be, as indicated above, similar to enzyme–small ligand effector interaction but with some added complications. These include the fact that a large protein may sterically block more than one site or one type of site and that the rate of association of two proteins will be slower than that of an enzyme with a small ligand (see Section 7.5). Ignoring these questions, treatment of the kinetic behavior of the enzyme in the presence of a protein effector raises many of the same concerns as expressed earlier with respect to mechanism and what binding steps may be considered rapid relative to the rate of the catalytic reaction. The situation in comparing kinetic and binding data is perhaps more complex for the enzyme-substrate-protein effector case than it is for the two substrate enzyme since in the former both the enzyme-substrate and enzyme-substrate-effector complexes are active while in the latter only the enzyme-substrate-substrate complex is active. A relatively simple kinetic analysis of the single substrate–single effector case has been presented elsewhere (2). As discussed earlier, it is not obvious that the kinetic expressions will be of the same form as the effector binding expressions, especially if the enzyme contains multiple binding sites for the substrate and effector.

If high concentrations of enzyme are required for the association to occur, necessitating stopped flow methods, it is quite possible that the rate of association of the enzyme and protein may become slow or of the same order of magnitude as the catalytic reaction. In such cases, one might expect to see hysteretic behavior (see Section 7.5) which of course will complicate the interpretation. Fundamentally, however, one wishes to examine the question of whether the kinetic parameters are affected by such interaction and the answer to that is not difficult to ascertain.

7.8.2 Enzyme–Structure Interactions

Least understood, but probably of considerable importance, are those interactions between enzymes and large structures: membranes, structural components of the cell, nucleic acids, and so on, provided that the interaction affects kinetic parameters. In cases of this sort it is almost certain that the kinetics will be altered even if only with relation to diffusion of the substrate to the immobilized enzyme compared to that free in solution. Very little in the way of enzyme kinetic analysis is available for this sort of system, primarily because of questions related to what the substrate (or product) concentration is in the environment of the enzyme. There is, however, a considerable literature on the properties of immobilized enzymes which avoids the question of any reversible association (50, 51 and references therein). Kurganov and Loboda (49) have analyzed the properties of the case where an enzyme is bound to an adsorbant. If they assume that the free and adsorbed enzymes are in rapid equilibrium, they can then show that the substrate dependence of the velocity may deviate from Michaelis–Menten behavior provided, of course, that the adsorbed enzyme has different kinetic properties from the enzyme free in solution. They show, for example, that positive cooperativity may occur when an oligomeric enzyme is reversibly bound to the absorbant. The situation may be viewed as analogous to the model of Monod et al. (8) which postulates two conformational forms in rapid equilibrium which differ in, for example, substrate affinity. In the case of the adsorbed enzyme, the two conformational forms are the free and bound enzyme. For cooperative behavior to occur the form which is present in excess binds substrate poorly relative to the substrate binding of the other form.

Goldstein (50) classifies the effects of immobilization as (a) conformational or steric effects, (b) partitioning effects, (c) microenvironmental effects, and (d) diffusional or mass-transfer effects. There is considerable evidence that the kinetic parameters of an immobilized enzyme generally do not reflect those of the soluble enzyme. Certainly determination of the kinetic parameters by the usual methods may be misleading at best and Michaelis constants, for example, may have little meaning with respect to the interpretation and over a wide range of substrate concentration, substantial deviation from Michaelis–Menten behavior may be observed. For a thorough analysis the effects listed by Goldstein would have to be evaluated. While microenvironmental partitioning effects (i.e., those due to charge) might be lessened at high ionic strength, diffusional effects are much more difficult to evaluate (50).

7.9 COUPLED ENZYME SYSTEMS

There are many reasons for believing that, in cells, interactions may occur between enzymes catalyzing successive steps in a metabolic pathway. There have been a number of tight complexes of enzymes that have been isolated and investigated. The subject has been extensively reviewed (52–55) and the issues associated with the advantage of this type of compartmentalization discussed (52, 53). Similarly the proposed role of loose complexes of enzymes has been raised (52), and most investigators seem to agree that such compartmentalization in terms either of flux of substrates through a metabolic pathway or its influence on the kinetic properties of an enzyme are an important part in metabolic regulation. It perhaps appears surprising therefore that so few weak interactions between enzymes have been observed in solution and even of these, some disagreement appears in the literature. At least one way to investigate this problem is to examine coupled enzyme systems as a function of enzyme and substrate concentration. Examination of kinetics of coupled enzymes is not a simple matter, but is relatively straightforward when comparing enzymes in solution relative to those which may interact in heterogeneous systems, that is, successive enzymes in a particular pathway being in close proximity on a macromolecular structure.

7.9.1 No Interactions Between Enzymes

To examine the question of whether enzyme-enzyme interaction is present, we shall first discuss the kinetics of coupled enzyme systems for which it is assumed that no such interaction occurs. Treatment of even the simplest systems has involved several assumptions, only some of which may be justified. Thus for two enzymes the usual description is represented as

$$A \overset{k_1}{\underset{E_A}{\rightarrow}} B \overset{k_2}{\underset{E_B}{\rightarrow}} C$$

where E_A and E_B are the enzymes of interest with the rate constants k_1 and k_2. Kinetic treatments usually assume (a) that both reactions are irreversible; (b) that A (and other substrates for E_A and E_B) are either at saturating levels or do not change in concentration during the assay; and (c) that the level of the intermediate B is considerably less than the apparent Michaelis constant for B as catalyzed by E_B.

The last assumption is not so much of an assumption, but a necessity. The steady-state level of the intermediate B can be shown (56–59) to be equal to

$$(m_B)_{ss} = \frac{k_1 K_B}{V_{B}}$$

and since V_B (the maximum velocity of E_B) must be larger than k_1 to prevent piling up of the intermediate B, $(m_B)_{ss}$ must be less than K_B.

With the above assumptions, a lag in the appearance of product (C) occurs (similar to that seen in Figure 1) with the time dependence of product formation being exactly the same as observed for hysteretic effects (10), except that the initial portion of the curve has a slope of zero. The equation for the time dependence of product formation is

$$m_C = k_1 \frac{t - K_B(1 + e^{-V_B t/K_B})}{V_b} \tag{13}$$

The intercept on the abscissa (see Figure 1) is K_B/V_B, while the intercept on the ordinate is the negative of the steady-state concentration of the intermediate. The thrust of these derivations (56–59) has been to be able to get an indication of the lag time so that coupled assays could be used successfully. Thus one can calculate, given k_1 and the kinetic parameters (V_B/K_B), the lag time that would occur before the steady-state velocity is reached. Provided that the correct velocity is reached at any substrate concentration used, one can then determine V_A and K_A by measuring the velocity as a function of A in the usual way. From the linear portion of the plot, one determines the velocity of reaction E_A, which can then be measured as a function of the concentration of A to determine the kinetic parameters of E_A.

Since the primary interest in the above derivations was related to the extent of the lag time, variations in the level of A were not considered. Rather, the treatment was extended to include several consecutive enzyme reactions. However the assumption that the concentration of A does not change with time becomes a critical one at low A concentrations and the analysis may fail without some type of computer simulation. The most useful experimental test of the correctness of the measured velocity is to see whether it remains constant when the concentration of the coupling enzyme is changed. It should be noted that another hidden assumption is that other substrates for either E_A or E_B (other than A or B) do not affect the velocity of the other enzymes.

The effect of a product on the activity of either enzyme may also invalidate the assay. For example phosphofructokinase can be strongly activated by low concentrations of fructose 1, 6-bisphosphate and the frequently used coupled enzyme system includes aldolase and glycerophosphate dehydrogenase in a nonphosphate containing buffer. However, with this assay system it is not possible to lower the fructose 1, 6-bisphosphate level enough to avoid activation even at high aldolase levels (60). As a consequence the velocity as a function of phosphofructokinase concentration is not linear. However, a different coupling assay system can be used to give valid results (60).

Recognizing that the above theoretical treatment could be too simplistic, Kuchel et al. (61) used Michaelis–Menten behavior for each of the enzymes and assumed a steady state of all enzyme-containing species. They then solved the equations by formulating them as a set of Maclaurin polynomials and showed that the concentration of C as a function of time could be represented as

$$(m_C)_t = \frac{V_A K_A V_B K_B (\overline{m}_A) t^2}{2[1 + K_A(\overline{m}_A)]} \tag{14}$$

A plot of $(m_C)_t$ vs t^2 will initially be linear and then slope off. The initial slope can then be plotted as a function of different initial concentrations of A. When a double reciprocal plot is constructed, the abscissa intercept is $-K_A$ and the ordinate intercept is $2/V_A V_B K_B$. Since one can experimentally determine V_B and K_B separately, one can then calculate V_A and K_A. The theory has been applied to the coupled arginase–urease system (62).

A somewhat different approach has been used by Kuchel and Roberts (63) which solves the steady-state and presteady-state equation for the coupled system. The solution of the equations giving the final product as a function of time consists of a linear term in t and a sum of exponentials with negative exponents in t. It is then necessary to compute individual rate constants assuming particular models.

7.9.2 Interactions Between Enzymes

There are several ways in which the kinetics of coupled enzyme systems could be influenced by interaction between the enzymes of the coupled system. These include (a) the effect of the coupling enzyme on the substrate kinetic parameters (V_A, K_A or the Michaelis constants for the other substrates of E_A); (b) the effect of the coupling enzyme on the binding of nonsubstrate ligands to E_A (i.e., allosteric effectors); (c) a change in the number of ligand binding sites due to steric effects (either substrate or other ligands); and (d) a channeling of the product of E_A to the substrate binding site of E_B resulting in a decreased diffusion time.

Nichol et al. (64) have formulated a set of differential rate equations for a system of two interacting enzymes. The equations were developed using Maclaurin polynomials similar to those given by the same authors (61) for the noninteracting system as described in Eq. (14). Some numerical solutions were presented in this paper and it was shown that when the interaction of the two enzymes leads to a species with different activity toward one of the substrates, kinetic studies may detect this interaction. Furthermore, under many conditions, it is possible that the interaction could give rise to deviations from the kinetic behavior observed for either enzyme alone.

In general, however, the kinetic theory for interacting enzymes in a coupled system has not been thoroughly examined. Yet there are several experimental approaches available to the investigator. These include, aside from initial velocity experiments, examination of the nature of the lag discussed in the previous section, the use of the full time course of the reaction, variation of the ratio of one enzyme to another, variation of the total enzyme concentration keeping the ratio E_A/E_B constant, the physical measurement of interaction in the absence or presence of substrate, and computer simulation of the kinetic data.

If there is nonkinetic evidence for interaction, the best way to approach the overall problem might be to examine the kinetic behavior of the system as a function of the total enzyme concentration maintaining the ratio E_A/E_B constant. Corrected for the total enzyme concentration then, the results should be identical if there is no interaction and may be expected to change if interaction occurs. One could compare either the velocity of E_A as a function of substrate concentration or the relative lag time, but it is important that a wide range of enzyme concentration be used. Thus it is likely that stopped flow techniques will be required.

It might be useful to make some comments about the correct E_A/E_B ratio. If the interaction affects the specific activity of E_A or its Michaelis constant, an excess of E_B over E_A would be desirable for the measurement of coupled enzyme syste and detection of these changes. If, however, the specific activity of E_B or its Michaelis constant for B is altered, an excess of E_B might lead to most of the substrate B being channelled through the free E_B rather than the E_B in the complex. Under these conditions, the effect of interaction between the two enzymes might be difficult to detect. Thus, under such conditions, the E_A/E_B ratio should be $\leqslant 1$. This in turn might invalidate the derivation given in Eqs. (13) and (14) and computer simulation would again be required. Clearly the kinetic approach to the question of interaction in coupled enzyme systems is not a simple matter.

This type of experimental approach is suggested here because there are only very few theoretical approaches to those questions. Some of the theoretical approaches made recently have been sufficiently complex so as not to be readily available to the experimentalist (65, 66).

7.10 CONCLUSION

In this chapter we discussed how the kinetic parameters of an enzyme may be used to determine some issues related to protein-protein interactions. Points which have been stressed are the importance of performing experiments over as wide a range of enzyme concentrations as possible, the use of the full time course of the reaction, and the usefulness of computer simulation to avoid some of the mathematical complexities. Of course, the kinetic measurements must be coupled with independent measurements of protein-protein interactions by physical methods. It is clear that even in solution such interactions can influence kinetic behavior and presumably therefore the flux of the metabolites through a given pathway in vivo. Despite the intuitive feeling that such interactions are crucial in metabolic regulation, surprisingly few experimental systems which undergo relatively weak interactions have been demonstrated. It is quite likely that this reflects the fact that when association of several enzymes in a metabolic pathway occurs, it occurs on the surface of some structure such as a membrane or large protein matrix. It is exactly the kinetic parameters of this type of system which have not been discussed in this chapter. This does not reflect negligence on the author's part but rather the feeling that there is a dearth of experimental data and a fairly wide gap between the theoretical approaches to these difficult problems and the data which are available. It is to be hoped that this gap might be closed when more of the appropriate kinetic data become available and when the theory becomes more amenable to direct test by the kineticist.

REFERENCES

1. C. Frieden, *Annu. Rev. Biochem.* **40**, 653 (1971).
2. C. Frieden, *J. Biol. Chem.* **239**, 3522 (1964).
3. I. H. Segel, *Enzyme Kinetics*, Wiley, New York, 1975.
4. H. J. Fromm, *Initial Rate Enzyme Kinetics*, New York: Springer-Verlag, New York, 1975.
5. J. F. Hearnon, S. J. Bernard, S. L. Freies, D. J. Botts, and M. F. Morales, in P. D. Boyer et al., Eds., *The Enzymes*, Vol. 1, Academic Press, New York, 1959, p. 49.
6. D. W. Pettigrew and C. Frieden, *J. Biol. Chem.* **252**, 4546 (1977).
7. L. W. Nichol, K. O'Dea, and P. A. Baghurst, *J. Theor. Biol.* **34**, 255 (1972).
8. J. Monod, J. Wyman, and J.-P. Changeux, *J. Mol. Biol.* **12**, 88 (1965).
9. E. Whitehead, *Biochemistry* **9**, 1440 (1970).
10. C. Frieden, *J. Biol. Chem.* **245**, 5788 (1970).
11. C. Frieden, *Ann. Rev. Biochem.* **48**, 471 (1979).
12. L. Garfinkel, M. C. Kohn, and D. Garfinkel, *Crit. Rev. Bioeng.* **2**, 329 (1977).
13. D. J. Bates and C. Frieden, *Comput. Biomed. Res.* **6**, 474 (1973).
14. C. Frieden and J. Fernandez-Sousa, *J. Biol. Chem.* **250**, 2106 (1975).
15. D. J. Bates, and C. Frieden, *J. Biol. Chem.* **248**, 7885 (1973).
16. A. T. Phillips, *Crit. Rev. Biochem.* **2**, 343 (1974).
17. B. I. Kurganov, Z. S. Kagan, A. I. Dorozhko, and V. A. Yakovlev, *J. Theor. Biol.* **47**, 1 (1974).
18. C. Y. Huang, and D. J. Graves, *Biochemistry* **9**, 660 (1970).
19. B. I. Kurganov, *J. Mol. Biol.* **2**, 430 (1968).
20. B. I. Kurganov, *J. Theor. Biol.* **68**, 521 (1977).
21. L. W. Nichol, W. J. H. Jackson, and D. J. Winzor, *Biochemistry* **6**, 2449 (1967).
22. C. Frieden, *J. Biol. Chem.* **242**, 4045 (1967).
23. L. W. Nichol and D. J. Winzor, *Biochemistry* **14**, 3015 (1976).
24. D. E. Koshland, Jr., G. Nemethy, and D. Filmer, *Biochemistry* **5**, 365 (1966).
25. G. Kegeles, *Methods Enzymol.* **68**, 308 (1978).
26. B. Finlayson and E. W. Taylor, *Biochemistry* **8**, 802 (1969).
27. C. Y. Huang and C. Frieden, *J. Biol. Chem.* **247**, 3638 (1972).
28. P. F. Liddle, D. J. Jacobs, and G. L. Kellett, *Anal. Biochem.* **79**, 276 (1977).
29. R. Koren and G. G. Hammes, *Biochemistry* **15**, 1165 (1976).
30. R. W. Noble, M. Reichlin, and Q. Gibson, *J. Biol. Chem.* **244**, 2403 (1969).
31. K. Neet, *Biophys. Chem.* **2**, 102 (1974).
32. P. E. Bock and C. Frieden, *J. Biol. Chem.* **251**, 5630 (1976).
33. P. E. Bock and C. Frieden, *J. Biol. Chem.* **251**, 5637 (1976).
34. C. Frieden, H. R. Gilbert, and P. E. Bock, *J. Biol. Chem.* **251**, 5644 (1976).
35. D. W. Pettigrew and C. Frieden, *J. Biol. Chem.* **254**, 1887 (1979).
36. D. W. Pettigrew and C. Frieden, *J. Biol. Chem.* **254**, 1896 (1979).
37. C. P. Dunne and W. A. Wood, *Curr. Top. Cell. Regul.* **9**, 65 (1975).

38. P. E. Bock and C. Frieden, *Trends Biochem. Sci.* **3**, 100 (1978).

39. B. I. Kurganov, A. I. Dorozhko, Z. S. Kagan, and V. A. Yankovlev, *J. Theor. Biol.* **60**, 287 (1976).

40. B. I. Kurganov, A. I. Dorozhko, Z. S. Kagan, and V. A. Yankovlev, *J. Theor. Biol.* **60**, 271 (1976).

41. J. Eisenger and N. Gross, *Biochemistry* **14**, 4031 (1975).

42. Y.-Y. Chien, *J. Am. Chem. Soc.* **70**, 2256 (1948).

43. R. Rudolph and R. Jaenicke, *Eur. J. Biochem.* **63**, 409 (1976).

44. R. Cohen, *Comp. Rend.* **256**, 3513 (1963).

45. D. L. Kemper and J. Everse, *Methods Enzymol.* **27**, 67 (1973).

46. D. J. Llewellyn and G. O. Smith, *Arch. Biochem. Biophys.* **190**, 483 (1978).

47. B. L. Taylor, W. H. Frey, R. E. Barden, M. C. Scrutton, and M. F. Utter, *J. Biol. Chem.* **253**, 3062 (1978).

48. G. J. Wei and W. C. Deal, Jr., *Biochemistry* **18**, 1129 (1979).

49. B. I. Kurganov and N. I. Loboda, *J. Theor. Biol.* **79**, 281 (1979).

50. L. Goldstein, *Methods Enzymol.* **44**, 397 (1976).

51. J.-M. Engasser and C. Horvath, in L. W. Wingard et al, Eds., *Applied Biochemistry and Bioengineering*, Vol. 1, Academic Press, New York, 1976, p. 127.

52. G. R. Welsh, *Prog. Biophys. Mol. Biol.* **32**, 103 (1977).

53. P. A. Srere and K. Mosbach, *Annu. Rev. Microbiol.* **28**, 61 (1974).

54. L. J. Reed and D. J. Cox, *Annu. Rev. Biochem.* **35**, 57 (1966).

55. A. Ginsburg and E. R. Stadtman, *Annu. Rev. Biochem.* **39**, 429 (1970).

56. W. R. McClure, *Biochemistry* **8**, 2782 (1969).

57. J. Easterby, *Biochim. Biophys. Acta* **293**, 552 (1973).

58. F. B. Rudolph, B. W. Bauger, and R. S. Beissner, *Methods Enzymol.* **63**, 22 (1979).

59. A. C. Storer and A. Cornish-Bowden, *Biochem. J.* **141**, 205 (1974).

60. K. Emerk and C. Frieden, *Arch. Biochem. Biophys.* **168**, 210 (1975).

61. P. W. Kuchel, L. W. Nichol, and P. D. Jeffrey, *J. Theor. Biol.* **48**, 39 (1974).

62. P. W. Kuchel, L. W. Nichol, and P. D. Jeffrey, *J. Biol. Chem.* **250**, 8222 (1975).

63. P. W. Kuchel and D. V. Roberts. *Biochim. Biophys. Acta* **364**, 181 (1974).

64. L. W. Nichol, P. W. Kuchel, and P. D. Jeffrey, *Biophys. Chem.* **2**, 354 (1974).

65. T. L. Hill, *Proc. Natl. Acad. Sci. USA* **74**, 4111 (1977).

66. T. L. Hill and Y.-D. Chen, *Proc. Natl. Acad. Sci. USA* **75**, 5260 (1978).

CHAPTER 8

The Self-Assembly of Long Rodlike Structures

SERGE N. TIMASHEFF

8.1   INTRODUCTION

One of the ways to characterize protein self-associations is according to the geometry of the final assembled structure. The vast majority of systems studied by physical chemical techniques have for end product well-defined small compact aggregates with not very large degrees of polymerization, usually in the range of 2–16. To these belong hemoglobin, β-lactoglobulin, and the majority of subunit enzyme systems. Such self-associations can be examined best by standard macromolecular techniques, such as the transport methods of velocity sedimentation and gel permeation chromatography, with the application of the Gilbert theory and its various extensions (Chapters 3 and 4), or by equilibrium methods, such as light scattering, sedimentation equilibrium, or small-angle X-ray scattering (Chapter 5). Examples of such analyses are now abundant in the literature, following the pioneering studies on β-lactoglobulin (1), α-chymotrypsin (2,3), insulin (4), and hemoglobin. Since these approaches are treated elsewhere in this volume, they will not be discussed here. Another mode of self-association generates long rodlike structures, frequently of an indefinite degree of polymerization, which depends on the environmental conditions, such as temperatures or the presence of ligands, for example, metal ions, cofactors or hydronium ions. These structures can attain very large dimensions, of the order of microns, and their assembly is frequently found to be highly cooperative. In fact the sharpness with which polymers appear as a function of total protein concentration is highly similar to a phase transition and the assembly process can be regarded as a one-dimensional crystallization. The high molecular weight, length, and asymmetry of these assemblies usually places their study outside the range of the classical techniques, such as analytical ultracentrifugation or gel permeation chromatography. Therefore, other techniques must be sought to characterize both the equilibria and kinetics involved in these self-assembly reactions. A number of systems that assemble in this mode have been identified and characterized. These include the polymerization of G-actin into F-actin (5,6), the assembly of bacterial flagella (7), the polymerization of tobacco mosaic virus protein in the absence of the viral RNA (8,9), the self-association of glutamate dehydrogenase (10), and the self-assembly of tubulin to form microtubules (11,12). In the characterization of these processes four principal questions are normally asked: (*a*) What is the structure (geometry) of the final product? (*b*) What are the free energy relations in the assembly process? (*c*) What is the mechanism of the process? (*d*) What are the intermediates formed in the assembly process? While the first question can be answered best by electron microscopy or X-ray diffraction (Chapter 2), these techniques are not amenable to the examination of the dynamics of the assembly process. The second and third questions can be approached by nondestructive techniques, such as light scattering, viscosity, and flow birefringence. The last question is the most difficult one to answer (13). It can be pursued by a variety of methods, including those normally developed for small assembled structures. This question, however, is complicated by the very difficult problem of differentiation between true intermediates on the assembly pathway and nonfunctional trivial aggregates formed by the given protein. In this chapter we shall limit ourselves strictly to a discussion of the equilibria involved in the assembly, with some remarks on the kinetic analysis of the pathway. Furthermore, our discussion will be restricted to highly elongated structures, which may be regarded macroscopically as linear and microscopically as helical.

8.2 THEORY

The polymerization of a protein into long rodlike structures can be examined thermodynamically in terms of two possible pathways. First, it can occur through linear polymerization in which the assembled structure is formed by the sequential addition of the monomeric species to a growing chain, all interactions occurring with an identical standard free-energy change. The second, more complicated mechanism is that of a two-stage nucleated polymerization. In this pathway the first stage consists of a simple linear polymerization, which leads to the formation of an aggregate with a low degree of polymerization. This aggregate can then act as a nucleation center for the growth of the large structure, monomeric units still adding sequentially with an identical free energy change, which, however, is more negative than that characteristic of the first reaction. In fact, the nucleated polymerization pathway is simply the sequential combination of two linear polymerization reactions, with the restriction that the one with a larger free energy change can proceed only after the termination of the first one. Let us, therefore, examine these two in turn.

8.2.1. Linear Polymerization

As pointed out by Lauffer (8), a linear polymerization process can be treated in two ways, namely, in terms of equilibrium self-association or of the Flory linear condensation polymerization theory (14). The latter is based on the assumption that the chemical reactivity of a site of interaction is independent of the length of the chain, that is, of previous additions to the growing chain. This coincides with one of the requirements of an isodesmic self-association, in which all monomers add to the growing structure with an identical change in free energy (Chapter 1). Consider an isodesmic reaction:

$$
\begin{aligned}
P_1 + P_1 &\rightleftharpoons P_2 \\
P_2 + P_1 &\rightleftharpoons P_3 \\
\vdots \quad &\qquad \vdots \\
P_{i-1} + P_1 &\rightleftharpoons P_i \\
\vdots \quad &\qquad \vdots
\end{aligned}
\tag{1}
$$

The equilibrium constant for each step is given by

$$K_i = \frac{[P_i]}{[P_{i-1}][P_1]} \tag{2}$$

and since all K_i are identical the concentration of each i-mer is given by

$$[P_i] = [P_1]^i K_1^{i-1} \tag{3}$$

where

$$K_1 = K_2 = K_3 = \text{all } K_i$$

The total concentration of protein, C_t, expressed in terms of moles of monomer, is

$$C_t = C_1 + C_l = \sum_{i=1}^{\infty} iC_i \tag{4}$$

where C_1 is the molar concentration of monomer, C_l is the total concentration of species of degree of polymerization of two or greater, and C_i is the molar concentration of each i-mer. Combining Eqs. (3) and (4), and setting $[P_i] = C_i$, we obtain, for $K_1 C_1 < 1$,

$$C_t = \frac{C_1}{(1 - K_1 C_1)^2} \tag{5}$$

which is identical with Eq. (9) of Chapter 1.

Treating the same process in terms of the Flory theory of linear condensation polymerization (14), let us consider that we have in solution a total of N particles per unit volume; let N_i be the number of particles containing i monomer units, and N_0 be the total number of monomer units in the system, whether in the free or combined state. Let each uncombined monomer and each polymer have a free interaction site. Let p be the probability that this site is combined. The number of free sites, as well as the number of particles, N, is $N_0(1-p)$. It follows that $N_i/N_1 = p^{i-1}$, and

$$K_1 = \frac{p}{C_t(1-p)^2} \tag{6}$$

The probability, p, can be obtained by a number of techniques, such as light scattering. If the particles are small relative to the wavelength of the light and conditions such that the viral coefficients are vanishingly small, Lauffer (8) has shown that

$$p = \frac{(\tau/\tau_0) - 1}{(\tau/\tau_0) + 1} \tag{6a}$$

where τ is the experimentally measured turbidty and τ_0 is the turbidity of the monomer. When the particles become large, however, the Rayleigh approximation is invalid, these relations become complex and must be treated in terms of the Rayleigh–Gans (15), or even the Mie (16), theory of scattering (17, 18).

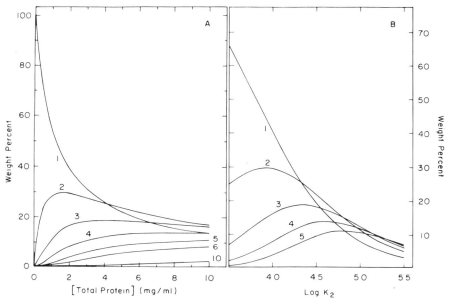

FIGURE 1

Mass distribution of tubulin among different size polymers for an isodesmic, indefinite self-association induced by vinblastine. (A). Dependence on the total protein concentration; $K_2^{app} = 5.2 \times 10^4\ M^{-1}$. ($B$) Dependence on the polymerization constants, total protein concentration = 10 mg/ml. The numbers next to each curve are degrees of polymerization. [Reprinted form G. C. Na and S. N. Timasheff, *Biochemistry* **19**, 1347 (1980)].

For a linear polymerization mechanism, the distribution of polymerized species may be calculated from Eqs. (3) and (5). The results of such a typical calculation are shown in Figure 1. It is evident that when the polymerization is of a linear isodesmic type, no predominant species are formed. In fact, as total protein concentration increases, the mass distribution of the various polymers tends toward uniformity. As is evident, this mechanism does not predict any cooperativity in the self-assembly.

8.2.2 Nucleated Polymerization

The theory of nucleated polymerization of proteins was first developed by Oosawa and co-workers for the helical polymerization of actin (19–22). According to this theory, the polymerization can be described as a two-step process, shown schematically in Figure 2. The first step is a nucleation step, which consists of a linear polymerization, as described above. The addition of each monomer involves the formation of a single contact with another monomer and it can be characterized by an association constant, K_n. This results in the assembly of a nucleus of degree of polymerization, n. At this

Oosawa Helical Polymerization Theory

Two Steps:

I. Nucleation

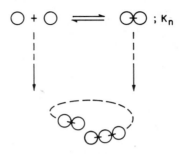

Kₙ at Each Step (One Contact)

2. Helix Propagation

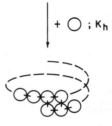

Kₕ at Each Step (Two Contacts)

FIGURE 2
Schematic representation of the Oosawa nucleated polymerization mechanism.
[Adapted from "Thermodynamic Examination of the Self-Association of Brain Tubu-
lin to Microtubules and Other Structures," Serge N. Timasheff, in *Physical Aspects of
Protein Interactions*. (N. Catsimpoolas, Ed.) Elsevier North-Holland, Amsterdam (1978)
pp. 219–273.]

point the addition of one further monomer starts the second turn of the helix
and the growth that continues with each additional unit involves the formation of two or more contacts between the unit and the existing structure. All
further monomeric units are then added on in similar manner, the assembly
progressing in helical array. The association constant for the helical growth
process, K_h, for the addition of each monomer must be greater than K_n
because of the free-energy contributions of the additional intersubunit contacts. It is the condition that $K_h > K_n$, which renders the process cooperative.
Let us examine this formally. Following Oosawa and co-workers (19–22), let
us assume that the process proceeds first by an isodesmic pathway to the
formation of the nucleus of degree of polymerization n, that is, P_n.

Let us consider the reaction $P_{(n+i),h} \rightarrow P_{(n+i+1),h}$, that is, the addition of a monomer to the growing helical structure. This step can be decomposed into several contributions: (a) Addition of the monomer to the growing chain, with a standard free-energy change, $\Delta G_n^0 = -RT\ln K_n$; ($b$) Formation of additional contacts with other monomers of the helix, with a contribution, K_c, to the equilibrium constant; (c) The gain in cratic free energy when the additional contacts are made, since once the monomer is attached to the growing chain, additional bond formation does not involve the loss of the entropy of mixing of the monomer, that is, there is no decrease in the number of independent kinetic units in solution, as occurs in the formation of the first bond. The free-energy change in the formation of these additional contacts is, then, $\Delta G_c^0 = -RT\ln K_c - RT\ln \{X_j/(X_{j-1}X_1)\}$, where X_l is the mole fraction of species l. This last contribution can amount to -2.5 kcal/mol. Therefore

$$\Delta G_h^0 = -RT\ln K_n K_c \left\{ \frac{X_j}{X_{j-1}X_1} \right\} = -RT\ln K_h$$

$$\Delta G_n^0 = -RT\ln K_n \tag{7}$$

and $K_h \gg K_n$. This analysis also implies, if the intersubunit bonds are regarded as being of two types, namely, longitudinal (K_n) and lateral (K_c), that $K_n > K_c$; otherwise, the initial linear polymerization could not occur in the direction in which it actually does. It is the contribution of the cratic free energy and the probability that the helical assembly involves the formation of more than one additional bond, which makes $K_h \gg K_n$.

The first step in the formation of the helix involves the transformation of the linear array of monomer units into a helical structure. This involves the free energy of the structural change, ΔG_s^0. While this change mechanistically should accompany the addition of the $(n+1)$th unit, since the helical structure is formed only at that stage, thermodynamically, this reaction can be incorporated into the nucleation process since it must precede further polymerization. Let s be the equilibrium constant for the unimolecular reaction $P_n \rightleftharpoons P_{n,h}$; $\Delta G_s^0 = -RT\ln s$. If the initial formation of the helix involves the introduction of rigidity, that is, a reduction in the rotational and bending entropy of the linear structure, this reaction should be unfavorable and should be characterized by a positive change in free energy and a value of $s \ll 1$. On the other hand, if addition of each unit to the growing chain takes place in the proper geometry modulated by intersubunit bond angles and directions, and with proper rigidity due to multiple point contact in the bonding site, then no additional entropy loss need occur on the first formation of the helix, and this contribution can be neglected. In terms of these considerations, the concentration of the completed nucleating structure in helical conformation, $C_{n,h}$, and that of any species polymerized in helical form, $C_{(n+i),h}$, are given by

$$C_{n,h} = sK_n^{n-1}C_1^n \tag{8}$$

and

$$C_{(n+i),\,h} = s\left(\frac{K_n}{K_h}\right)^{n-1} K_h^{-1}(K_hC_1)^{n+i} \tag{9}$$

The total concentration of protein contained in the helical polymers, expressed in terms of moles of monomer, is

$$C_h = \sum_{j=n+1}^{\infty} jC_{j,\,h} = \sum_{j=n+1}^{\infty} jAK_h^{-1}(K_hC_1)^j \tag{10}$$

where $A = s(K_n/K_h)^{n-1}$. With $K_hC_1 < 1$, this becomes

$$C_h = A\left[\frac{C_1}{(1-K_hC_1)^2} - C_1\sum_{j=1}^{n} j(K_hC_1)^{j-1}\right] \tag{11}$$

The first terms in the brackets corresponds to an isodesmic polymerization from monomer up, with a single association constant K_h. The second term corrects for the polymers up to degree of polymerization, n, which, by definition, cannot exist, since the second phase of the polymerization can start only after termination of nucleation, that is, its first step is the addition of the $(n+1)$th monomeric unit. Following the addition of that unit, the process may be regarded as an isodesmic polymerization with growth constant K_h, the number of growing polymers being limited by the number of nuclei formed. Since the concentration of protein in linear polymers (nucleation step) is given by the series of Eqs. (4) and (5), starting with $i=2$ and truncated at degree of association, n, the total protein concentration, expressed as moles of monomeric unit is

$$C_t = C_1\left\{1 + \sum_{j=2}^{n} j(K_nC_1)^{j-1} + A\left[\frac{1}{(1-K_hC_1)^2} - \sum_{j=1}^{n} j(K_hC_1)^{j-1}\right]\right\} \tag{12}$$

In this equation the first term inside the braces is the monomer concentration, the second term is the concentration of linear polymers up to the nucleated structure, the third term is the concentration of helical polymers.

Let us analyze the significance of this equation. Starting with the first term in the brackets, we find that for a constant value of K_h, this term increases as K_hC_1 increases and assumes very large values as $K_hC_1 \to 1.0$. For $K_hC_1 > 1.0$ this summation breaks down, and examination of Eq. (10) shows that the concentration of polymer goes to infinity. Therefore, the concentration of monomer must always be less than K_h^{-1}, all other protein existing only in the state of polymers. Now by definition, the coefficient A is very small. Oosawa and Asakura estimate it to be $< 10^{-10}$ (22). But for values of A even as large as 10^{-5}, C_h becomes greater than $0.01C_1$ only at $K_hC_1 > 0.97$. At smaller values of A, helical polymers appear in significant amounts at values of K_hC_1 which differ from unity by only an infinitesimal amount. The second term in the brackets is negligibly small relative to the first term, and polymers appear in significant amounts only when the monomer concentration becomes close to equal to K_h^{-1}. Since $K_n \ll K_h$, the term corresponding to the concentration of linear polymers is always $\ll 1.0$. Therefore, at protein concentrations just below the appearance of significant amounts of helical polymers, $C_t \simeq C_1$. These considerations lead to three consequences. First, the formation of helical polymers is characterized by a critical concentration, C_r. Below C_r, the protein is found essentially only in the monomeric state, with linear polymers of degree of polymerization $\leqslant n$ being present in extremely small amounts ($C_l < \text{or} \ll 0.1C_1$), and helical polymers being present in vanishingly small amounts. Second, essentially all protein in excess of C_r is incorporated into the high polymers, the concentration of protein not so incorporated remaining virtually constant at C_r. Third, the critical concentration is related to the growth constant, K_h, by the simple relationship

$$K_h = C_r^{-1} \tag{13}$$

Therefore, a measurement of the critical concentration leads directly to the value of the standard free energy of monomer addition to the cooperatively growing structure at the specific conditions of the experiment,

$$\Delta G_h^0 = -RT \ln K_h = RT \ln C_r \tag{14}$$

where R is the universal gas constant and T is the thermodynamic (Kelvin) temperature.

At this point, prior to a discussion of the methods available for measuring C_r, it seems desirable to examine further some of the properties of this model system. Returing to Eq. (12), it is evident that the cooperativity of the growth phase is modulated by the value of $A = s(K_n/K_h)^{n-1}$. This parameter depends on two factors, the free-energy change of the "strain" reaction and the ratio of the growth constants for the nucleation and propagation phases. Now the "strain" reaction, that is, the transformation of the linear polymer into the first element of helical geometry, may involve the loss of freedom of rotation of the monomer unit, that is, freedom of the linear polymeric chain to bend and twist. This would mean that the entropy change for this reaction, ΔS_s, would be negative, resulting in a positive value of ΔG_s^0 and $s < 1.0$. In fact values of $s \sim 10^{-3}$ can easily be expected (21). On the other hand, because of intersubunit bond orientation and rigidity, the linear polymer could assemble in the geometry necessary for subsequent helical growth, so that the structure of P_n would be identical to that of $P_{n,h}$. In this case, all the entropy factors would be incorporated already in ΔG_n^0, that is, K_n, rendering $\Delta G_s^0 = 0$, and $s = 1$. Using this simplifying assumption, let us examine again the relation between K_n and K_h. Cooperativity requires that $K_n < K_h$. In the case of $K_n = K_h$ Eq. (12) reduces to Eq. (5), and the system becomes one of simple isodesmic polymerization. As the ratio K_n/K_h decreases, A takes on progressively smaller values depending on n, the degree of cooperativity required to form the nucleus.

Now, what are the highest values of A that would permit the formation of long rodlike structures in helical array of monomeric units? This is restricted by two factors: (a) the degree of cooperativity needed to give rise to a critical concentration, and (b) the average degree of polymerization, $\langle i \rangle$, compatible with the rodlike geometry. Taking these in turn, when $K_n > 0.1K_h$, and the order of cooperativity is set at 5, the concentration of helical polymers becomes significant at values of $K_h C_1$ considerably smaller than 1.0, so that no true critical concentration is observed, but the increase in large polymer concentration assumes a sigmoidal shape, with the linear polymer concentration remaining at significant levels. For example, when $(K_n/K_h) = 0.5$, $n = 5$, at $K_h C_1 = 0.5$, 12% of the protein is already in helical form, and 38% is in the form of linear polymers. For $(K_n/K_h) = 0.1$, $n = 4$, at $K_h C_1 = 0.9$, 9% of the protein is already in helical form, while only 1.5% is in the form of linear polymers. Typical shapes of monomer and polymer distributions for the various cases are depicted in Figure 3. The existence of a sharp break, that is, a critical concentration, in the formation of the helical polymers requires that $K_n \ll K_h$. This is easily realized from the considerations on the number of contacts formed, as seen from Eq. (7). The cratic entropy term alone contributes a factor of $\sim 1/55$. Nevertheless the above-discussed intermediate cases are quite possible. These, however, will not give rise to large polymeric structures. Oosawa and co-workers (21) have shown that the average degree of polymerization $\langle i \rangle$, is

$$\langle i \rangle = \left(\frac{C_h}{C_r} \right)^{1/2} A^{-1/2} \tag{15}$$

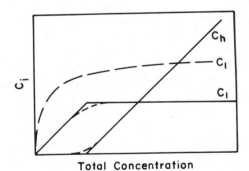

Total Concentration

FIGURE 3

Concentration distribution of species in self-assembling systems. (−−) Monomer concentration in linear polymerization. (——) Monomer and helical polymer concentrations in nucleated cooperative self-assembly system, when A is very small; (---) Concentration distributions when A is intermediate (Adapted from F. Oosawa and M. Kasai, in *Subunits in Biological Systems*, Part A, S. N. Timasheff and G. D. Fasman, Eds. Marcel Dekker, New York, 1971, pp. 261–322.)

Setting $C_h/C_r = 1$, or $C_t \geqslant 2C_r$, for the above two cases, $\langle i \rangle$ is found to be 4 and 32, respectively, that is, there will be no large helical polymers formed, and certainly no long rodlike structures. These cases do not fall, therefore, into the category of large helical assemblies. For long rodlike structures to appear, that is, for $\langle i \rangle \geqslant 10^3$, at $C_t = 2C_r$, A must assume values of $\leqslant 10^{-6}$, or for $n = 4$, $(K_n/K_h) \leqslant 0.01$. Such values of A will also give rise to the appearance of a sharp critical concentration. In view of these considerations, we may eliminate from further consideration systems for which $(K_n/K_h) > 0.01$, and consider only those systems which give rise to long rodlike structures in cooperative fashion.

Since for this system the standard free-energy change of helical growth can be deduced from the critical concentration by means of Eq. (14), it becomes relatively easy to characterize the polymerization in terms of all the standard thermodynamic parameters, namely, the enthalpy, ΔH^0, entropy, ΔS^0, heat capacity, ΔC_p and the volume, ΔV, changes, since

$$\Delta H^0 = -R \frac{d\ln K}{d(1/T)}$$

$$\Delta S^0 = \frac{\Delta H^0 - \Delta G^0}{T} = -\left(\frac{\partial \Delta G^0}{\partial T}\right)_P \tag{16}$$

$$\Delta C_p = \left(\frac{\partial \Delta H^0}{\partial T}\right)_P = \left(\frac{\partial \Delta S^0}{\partial \ln T}\right)_P$$

$$\Delta V = -RT\left(\frac{\partial \ln K}{\partial P}\right)_T$$

The significance of the entropy and heat capacity changes depends on an understanding of the exact meaning of the enthalpy change determined from a van't Hoff plot of the critical concentration data. Operationally such a measured change in standard enthalpy, ΔH^0_{exp}, is

$$\Delta H^0_{exp} = -R \frac{d\ln K_h}{d(1/T)} = R \frac{d\ln C_r}{d(1/T)} \tag{17}$$

Since, at the critical concentration, helical polymers are not present in significant amounts, the total protein concentration at C_r can be expressed as a close approximation by

$$C_t = C_r = C_1 \left[\frac{1}{(1 - K_n C_1)^2} + s(K_n C_1)^{n-1}\right] \tag{18}$$

At the critical concentration $C_1 \simeq K_h^{-1}$, and within a close approximation, Eq. (18) can be rewritten as

$$C_r = K_h^{-1}\left(\frac{K_h - K_n}{K_h}\right)^{-2}\left[1 + s\left(\frac{K_n}{K_h}\right)^{n-1}\left(\frac{K_h - K_n}{K_h}\right)^2\right] \tag{19}$$

Since s and (K_n/K_h) are $\ll 1.0$, Eq. (19) reduces to

$$\ln C_r = \ln K_h - 2\ln\ (K_h - K_n) \simeq -\ln K_h \qquad (20)$$

and

$$\Delta H_{exp}^0 = -\Delta H_h + 2R\frac{d\ln(K_h - K_n)}{d(1/T)} \simeq \Delta H_h \qquad (21)$$

The relative contributions of the heats of nucleation and growth to the van't Hoff enthalpy can be readily examined by setting $s = 1$ and simplifying Eq. (18) and (19) to

$$C_r = \frac{C_1}{(1 - K_n C_1)^2} = \frac{K_h^{-1}}{\left[1 - (K_n/K_h)\right]^2} \qquad (22)$$

This leads to the result that

$$\Delta H_{exp}^0 = \Delta H_h^0\left(\frac{K_h + K_n}{K_h - K_n}\right) + \Delta H_n^0\left(1 - \frac{K_h + K_n}{K_h - K_n}\right) \qquad (23)$$

For a value of $K_n/K_h = 10^{-2}$, this gives $\Delta H_{exp}^0 = 1.02\,\Delta H_h^0 - 0.02\,\Delta H_n^0$, that is, just as in Eq. (21), the measured van't Hoff enthalpy change is found to be essentially the standard enthalpy change of helical growth. Similarly, in calorimetric measurements, the heat uptake or evolution measured during the reaction at concentrations above the critical concentration should be essentially that of the helical growth, since according to Eq. (12) the total concentration of linear polymers would be negligible relative to that of helical polymers, and the heat generated by the nucleation reaction would be undetectable by present-day instrumentation.

The above equilibrium analysis permits the thermodynamic characterization of the cooperative growth of the elongated structure. It does not yield any information, however, on the actual pathway of the polymerization. Such information must be obtained from nonequilibrium experiments, for example from the kinetics of the process. This, however, involves a priori assumptions concerning the mechanism. Oosawa et al. (19–22) have treated the kinetics of this process in terms of a simple model, namely, that of a nucleated polymerization–depolymerization reaction at one end of the assembled structure. The results of their analysis are lucidly presented in their publications and will not be reproduced here. The two principal conclusions are: the rate of formation of helical polymers follows a sigmoidal dependence on time, and it is a strong function of total protein concentration.

While a number of self-assembling systems have been found to conform to the general characteristics of the nucleated polymerization mechanism, it is not necessarily true that the process is fully described by this simple mechanism. For example, addition and departure of monomers may occur at both ends; breaks may occur in the middle; assembled oligomers may combine to form large polymers. In fact, the nucleation process may be kinetically much more complicated than simple linear polymerization. For example, Carlier and Pantaloni (23) have carried out a statistical thermodynamic analysis of such an assembling system, with the conclusion that, given certain assumptions concerning the relative free energies of formation of longitudinal and lateral bonds, assembly should proceed through stages of linear growth, two-dimensional polymerization into elongated sheets and closing of the sheets to form short helices, the growing then proceeding according to the Oosawa et al., helical polymerization model. While this model follows an initial pathway drastically different from the nucleated polymerization model of Oosawa et al., and may strongly affect the kinetic analysis of nucleation and the initial growth stages, it in no way invalidates the thermodynamic analysis of helical growth, since the latter describes the system only after it had reached equilibrium, and is obviously independent of pathway. Furthermore, the equilibrium description of the process maintains its validity even if the process consists of two simultaneous equilibria occurring at the two ends of the structure, or if it is a steady state process in which a component of the solution, present in large excess, is altered irreversibly during the reaction, as by hydrolysis, for example, ATP to $ADP + P_i$. In the first case, for example, at steady state, the apparent growth constant, K_h, measured as C_r^{-1} could be equal to the sum of the assembly equilibrium constants at the two ends of the structure, $K_h^{(1)} + K_h^{(2)}$. In the case where $K_h^{(1)} > K_h^{(2)}$, a steady state assembly will be favored at end (1), and disassembly at end (2). This results in the treadmilling mechanism proposed by Wilson and co-workers for cytoplasmic microtubules (24). In fact, unless the two constants are identical or the reaction is blocked completely at one end, treadmilling must occur. Furthermore, the two-end assembly–disassembly pathway provides also a mechanism for limiting the length of the assembled structures without requiring any growth–terminating factors.

8.3 METHODS

The geometry and dimensions of the assembled structures under consideration impose strong limitations on the techniques available for following their assembly. The techniques most frequently used for these systems are: (*a*) light scattering; (*b*) pelleting of assembled material by high speed centrifugation; (*c*) hydrodynamic methods, such as viscosity and flow birefringence; (*d*) electron microscopy; and (*e*) progress of a coupled chemical reaction such as $ATP \rightarrow ADP + P_i$. We shall not discuss the last two methods, since this chapter is restricted to nondestructive physical techniques easily amenable to equilibrium studies. Let us take the other three in order. All are subject to strict assumptions and definite limitations.

8.3.1 Light Scattering

At present, the most widely used method for following the assembly of large linear structures seems to be that of light scattering or turbidimetry, that is, measurement of the total light scattered by attenuation of the incident beam. While this method has been in use for many years, it is only six years ago that it received a solid theoretical foundation for the case under consideration, namely for systems in which the assembled structure has the geometry of long thin rods relative to the incident wavelength. The theoretical analysis was performed by Berne (25) and his conclusions were verified experimentally by Gaskin et al. (11) using the microtubule assembly system. Working within the Rayleigh–Gans approximation, Berne took as his model a solution of rigid rods, which were (a) composed of optically isotropic identical monomeric units distributed uniformly along the rod axis, (b) randomly oriented in solution, (c) monodisperse, and (d) whose thickness was small relative to the wavelength of the incident light, λ, and to the length of the rod, L. Requirements (a) and (d) are easily satisfied. Requirement (b) can be satisfied by extrapolation to infinite dilution. Requirement (c) is rarely met; this, however, does not vitiate any of the practical conclusions of the theory, which remains valid for polydisperse systems, as long as the rods are long relative to the wavelength of the light.

Working within these assumptions, Berne showed that, for this geometric model, turbidity τ, (or the scattering intensity, I, at any given angle) is a direct measure of the mass of material polymerized, provided that $L/\lambda \gg \frac{1}{6}$. This is a direct consequence of the result that, within the assumptions of this theory, the dependence of turbidity on the wavelength reduces to inverse proportionality to the third power of the wavelength, instead of the more familiar inverse fourth power dependence. For any value of L/λ, turbidity is related to dimensions by

$$\tau = C \frac{H(Q_0)}{Q_0^{\,2}} \left(\frac{\pi\mu^2\alpha_0^2}{16(\varepsilon')^2\lambda^2} \right) \tag{24}$$

where

$$Q_0 = \sqrt{2}\,\pi\mu\left(\frac{L}{\lambda}\right)$$

where C is the number concentration of macromolecules, μ is the refractive index of the medium, α_0 is the macromolecular polarizability, ε' is the dielectric constant of the medium and $H(Q_0)$ is a function of rod length, distribution of rod orientations and angle of scattering. For small $Q_0(<1)$, $H(Q_0)$ and, therefore τ, varies as $Q_0^{\,4}$, that is, the inverse fourth power dependence on the wavelength holds. When $Q_0 \gg 1$, the dependence of $H(Q_0)$ on Q_0 decreases to the third power, that is, turbidity becomes proportional to $(L/\lambda)^3$. Theoretical calculations show that this becomes valid for $L/\lambda > 3.5$. For the usual wavelengths of turbidity measurements, for example, 350 nm, this corresponds to particle lengths of $> 12,000$ Å. For an assembly of monomeric units 100 Å in length this means that > 120 turns of the helix would have to form before reaching the validity of this law. Furthermore, Berne has examined the dependence of the quantity

$H(Q_0)/Q_0{}^2$, that is, of τ, on Q_0. At low values of Q_0, τ shows little dependence on Q_0. This dependence increases with increasing Q_0 and at sufficiently large Q_0, $H(Q_0)/Q_0{}^2$ becomes a linear function of Q_0. In this range the turbidity becomes proportional to CL, that is, to the total number of monomeric units in the assembled system in solution. Therefore, at high values of L/λ, turbidity (or scattering intensity) becomes a direct measure of the mass of protein polymerized into long rigid rodlike structures.

Since its development, this theory has received extensive application, in particular in studies on the self-assembly of microtubules from purified brain tubulin (11, 12, 26). Typical results of equilibrium and kinetic studies are presented in Figures 4 and 5 for the microtubule assembly system. In this system polymerization of 110,000 molecular weight tubulin monomers is induced by heating the solution. The polymers formed are known to be long assembled structures (typically several microns in length) having the geometry of hollow cylinders with an outer diameter of 25 nm. Thus geometrically this system satisfied the requirement of the Berne theory (25). Indeed, careful testing by Gaskin et al. (11) has shown that turbidity (measured as the attenuation of light in a spectrophotometer at 350 nm) is proportional to $\lambda^{-3.3}$, or close to the prediction of the Berne theory. The slight deviation from the inverse third power law is most probably the result of the crude methods by which turbidity is normally measured, namely, by the attenuation of the incident light measured in a standard spectrophotometer, using a one centimeter absorption cell and poorly collimated optics. Another contributing factor may be deviation of the real experimental system from the basic assumptions of the Berne theory.

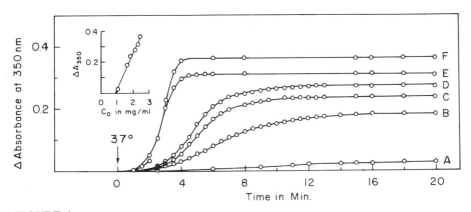

FIGURE 4

Turbidimetric determination of the critical concentration of tubulin self-assembly into microtubules at 37°C in a pH 7.0, 0.1 M phosphate buffer, containing 1.6×10^{-2} M MgCl$_2$, 10^{-4} M GTP, 3.4 M glycerol and 10^{-3} M EGTA. (Reprinted from "Thermodynamic Examination of the Self-Association of Brain Tubulin to Microtubules and Other Structures" Serge N. Timasheff, in *Physical Aspects of Protein Interactions* (N. Catsimpoolas, Ed.) Elsevier North-Holland, Amsterdam, 1978, pp. 219–273.)

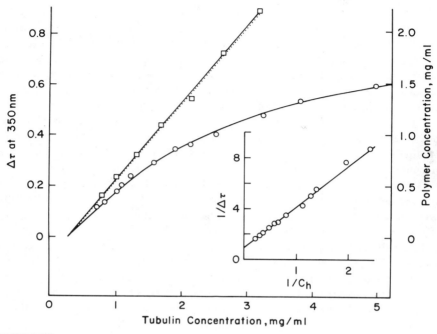

FIGURE 5

Dependence of the turbidity increment at 350 nm on total protein concentration in the self-assembly of tubulin to microtubules. (O) Turbidity measurement; (□) Concentration of polymerized tubulin in the same solutions, determined by high-speed centrifugation. Dotted line: turbidity corrected for the concentration effect. Inset: Plot of $(\Delta\tau)^{-1}$ as a function of $(C_h)^{-1}$, according to Eq. (26). [Adapted from M. -F. Carlier and D. Pantaloni, *Biochemistry* **17**, 1908 (1978).]

Within these uncertainties, assembly of pure tubulin into microtubules proceeds in a manner consistent both with the Berne theory of light scattering and the Oosawa theory of nucleated helical polymerization and it may be used as a good example of how these concepts can be applied. Examination of the data of Figure 4 shows three basic features. First, induction of polymerization by changing the temperature to 37°C leads to an increase in turbidity, which reaches a plateau value after a definite amount of time. The turbidity values in the plateau region are linerally dependent on protein concentration, as shown in the inset of Figure 4. This is consistent with the conclusion of the Berne theory that, for polymers such as microtubules, turbidity should be proportional to the total mass of protein polymerized. Second, extrapolation of the turbidity increment (i.e., $\tau_{exp} - \tau_{unpolymerized} = \Delta\tau$) to zero crosses the abcissa at a finite nonzero protein concentration below which turbidity remains at a constant value equal to that of the unpolymerized system. The concentration at which $\Delta\tau \to 0$ is, therefore, the critical concentration, indicating that the polymerization is cooperative, that is, it conforms to the Oosawa et al. nucleated helical assembly model. Finally, examination of Figure 4 reveals that both the lag period between the temperature change and the onset of turbidity and the rate of increase of turbidity with time are strong functions of total protein concentration, again in full conformity with the predictions of the Oosawa et al. theory.

When the turbidity method is used in equilibrium thermodynamic studies, that is, when its use is linked strictly to the determination of the critical concentration and K_h, extrapolation to zero $\Delta\tau$ involves essentially an extrapolation of C_h to zero, eliminating various concentration-dependent effects. On the other hand, turbidimetry has also been used frequently to follow the kinetics of the assembly–disassembly reactions. This type of experiment imposes several requirements: first, the exact relationship between $\Delta\tau$ and the mass of protein polymerized must be known over the protein concentration used; second, the measurements must be restricted to rod lengths (i.e., degrees of assembly) sufficiently long to satisfy the λ^{-3} dependence of τ; third, contributions of aggregates of smaller lengths and of all other geometries must be corrected for. The first requirement can be satisfied by properly calibrating $\Delta\tau$ in terms of the mass of assembled material established by some other technique, such as pelleting in a centrifuge. The second and third requirements can be met by restricting the measurements only to the late stages of the assembly process or the beginning of disassembly. The third requirement is probably satisfied by subtracting background turbidity measured just prior to the onset of rapid assembly. In the case of microtubule assembly, the first requirement has been tested by various investigators with the conclusion that, while at low total protein concentration, $\Delta\tau$ varies essentially linearly with total protein concentration, significant deviation sets in relatively early and much of the experimental work has to be done in a concentration range which is above linearity. Typical results are presented in Figure 5 taken from the studies of Carlier and Pantaloni (23). It is evident that the experimental turbidity values display a strong downward curvature from a straight-line dependence on protein concentration. Such results reflect a departure from the basic assumption of the theory that the assembled rods must be randomly oriented, that is, that their freedom of motion (rotation or tumbling) in solution must not be hindered by attractive or repulsive interactions with other assembled particles, or even by simply mechanical interference. Long rods would tend to align parallel to each other leading to long-range ordering effects (27,27a). Such long-range ordering results in external interference of the scattered light (28) which, at low concentrations, can be described by virial coefficients (28). At high concentrations it can actually give rise to effects similar to diffraction (29).

Carlier and Pantaloni (23) developed an empirical method for correcting for the curvature in the turbidity-concentration plot. Fundamentally, their method is based on a virial expansion of the turbidity. Formally, this can be expressed in general form as:

$$K\frac{C_h}{\Delta\tau} = \frac{1}{M_w} + 2BC_h + 3CC_h{}^2 + \cdots \qquad (25)$$

where K is a proportionality constant, which includes all optical and shape factors, M_w is the weight-average molecular weight of the polymers, C_h is the concentration of protein assembled in helical array, $C_h = C_{total} - C_{crit}$, and B, C, and so on are the second, third, and so on virial coefficients. Carlier and Pantaloni present their data by the empirical expression

$$\frac{C_h}{\Delta \tau} = \frac{1}{\alpha} + \beta C_h \qquad (26)$$

where α and β are arbitrary empirical coefficients. A plot of $1/\Delta \tau$ vs $1/C_h$ yields α and β, permitting the calculation of the turbidity, $\Delta \tau = \alpha C_h$, corrected for the effect of concentration, since

$$\Delta \tau' = \frac{\Delta \tau}{1 - \beta \Delta \tau} \qquad (27)$$

This results in the straight line of Figure 5, which must be used in further analysis of the data. In fact, in a kinetics experiment, every point must be properly corrected for the deviation from the ideal straight-line relation.

The other limitations imposed by the basic assumptions of the Berne theory are less amenable to simple treatment. First, let us examine the validity of the Rayleigh–Gans approximation (17, 18). This approximation, known also as the Rayleigh-Debye approximation, is based on the requirement that the "phase shift" corresponding to any point in the scattering particle be negligible, that is, that $(4\pi a/\lambda)(m-1) \ll 1$, where a is a characteristic dimension through the particle and m is the relative refractive index of the particle, defined as $m = \mu_p/\mu$ (where μ_p is the refractive index of the particle and μ is that of the medium). Since for proteins m is not far from unity, this criterion is satisfied for rods with lengths of the order of micrometers in length. Therefore, the Berne theory can be safely applied for particles with lengths between 3.5λ (lower limit for $\Delta \tau$ proportionality to λ^{-3}) and several microns (upper limit for the validity of the Rayleigh–Gans–Debye approximation).

The criterion of rods thickness small relative to λ can be examined in terms of the calculations of Farone et al. (30) of the scattering from infinitely long cylinders. From these calculations, it can be estimated that, for proteins in aqueous medium the Rayleigh–Gans approximation should be valid for rods with a cross-section radius, $r < 0.2\lambda$, or for a wavelength of 350 nm, the assembled structure should have a radius of not more that 70 nm.

A further assumption of the Rayleigh–Debye theory is that light scattered from a particle proceeds to the detector without further scattering events, that is, that there is no multiple scattering (31). This can be minimized by using small solution volumes and dilute sample solutions.

A further question to be addressed in using turbidity as a measure of polymerization is the contribution from smaller aggregates and from structures other than rods. The turbidity for rods of any length is related to length by Eq. (24). For long rods, this reduces to $\Delta \tau \propto NM$, where N is the number of assembled polymers and M is their molecular weight. For short rods, $\Delta \tau \propto \lambda^{-4}$ and the usual relations holds that $\Delta \tau \propto NM^2$. For intermediate lengths of rods, the power of M gradually changes from 2 to 1. As a result in the initial state of growth the rate of change of turbidity with increase in length of the rod will be greater than in the later stages, $d\tau/dL$ decreasing from 2 to 1 in the region between $L=\lambda$ and $L=3.5\lambda$ (25). Therefore, any use of turbidity for assembly kinetics measurements should be approached with great caution, since for $L<3.5\lambda$ the change in turbidity becomes a complex function of the change in particle length. Furthermore, in such measurements, proper correction should be made for the contribution to the light scattering of aggregates other than linear. When such aggregates are small, their contribution to the turbidity is proportional to $C_i M_i$, where C_i is the mass concentration of aggregated species i and M_i is its molecular weight. For large nonlinear aggregates, turbidity will deviate from proportionality to CM. However, there is no a priori requirement that the scattering law will reduce to $\tau \propto NM$, as for long thin rods. To the contrary this is very unlikely. Therefore, turbidity should not be used routinely as a quantitative measure of assembly for polymer whose structure corresponds to geometries other than that of long, thin rods. In fact, when the aggregated species are spherical, it has been shown (32) that, once spheres of a certain size have been reached, turbidity may decrease with a further increase in radius.

A further complication in the use of turbidity to follow assembly is strictly instrumental. This is due to the large angles subtended by detectors in the usual spectrophotometers. The definition of turbidity contains the assumption that only unscattered light is measured by the detector. For large particles, however, scattering is predominantly in the forward direction. Therefore, part of the light registered on the detector as transmitted light is, in fact, light scattered at very low angles. This results in apparent turbidity values that are too low. Correction for this requires the introduction of a fine aperture at the detector with good collimation of the transmitted beam, or a theoretical correction for the amount of light scattered in a cone described by rotating about the axis of the incident light the maximal angle viewed by the detector.

In summary, turbidity can be a useful method for following the assembly of long rodlike structures, if the assembled structures are sufficiently long. From Eq. (15), this will be generally true if the degree of cooperativity is very high. No great errors are introduced when the measurements entail extrapolation to zero concentration of polymers, as in the measurement of the critical concentration. On the other hand, great caution must be exercised in using this technique for kinetic measurements, in view of its validity as a quantitative tool over only a relatively narrow range of rod lengths and of the technical problems which must be overcome.

8.3.2 Pelleting

The amount of material assembled can also be measured directly by high speed centrifugation in which the high polymers become pelleted at the bottom of the cell, only monomers and small aggregates remaining in the supernatant. This approach is based on two assumptions: (a) The rate of depolymerization is slow relative to the length of the centrifugation, so that the equilibrium distribution is not disturbed during the course of the experiment. (b) The assembly equilibrium is not disturbed by pressure, since $\ln\{K(0)/K(P)\} = M_p \triangle \bar{v}(P - P_0)$, where $K(0)$ and $K(P)$ are the equilibrium constants at pressures P_0 and P, M_p is the molecular weight of the polymer and $\triangle \bar{v}$ is the difference in partial specific volumes between polymer and monomer. Many assembly reactions are accompanied by significant values of $\triangle \bar{v}$ (33). Since pressures of several hundred atmospheres may be generated at the bottom of tubes in high-speed centrifuges, the second criterion may at times be difficult to meet. The validity of this technique can be tested, however, (a) by examining critically whether the protein in the supernatant can be induced to assemble at atmospheric pressure, and (b) by ascertaining that the total protein concentration in the supernatant is equal to the known critical concentration prior to centrifugation.

8.3.3   Viscosity and Flow Birefringence

Finally, assembly of long helical polymers has been followed also by transport techniques in particular viscosity and flow birefringence. While, qualitatively, these approaches can give information on the critical concentration and the general pattern of the rate of assembly, the validity of these approaches is based to a great extent on empirical correlation with other techniques (22). We shall limit our remarks to viscosity, although similar considerations apply to flow birefringence. In viscosity experiments, the quantity normally recorded is the specific viscosity, η_{sp}, which is plotted either as a function of time to obtain the plateau values at various protein concentrations, or as a function of protein concentration at the plateau values to obtain the critical concentration. Using the Huggins equation (34), η_{sp} is related to the intrinsic viscosity $[\eta]$ by

$$\eta_{sp} = [\eta]C + k[\eta]^2 C^2 \tag{28}$$

Combining with the Mark–Houwink equation

$$[\eta] = KM^\alpha \tag{29}$$

where M is the molecular weight of the polymer and K and α are constants defined by the shape of the polymer, we get

$$\eta_{sp} = KM^\alpha C + K'M^{2\alpha}C^2 \tag{30}$$

Therefore, a plot of η_{sp} as a function of C, or C_{hel} cannot a priori be expected to give a straight line. This may be approached at very low values of C and high M, since the dependence of $[\eta]$ on M changes with molecular weight and α attains a constant value at large M (35). Detailed kinetic analysis is even more complicated, since even in the approximation that $\eta_{sp}/C = [\eta]$, the rate of viscosity change follows a complex dependence on both concentration of polymers and their molecular weight, as is evident from the time derivative of Eq. (30), where $C = C_{hel}$ and both C_{hel} and M change with time. Furthermore, the constants K and α are functions of exact shape. Therefore, the presence of bends, nicks, torsion, flexibility or an occasional cross-link will strongly affect the viscosity of the solution, subjecting to serious errors any quantitative conclusions drawn about the assembly process.

8.4 CONCLUSION

At present the self-assembly of proteins to long rigid rodlike structures is amenable to quantitative thermodynamic analysis, both from the theoretical and the experimental points of view. The basic theory is that of nucleated helical polymerization developed by Oosawa and co-workers. This permits the exact evaluation of the standard free energy change of growth, that is, of the addition of a monomeric unit to the growing helical array, once nucleation is complete. The principal requirement is that $K_h \gg K_n$, which leads to the formation of long structures, the manifestation of a sharp critical concentration and the essential absence of any low polymers, once formation of high polymers sets in. Experimentally, this process can be followed best by light scattering (or rather turbidity) measurements, since as has been shown by Berne, for long rods the scattering intensity is a direct measure of the mass of protein polymerized. This method, however, should be used with great caution, particularly in kinetic experiments, in view of its validity only over a rather limited range of rod lengths, that is, between the minimal length at which turbidity becomes proportional to λ^{-3} and the length at which the Rayleigh–Gans–Debye approximation loses its validity, that is, over a range in which the length of the helix increases by not more than a factor of 10.

ACKNOWLEDGMENT

This work was supported by grants from the National Institutes of Health, CA 16707 and GM 14603.

REFERENCES

1. R. Townend, R. J. Winterbottom, and S. N. Timasheff, *J. Am. Chem. Soc.*, **82**, 3161 (1960).

2. V. Massey, W. F. Harrington, and B. S. Martley, *Discuss. Faraday Soc.*, **20**, 24 (1955).

3. K. C. Aune and S. N. Timasheff, *Biochemistry* **10**, 1609 (1971).

4. R. F. Steiner, *Arch. Biochem. Biophys.* **39**, 333 (1952).

5. S. Asakura and F. Oosawa, *Arch. Biochem. Biophys.* **87**, 273 (1960).

6. S. Asakura, M. Kasai, and F. Oosawa, *J. Polymer Sci.* **44**, 35 (1960).

7. B. R. Gerber, L. M. Routledge, and S. Takashima, *J. Mol. Biol.* **71**, 317 (1972).

8. M. A. Lauffer, in S. N. Timasheff and G. D. Fasman, Eds., *Subunits in Biological Systems*, Part A, Marcel Dekker, New York, 1971, pp. 149–199.

9. A. Durham, J. T. Finch, and A. Klug, *Nature, New Biol.* **229**, 37 (1971).

10. H. Eisenberg, R. Josephs, and E. Reisler, *Adv. Protein Chem.* **30**, 101 (1976).

11. F. Gaskin, C. R. Cantor, and M. L. Shelanski, *J. Mol. Biol.* **89**, 737 (1974).

12. S. N. Timasheff, in N. Catsimpoolas, Ed., *Physical Aspects of Protein Interactions*, Elsevier North-Holland, Amsterdam, 1978, pp. 219–273.

13. A. C. H. Durham and A. Klug, *J. Mol. Biol.* **67**, 315 (1972).

14. P. J. Flory, *J. Am. Chem. Soc.*, **58**, 1877 (1936).

15. Lord Rayleigh, *Phil. Mag.*, 81 (1881).

16. G. Mie, *Ann. Physik* **25**, 377 (1908).

17. M. Kerker, *The Scattering of Light*, Academic Press, New York, 1969.

18. H. C. van de Hulst, *Light Scattering by Small Particles*, Wiley, New York, 1957.

19. F. Oosawa and S. Higashi, *Prog. Theor. Biol.* **1**, 28 (1967).

20. F. Oosawa and M. Kasai, *J. Mol. Biol.* **4**, 10 (1962).

21. F. Oosawa and M. Kasai, in S. N. Timasheff and G. D. Fasman, Eds., *Subunits in Biological Systems*, Part A, Marcel Dekker, New York, 1971, pp. 261–322.

22. F. Oosawa and S. Asakura, *Thermodynamics of the Polymerization of Protein*, Academic Press, New York, 1975.

23. M. F. Carlier and D. Pantaloni, *Biochemistry* **17**, 1908 (1978).

24. R. L. Margolis and L. Wilson, *Proc. Natl. Acad. Sci. USA* **74**, 3466 (1977).

25. B. J. Berne, *J. Mol. Biol.* **89**, 756 (1974).

26. S. N. Timasheff and L. M. Grisham, *Annu. Rev. Biochem.* **49**, 565 (1980).

27. L. Onsager, *Ann. N.Y. Acad. Sci.* **51**, 627 (1949).

27a. P. J. Flory, *Proc. R. Soc.* **A234**, 73 (1956).

28. G. Fournet, *Acta Cryst.* **4**, 293 (1951).

29. S. N. Timasheff and B. D. Coleman, *Arch. Biochem. Biophys.* **87**, 63 (1960).

30. W. A. Farone, M. Kerker, and E. Matjeivic, in M. Kerker, Ed., *Electromagnetic Scattering*, Pergamon Press, New York, 1963, pp. 55–71.

31. W. B. Dandliker and J. Kraut, *J. Am. Chem. Soc.* **78**, 2380 (1956).

32. S. N. Timasheff, *J. Colloid Interface Sci.* **21**, 489 (1966).

33. W. F. Harrington and G. Kegeles, *Methods Enzymol.* **27**, 306 (1973).

34. C. Tanford, *Physical Chemistry of Macromolecules*, Wiley, New York, 1961, Chapter 6.

35. D. M. Crothers and B. H. Zimm, *J. Mol. Biol.* **12**, 525 (1965).

CHAPTER **9**

Binding Equations and Control Effects

L.W. NICHOL AND D. J. WINZOR

In biological systems the binding of a ligand to a protein is an extremely common event that can have pronounced consequences upon the functional state and role not only of the protein but also of the entire physiological system. For example, drug therapy can frequently be traced to reversible inhibition of a single enzyme; immunological protection is a consequence of antigen-antibody interactions; reversible binding of Ca(II) to proteins plays an important role in muscle action and in blood coagulation, while the oxygen-hemoglobin system serves to illustrate the vital role of proteins as transporters of small molecules. Moreover, the regulation of metabolic pathways entails an interplay between a series of reversible equilibria involving enzymes and metabolites. Because of the diversity and biological importance of their occurrence, the study of such interactions has received considerable attention.

Generally, experimental results in this field are formulated as binding curves, which display the relationship between the amount of ligand bound and its unbound concentration. The simplest form of such a curve is a rectangular hyperbola but deviations from this form are common. An example is provided by a sigmoidal binding curve which around its point of inflection exhibits the property that the amount of ligand bound is an extremely sensitive function of the free ligand concentration. Such curves, therefore, provide insight into the operation of important biological control effects and form the bases of molecular interpretations of such phenomena. The present chapter discusses binding curves of diverse types in terms of their experimental determination, their use in molecular interpretation and their biological significance.

9.1   THE DEFINITION AND MEASUREMENT OF THE BINDING FUNCTION

In studies of mixtures in solution of an acceptor A and a ligand S it is appropriate to define operationally a binding function, r, as the ratio of the moles of ligand bound to the total moles of acceptor (1). Thus

$$r = \frac{\overline{m}_S - m_S}{\overline{m}_A} \tag{1}$$

where $\overline{m}_S$ and $\overline{m}_A$ denote the total molar concentrations of ligand and acceptor, respectively, in the mixture, and m_S is the corresponding equilibrium concentration of free ligand. This function corresponds to the *average* number of molecules of ligand associated with each molecule of A (2). Provided that $\overline{m}_S$ and $\overline{m}_A$, the initial mixing composition, may be determined, evaluation of one point on a binding curve requires the determination of m_S or $(\overline{m}_S - m_S)$. The latter quantity may be available for specific systems by application of such techniques as spectrophotometry (3–5), fluorimetry (6–8), and nmr spectrometry (9–12), but more frequently it is m_S that is determined.

In the specific instance of the study of antigen–antibody binding by radioim-munoassay, it is possible to label radioactively one reactant and after ensuring complete precipitation of all complexes (by, for example, the addition of ammonium sulfate), to estimate the equilibrium concentration of the labeled reactant in the supernatant. However, more general procedures entail the evaluation of m_S by creation of a solution phase containing only ligand, the concentration of which may be related to that in the solution phase comprising the equilibrium mixture. Two types of situation are encountered in practice, the binding to a macromolecular acceptor of either a small ligand or of a ligand that is also macromolecular: the choice of a method for creating the appropriate ligand phase is dictated by this distinction.

9.1.1 Equilibrium Dialysis

In this technique a membrane that is permeable to ligand but not to acceptor or acceptor-ligand complex(es) is used to divide the dialysis cell into two compartments. Acceptor or an acceptor-ligand mixture is introduced into one compartment (α) and ligand or buffer into the other (β). At equilibrium the chemical potential of ligand is identical in the two phases, and hence its thermodynamic activity in the β (i.e., pure ligand) phase equals the activity of unbound ligand in the mixture. Thermodynamic ideality is generally assumed to enable activities to be replaced by concentrations, a reasonable assumption for many, but not all, systems (13). The fact that the β-phase contains only free ligand expands greatly the number of methods that may be used to determine its equilibrium concentration, photometric, enzymatic or radioisotopic labeling procedures being most commonly used. Preference is usually given to an analytical procedure that can also be used to measure the total concentration of ligand in the α-phase, whereupon the numerator of the binding function, namely ($\overline{m}_S - m_S$), is obtained directly. Otherwise, the concentration of bound ligand must be inferred from the difference between the total amount of ligand introduced into the system and that present as free ligand. This indirect method may require quantitative correction for any absorption of ligand to the membrane (14). Moreover, application of the procedure to systems involving the binding of a charged ligand to a protein assumes implicitly the absence of a significant Donnan effect. In fact, the concentrations of a charged ligand in the two phases are related by the expression (15),

$$\left(\frac{m_S^\alpha}{m_S^\beta} \right)^{1/z_S} = 1 - \left(\frac{\bar{z}_A \overline{m}_A^\alpha}{2I} \right) \tag{2}$$

where $\bar{z}_A$, z_S denote the valencies of acceptor constituent and ligand respectively, and I denotes the ionic strength of the medium. In many studies performed at an ionic strength of 0.1 or higher the Donnan correction is negligible, but with highly charged systems studied at low ionic strengths a correction via Eq. (2) is necessary, which requires an iterative determination of $\bar{z}_A$.

A major disadvantage of equilibrium dialysis is the time required for attainment of equilibrium across the semipermeable membrane. In an attempt to overcome this time factor, Colowick and Womack (16) have developed a steady-state dialysis procedure. The apparatus comprises a dialysis cell with an upper compartment, containing an acceptor-ligand mixture, separated by a membrane from a lower compartment, through which buffer is pumped at a constant rate. Analysis of the ligand concentration in the effluent has indicated that only a few minutes are required to establish a steady-state between the rates at which ligand is entering (via dialysis) and leaving (via pumping) the lower compartment. The concentration of free ligand in the equilibrium mixture is then estimated from this steady-state concentration by calibration of the system with ligand but not acceptor in the upper compartment. This calibration step has no rigorous thermodynamic basis, since (unlike equilibrium dialysis) chemical potentials of ligand in the two phases cannot be explicitly related. Other methods of achieving a reduction of the time have therefore been sought.

9.1.2   Diafiltration and Ultrafiltration

In the initial application of the ultrafiltration assembly to studies of ligand binding (17), the technique of fixed-volume diafiltration was used in which a solution of ligand from a reservoir is passed through a fixed volume of stirred protein solution (concentration $\bar{m}_A^\alpha$) until the ligand concentration in the effluent taken from below the membrane is equal to that (m_S^α) in the reservoir. The contents of the filtration cell are then assayed for total ligand concentration ($\bar{m}_S^\alpha$), and hence r is determined from Eq. (1). It is possible to obtain r in even shorter time by dispensing with the reservoir (18). A mixture containing known total concentrations of acceptor and ligand is placed in the filtration cell and small aliquots of the effluent containing free ligand are collected. The concentration of ligand in this effluent at any given time defines exactly (18) the corresponding concentration of free ligand (m_S^α) in the reaction mixture. Under the conditions employed an experimental value of r for the binding of Mn(II) to concanavalin A could be obtained within 10–20 min.

A major precaution to be taken with the second technique (18) concerns the progressive decrease in volume of the reaction mixture as effluent is removed from below the membrane. As a consequence the total concentrations of acceptor and ligand are constantly changing, and hence an extremely accurate record of the volume and ligand concentration of the effluent is required to determine the values of $\bar{m}_A^\alpha$ and $\bar{m}_S^\alpha$ appropriate to a particular aliquot of effluent. Moreover, this method is not recommended when the acceptor self-associates, since the relative proportions of oligomeric acceptor species would then vary with the changing $\bar{m}_A^\alpha$. In the diafiltration method

(17), the collection and treatment of results is simpler and to be preferred for self-associating acceptor systems inasmuch as $\bar{m}_A^\alpha$ remains constant. However, evaluation of $\bar{m}_S^\alpha$ requires the availability of an analytical method that yields the combined concentration of ligand in free and bound form. If such an analytical method were unavailable, conventional equilibrium dialysis would be the method of choice from those discussed thus far.

9.1.3 Migration Methods

Another method of separating pure ligand from an equilibrium mixture of acceptor and ligand is to employ mass migration methods such as electrophoresis, sedimentation velocity or chromatography. Since the dilution that occurs in any zonal experiment must clearly perturb the composition of an interacting mixture from its initial equilibrium state, investigations of acceptor-ligand systems are made more amenable to interpretation by performing the migration experiments in a manner that preserves a plateau of original composition. Conventional velocity sedimentation, moving boundary electrophoresis and the frontal technique of gel chromatography (19,20) are three commonly used methods that retain plateau regions.

In addition to exhibiting this plateau region of original composition (the α-phase) the migration pattern for an interacting acceptor-ligand mixture also contains a second plateau region corresponding to pure ligand. However, the concentration of ligand in this region may differ significantly from its equilibrium concentration in the initial reaction mixture (21,22). Only in the event that unbound acceptor and all complexes comigrate does $m_S^\beta = m_S^\alpha$ (20–22). Consider, for example, a typical "sedimentation dialysis" experiment in which the tube of a preparative rotor or airfuge rotor (23) is filled with the acceptor-ligand mixture of known composition, $\bar{m}_A^\alpha$ and $\bar{m}_S^\alpha$ and then subjected to ultracentrifugation for a time sufficiently long to ensure the complete removal of acceptor from the meniscus region. The concentration of ligand in this region, m_S^β, may be obtained and equated to m_S^α provided the sedimentation coefficients of unbound A and of all complexes are identical, or nearly so. This assumed identity of the migration rates of all acceptor-containing species certainly seems a reasonable approximation in instances where S is a small ligand such as a metal ion (24) or NADH (25), or where the acceptor is an insoluble matrix, the situation pertaining in studies of the binding of glycolytic enzymes to structure proteins of muscle (26,27). However, in studies of interactions between soluble macromolecules of comparable size it is quite unrealistic to assume that velocities of acceptor and its complexes are identical: in this case, although the concentration of ligand in the protein-free phase may be determined, it is not the equilibrium concentration pertaining in the plateau region (21,22).

The latter problem may be overcome by the use of gel chromatography because of the availability of gels with a variety of permeation characteristics. Thus it is frequently a relatively simple matter to select a gel from which free

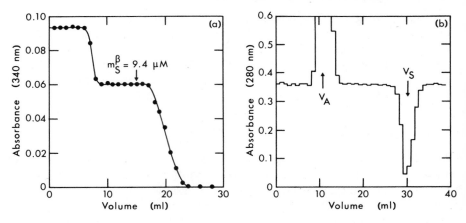

FIGURE 1
Evaluation of the binding function r by gel chromatography. (a) Trailing elution profile obtained in a frontal study of the binding of NADH to lactate dehydrogenase (adapted from ref. 29). Since the original mixing concentrations of NADH and enzyme were 15 μM and 2.8 μM, respectively, the value of r from Eq. (1) is 2.0. (b) Profile obtained in a study of the binding of tryptophan to bovine serum albumin by the Hummel and Dreyer procedure. The area enclosed by the negative peak at V_S equals the amount of ligand bound, which on division by the amount of acceptor applied yields r. (Adapted from ref. 34 with permission. Copyright by American Chemical Society.)

acceptor and all acceptor-ligand complexes are excluded and thus ensure the comigration of A and all complexes. To create a plateau of initial composition, acceptor-ligand mixture is added to a column of appropriate gel until the composition of the effluent is identical with that being applied. On subsequent elution with buffer, the concentration of ligand in the acceptor-free region, observed optically on the column (28) or in a conventional elution profile, yields the equilibrium concentration directly. Figure 1a presents the elution profile obtained in a study of the interaction between lactate dehydrogenase and NADH on Sephadex G-25 (29). This frontal procedure has been used to study protein-protein interactions (20) as well as other protein–small molecule interactions (30–32).

A disadvantage of the frontal technique is the relatively large volume of acceptor-ligand mixture that is required for its use. Consequently, preference has been shown for the Hummel and Dreyer (33) technique, which entails application of a relatively small zone of acceptor solution to a column preequilibrated with a known concentration of ligand; the identity of acceptor and complex elution volumes is again required for valid application of the technique. An excellent example of the use of this method is the study of tryptophan binding by bovine serum albumin (34). The increase of total concentration coincident with the acceptor peak at V_A (Figure 1b) reflects the binding of ligand, whereupon the amount bound may be calculated by trapezoidal integration to find the area of this peak. Alternatively, the area of the negative peak that occurs at V_S, the elution volume of ligand, may be used for this purpose. Greater economy in regard to amount of acceptor required is certainly an advantage of this technique over the frontal procedure described above; but the required trapezoidal integration places stringent demands not only on the accuracy with which differences in ligand concentrations may be measured, but also on the accuracy with which the volume increments must be measured. In experiments involving discontinuous analysis of the effluent, estimation of fraction volumes by weight seems essential. Provided that measurement of total ligand concentration is feasible in the presence of acceptor, the need for trapezoidal integration in the Hummel and Dreyer procedure can be obviated by increasing the volume of the applied zone sufficiently for the elution profile to contain a plateau region of acceptor, instead of a peak. The concentration of bound ligand is then simply obtained as the difference between the total ligand concentrations associated with this acceptor plateau and the preequilibrating concentration of ligand (35).

The study by frontal chromatography of the binding of charged ligands requires special mention. Gel chromatographic studies of ligand binding are subject to Donnan redistribution of ions in the same manner as equilibrium dialysis is affected (36). Indeed, the analogy is complete when it is realized that m_S^β, the concentration of ligand obtained from a frontal binding experiment (Figure 1a) refers to the concentration of free ligand in the acceptor-free phase within the gel beads (36), rather than that (m_S^α) in the equilibrium mixture surrounding the beads. The use of relatively high ionic strengths to decrease the differences between m_S^α and m_S^β has already been discussed in relation to the application of Eq. (2) to equilibrium dialysis studies. If the neglect of the Donnan redistribution cannot be justified, a protocol has been suggested (35) involving both types of plateau chromatographic experiments, which leads directly to m_S^α appropriate for use in Eq. (1) to calculate r.

In the final migration method, moving boundary electrophoresis, it cannot be assumed even for acceptor–small ligand interactions that the electrophoretic mobilities of acceptor and all complexes are identical. Accordingly, the observable concentration of free ligand is not the appropriate m_S^α, calculation of which from the observed m_S^β may proceed only indirectly via use of a moving boundary equation and the concept of a constituent velocity (37–41).

9.1.4   Sedimentation Equilibrium

On subjecting an interacting acceptor-ligand mixture to sedimentation equilibrium at angular velocity ω, the acceptor, the ligand, and each complex are distributed such that the concentration of each species i at radial distance x is related to $m_i(x_m)$, its concentration at the air-liquid meniscus, by the expression

$$m_i(x) = m_i(x_m) \exp\left\{ \frac{M_i(1-\bar{v}_i\rho)\omega^2(x^2 - x_m^2)}{2RT} \right\} \tag{3}$$

in which M_i denotes the molecular weight of solute i with partial specific volume $\bar{v}_i$. Application of the $\Omega(x)$ analysis (42), based on Eq. (3) and described in detail in Chapter 5, yields the concentration $m_S(x)$ of unbound S at each radial position x. If values of $\bar{m}_A(x)$ and $\bar{m}_S(x)$ are also available by use of absorption optics and isobestic points, it is evident from Eq. (1) that a range of (r, m_S) points may be found from a single experiment. This method is of greater value when S is relatively large, because when the ligand is small $m_S(x)$ becomes virtually constant according to Eq. (3). In this case a plot of $\bar{m}_S(x)$ vs $\bar{m}_A(x)$ yields from the slope and intercept, respectively, a single value of r and the corresponding m_S, as discussed in relation to the sedimentation equilibrium of mixtures of bovine serum albumin and methyl orange (43). This system has, of course, been studied by the far simpler methods of equilibrium dialysis (44) and gel chromatography (28,31).

9.2   THE GENERAL BINDING EQUATION FOR A SINGLE ACCEPTOR STATE

In considering binding equations that are of use in interpreting plots of r vs m_S, it is convenient to examine first a situation where ligand binds to p sites on a single acceptor state, the successive equilibria being described in stoichiometric terms by

$$AS_{i-1} + S \rightleftharpoons AS_i; \qquad K_i = \frac{m_{AS_i}}{m_{AS_{i-1}} m_S}; \qquad (i = 1, 2, \ldots, p) \tag{4}$$

where K_i is the association equilibrium constant on a molar scale. By successive substitution it follows that

$$m_{AS_i} = \left\{ \prod_{l=1}^{l=i} K_l \right\} m_A m_S^i \tag{5}$$

and that the total concentrations of acceptor and ligand are given, respectively, by

$$\bar{m}_A = m_A + \sum_{i=1}^{i=p} m_{AS_i} = m_A \left(1 + \sum_{i=1}^{i=p} \left\{ \prod_{l=1}^{l=i} K_l \right\} m_S^i \right) \tag{6}$$

$$\bar{m}_S = m_S + \sum_{i=1}^{i=p} i m_{AS_i} = m_S + m_A \sum_{i=l}^{i=p} i \left\{ \prod_{l=1}^{l=i} K_l \right\} m_S^i \tag{7}$$

Combination of Eqs. (1), (6), and (7) yields the general binding equation, of form originally proposed by Adair (45),

$$r = \frac{\sum\limits_{i=1}^{i=p} i\left\{ \prod\limits_{l=1}^{l=i} K_l \right\} m_S^i}{1 + \sum\limits_{i=1}^{i=p} \left\{ \prod\limits_{l=1}^{l=i} K_l \right\} m_S^i} \tag{8}$$

which is a ratio of polynomials in m_S, independent of m_A and hence of the total acceptor concentration $\overline{m}_A$.

Equation (8) may be transformed (46,47) by defining,

$$\lambda = 1 + \sum\limits_{i=1}^{i=p} \left\{ \prod\limits_{l=1}^{l=i} K_l \right\} m_S^i \tag{9a}$$

so that

$$\frac{d\lambda}{dm_S} = \sum\limits_{i=1}^{i=p} i\left\{ \prod\limits_{l=1}^{l=i} K_l \right\} m_S^{i-1} \tag{9b}$$

It follows from Eq. (8) that

$$r = \frac{d\ln \lambda}{d\ln m_S} ; \qquad \ln \lambda = \int_0^{m_S} \frac{r\, dm_S}{m_S} \tag{9c}$$

It has been suggested (48) that a high power polynomial in m_S be used in a least squares fit to describe experimental data in the form of r/m_S vs m_S: this function can then be used in performing the integration in Eq. (9c) to determine λ as a function of m_S. A least-squares regression analysis then yields, on the basis of Eq. (9a), values of K_i. This provides a general procedure amenable to statistical criteria, for evaluating the stoichiometric equilibrium constants governing a system describable by Eq. (8): other procedures are also available for this purpose (49). We need now to consider the meaning and implications of the relative magnitudes of the K_i.

9.2.1 Binding to Equivalent and Independent Sites: The Rectangular Hyperbola

Considerable simplification of Eq. (8) was effected by Klotz (1), who noted that provided the binding sites on the acceptor were equivalent and independent, all stoichiometric equilibrium constants K_i could be related to a single intrinsic association constant k_A, also termed a site-binding constant. In these terms, for example, when there are two equivalent sites on acceptor, one visualizes two forms of the $1:1$ complex, -A-S and S-A-, and writes $m_{AS} = 2k_A m_A m_S = C_1^2 k_A m_A m_S$: for this system, there is one form of the $1:2$ complex, S-A-S, and provided the binding of S at either site is unaffected by occupation of the other site with S (the concept of independence), $m_{AS_2} = k_A^2 m_A m_S^2 = C_2^2 k_A^2 m_A m_S^2$. In general, according to the formulation of Klotz

(1,14),

$$m_{AS_i} = C_i^p k_A^i m_A m_S^i; \qquad \left\{ \prod_{l=1}^{l=i} K_l \right\} = C_i^p k_A^i \tag{10}$$

where C_i^p is the number of combinations of p sites taken i at a time. It follows by induction from Eq. (10) that,

$$K_i = \frac{C_i^p k_A}{C_{i-1}^p} = \frac{(p-i+1)k_A}{i} \tag{11}$$

Equation (11) provides the first insight into the interpretation of the relative magnitudes of the K_i. For example, with a system characterized by $p=2$ and a single intrinsic constant, k_A, the relation $K_1 = 4K_2$ is consistent with the binding sites being equivalent and independent. The intrinsic k_A is a pseudo-thermodynamic quantity, associated with the constant intrinsic standard free energy change, $(\Delta G^0)_{int} = -RT \ln k_A$, for each addition of a molecule of S to a single site on A. However, if it and p may be found from the experimental binding results, it follows that Eq. (11) may be used to calculate the successive association constants which govern the composition of any equilibrium mixture in terms of stoichiometric complexes.

Combination of Eqs. (8) and (10) yields, on noting that $iC_i^p = pC_{i-1}^{p-1}$

$$r = \frac{pk_A m_S \left(1 + \sum_{i-1=1}^{i-1=p-1} C_{i-1}^{p-1}(k_A m_S)^{i-1} \right)}{1 + \sum_{i=1}^{i=p} C_i^p (k_A m_S)^i} \tag{12a}$$

Both the numerator and denominator of Eq. (12a) are written in a form suitable for direct collection by the binomial theorem, and thus it follows that

$$r = \frac{pk_A m_S (1 + k_A m_S)^{p-1}}{(1 + k_A m_S)^p} = \frac{pk_A m_S}{1 + k_A m_S} \tag{12b}$$

Equation (12b) embodies the simple conclusion that the curve describing the binding of a ligand to equivalent and independent sites on a single acceptor state is a rectangular hyperbola, which may be linearized according to

$$\frac{1}{r} = \frac{1}{pk_A m_S} + \frac{1}{p} \qquad \text{Double-reciprocal plot} \tag{13a}$$

$$\log \left\{ \frac{r}{(p-r)} \right\} = \log k_A + \log m_S \qquad \text{Hill plot} \tag{13b}$$

$$\frac{r}{m_S} = -rk_A + pk_A \qquad \text{Scatchard plot} \tag{13c}$$

An illustrative Scatchard plot (2) is shown in Figure 2a. Clearly, a least-squares regression fit with appropriate weighting of (r, m_S) points would lead to evaluation of the required parameters p and k_A. Thompson and Klotz (50)

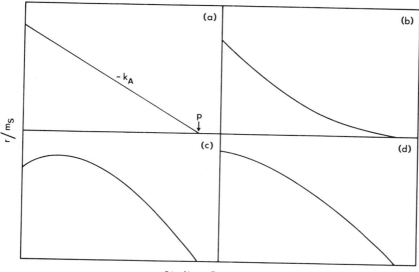

FIGURE 2

Basic forms of Scatchard plots referring to a variety of acceptor-ligand systems delineated throughout the text. (a) A straight line with first derivative $d(r/m_S)/dr < 0$ and second derivative $d^2(r/m_S)/dr^2 = 0$. (b) A plot convex to the r-axis with negative first derivative and positive second derivative. (c) and (d), Curves concave to the r-axis with negative second derivatives: in the former case the first derivative changes sign, and when it equals zero a maximum is observed, which reflects a point of inflection in the corresponding binding curve. In the latter case the first derivative is negative for all r.

have discussed nonlinear forms of graphical representation (in particular, plots of log r vs log m_S), which offer advantage in the interpretation of experimental results conforming to Eq. (12b) in cases where values of (r, m_S) cover a limited range.

The analog in enzyme kinetics of Eq. (12b) is the Michaelis–Menten expression obtained with the transformation (51) $r/p = v/V$, where v is the initial velocity, V is the maximal velocity and k_A is now viewed as the reciprocal Michaelis constant, a ratio of rate constants. In both the binding and kinetic areas, the rectangular hyperbolic relation between the amount of ligand bound (or v/V) and the concentration of unbound ligand, itself a form of regulatory response to varying metabolite concentration, serves as a reference for the delineation of more complicated behavior. Deviations of binding curves from the form of a rectangular hyperbola are common, and as these deviations assume particular significance in relation to metabolic control, they will now be examined in detail.

9.2.2   Sums of Rectangular Hyperbolae

Consider first a system in which two sites on an acceptor are nonequivalent toward the binding of the same ligand, such that $m_{\text{S-A}} = k_1 m_A m_S$ and $m_{\text{-A··S}} = k_2 m_A m_S$, where k_1 and k_2 are site-binding constants. If also the binding processes are independent, it follows that $m_{AS_2} = k_1 k_2 m_A m_S^2$, so that with the use of the method of partial fractions,

$$\overline{m}_A = m_A(1 + k_1 m_S)(1 + k_2 m_S) \tag{14a}$$

$$\overline{m}_S - m_S = m_A\{(k_1 + k_2)m_S + 2k_1 k_2 m_S^2\} \tag{14b}$$

$$r = \frac{k_1 m_S}{1 + k_1 m_S} + \frac{k_2 m_S}{1 + k_2 m_S} \tag{14c}$$

The form of the Scatchard plot obtained on the basis of Eq. (14c) is shown in Figure 2b. The deviation from linearity is termed convex to the r-axis. It is possible to fit such a curve (52) to determine k_1 and k_2, but it is also noted with the use of Eq. (5) that

$$K_1 = k_1 + k_2; \qquad K_2 = \frac{k_1 k_2}{k_1 + k_2} \tag{14d}$$

Thus, determination of the stoichiometric constants K_1 and K_2, as described previously, provides an alternative method of analysis for such a system.

For an acceptor possessing F classes of independent binding sites, each class being constituted of p_J equivalent sites associated with intrinsic binding constant k_J, the generalized form of Eq. (14c) is (53)

$$r = \sum_{J=1}^{J=F} \left\{ \frac{p_J k_J m_S}{1 + k_J m_S} \right\} \tag{14e}$$

It has been shown (40) that the same form of equation (a sum of terms each describing a rectangular hyperbola) will arise when the same ligand binds to two or more acceptor states comprising a noninteracting mixture; or to a mixture of acceptor states in slowly attained equilibrium where detailed balance between them is not maintained during the course and measurement of binding (54). The appropriate equation is (1.35) of ref. 40. Studies on the binding of α-D-methylglucopyranoside at pH 7.0 to a mixture of dimeric and tetrameric states of concanavalin A (55) provide an example of the type of deviation under discussion and its interpretation in these terms.

It becomes apparent that detailed knowledge of the homogeneity or otherwise of the acceptor state is a necessary precursor to the interpretation of binding curves in terms of site interaction parameters. Moreover, as we shall now see, deviations of binding curves from the form of a rectangular hyperbola may arise from causes other than the nonequivalent site proposal. It is well to recognize at the outset that these deviations (whatever their cause) will be describable by Eq. (8), provided binding results are independent of acceptor concentration. We are required, therefore, to understand the different meanings ascribed to the $\{\Pi K_I\}$ coefficient in Eq. (8), as in Eqs. (10) and

(14d), if we are to understand the different molecular models proposed to account for the deviations. It follows as a necessary corollary that it will not always be possible to distinguish on the basis of binding data alone between certain models (47).

9.3 CONFORMATIONAL TRANSITIONS OF ACCEPTOR

9.3.1 Ligand-Induced Transitions

With the above warning in mind it is necessary to point out that a binding curve of the form shown in Figure 2b does not necessarily imply binding to non-equivalent sites that are independent. Indeed, there are several examples of this form of curve being obtained in binding studies of enzymes whose subunit structures are such that the nonequivalent site hypothesis seems most unlikely. In these instances it is more probable that the binding sites are initially equivalent but dependent, the mutual interaction between sites being a consequence of protein conformational changes induced by ligand binding (56,57). Even when dependent (cooperative) site interactions are encountered Eq. (8) still suffices to describe the binding curve in terms of stoichiometric constants provided that the acceptor does not undergo self-association. It follows, therefore, that an experimenter may apply the previously described procedures to evaluate the stoichiometric equilibrium constants K_i, the number of significant terms in the polynomial solution giving p, the maximum number of sites: values of p may also be deduced from the known subunit structure of a protein or be determined by extrapolation procedures as the limiting value of r as $m_S \rightarrow \infty$.

It is not sufficient, however, merely to compare the relative magnitudes of these K_i in an attempt to obtain insight into the molecular mechanism responsible for the cooperativity. To put this more clearly, for the case $p=2$ the relation $K_1 > K_2$ does not necessarily imply that a curve such as that shown in Figure 2b need be obtained because, as we have seen from Eq. (11), the equality $K_1 = 4K_2$ is precisely the requirement for a linear Scatchard plot. Accordingly, it is suggested that stoichiometric constants K_i be transformed into site-binding constants k_i via the relation,

$$K_i = \frac{(p-i+1)k_i}{i} \tag{15}$$

A curve such as that shown in Figure 2b is only obtained when $k_1 > k_2$. This inequality written in terms of site-binding constants defines what is meant by negative cooperativity. Ligand-induced changes in acceptor conformation may also lead to situations where site-binding constants progressively increase in magnitude: such systems are termed positively cooperative.

In practice distinction between positive and negative cooperativity is usually sought not by evaluating the k_i, as has been suggested, but rather by graphical procedures. Two such procedures will be discussed. First, if Scatchard plots are constructed, the following criteria may be used.

$$\frac{d^2(r/m_S)}{dr^2} > 0 \qquad \text{for all } r; \text{ homogeneous negative cooperativity} \quad (16a)$$

$$\frac{d^2(r/m_S)}{dr^2} < 0 \qquad \text{for all } r; \text{ homogeneous positive cooperativity} \quad (16b)$$

Inequality (16a) is in accord with the form of Figure 2b; inequality (16b) is in accord with Figure 2c, while the condition $d^2(r/m_S)/dr^2 = 0$ describes a linear Scatchard plot, Figure 2a. Differentiation of the combined Eq. (8) and (15) written for $p = 2$ indeed leads to the conclusion that inequality (16a) is obeyed when $k_1 > k_2$ ($K_1 > 4K_2$) and inequality (16b) is obeyed when $k_1 < k_2$ ($K_1 < 4K_2$).

As an alternative to this procedure, other workers (58, 59) favor interpretation of binding results by the use of the Hill plot, that is, a plot of log $\{r/(p-r)\}$ vs log m_S, which is linear with unit slope for all m_S when sites are equivalent and independent. Bardsley and Waight (58), who have based their studies on the linked-functions theory of Wyman (60, 61), choose to assign the nature of cooperativity on the basis of the sign of $f(x)$ in the expression

$$\frac{d \log\{r/(p-r)\}}{d \log m_S} = 1 + f(x) \qquad (17a)$$

The sign of $f(x)$ depends on the sign of the Hessian of the polynomial given by λ [Eq. 9(a)]. The Hessian is defined as

$$H(m_S) = \frac{\{p\lambda\lambda'' - (p-1)(\lambda')^2\}}{p^2(p-1)} \qquad (17b)$$

where λ' and λ'' are first and second derivatives of λ with respect to m_S. It is a simple matter to show that for $p = 2$, $f(x) < 0$ only when $k_1 > k_2$, a condition termed negative cooperativity: likewise, there is consistency between defining positive cooperativity, $k_1 < k_2$, on the basis of either inequality (16b), or on the basis of a positive sign for the Hessian, which implies that the slope of the Hill plot is greater than unity for all m_S.

After the sign of the cooperativity has been established, the worker may choose to probe the molecular basis of the effect in finer detail. Let us consider the case $p = 4$ and write Eq. (8) with the substitution for K_i given in Eq. (15) to obtain

$$r = \frac{4k_1 m_S + 12k_1 k_2 m_S^2 + 12k_1 k_2 k_3 m_S^3 + 4k_1 k_2 k_3 k_4 m_S^4}{1 + 4k_1 m_S + 6k_1 k_2 m_S^2 + 4k_1 k_2 k_3 m_S^3 + k_1 k_2 k_3 k_4 m_S^4} \qquad (18)$$

If this equation is compared with Eq. (13) of ref. 56, pertinent to a particular case of the model proposed by Koshland, Némethy, and Filmer, we note that the numerical coefficients of each term in the corresponding power of m_S are identical. This emphasizes that Koshland and co-workers (56) also consider that the vacant sites on the complexes AS_i are equivalent within each complex, even though the site-binding constant differs for each complex. The comparison also shows the equations to be equivalent upon substitution of the identities

$$k_1 \equiv K_{AB}^3 K_S K_T \tag{19a}$$

$$k_2 \equiv K_{AB} K_{BB} K_S K_T \tag{19b}$$

$$k_3 \equiv \frac{K_{BB}^2 K_S K_T}{K_{AB}} \tag{19c}$$

$$k_4 \equiv \frac{K_{BB}^3 K_S K_T}{K_{AB}^3} \tag{19d}$$

where K_S represents the intrinsic affinity of ligand for an individual subunit, K_T the isomerization constant for the conformational change from a subunit in state A to state B, and K_{AB}, K_{BB} define the subunit-subunit interactions that give rise to the nonequivalence of successive ligand binding.

This type of approach (56) thus attempts to ascribe a more detailed meaning to the overall site-binding constants k_i, which, by standard thermodynamic procedures, may certainly be expressed as products of any notional set of equilibrium constants. Reference has been made to Eq. (13) of ref. 56, which refers to a tetrahedral arrangement of subunits in the acceptor, but similar identifications may be made between Eq. (18) and Eqs. (18), (19), and (24) of ref. 56, which refer to different geometrical arrangements of the four subunits. Attempts to distinguish between the various models may thus be made by solving the set of Eq. (19a)–(19d) and the corresponding sets for the other geometries, and then rejecting the cases that do not yield physically realistic values for the parameters. Koshland and co-workers (56, 57, 62, 63) have in fact suggested more direct procedures for these evaluations. However, we wish to emphasize that such endeavors, intrinsically useful in attempting to define molecular hypotheses, merely yield parameters that are an alternative means of representing the $\{\Pi K_I\}$ coefficients of Eq. (8). The question remains whether still other interpretations of these coefficients are possible.

In this connection, it is noted that a convex Scatchard plot (Figure 2b) would be obtained if the binding of a charged ligand to initially equivalent sites on an acceptor were to alter significantly the electrostatic potential at the acceptor surface such that the successive binding of ligand molecules became more difficult. This effect, which does not necessarily involve a conformational change in acceptor structure, can be described in either of two ways. First, the results could be analyzed to yield the K_i appropriate to Eq. (8) and hence the k_i from Eq. (15), whereupon the effect would be reflected quantitatively as a series of k_i which progressively decrease in magnitude. Second, such results could be fitted to a binding equation of similar form to Eq. (12b) but modified with exponential terms to account for the electrostatic potential, which itself is a function of r (64, 65). These electrostatic contributions are not generally considered in the binding of specific ligands to a limited number of spatially distant sites on an enzymic acceptor, but they may be an important consideration in other circumstances such as the binding of Ca(II) ion to fragment 1 of prothrombin (66), where negatively charged acceptor sites are in close proximity.

Moreover, an alternative interpretation of the $\{\Pi K_l\}$ coefficients in Eq. (8) has been given for systems where the Scatchard plots are *concave* to the r-axis, as detailed in the next section.

9.3.2   Preexisting Acceptor Isomerization

An alternative concept to ligand-induced positively cooperative effects is embodied in the proposal (67) that, even in the absence of ligand, the flexibility of protein structure may ensure a variety of isomeric states coexisting in equilibrium in solution. It is possible, as originally proposed (67), that within individual states binding sites may be equivalent and independent; but that the site-binding constants (or, indeed, the numbers of binding sites per molecule) may differ between states due to their different conformations. It suffices to consider two isomeric states, $R \rightleftharpoons T$, possessing, respectively, p and q binding sites per molecule associated with site-binding constants, k_R and k_T: the equations which follow may readily be summed to encompass a multiisomeric state system. Equations (6), (7), and (10) apply to each isomeric state, and thus,

$$\overline{m}_A = m_R(1 + k_R m_S)^p + m_T(1 + k_T m_S)^q \tag{20}$$

$$\overline{m}_S - m_S = p k_R m_R m_S (1 + k_R m_S)^{p-1} + q k_T m_T m_S (1 + k_T m_S)^{q-1} \tag{21}$$

where $\overline{m}_A$ and $\overline{m}_S$ are the total molar concentrations of acceptor and ligand, respectively. The ratio of Eqs. (21) and (20) may be divided throughout by m_R to yield,

$$r = \frac{p k_R m_S (1 + k_R m_S)^{p-1} + q k_T X m_S (1 + k_T m_S)^{q-1}}{(1 + k_R m_S)^p + X(1 + k_T m_S)^q} \tag{22}$$

where $X = m_T / m_R$ is the acceptor isomerization constant which is independent of $\overline{m}_A$. This implies, as with all models discussed thus far, that binding points found with different acceptor concentrations will lie on the same curve: no acceptor concentration-dependence is predicted.

9.3.2.1   The forms of binding curves

For particular systems, namely, $p = q$ and $k_R = k_T$; p and/or $k_R = 0$ and $q = 1$; q and/or $k_T = 0$ and $p = 1$; $p = q = 1$ and $k_R \neq k_T$ (61), Eq. (22) simplifies to a form describing a rectangular hyperbolic plot of r vs m_S. Except with the first of these cases, the extent of binding depends on the magnitude of the isomerization constant X; but the existence of the isomerization equilibrium itself will not be detectable from Scatchard, Hill or double-reciprocal plots which will all be linear. For other systems, deviations from the form of a rectangular hyperbola must arise, since Eq. (22) is of the same form as Eq. (8). This may be illustrated for the case $p=q=2$, for which Eq. (22) becomes on expansion,

$$r = \frac{K_1 m_S + 2 K_1 K_2 m_S^2}{1 + K_1 m_S + K_1 K_2 m_S^2} \tag{23a}$$

$$K_1 = \frac{2(k_R + k_T X)}{1 + X} \tag{23b}$$

$$K_1 K_2 = \frac{k_R^2 + k_T^2 X}{1 + X} \tag{23c}$$

Again we note a particular interpretation of the $\{\Pi K_i\}$ coefficient in Eq. (8) and we may well inquire whether or not the preexisting isomerization model will display binding behavior any different from that encountered with allosteric systems.

In fact, such a difference does exist. This may be delineated by examining the sign of the Hessian of the binding polynomial, $\lambda = (1 + k_R m_S)^p + X(1 + k_T m_S)^p$, the denominator of Eq. (22) with $p=q$. The Hessian is

$$X(1 + k_R m_S)^{p-2}(1 + k_T m_S)^{p-2} \{k_T(1 + k_R m_S) - k_R(1 + k_T m_S)\}^2 > 0 \tag{24}$$

This implies according to the criterion described earlier (58) that $f(x)$ in Eq. (17) is necessarily positive and that slopes of tangents to the Hill plot at any point are greater than unity. Consistent with this observation is the finding (68) that the isomerization model (67) cannot yield a Scatchard plot characterized by $d(r/m_S)/dr < 0$ and $d^2(r/m_S)/dr^2 > 0$ for all r. In other words, the type of plot shown in Figure 2b, relevant to nonequivalent site binding or a negatively cooperative allosteric system, cannot be obtained with a preexisting acceptor isomerization regardless of whether ligand binding is to both isomeric states or (in the extreme case of preferential binding) exclusive to either isomeric state. It follows then that, in general, the form of binding results obtained with a preexisting isomerizing acceptor system will assume graphical representations reminiscent of positively cooperative allosteric effects. In this connection, it is noteworthy that the detailed form of the binding plot described by Eq. (22), to which we now turn, has received considerable attention (58, 68–72).

9.3.2.2 Domains of sigmoidality

It cannot be assumed that the isomerizing acceptor model will lead to a sigmoidal binding curve under all circumstances. Such a curve is characterized by a point of inflection and attention has been focused on the conditions for its existence. The essence of the findings may be exemplified with the particular case $p=q=2$, $\beta = k_T/k_R \neq 1$. For this case, the condition

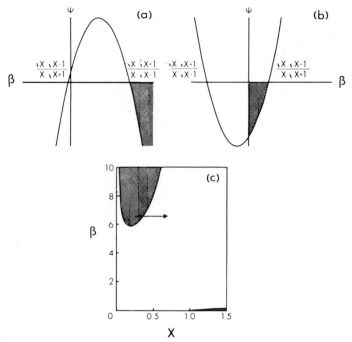

FIGURE 3
Plots illustrating the concept of domains of sigmoidality for ligand binding to a self-interacting acceptor. The particular case refers to Eqs. (25) and (26) of the text and is discussed therein. (Adapted from ref. 72 with permission. Copyright by Academic Press Inc. (London) Ltd.)

for the existence of a point of inflection is given by (72),

$$\psi = (1-X) + \beta^2 X(X-1) + 4\beta X < 0; \qquad \frac{d^2 r}{dm_s^2} = 0 \qquad (25)$$

This condition is identical with that formulated for the existence of a critical point (a maximum) in the corresponding Scatchard plot.* Inequality (25) introduces the concept of domains of sigmoidality which may be explored in the following way. When $0 < X < 1$, a plot of ψ vs β exhibits a maximum ($d^2\psi/d\beta^2 < 0$) and intersects the β-axis at the points shown in Figure 3a. When $X > 1$, the parabola is inverted, Figure 3b. It follows that the conditions

---

*For systems where $p = q > 2$ and $\beta \neq 1$, it is possible that more than one point of inflection will appear in the binding curve (70,72), there being an exact correspondence between the numbers of, and conditions of existence for, critical points in Scatchard plots and points of inflection in binding curves (72).

for the binding curve to be sigmoidal (denoted by the shaded areas in Figure 3a,b) are

$$\beta > \frac{-(\sqrt{X}+1)}{\sqrt{X}\,(\sqrt{X}-1)}; \qquad X < 1 \tag{26a}$$

$$\beta < \frac{\sqrt{X}-1}{\sqrt{X}\,(\sqrt{X}+1)}; \qquad X > 1 \tag{26b}$$

The shaded areas in Figure 3c show in part the two domains of X and β which satisfy these inequalities. Inside these domains, the Scatchard plot exhibits a single maximum as illustrated in Figure 2c: outside the domains, the Scatchard plot assumes the form depicted in Figure 2d, characterized by $d(r/m_S)/dr < 0$ and $d^2(r/m_S)/dr^2 < 0$ for all r. It is noted from Figure 3c that to obtain a sigmoidal binding curve when the R isomer is initially favored ($X < 1$), it is required that this isomer exhibit a much lower affinity for the ligand than the T isomer (β large). Similarly, when T is favored ($X > 1$), the R isomer must be the more active. Thus, the essence of a sigmoidal control response in these terms is a large reservoir of relatively inactive isomer.

9.3.2.3 Effectors

It is pertinent now to investigate the possible biological significance of the existence of domains of interaction parameters within which sigmoidal binding responses will be encountered. Consider first the effect of variation of temperature from T_1 to T_2 at constant pressure P; if the equilibrium reactions operating in the acceptor-ligand system are associated with finite enthalpy changes, then the appropriate equilibrium constants will vary according to

$$(X_1)_P = (X_2)_P \exp\{\Delta H^0(1/T_2 - 1/T_1)/R\} \tag{27a}$$

$$(\beta_1)_P = (\beta_2)_P \exp\{(1/T_2 - 1/T_1)(\Delta H_T^0 - \Delta H_R^0)/R\} \tag{27b}$$

where ΔH^0 is the enthalpy change associated with the acceptor isomerization, R$\rightleftharpoons$T, and $(\Delta H_T^0 - \Delta H_R^0)$ is the difference in total enthalpy changes associated with the binding of ligand to the R and T isomers. In the event that the latter difference is small, the locus of (X, β) for various temperatures is a straight line parallel to the X-axis, which may cross a boundary of a domain of sigmoidality, as illustrated in Figure 3c. It follows that the form of binding response may be critically dependent on temperature variation and, indeed, the experimental studies on the binding of NAD to D-glyceraldehyde-3-phosphate dehydrogenase (73) serve to illustrate this point. In general, any parameter (such as temperature, pressure, or pH) whose variation affects the magnitude of the operative equilibrium constants, and in particular the acceptor isomerization constant X, may properly be termed an effector.

Several authors (51, 74–76) have considered the related problem of the binding of two ligand species S and E to different sites on the R isomer and also to distinct sites on the T isomer. Analysis of this problem has led to the conclusion that the binding equation for S given in Eq. (22) continues to apply, provided X is replaced by X', where,

$$X' = \frac{X(1 + N_T m_E)^y}{(1 + N_R m_E)^w}$$ (28)

and w and y denote, respectively, the number of binding sites for E on the R and T isomers associated with site-binding constants N_R and N_T. Except for the case $w = y$ and $N_R = N_T$ (when $X = X'$) variation of the concentration of E will result in variation of X' and in a resultant shift in the form of the binding curve. If E binds preferentially to the isomer which is less active toward S, an increased tendency toward sigmoidal form will be observed on increasing $\bar{m}_E$: conversely, an activation effect is predicted if E binds preferentially to the same isomer as does S (76). It is indeed possible that a domain of sigmoidality may be crossed by introducing such an effector. Figure 4a presents an example of the inhibitory effect of CTP and of the activating effect of ATP on the kinetics of the reaction catalyzed by aspartate transcarbamylase with aspartate and carbamyl phosphate (saturating) as substrates. The experimental points were obtained by Gerhart (77) and the solid lines were calculated by Smith (78) on the basis of the combined Eqs. (22) and (28) written in kinetic format. The basis of Smith's interpretation was that the enzyme in the absence of added ligands comprises an equilibrium mixture of isomeric forms R (enzymatically active with $p = 6$) and T (inactive, q and/or $k_T = 0$), the isomerization equilibrium being governed by $X = 8$. For this type of system involving an inactive isomer, the condition for it being within a domain of sigmoidality is $X > 1/(p - 1)$ as shown in ref. 72. A sigmoidal curve is predicted provided $X > 0.2$, and thus its observation as curve B in Figure 4a is not surprising. When CTP is added, for which $N_R = 5.13 \times 10^4 \ M^{-1}$, $N_T = 7.41 \times 10^4 \ M^{-1}$ and $w = y = 6$ (78), it follows from Eq. (28) that X' is even greater than X at all m_E: increased sigmoidality is predicted and observed (curve C). In contrast, with ATP for which $N_R = 1 \times 10^5 \ M^{-1}$ and $N_T = 1 \times 10^{-2} \ M^{-1}$ with $y = w = 6$, we find $X' < X$, and indeed for realistic values of m_E, $X' < 0.2$. The boundary of the domain of sigmoidality has been crossed and curve A is obtained.

The formulation of Eq. (28) is based on the proposal that for complexes RS_iE_j, $i = 1, 2, \ldots, p$ and $j = 1, 2, \ldots, w$, which specifies that ligands S and E bind to different sites, similar relations holding for TS_kE_l. However, situations may arise where two different ligand species compete for the same p sites on R ($i = 0, 1, 2, \ldots, p$; $j = 0, 1, 2, \ldots, p$; $0 \leqslant i + j \leqslant p$) and for the same q sites on T ($k = 0, 1, 2, \ldots, q$; $l = 0, 1, 2, \ldots, q$; $0 \leqslant k + l \leqslant q$). The result of this formulation is that the basic binding equation is modified to (78–80)

$$r = \frac{p k_R m_S (1 + k_R m_S + N_R m_E)^{p-1} + q k_T X m_S (1 + k_T m_S + N_T m_E)^{q-1}}{(1 + k_R m_S + N_R m_E)^p + X(1 + k_T m_S + N_T m_E)^q}$$ (29)

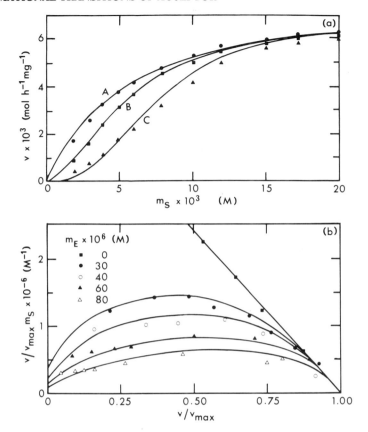

FIGURE 4
The action of effectors on the initial velocities of enzyme-catalyzed reactions. (*a*) Reaction catalyzed by aspartate transcarbamylase with aspartate and carbamyl phosphate (saturating) as substrates: *B*, curve obtained in the absence of effectors; *A* and *C*, curves obtained in the presence of ATP and CTP, respectively. (Adapted from ref. 78 with permission. Copyright by Academic Press Inc. (London) Ltd.) (*b*) Scatchard plots referring to the kinetics of the reaction catalyzed by deoxythymidine diphosphate D-glucose pyrophosphorylase with dTDP-glucose as substrate: the effector *E* in this case is dTDP-rhamnose. (Adapted from ref. 80 with permission. Copyright by Elsevier/North-Holland Biomedical Press.)

A kinetic analog of Eq. (29) was used by Smith (78) to fit quantitatively the activation effect on aspartate transcarbamylase by maleate observed at low aspartate concentration (81). Maleate in this system is an example of an enzyme active-site directed effector and several other enzyme systems have been cited (80) for which the similarity of substrate and effector structures suggests that a competitive effect is operative. In such cases Eq. (29) with summed terms introduced inside parentheses is more likely appropriate in describing results than the combined Eq. (22) and (28), involving product relationships. In practice, it may prove difficult to distinguish between these choices. Figure 4*b* presents experimental results (82) for the reaction catalyzed by deoxythymidine diphosphate *D*-glucose pyrophosphorylase with dTDP-glucose as substrate and dTDP-rhamnose, a product of the metabolic pathway, as effector. Sigmoidality of the Michaelis plot, as evidenced by the maxima in the Scatchard plots, was introduced and increased as the concentration of the effector was increased. Frieden (51) in his Figure 4 fitted these results with reasonable precision on the basis of the kinetic analog of the combined Eq. (22) and (28): the solid lines in Figure 4b, however, are based (80) on Eq. (29), which is appropriate if the effector were active-site directed. Evidently, a choice between the two possibilities cannot be made on the basis of these data alone.

These developments of the isomerizing acceptor model illustrate its flexibility in describing a diverse range of binding and kinetic results. In the latter connection, it is not implied that binding equations are in all cases directly transformable to kinetic analogs: for example, when two substrates are involved in enzyme action, theoretical binding equations account for the contribution of all complexes while in the kinetic measurement only some of these are capable of leading to product formation, a difference which must be taken into account in formulating kinetic equations (83). The flexibility exhibited by the isomerizing acceptor model is shared by allosteric models and, in this regard, we are reminded that both types of basic formulation are in accord with Eq. (8). It is noted, however, that if the isomerization model is to be applicable, it is required that for any particular value of $p = q$ the three interaction parameters, k_R, k_T, and X, suffice to describe experimental binding results, which does place restrictions on the inter-relationships between the $\{\Pi K_i\}$ coefficients in Eq. (8). Considerable effort (84–86) has been expended in attempting to distinguish between the isomerization and allosteric proposals for particular systems, but, in general, it is difficult to answer the basic question: *in a fixed solution environment*, do isomeric states of acceptor coexist in equilibrium prior to the addition of ligand or are conformational transitions induced by addition of ligand? This difficulty does not arise in the consideration of other types of self-interacting acceptor systems, which may also form the basis of control binding responses.

9.4   SELF-ASSOCIATION OF ACCEPTOR

9.4.1   Perturbation of Preexisting Acceptor Association by Ligand Binding

Many proteins exist in particular aqueous environments as equilibrium mixtures of monomers (comprised of subunits or not) and higher polymeric states. The detection and characterization of such protein-protein interactions by mass migration and equilibrium methods (Chapter 3–5) is facilitated by the study of the dependence on total protein concentration of weight-average properties (molecular weight, elution volume or sedimentation coefficient) of the system: isomerizing systems exhibit no concentration-dependence of weight-average properties. Consider now a simple self-association, $nM \rightleftharpoons P$, in which monomer M coexists in equilibrium with a single higher polymer P and ligand S binds to p equivalent and independent sites on M with intrinsic association constant k_M and to q such sites on P with intrinsic constant k_P. The total base-molar concentration of protein in the equilibrium mixture is given by

$$\overline{m}_A = \overline{m}_M + n\overline{m}_P = m_M(1+k_M m_S)^P + nm_P(1+k_P m_S)^q \tag{30}$$

where $\overline{m}_M$ and $\overline{m}_P$ are the constituent concentrations of monomer and polymer, respectively. The effect of the constraint inherent on the addition of S to the system may be exemplified by defining the quantity X^* as,

$$X^* = \overline{m}_P / \overline{m}_M^n = \frac{X(1+k_P m_S)^q}{(1+k_M m_S)^{np}} \tag{31}$$

where $X = m_P / m_M^n$ is the acceptor association constant, and it is noted that the variable, X^*, may be found as a function of m_S experimentally (87). When numbers of binding sites are conserved on polymerization ($q = np$) and $k_P = k_M$, Eq. (31) becomes $X^* = X$, implying, if S is small, that its addition will be without effect on weight-average properties of the system. However, if either or both of the conditions q = np, $k_P = k_M$ were disobeyed, it follows from Eq. (31) that X^* must vary with m_S, and that this variation may take several forms. The first is exemplified by the binding of the competitive inhibitor N-acetylglucosamine to the associating lysozyme system, for which the weight-average molecular weight decreases towards that of monomeric constituent with increasing inhibitor concentration. This is in accord with a decrease in X^* towards a zero limit as $m_S \to \infty$, in keeping with the observation (88,89) that $q < np$, $k_M = k_P$. The second type of situation is encountered in the binding of phenylpropiolate to the dimerizing a-chymotrypsin system (32) for which $q = np$ but $k_P < k_M$. Again a decrease of X^* with increasing m_S is observed, but X^* tends to a finite (nonzero) limit given by

$$\lim_{m_S \to \infty} X^* = X\left(\frac{k_P}{k_M}\right)^q \tag{32}$$

The third set of cases involves an increase in X^* with increasing m_S toward either an infinite limit or to that given by Eq. (32). The former situation is exemplified by the binding of Zn(II) to the dimerizing α-amylase system, where only the dimer possesses a binding site for the ligand (90). The latter is encountered in the binding of oxytocin to neurophysin, a system for which $q = np$ with $k_P > k_M$ (91). With the fourth possibility, $q \neq np$ and $k_M \neq k_P$, it has been shown that a critical point may exist in the plot of X^* vs m_S: this has been discussed in relation to results obtained on the interaction of organic phosphates with human methemoglobin A which in 0.25 M sodium acetate, pH 5.4, exists as a monomer-dimer $(2\alpha\beta \rightleftarrows \alpha_2\beta_2)$ system (87).

9.4.2 Acceptor Concentration-Dependent Binding Curves

Several other examples, including the binding of effectors to the isodesmically indefinitely self-associating glutamate dehydrogenase system (92–94), the binding of Zn(II) to the polymerizing insulin system (95) and the interaction of ATP or UTP with cytosine triphosphate synthetase (96), could be cited where addition of a ligand disturbs a pre-existing acceptor association equilibrium. As Steiner (97) notes, examples of this kind of behavior are numerous. It is timely, therefore, to consider the forms of binding curves which will arise with such systems. The appropriate binding equation (98) for a two-state self-associating acceptor system $(n\text{M} \rightleftarrows \text{P})$ is

$$r = \frac{pk_M m_M m_S (1 + k_M m_S)^{p-1} + qk_P m_P m_S (1 + k_P m_S)^{q-1}}{m_M (1 + k_M m_S)^p + nm_P (1 + k_P m_S)^q} \tag{33}$$

which may readily be generalized as in Eq. (8) of ref. 98 to describe a multistate acceptor system. When $q = np$ and $k_M = k_P$, Eq. (33) simplifies to Eq. (12b), and thus under conditions of nonpreferential binding of ligand to acceptor states (where $X^* = X$) the binding curve will be a rectangular hyperbola independent of total acceptor concentration, $\overline{m}_A$. However, when $q \neq np$ and/or $k_M \neq k_P$, binding curves deviating from hyperbolic form are predicted. In this connection, we first note that when $n = 1$ (acceptor isomerization) Eq. (33) becomes Eq. (22). Thus the model proposed by Monod and co-workers (67) is a special case of the more general oligomerization scheme: it is the only case in this scheme where r is independent of $\overline{m}_A$. Thus, when $n > 1$, division of the numerator and denominator of Eq. (33) by m_M does not permit the introduction of an equilibrium constant [as it did with Eq. (22)], since $X = m_P / m_M^n$. This observation has the important implication that, for the first time, we have encountered in Eq. (33) a binding equation which is not formally identical with Eq. (8). In explicit terms, this means that for associating acceptor systems, binding curves are acceptor concentration-dependent, each curve at a fixed $\overline{m}_A$ being defined by Eq. (33) and the simultaneous Eq. (30) which may be rewritten as

$$nX(1 + k_P m_S)^q m_M^n + (1 + k_M m_S)^p m_M - \overline{m}_A = 0 \tag{34}$$

Numerical examples of the family of binding curves arising as $\overline{m}_A$ is varied may readily be constructed by solving the polynomial Eq. (34) for m_M (with assigned interaction parameters and for a range of m_S), calculating $m_P = X m_M^n$ and inserting corresponding values of m_S, m_M, and m_P into Eq. (33) to calculate (r, m_S) points. Further use of these relations in curve-fitting experimental binding results has been discussed previously (40, 99).

Figure 5 presents three examples of systems which exhibit acceptor concentration dependence in their binding behavior. In each case, each curve was constructed at a fixed $\bar{m}_A$ and the importance of so doing cannot be overstressed. With an associating system, variation of both $\bar{m}_A$ and $\bar{m}_S$ in a series of experiments would lead to a plot of r vs m_S which is a traverse of the family of binding curves, even though r is expressed per base-mole of acceptor. Figure 5a presents results for the binding of oxygen to hemoglobin near neutral pH where at low protein concentrations comparable proportions of the $\alpha\beta$ and $\alpha_2\beta_2$ species coexist in equilibrium, $2\alpha\beta \rightleftharpoons \alpha_2\beta_2$ (100): the curves are sigmoidal and approach hyperbolic form as dilution favors the $\alpha\beta$ form which binds oxygen preferentially. Likewise, the maxima in the Scatchard plots of Figure 5b correspond to points of inflection in sigmoidal binding curves describing the binding of GTP to indefinitely self-associating glutamate dehydrogenase (101). Again, decrease of $\bar{m}_A$ results in enhanced binding, indicating that it is the monomeric form of the enzyme which binds GTP preferentially. Figure 5 c, pertaining to the binding of zinc(II) to the dimerizing α-amylase system (90) also exhibits acceptor concentration dependence; but is strikingly different from the other examples in that the form of the curves is convex to the r-axis. It follows that preferential binding of a ligand to a self-associating acceptor system differs from the isomerization model, not only with regard to acceptor concentration-dependent binding, but also in particular circumstances in leading to Scatchard plots convex to the r-axis.

9.4.3 Domains of Sigmoidality: Effectors

The latter point is properly explored by considering values of interaction parameters which determine domains of sigmoidality. For simplicity these are discussed in relation to situations where ligand binding is exclusive to the monomeric ($q=0$) or to the polymeric ($p=0$) form of acceptor. If the following conditions are met (72) such systems will exhibit sigmoidal binding behavior characterized by a Scatchard plot with a maximum.

$$X\bar{m}_A^{n-1} > \frac{\{n^2(p-1)+n\}^{n-1}}{\{n^2(p-1)\}^n} \; ; \quad q=0 \tag{35a}$$

$$X\bar{m}_A^{n-1} < \frac{(q-1)(n+q-1)^{n-1}}{n^{n+1}} \; ; \quad p=0 \tag{35b}$$

These conditions also apply when $n=1$ (acceptor isomerization). In contrast to the isomerization case, however, it is now evident for an associating acceptor ($n>1$) that introduction of the dimensionless product $X\bar{m}_A^{n-1}$ delineates the concept that $\bar{m}_A$ is important in determining not only the form of binding curves as members of a family (Figure 5), but also the conditions for the onset of sigmoidal binding behavior. It could be noted that this product is extremely sensitive to variation of $\bar{m}_A$ if n is large and, indeed, may similarly be sensitive to variation of a parameter, such as temperature. For example, a temperature change from 5 to 35°C with $\Delta H° = 50$ kcal/mol (that for the

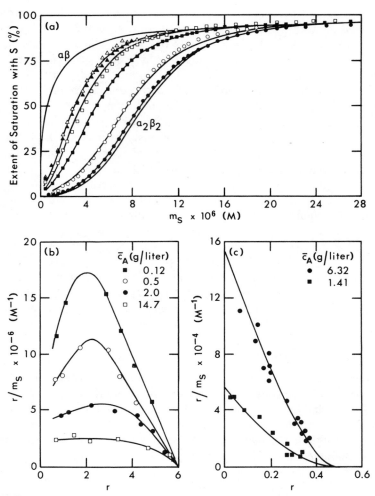

FIGURE 5

Experimental systems exhibiting acceptor concentration dependence in their ligand binding behavior. (a) The binding of oxygen to human hemoglobin at pH 7.4; the acceptor concentration, fixed for each binding curve, varied between 4×10^{-8} and 4×10^{-4} M heme. (Adapted from ref. 100 with permission. Copyright by American Chemical Society.) (b) The binding of GTP to glutamate dehydrogenase at pH 7.1 in the presence of 400 μM NADH; the concentration of enzyme used for each binding curve is cited in the figure. (Adapted from ref. 101 with permission. Copyright by American Society of Biological Chemists, Inc.) (c) The binding of Zn(II) to bacterial α-amylase at pH 7; α-amylase concentrations as indicated. (Adapted from ref. 90.)

tetramerization of β-lactoglobulin A) changes X and hence the product by a factor of about 10^4. It is possible, therefore, in cases of exclusive binding to one oligomeric state to obtain a sigmoidal binding response under one set of conditions (temperature, pressure, pH, ionic strength, and $\overline{m}_A$) and to move outside the domain of sigmoidality by varying one or more of these conditions. Recently the forms of binding curves outside of the domains of sigmoidality have been elucidated for these systems (68) by examining the sign of the second derivative of the Scatchard function. When binding is exclusive to monomer and inequality (35a) is disobeyed, Scatchard plots are of the form shown in Figure 2d with negative second derivative for all r. This is also true when ligand binds exclusively to the polymeric state when inequality (35b) is disobeyed and $q \geqslant n$. If, however, binding is exclusive to a *single site* on the polymer ($p=0$, $q=1$), inequality (35b) is never obeyed and it has been shown (72) that the second derivative is positive for all r. This means that the Scatchard plot is necessarily of the form shown in Figure 2b, and we see in explicit terms the origin of the convex plots shown in Figure 5c, pertaining to the exclusive binding of zinc(II) to one site on the dimeric form of α-amylase.

It remains to explore the case where $p=0$ and $1<q<n$. Figure 6 presents numerical examples calculated using Eq. (33) and (34) for such a case ($n=4$, $p=0$, $q=2$). The striking feature is apparent not only that the forms of the Scatchard plots change dramatically with a tenfold variation of the total acceptor concentration but also that the sign of the second derivative is no longer fixed. In Figure 6a the second derivative is positive for all r, which has been given theoretical justification in ref. 68. In Figure 6b the sign of the second derivative changes from negative to positive, as also reasoned in ref. 68. In Figure 6c the parameters are such that inequality (35b) is obeyed and the system has entered a domain of sigmoidality, which is clearly evidenced by the maximum in the Scatchard plot.

Parameters which govern the product $X\overline{m}_A^{n-1}$ are in a real sense effectors of the binding behavior encountered with self-associating acceptor systems; and so too are certain specific compounds which bind at the same sites as primary ligand S or at different sites. The action of these types of effectors is describable in the same terms as used in Section 9.3.2.3, and thus it suffices in this context to present the following general binding equation,

$$r = \frac{\displaystyle\sum_j \left\{ \tau_{j,s} k_{j,s} m_S m_j \left(1 + k_{j,s} m_S + \sum_g k_{j,g} m_g\right)^{\tau_{j,s}-1} \prod_h (1 + k_{j,h} m_h)^{\tau_{j,h}} \right\}}{\displaystyle\sum_j \left\{ j m_j \left(1 + k_{j,s} m_S + \sum_g k_{j,g} m_g\right)^{\tau_{j,s}} \prod_h (1 + k_{j,h} m_h)^{\tau_{j,h}} \right\}}$$

(36)

where j refers to the oligomeric acceptor states ($j=1$, monomer; $j=2$, dimer; etc.), $k_{j,s}$ is the site-binding constant for the interaction of S with that

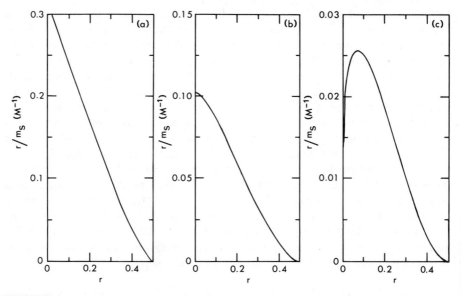

FIGURE 6

A numerical example illustrating a change in the basic form of the Scatchard plot consequent upon a change in acceptor concentration. The system comprised a monomer–tetramer equilibrium ($X = 10^{12} \ M^{-3}$) with only tetramer binding ligand at two sites ($k_P = 1 \ M^{-1}$): (a) $\bar{m}_A = 2 \times 10^{-4} \ M$; (b) $\bar{m}_A = 5 \times 10^{-5} \ M$; (c) $\bar{m}_A = 2 \times 10^{-5} \ M$. (Adapted from ref. 68 with permission. Copyright by Academic Press Inc. (London) Ltd.)

oligomer, $\tau_{j,S}$ is the number of binding sites per molecule of the oligomer, and the subscripts (j,g) and (j,h) define similar parameters for the binding to oligomer j of, respectively, active-site directed effectors g and those of the noncompetitive type h. First, it is noted that in the absence of effectors Eq. (36) becomes the general form of Eq. (33) and thus we see that binding equations are available for other than two-state acceptor systems: protein self-associations are either of the definite or indefinite types, and even in the former situation a series of intermediate oligomers may coexist in appreciable amounts when $n > 2$. Second, it is apparent from Eq. (36) that product terms are introduced, as in Eq. (28), to account for the operation of noncompetitive effectors, while summation terms reflect the consequences of active-site directed effectors, as in Eq. (29). Thus Eq. (36) predicts activation and inhibition effects of various types. Third, in a biological context Eq. (36) may indeed be appropriate since various ligands are jointly present, but in an experimental context it is apparent that evaluation of the numerous interaction parameters in it would require systematic investigation of the self-association of acceptor alone and in the separate presence of each ligand.

9.4.4   Joint Operation of Allosteric and Self-Association Effects

In the past there has been a tendency to attempt to distinguish between molecular mechanisms for control effects as though alternative schemes were mutually exclusive. It now appears that the control of some systems may be based solely on cooperative effects between subunits (or isomerization of the acceptor) and with others that self-association of the acceptor is the underlying cause. The pertinent point emerges, however, that with yet other systems these molecular events may jointly operate, both contributing to the form of binding curves, but with only the latter providing overall control dictated by acceptor concentration levels (102). It seems timely, therefore, to emphasize this point by formulating the following binding equation which encompasses both types of effect for a system with a single ligand.

$$
r = \frac{\sum\limits_{j} \left\{ m_j \sum\limits_{i=1}^{i=\tau_j} i \left\{ \prod\limits_{l=1}^{l=i} K_{j,l} \right\} m_S^i \right\}}{\sum\limits_{j} \left\{ jm_j \left(1 + \sum\limits_{i=1}^{i=\tau_j} \left\{ \prod\limits_{l=1}^{l=i} K_{j,l} \right\} m_S^i \right) \right\}}
\tag{37}
$$

In this expression j denotes the acceptor states (monomer, dimer, etc.), τ_j the numbers of binding sites per molecule of each acceptor state, and $K_{j,l}$ the stoichiometric equilibrium constant, as in Eq. (8), describing the binding of S to acceptor state j.

There are some who would argue that the total acceptor concentrations encountered *in vivo* are likely to be sufficiently low to obviate effects due to protein association. If this were the case Eq. (37) simplifies directly to Eq. (8), which has already been discussed in considerable detail in the light of allosteric and other effects. While this may be true for certain systems, we would warn against general adoption of this view for the following reasons. First, it is obvious that not all proteins exist *in vivo* at low total concentrations. For example, the concentration level of glutamate dehydrogenase (103) is in the g/liter range (cf. Figure 5b), while hemoglobin exists in the erythrocyte at a concentration of approximately 320 g/liter. The allosteric effects operative in the binding of oxygen and organic phosphates to the $\alpha_2\beta_2$ form of hemoglobin are well accepted (84, 86); but nevertheless questions remain concerning the control of oxygen binding at high hemoglobin concentrations, where association of oxyhemoglobin has been detected (104) and where oxygen binding curves exhibit dependence on acceptor concentration (105, 106). The association in question is not $2\alpha\beta \rightleftarrows \alpha_2\beta_2$ (Figure 5a), which is only significant at very low hemoglobin concentrations in the physiological pH range, but rather an association of the type $n\,\alpha_2\beta_2 \rightleftarrows (\alpha_2\beta_2)_n$. Second, measured protein association constants vary widely in magnitude, such that, for example, the concentration range appropriate to the coexistence of comparable proportions of sulfatase A oligomers is not g/liter but

μg/liter (107, 108). Studies on the concentration dependence of activities of other enzymes suggest that they too dissociate at high dilution (109, 110). Finally, we note that the total biological environment of the acceptor must be taken into account, for indeed, considerations of excluded volume, charge interactions, and the presence of relevant effectors determines the composition of the mixture in terms of the relative proportions of acceptor constituents.

9.5 HETEROGENEOUSLY ASSOCIATING ACCEPTOR SYSTEMS: INTERACTIONS OF LIGAND

9.5.1 Two-State Acceptor Systems

As noted in Chapter 1, protein interactions of types other than isomerizations or self-associations may be encountered; perhaps those of greatest potential interest yet to be considered involve complexing of a protein A with a dissimilar macromolecular entity B. In this connection, the entity B may be a cellular membrane (111), any type of macromolecule unrelated to A, or (if A is itself an enzyme) B may be the enzyme catalyzing a consecutive reaction in a pathway involving enzymes A and B. In relation to ligand binding, these examples share the common feature that a preexisting acceptor interaction again creates a situation in which different acceptor states of species A, that may have different affinities for a specific ligand S, coexist in equilibrium. For acceptor interactions of the type $A + B \rightleftarrows C$, where only A and C bind ligand at p and q sites, respectively, which are equivalent and independent, it may be shown that

$$r = \frac{p k_A m_A m_S (1 + k_A m_S)^{p-1} + q k_C m_C m_S (1 + k_C m_S)^{q-1}}{m_A (1 + k_A m_S)^p + m_C (1 + k_C m_S)^q} \tag{38}$$

in which the denominator equals the total concentration of A in the system. Equation (38) shows that provided $p \neq q$ and/or $k_A \neq k_C$ the binding curve must deviate from the form of a rectangular hyperbola. To obtain expressions suitable for analysis of experimental results it is necessary to appreciate that r is a function of the initial composition of the mixture, $\bar{m}_A$ and $\bar{m}_B$, and of the association constant $X = m_C / m_A m_B$. Thus

$$\bar{m}_A = m_A \alpha^p + m_C \beta^q; \qquad \bar{m}_B = m_B + m_C \beta^q \tag{39}$$

where $\alpha = (1 + k_A m_S)$ and $\beta = (1 + k_C m_S)$: combination of these relationships shows that

$$m_B = \frac{\left\{ (\bar{m}_B - \bar{m}_A) X \beta^q - \alpha^p + \sqrt{\Delta} \right\}}{2X\beta^q} \tag{40a}$$

where

$$\Delta = \left\{ (\bar{m}_B - \bar{m}_A) X \beta^q - \alpha^p \right\}^2 + 4X\bar{m}_B \alpha^p \beta^q \tag{40b}$$

The set of simultaneous equations (38–40) permits evaluation of r as a function of m_S for any given system whose initial mixing composition is defined: in this connection it is noted that the parameters X, p, and k_A may be evaluated from separate studies, which aids in the curve-fitting of binding results to obtain the remaining parameters q and k_C.

The forms of curves that arise have been discussed in a kinetic format for the particular case where A and B are enzymes catalyzing consecutive reactions of a pathway (112). An interesting point was made that the situation could well be encountered where separate *in vitro* studies on A and B could reveal classical Michaelis–Menten kinetics, whereas in their joint presence a sigmoidal regulatory response (defining the rate of final product formation as a function of the initial substrate concentration for enzyme A) could arise as the sole consequence of the enzyme-enzyme interaction.

9.5.2 Interacting Ligand Systems: Self-and Heterogeneous Associations

In discussions of binding theory there is a tendency to regard the protein as the acceptor species and, as in previous sections, to discuss self-association phenomena in this light. There are, however, situations in which the protein undergoing self-association is the ligand. Such is the case in the binding of prothrombin to the phospholipid micelle, where the acceptor (the micelle) is not self-interacting but the ligand (prothrombin) exists as an equilibrium mixture of monomeric and dimeric forms in the presence of Ca(II) ions (66). A similar situation arises in the binding to membrane receptor sites of insulin, which is known to associate indefinitely near neutral pH (95, 113). The question of control effects introduced by the concept of a self-interacting ligand assumes even greater proportion when it is recalled that ligands with low molecular weight may also isomerize or self-associate. Examples include the isomerization of *N*-acetylglucosamine (114), and the self-associations of ATP (115, 116), organic dyes (117), cholesterol (118), purines (119), and pyrimidines (120).

Consider a relatively simple situation in which each state of a self-interacting ligand ($nM \rightleftharpoons P$) binds competitively to the same p equivalent and independent sites on an acceptor A with respective site-binding constants k_M and k_P. It is relevant in an experimental and also a biological context to define the binding function as the base-moles of all forms of ligand bound per mole of acceptor, such that

$$r = \frac{\overline{m}_S - m_M - nm_P}{\overline{m}_A} \tag{41}$$

Nichol and co-workers (79) formulated the following binding equation for this situation.

$$r = \frac{p(k_M m_M + nk_P m_P)}{1 + k_M m_M + k_P m_P} \tag{42}$$

Equation (42) predicts a rectangular hyperbola for the plot of r versus $(m_M + nm_P)$ when $n = 1$ (ligand isomerization), irrespective of the relative magnitudes of k_M and k_P (79). At the same time the relation predicts two basic forms of control response when $n > 1$, which may be exemplified by considering the extreme cases where the monomeric form of ligand binds exclusively to acceptor ($k_P = 0$), and the converse situation where polymer is the sole active ligand species ($k_M = 0$). In the latter case a plot of r vs total free ligand concentration ($m_M + nm_P$) is sigmoidal, the corresponding Scatchard plot being concave to the r-axis (Figure 2c). However, when the monomeric form of ligand binds exclusively, a similar Scatchard plot exhibits convex behavior, as shown in Figure 2b. Such a result has been obtained in the binding of prothrombin fragment 1 to single-layer phospholipid vesicles (66), in accord with the hypothesis that the interaction of the monomeric form of fragment 1 with the vesicles is competitive with its dimerization. Clearly, in such situations there is a reservoir of inactive ligand (dimer), and the amount of ligand bound is less than it would have been if the ligand had not self-interacted; these are salient points in the regulation of blood coagulation (121).

Cases may well be encountered involving self-association of both ligand and acceptor, a situation for which Eq. (11) of ref. 79 is the appropriate binding equation. Moreover, systems may also be encountered where ligand interactions of other types operate. An example is provided by the work of Denburg and De Luca (122), who showed that in the presence of excess Mg(II) ions Michaelis–Menten kinetics were exhibited by firefly luciferase with magnesium-pyrophosphate complex as substrate: with a decreased concentration of Mg(II) ions the plot of initial velocity versus total pyrophosphate concentration was sigmoidal. This sigmoidal curve was fitted quantitatively (123) by considering specifically the equilibrium reaction $Mg(II) + PP_i \rightleftarrows Mg(II)—PP_i$. It is interesting to note that in this case the complex is the active species, which parallels the situation discussed above in which the polymeric form of ligand binds exclusively to acceptor: the prediction of a sigmoidal response in both cases is accordingly consistent. There are, of course, other examples where heterogeneous association reactions between a metal ion and ligand may require similar consideration. Certainly, in the field of bioenergetics most important reactions involve the participation of Mg(II) complexes of adenine dinucleotides which exist in equilibrium with their ionic constituents (124).

9.6 EQUILIBRIUM CROSS-LINKING REACTIONS

In all previous sections discussion is confined to situations in which the ligand S (whether it be macro molecular or of low molecular weight) is univalent and hence the operative equilibria for any multivalent acceptor state have been describable by Eq. (4). A more comprehensive consideration of the biological relevance of acceptor–ligand systems also requires formulation of binding equations governing the interactions between a bivalent ligand S and a multivalent acceptor A. A situation is thereby encountered where cross-linking of reactants leads to an array of complexes comprising three-dimensional networks of alternating A and S units. This type of cross-linking association has been studied in relation to the irreversible formation of synthetic nonlinear polymers (125–127); and it has long formed the conceptual basis for elucidating reversible interactions between antigens and bivalent antibodies (128–130).

9.6.1 Model Antigen–Antibody Systems

To illustrate the basic forms of binding responses obtained with such systems, we consider an idealized situation where both reactants are homogeneous and bear functional groups of equal reactivity, so that one site-binding constant, k, governs all equilibria. With a multifunctional reactant, A, possessing p sites and a bivalent reactant, S, there coexist at equilibrium unbound S and a series of complexes, $A_i S_j$ [$i = 1, 2, \ldots, \infty$; $j = (i-1), i, (i+1), \ldots, i(p-1)+1$], where $i = 1, j = 0$ denotes unbound A. It follows that the array of complexes may be formulated in stoichiometric terms as

$$
\overbrace{
\begin{array}{llllll}
 & & & A_i S_j & & \\
i = 1 & A, & AS, & AS_2, & \ldots, & AS_p \\
i = 2 & A_2 S, & A_2 S_2, & A_2 S_3, & \ldots, & A_2 S_{2p-1} \\
i = 3 & A_3 S_2, & A_3 S_3, & A_3 S_4, & \ldots, & A_3 S_{3p-1} \\
\vdots & \vdots & \vdots & \vdots & \vdots & \vdots
\end{array}
}
\tag{43}
$$

The first row of the array lists the type of complex previously described in relation to the binding of a ligand to a multivalent acceptor, whereas the first column of the array delineates complexes in which A molecules have been cross-linked via ligand bridges. Each of the latter complexes may also successively bind S to become fully saturated. Such an equilibrium system exhibits two basic properties, which will now be examined in detail according to previously presented (131) theory.

9.6.1.1 Binding responses

A reacted-site probability function P_A is defined as the probability that any given site on an A molecule has reacted with a site on an S molecule, such that the free (m_A) and total ($\overline{m}_A$) acceptor concentrations are related by

$$
m_A = \overline{m}_A (1 - P_A)^p \tag{44a}
$$

With similar notation for the bivalent ligand molecule we may write

$$
m_S = \overline{m}_S (1 - P_S)^2 \tag{44b}
$$

In these terms the site-binding constant, k, may be defined as the ratio of the concentration of reacted A sites ($pP_A\overline{m}_A$) to the product of the concentrations of unreacted A sites ($p(1-P_A)\overline{m}_A$) and unreacted S sites ($2(1-P_S)\overline{m}_S$). Thus

$$k = \frac{P_A}{2(1-P_A)(1-P_S)\overline{m}_S} \tag{45a}$$

It also follows that the total concentration of reacted A sites must equal the total concentration of reacted S sites, so that,

$$pP_A\overline{m}_A = 2P_S\overline{m}_S \tag{45b}$$

Combination of the usual definition of r, that is, Eq. (1), with Eqs. (44) and (45) leads (131) to

$$r = \left\{ \frac{p\alpha}{1+\alpha} \right\} + \Omega \tag{46a}$$

where

$$\Omega = \frac{(1-\alpha^2)}{4k\overline{m}_A\alpha} \left\{ 1 + \frac{2pk\overline{m}_A\alpha}{(1+\alpha)^2} - \left[1 + \frac{4pk\overline{m}_A\alpha}{(1+\alpha)^2} \right]^{1/2} \right\} \tag{46b}$$

and $\alpha = 2km_S$. It is clear from the dependence of r on $k\overline{m}_A$ that binding curves for such a cross-linking system exhibit dependence on acceptor concentration, a point illustrated numerically in Figure 7a. These curves, constructed with different but fixed values of $k\overline{m}_A$, intersect at the point ($r=p/2$, $\alpha=2km_S=1$), which is seen from Eq. (46b) to correspond to $\Omega=0$. The sign of Ω at other values of α depends solely on the sign of $(1-\alpha^2)$, since its coefficient in Eq. (46b) may be shown to be positive. When $\alpha < 1$ (or $m_S < 1/2k$) prior to the point of intersection, Ω is positive and values of r lie above those for the rectangular hyperbola described by the first term of Eq. (46a): conversely, when $\alpha > 1$, Ω is negative and the binding curves for the cross-linking system are below this rectangular hyperbola. Thus particularly effective binding (compared to the hyperbolic response) arises prior to the intersection point. Figure 7b presents the corresponding Scatchard plots, their form but not their dependence on $k\overline{m}_A$ being reminiscent of that obtained in the binding to a single acceptor state of a monofunctional ligand at sites which are nonequivalent or negatively cooperative. The important point emerges, however, that for cross-linking systems such deviations cannot be taken alone as an indication of site nonequivalence or mutual interaction of sites.

It is now observed that it is by no means mandatory to collect binding results on crosslinking systems in the form of corresponding values of r and m_S at fixed $\overline{m}_A$. For example, in certain radioimmunoassays (132) the experiment is conducted with fixed antibody concentration, $\overline{m}_S$, using radioactively labelled antigen, the results being presented as the percentage of antigen bound vs the logarithm of the total antigen concentration, $\overline{m}_A$.

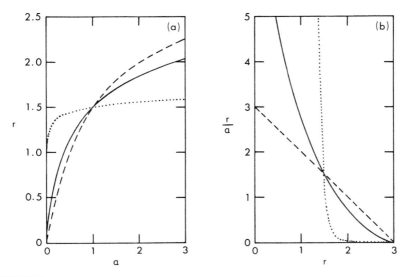

FIGURE 7
Binding behavior of a crosslinking system in which a bivalent ligand interacts with a trivalent acceptor. (a) Direct binding curves and (b) the corresponding Scatchard plots calculated using Eq. (46) with $k\overline{m}_A = 100$ ($\cdots$) and 1 (———). The rectangular hyperbola (---) and the corresponding straight line in Scatchard format are reference plots calculated with the first term of Eq. (46a).

Analysis of such results is facilitated by expressing P_A as a function of $\overline{m}_A$ and $\overline{m}_S$, which is achieved by eliminating P_S between Eqs. (45a) and (45b). The result is (131)

$$P_A = 1 + \left\{ \left(1 + 2k\overline{m}_S - pk\overline{m}_A - \sqrt{\Delta} \right) / 2pk\overline{m}_A \right\} \qquad (47a)$$

where

$$\Delta = \left(1 + 2k\overline{m}_S - pk\overline{m}_A \right)^2 + 4pk\overline{m}_A \qquad (47b)$$

Clearly, Eq. (47) may be used to construct a theoretical plot (for any given set of values of p, k, and $\overline{m}_S$) of the percent antigen bound vs log $\overline{m}_A$, since

$$\% \text{ antigen bound} = 100\frac{(\overline{m}_A - m_A)}{\overline{m}_A} = 100\left\{ 1 - (1 - P_A)^p \right\} \qquad (48)$$

Figure 8 presents a curve of this type constructed (131) in an attempt to fit results obtained on the interaction of sperm whale myoglobin and its specific antibodies. Evidently, the basic form of the experimental curve is described in terms of a minimum number of parameters implicit in the theory of cross-linked interactions. Nevertheless, in general one might expect further extensions to this basic binding theory to account for antibody population and reactive site heterogneity (133–135).

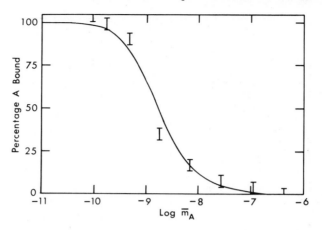

FIGURE 8

Application of the cross-linking theory to the description of radioimmunoassay results obtained with sperm whale myoglobin (antigen, A) and its specific antibodies (S). Experimental results are denoted by error bars and the solid line has been computed using Eqs. (47) and (48) with $p = 5$, $\overline{m}_S = 6 \times 10^{-10}$ M and $k = 8 \times 10^8$ M^{-1}. (Adapted from ref. 131 with permission. Copyright by Academic Press Inc. (London) Ltd.)

9.6.1.2   Precipitin effects

It follows directly from Eq. (46) that the limit of r as $m_S \to \infty$ is p, which means that in this limit the only complex of the array [Eq.(43)] remaining is AS_p. With increasing m_S, therefore, the concentrations of all other complexes must increase, pass through maxima and then decrease to zero. This behavior, which is the second basic property of all cross-linking systems, may be explored further in either of two ways. First, it is possible (131, 136) to formulate, with the use of appropriate statistical factors (125, 126), an explicit expression for the concentrations of all complexes, as

$$m_{A_i S_j} = \frac{2^j p^i (pi - i)! \{ C_{j-i+1}^{pi-2i+2} \} k^{j+i-1} m_A^i m_S^j}{(pi - 2i + 2)! \, i!} \tag{49}$$

The detailed composition of any mixture with initial composition defined by the total concentrations $\overline{m}_A$ and $\overline{m}_S$ may thus be determined with the joint use of Eqs. (44),(45), and (49). It is, of course, not possible to represent graphically the distribution of all complexes in the array [Eq. (43)], and accordingly a second approach has been formulated. This has involved differentiation of Eq. (49) with respect to m_S at fixed $\overline{m}_A$ (131) and has led to the finding that all $A_i S_j$ complexes (except AS_p) attain maximal values of concentration, those for which $j/i = p/2$ doing so together when $m_S = 1/2k$. Consistently, this is also the point at which $d(P_A P_S)/dm_S = 0$ (a maximum), showing that the extent of reaction reaches a maximum. In the vicinity of this point it is likely that a maximum precipitation effect may be observed (129, 130, 136, 137), the precipitated complexes redissolving on addition of excess S.

Reference to Figure 7 shows that the intersection point for binding curves also occurs at $m_S = 1/2k$ (or $\alpha = 1$), where $r = p/2$, and that more extensive binding of A and S (compared to the hyperbolic reference curve) occurs prior to this point of maximum precipitation. This has direct relevance to antigen-antibody reactions, which result in precipitate formation and macrophage ingestion.

It is well to note that cross-linking interactions between dissimilar macromolecules may not be restricted to antigen-antibody systems. For example, when any two macromolecules bearing opposite charge are mixed in solution with sufficiently low ionic strength, a spectrum of electrostatic forces must operate, and indeed such a system (ovalbumin-lysozyme at pH 6.8) has recently (138) been formalized in terms of the array of complexes in Eq. (43): the binding behavior was described by Eq. (46) and a classical precipitin curve was obtained. It would appear that the two basic properties of cross-linking systems, thereby illustrated with a model system, may have biological relevance extending beyond their operation in the immunological response.

9.6.2 A Model for Lymphocyte Activation

Lymphocyte activation initiates numerous biochemical events, summarized in ref. 139. While antigens trigger the transformation of resting lymphocytes into blast cells *in vivo*, they activate only approximately one cell in 10^4 (140) and, thus, experimental studies of the activation and subsequent transformation are often performed with mitogens, such as proteins of the plant lectin type, that act generally on T or B cell populations. The activation is often monitored by the incorporation of a radioactively labeled precursor into cellular DNA, the results being presented as a plot of the amount of marker incorporated as a function of total mitogen concentration used in the initial activation. Such dose-response curves, while differing in their width and symmetry, tend to be peaks exhibiting single maxima. The question is whether such maxima may arise from a cross-linking of membrane receptor sites by a bivalent mitogen.

On the interaction of a bivalent mitogen, S, with a p-valent receptor membrane A, account must first be taken of the equilibria $AS_{i-1} + S \rightleftarrows AS_i$ where complexes are formed involving the attachment of one bond of S to each receptor site. Assuming equal site reactivity, we may conclude from Section 9.2.1 that the constituent concentration of A, unbound and in these complexes, is $m_A(1 + 2k_A m_S)^p$ where $K_i = 2(p - i + 1)k_A/i$, a reformulation of Eq. (11) to account for the bivalency of S. Fuller accounts of binding theory to allow for membrane receptor site cooperativity (141) or phase-distribution and surface charge effects (142) may be found elsewhere. Of greater interest in the present context is the postulate that complexes may also be present in which both bonds of S are linked intracellularly to (say) adjacent receptor sites on A. The situation differs conceptually from the antigen-antibody case, in that cross-linking of acceptor entities (intercellularly) is not considered, a reasonable premise for the activation of lymphocyte cultures by certain mitogens at low concentration level(143). The bridging of adjacent pairs of receptor sites may well introduce strain into the membrane structure so that a different site-binding constant k_B must be introduced to describe this type of cross-linking interaction. There may be complexes with two or more cross-linked pairs of receptor sites; but we will suppose that the formation of just one cross-link is sufficient to disrupt the membrane and to allow a radioactive precursor to enter the cell, the event monitored in a dose-response curve. The contribution to the total concentration of A due to these complexes involving any single adjacent pair of receptor sites ($p-1$ sets being cross-linked, with the remaining $p-2$ sites unoccupied or partly or wholly occupied by S molecules bound by a single bond) is given by $2(p-1)k_B m_A m_S(1+2k_A m_S)^{p-2}$. It is thus possible to define a function Y as the ratio of this constituent concentration to the total concentration of A.

$$Y = \frac{2(p-1)k_B m_S(1+2k_A m_S)^{p-2}}{(1+2k_A m_S)^p + 2(p-1)k_B m_S(1+2k_A m_S)^{p-2}} \tag{50}$$

In this simplified approach, Y may be viewed as being proportional to the ordinate of a dose-response curve with m_S as the abscissa. Differentiation of Eq. (50) with respect to m_S shows that $dY/dm_S = 0$ (a maximum in the curve) when $m_S = 1/2k_A$. It does appear, therefore, with the reservations noted in

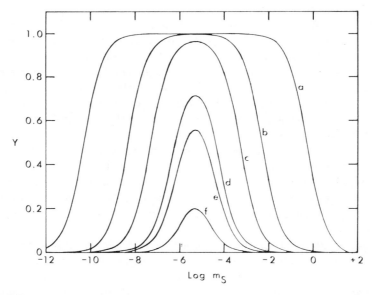

FIGURE 9
Simulation of dose response curves according to the cross-linking theory of lympho-cyte activation. Plots have been constructed on the basis of Eq. (50) for a bivalent receptor ($p=2$) with $k_A = 10^5 \ M^{-1}$ and the following values of k_B: (a) $10^{10} \ M^{-1}$; (b) $10^8 \ M^{-1}$; (c) $10^7 \ M^{-1}$; (d) $10^6 \ M^{-1}$; (e) $5 \times 10^5 \ M^{-1}$; (f) $10^5 \ M^{-1}$.

ref. 139, that the forms of experimentally observed dose-response curves for lymphocyte activation do imply a mechanism of membrane site cross-linkage, the extent of which increases and then decreases as m_S is varied. Figure 9 presents such curves calculated using Eq. (50) with $p = 2$, a fixed value of k_A and range of values of k_B. While the form of the plots and the values of Y at the maxima depend on p, k_A and k_B, the value of m_S (rather than $\bar{m}_S$) at the maxima is solely dependent on k_A. Thus, as Sawyer and Winzor (139) noted, this value of m_S provides a measure of the affinity constant of singly bonded mitogen rather than reflecting the cross-linking effect.

9.7 CONCLUDING REMARKS

A major point which has emerged from this discussion is that, in the area of acceptor-ligand binding, there are three basic forms of control response. These are summarized in Figure 2 in terms of Scatchard plots, which are linear (the rectangular hyperbolic response), convex to the r-axis (a steep hyperbolic response typified in Figure 7a), and concave to the r-axis with or without a maximum (the former corresponding to a sigmoidal binding curve as exemplified in Figure 5a): combination of effects, as in Figure 6, is also possible. We have attempted to discuss in some detail the underlying causes of these basic forms of control response and found that each may arise in different ways. The rectangular hyperbolic response in general arises when ligand binds to equivalent and independent sites on a single noninteracting state, but we have seen that the same effect is possible in particular cases involving an isomerizing acceptor or with systems in which the association of acceptor is not perturbed by the addition of ligand. The steep hyperbolic response may be due to binding at nonequivalent sites, to a negatively cooperative allosteric effect, to preferential ligand binding by a polymeric acceptor state (Figure 5c), to the operation of cross-linking equilibria, or to the binding of the monomeric form of a ligand which itself associates. Similarly, the sigmoidal binding response is encountered with positively cooperative allosteric systems; with preferential binding of ligand to different acceptor states coexisting in equilibrium regardless of whether the equilibria involve isomers, polymers or complexes of dissimilar reactants; with ligand-initiated association of acceptor by a modification pathway (144); or with a self-interacting ligand system when the larger species binds exclusively to acceptor. It is now recognized with this last class of systems that domains of sigmoidality exist, governed by the magnitudes of the interaction parameters and outside of which the binding curve loses its distinctive point of inflection. In listing these alternatives we would not wish to create the impression that it is no longer possible to distinguish between them on an experimental basis. Indeed there are several procedures, arising from theoretical considerations, that may aid in the delineation, not the least of which are physical studies on the acceptor and ligand systems alone and in combination, particular emphasis being placed on the systematic variation of acceptor concentration (Figures 5–7).

In addition to treating this whole area as an *in vitro* study of the molecular bases of binding phenomena, there is the biological relevance of such interactions to be considered. Indeed, it is here that the forms of the binding curves assume a different perspective. A sigmoidal curve is viewed in terms of the concept of sensitivity in the amount of ligand bound (or released) around the point of inflection (145). There is a similar region of sensitivity in the steep hyperbolic response at low ligand concentrations but at higher concentrations the effective plateau region is one in which the amount of ligand bound is relatively insensitive to variation in its unbound concentration: the possible importance of such a buffering effect has been discussed by Koshland and Neet (63). The existence of domains of sigmoidality is seen to be an expression of the way that environmental parameters may modify the aforementioned buffering and sensitivity effects. Acceptor concentration-dependence of binding curves is viewed in similar light, and possibly relates control at the enzyme level with control at the protein synthesis level, since the latter together with consideration of protein turnover determines acceptor concentrations. In other cases it is possible that the form of the binding curve is primarily symptomatic of the more important change in system composition consequent on ligand binding. For example, the change in relative amounts of polymeric constituents caused by the preferential binding of ligand to different association states of a protein may well bear on questions of acceptor permeation through, or localization within, the cell. Certainly, the basic property of a cross-linking system that the concentrations of most complexes pass through maxima is of direct relevance in the immunological response. Likewise, the section on lymphocyte activation stressed this same basic property of cross-linking systems rather than the forms of mitogen-lymphocyte binding curves. It is becoming increasingly clear that the formulation of relevant binding equations is but the first step in understanding their full implication; for it is now apparent that they contain hitherto unsuspected potential for describing regulatory responses of diverse biological systems.

REFERENCES

1. I. M. Klotz, *Arch. Biochem.* **9**, 109 (1946).

2. G. Scatchard, *Ann. N.Y. Acad. Sci.* **51**, 660 (1949).

3. I. M. Klotz, *J. Am. Chem. Soc.* **68**, 2299 (1946).

4. J. H. Lang and E. C. Lasser, *Biochemistry* **6**, 2403 (1967).

5. A. N. Glazer, *J. Biol. Chem.* **242**, 4528 (1967).

6. S. R. Anderson and G. Weber, *Biochemistry* **4**, 1948 (1965).

7. E. Daniel and G. Weber, *Biochemistry* **5**, 1893 (1966).

8. N. A. Attallah and G. F. Lata, *Biochim. Biophys. Acta* **168**, 321 (1968).

9. J. J. Fischer and O. Jardetzky, *J. Am. Chem. Soc.* **87**, 3237 (1965).

10. O. Jardetzky and N. G. Wade-Jardetzky, *Mol. Pharmacol.* **1**, 214 (1965).

11. A. S. V. Burgen, O. Jardetzky, J. C. Metcalfe, and N. G. Wade-Jardetzky, *Proc. Natl. Acad. Sci. USA* **58**, 447 (1967).

12. M. A. Raftery, F. W. Dahlquist, S. I. Chan, and S. M. Parsons, *J. Biol. Chem.* **243**, 4175 (1968).

13. J. Steinhardt and J. A. Reynolds, *Multiple Equilbria in Proteins*, Academic Press, New York, 1969, p.34.

14. I. M. Klotz, in H. Neurath and K. E. Bailey, Eds., *The Proteins*, Vol. 1B, Academic Press, New York, 1953, p.727.

15. H. Svensson, *Ark. Kemi Mineral. Geol.* **22A**, No. 10 (1946).

16. S. P. Colowick and F. C. Womack, *J. Biol. Chem.* **244**, 774 (1969).

17. W. F. Blatt, S. M. Robinson, and H. J. Bixler, *Anal. Biochem.* **26**, 151 (1968).

18. J. A. Sophianopoulos, S. J. Durham, A. J. Sophianopoulos, H. L. Ragsdale, and W. P. Cropper, Jr., *Arch. Biochem. Biophys.* **187**, 132 (1978).

19. D. J. Winzor and H. A. Scheraga, *Biochemistry* **2**, 1263 (1963).

20. L. W. Nichol and D. J. Winzor, *J. Phys. Chem.* **68**, 2455 (1964).

21. G. A. Gilbert and R. C. L. Jenkins, *Proc. R. Soc. London, Ser. A* **253**, 420 (1959).

22. L. W. Nichol and A. G. Ogston, *Proc. R. Soc. London, Ser. B* **163**, 343 (1965).

23. M. A. Bothwell, G. J. Howlett, and H. K. Schachman, *J. Biol. Chem.* **253**, 2073 (1978).

24. A. Chanutin, S. Ludewig, and A. V. Masket, *J. Biol. Chem.* **143**, 737 (1942).

25. S. F. Velick, J. E. Hayes, Jr., and J. Harting, *J. Biol. Chem.* **203**, 527 (1953).

26. H. Arnold and D. Pette, *Eur. J. Biochem.* **6**, 163 (1968).

27. F. M. Clarke and C. J. Masters, *Arch. Biochem. Biophys.* **153**, 258 (1972).

28. E. E. Brumbaugh and G. K. Ackers, *Anal. Biochem.* **41**, 543 (1971).

29. R. I. Brinkworth, C. J. Masters, and D. J. Winzor, *Biochem. J.* **151**, 631 (1975).

30. P. F. Cooper and G. C. Wood, *J. Pharm. Pharmacol.* **20**, 150S (1968).

31. L. W. Nichol, W. J. H. Jackson, and G. D. Smith, *Arch. Biochem. Biophys.* **144**, 438 (1971).

32. L. W. Nichol, W. J. H. Jackson, and D. J. Winzor, *Biochemistry* **11**, 585 (1972).

33. J. P. Hummel and W. J. Dreyer, *Biochim. Biophys. Acta* **63**, 530 (1962).

34. G. F. Fairclough, Jr. and J. S. Fruton, *Biochemistry* **5**, 673 (1966).

35. D. O. Jordan, S. J. Lovell, D. R. Phillips, and D. J. Winzor, *Biochemistry* **13**, 1832 (1974).

36. L. W. Nichol, W. H. Sawyer, and D. J. Winzor, *Biochem. J.* **112**, 259 (1969).

37. R. A. Alberty and H. H. Marvin, Jr., *J. Phys. Colloid Chem.* **54**, 47 (1950).

38. L. G. Longsworth, in M. Bier, Ed., *Electrophoresis, Theory, Methods and Applications*, Academic Press, New York, 1959, p. 91.

39. L. W. Nichol and A. G. Ogston, *J. Phys. Chem.* **69**, 1754 (1965).

40. L. W. Nichol and D. J. Winzor, *Migration of Interacting Systems*, Clarendon Press, Oxford, 1972.

41. L. W. Nichol, G. D. Smith, and D. J. Winzor, *J. Phys. Chem.* **77**, 2912 (1973).

42. L. W. Nichol, P. D. Jeffrey, and B. K. Milthorpe, *Biophys. Chem.* **4**, 259 (1976).

43. I. Z. Steinberg and H. K. Schachman, *Biochemistry* **5**, 3728 (1966).

44. I. M. Klotz, F. M. Walker, and R. B. Pivan, *J. Am. Chem. Soc.* **68**, 1486 (1946).

45. G. S. Adair, *J. Biol. Chem.* **63**, 529 (1925).

46. J. T. Edsall and J. Wyman, *Biophysical Chemistry*, Academic Press, New York, 1953, p. 635.

47. M. E. Magar and R. F. Steiner, *J. Theor. Biol.* **32**, 495 (1971).

48. M. E. Magar, R. F. Steiner, and J. E. Fletcher, *J. Theor. Biol.* **32**, 59 (1971).

49. J. E. Fletcher, A. A. Spector, and J. D. Ashbrook, *Biochemistry* **9**, 4580 (1970).

50. C. J. Thompson and I. M. Klotz, *Arch. Biochem. Biophys.* **147**, 178 (1971).

51. C. Frieden, *J. Biol. Chem.* **242**, 4045 (1967).

52. S. I. Rubinow, *Immunochemistry* **14**, 573 (1977).

53. A. Blake and A. R. Peacocke, *Biopolymers* **6**, 1225 (1968).

54. G. Weber, in B. Pullman and M. Weissbluth, Eds., *Molecular Biophysics*, Academic Press, New York, 1965, p. 369.

55. G. H. McKenzie and W. H. Sawyer, *J. Biol. Chem.* **248**, 549 (1973).

56. D. E. Koshland, Jr., G. Némethy, and D. Filmer, *Biochemistry* **5**, 365 (1966).

57. A. Conway and D. E. Koshland, Jr., *Biochemistry* **7**, 4011 (1968).

58. W. G. Bardsley and R. D. Waight, *J. Theor. Biol.* **72**, 321 (1978).

59. W. G. Bardsley and J. Wyman, *J. Theor. Biol.* **72**, 373 (1978).

60. J. Wyman, *Adv. Protein Chem.* **19**, 223 (1964).

61. J. Wyman, *J. Am. Chem. Soc.* **89**, 2202 (1967).

62. M. E. Kirtley and D. E. Koshland, Jr., *J. Biol. Chem.* **242**, 4192 (1967).

63. D. E. Koshland, Jr. and K. E. Neet, *Annu. Rev. Biochem.* **37**, 359 (1968).

64. G. Scatchard, I. H. Scheinberg, and S. H. Armstrong, *J. Am. Chem. Soc.* **72**, 535 (1950).

65. S. McLaughlin and H. Harary, *Biochemistry* **15**, 1941 (1976).

66. F. A. Dombrose, S. N. Gitel, K. Zawalich, and C. M. Jackson, *J. Biol. Chem.* **254**, 5027 (1979).

67. J. Monod, J. Wyman, and J.-P. Changeux, *J. Mol. Biol.* **12**, 88 (1965).

68. L. W. Nichol, P. R. Wills, and D. J. Winzor, *J. Theor. Biol.* **80**, 39 (1979).

69. F. W. Dahlquist, *FEBS Lett.* **49**, 267 (1974).

70. B. I. Kurganov, Z. S. Kagan, A. I. Dorozhko, and V. A. Yakovlev, *J. Theor. Biol.* **47**, 1 (1974).

71. G. Schwarz, *Biophys. Chem.* **6**, 65 (1977).

72. P. A. Baghurst, L. W. Nichol, and D. J. Winzor, *J. Theor. Biol.* **74**, 523 (1978).

73. K. Kirschner, M. Eigen, R. Bittman, and B. Voigt, *Proc. Natl. Acad. Sci. USA* **56**, 1661 (1966).

74. M. M. Rubin and J.-P. Changeux, *J. Mol. Biol.* **21**, 265 (1966).

75. J.-P. Changeux and M. M. Rubin, *Biochemistry* **7**, 553 (1968).

76. L. W. Nichol, K. O'Dea, and P. A. Baghurst, *J. Theor. Biol.* **34**, 255 (1972).

77. J. C. Gerhart, *Curr. Top. Cell. Reg.* **2**, 275 (1970).

78. G. D. Smith, *J. Theor. Biol.* **69**, 275 (1977).

79. L. W. Nichol, G. D. Smith, and A. G. Ogston, *Biochim. Biophys. Acta* **184**, 1 (1969).

80. G. D. Smith, D. V. Roberts, and P. W. Kuchel, *Biochim. Biophys. Acta* **377**, 197 (1975).

81. J. C. Gerhart and A. B. Pardee, *Cold Spring Harbor Symp. Quant. Biol.* **28**, 491 (1963).

82. A. Melo and L. Glaser, *J. Biol. Chem.* **240**, 398 (1965).

83. D. W. Pettigrew and C. Frieden, *J. Biol. Chem.* **252**, 4546 (1977).

84. M. F. Perutz, *Nature (London)* **228**, 726 (1970).

85. G. Markus, D. K. McClintock, and J. B. Bussel, *J. Biol. Chem.* **246**, 762 (1971).

86. A. Arnone, *Nature (London)* **237**, 146 (1972).

87. P. A. Baghurst and L. W. Nichol, *Biochim. Biophys. Acta* **412**, 168 (1975).

88. A. J. Sophianopoulos, *J. Biol. Chem.* **244**, 3188 (1969).

89. G. J. Howlett and L. W. Nichol, *J. Biol. Chem.* **247**, 5681 (1972).

90. R. Tellam, D. J. Winzor, and L. W. Nichol, *Biochem. J.* **173**, 185 (1978).

91. P. Nicolas, M. Camier, P. Dessen, and P. Cohen, *J. Biol. Chem.* **251**, 3965 (1976).

92. R. F. Colman and C. Frieden, *J. Biol. Chem.* **241**, 3661 (1966).

93. P. W. Chun, S. J. Kim, C. A. Stanley, and G. K. Ackers, *Biochemistry* **8**, 1625 (1969).

94. R. J. Cohen and G. B. Benedek, *J. Mol. Biol.* **108**, 151 (1976).

95. B. K. Milthorpe, L. W. Nichol, and P. D. Jeffrey, *Biochim. Biophys. Acta* **495**, 195 (1977).

96. A. Levitzki and D. E. Koshland, Jr., *Biochemistry* **11**, 247 (1972).

97. R. F. Steiner, *J. Theor. Biol.* **45**, 93 (1974).

98. L. W. Nichol, W. J. H. Jackson, and D. J. Winzor, *Biochemistry* **6**, 2449 (1967).

99. L. W. Nichol, G. D. Smith, and D. J. Winzor, *Nature (London)* **222**, 174 (1969).

100. F. C. Mills, M. L. Johnson, and G. K. Ackers, *Biochemistry* **15**, 5350 (1976).

101. C. Frieden and R. F. Colman, *J. Biol. Chem.* **242**, 1705 (1967).

102. L. W. Nichol, *Search* **8**, 395 (1977).

103. C. Frieden, *Annu. Rev. Biochem.* **40**, 653 (1971).

104. L. W. Nichol, R. J. Siezen, and D. J. Winzor, *Biophys. Chem.* **10**, 17 (1979).

105. G. Torelli, F. Celentano, G. Cortili, E. D'Angelo, A. Cazzaniga, and E. P. Radford, *Physiol. Chem. Phys.* **9**, 21 (1977).

106. R. E. Benesch, R. Adalji, S. Kwong, and R. Benesch, *Anal. Biochem.* **89**, 162 (1978).

107. L. W. Nichol and A. B. Roy, *Biochemistry* **4**, 386 (1965).

108. A. Jerfy, A. B. Roy, and H. J. Tomkins, *Biochim. Biophys. Acta* **442**, 335 (1976).

109. P. Bernfeld, B. J. Berkeley, and R. E. Bieber, *Arch. Biochem. Biophys.* **111**, 31 (1965).

110. R. M. Hemphill, C. L. Zielke, and C. H. Suelter, *J. Biol. Chem.* **246**, 7237 (1971).

111. C. J. Masters, R. J. Sheedy, D. J. Winzor, and L. W. Nichol, *Biochem. J.* **112**, 806 (1969).

112. L. W. Nichol, P. W. Kuchel, and P. D. Jeffrey, *Biophys. Chem.* **2**, 354 (1974).

113. P. D. Jeffrey, B. K. Milthorpe, and L. W. Nichol, *Biochemistry* **15**, 4660 (1976).

114. E. W. Thomas, *Biochem. Biophys. Res. Commun.* **24**, 611 (1966).

115. W. E. Ferguson, C. M. Smith, E. T. Adams, Jr., and G. H. Barlow, *Biophys. Chem.* **1**, 325 (1974).

116. M. P. Heyn and R. Bretz, *Biophys. Chem.* **3**, 35 (1975).

117. M. E. Lamm and D. M. Neville, Jr., *J. Phys. Chem.* **69**, 3872 (1965).

118. F. S. Parker and K. R. Bhaskar, *Biochemistry* **7**, 1286 (1968).

119. K. E. Van Holde and G. P. Rossetti, *Biochemistry* **6**, 2189 (1967).

120. P. O. P. Ts'o, I. S. Melvin, and A. C. Olson, *J. Am. Chem. Soc.* **85**, 1289 (1963).

121. L. W. Nichol, in K. G. Mann and F. B. Taylor, Jr., Eds., *The Regulation of Coagulation*, Elsevier/North-Holland, New York, 1980, p. 43.

122. J. Denburg and M. DeLuca, *Biochem. Biophys. Res. Commun.* **31**, 453 (1968).

123. G. D. Smith and L. W. Nichol, *Aust. J. Biol. Sci.* **24**, 955 (1971).

124. J. P. Belaich and J. C. Sari, *Proc. Natl. Acad. Sci. USA* **64**, 763 (1969).

125. W. H. Stockmayer, *J. Chem. Phys.* **11**, 45 (1943).

126. P. J. Flory, *Principles of Polymer Chemistry*, Cornell University Press, Ithaca, N. Y., 1953.

127. C. W. Macosko and D. R. Miller, *Macromolecules* **9**, 199 (1976).

128. M. Heidelberger and F. E. Kendall, *J. Exp. Med.* **61**, 563 (1935).

129. R. J. Goldberg, *J. Am. Chem. Soc.* **74**, 5715 (1952).

130. R. J. Goldberg, *J. Am. Chem. Soc.* **75**, 3127 (1953).

131. P. D. Calvert, L. W. Nichol, and W. H. Sawyer, *J. Theor. Biol.* **80**, 233 (1979).

132. J. G. R. Hurrell, N. A. Nicola, W. J. Broughton, M. J. Dilworth, E. Minasian, and S. J. Leach, *Eur. J. Biochem.* **66**, 389 (1976).

133. E. A. Kabat and M. M. Mayer, *Experimental Immunochemistry*, Charles C. Thomas, Springfield, Ill., 1961.

134. M. T. Palmiter and F. Aladjem, *J. Theor. Biol.* **5**, 211 (1963).

135. F. Aladjem and M. T. Palmiter, *J. Theor. Biol.* **8**, 8 (1965).

136. S. J. Singer, in H. Neurath, Ed., *The Proteins*, Vol. 3, Academic Press, New York, 1965, p. 269.

137. C. Delisi, *J. Theor. Biol.* **45**, 555 (1974).

138. P. D. Jeffrey, L. W. Nichol, and R. D. Teasdale, *Biophys. Chem.* **10**, 379 (1979).

139. W. H. Sawyer and D. J. Winzor, *Immunochemistry* **13**, 141 (1976).

140. G. J. V. Nossal and G. L. Ada, *Antigens, Lymphoid Cells and the Immune Response*, Academic Press, New York, 1971.

141. J.-P. Changeux, J. Thiéry, Y. Tung, and C. Kittel, *Proc. Natl. Acad. Sci. USA* **57**, 335 (1967).

142. E. A. Haigh, K. R. Thulborn, W. H. Sawyer, and L. W. Nichol, *Aust. J. Biol. Sci.* **31**, 447 (1978).

143. N. Sharon and H. Lis, *Science* **177**, 949 (1972).

144. L. W. Nichol and D. J. Winzor, *Biochemistry* **15**, 3015 (1976).

145. E. R. Stadtman, *Adv. Enzymol.* **28**, 41 (1966).

Author Index

Note: Numbers in parentheses are reference numbers and indicate that the author's work is referred to although his name is not mentioned in the text. Numbers in italics show the pages on which the complete references are listed.

Subject Index

4 6 5 0 5